PELICAN BOOKS

MAN, THE UNKNOWN

By

ALEXIS CARREL

published by

PENGUIN BOOKS

WEST DRAYTON MIDDLESEX ENGLAND
245 FIFTH AVENUE NEW YORK U.S.A.

First Published 1935
Published in Pelican Books 1948

*Made and Printed in Great Britain for Penguin Books Limited
by Butler & Tanner Ltd., Frome and London*

TO MY FRIENDS

FREDERIC R. COUDERT
CORNELIUS CLIFFORD

AND

BORIS A. BAKHMETEFF

THIS BOOK IS

DEDICATED

CONTENTS

PREFACE *page* ix

Chapter I. THE NEED OF A BETTER KNOWLEDGE OF MAN 15

II. THE SCIENCE OF MAN 40

III. BODY AND PHYSIOLOGICAL ACTIVITIES 64

IV. MENTAL ACTIVITIES 115

V. INWARD TIME 152

VI. ADAPTIVE FUNCTIONS 180

VII. THE INDIVIDUAL 218

VIII. THE REMAKING OF MAN 252

INDEX 294

PREFACE

THE AUTHOR of this book is not a philosopher. He is only a man of science. He spends a large part of his time in a laboratory studying living matter, and another part in the world, watching human beings and trying to understand them. He does not pretend to deal with things that lie outside the field of scientific observation.

In this book he has endeavoured to describe the known, and to separate it clearly from the plausible; also to recognize the existence of the unknown and the unknowable. He has considered man as the sum of the observations and experiences of all times and of all countries. But what he describes he has either seen with his own eyes or learned directly from those with whom he associates. It is his good fortune to be in a position to study, without making any effort or deserving any credit, the phenomena of life in their bewildering complexity. He has observed practically every form of human activity. He is acquainted with the poor and the rich, the sound and the diseased, the learned and the ignorant, the weak-minded, the insane, the shrewd, the criminal, etc. He knows farmers, proletarians, clerks, shopkeepers, financiers, manufacturers, politicians, statesmen, soldiers, professors, school-teachers, clergymen, peasants, bourgeois, and aristocrats. The circumstances of his life have led him across the path of philosophers, artists, poets, and scientists, and also of geniuses, heroes, and saints. At the same time, he has studied the hidden mechanisms which, in the depth of the tissues and in the immensity of the brain, are the substratum of organic and mental phenomena.

He is indebted to the techniques of modern civilization for the possibility of witnessing such a gigantic spectacle. These techniques have enabled him simultaneously to give his attention to several subjects. He lives in the New World, and also in the Old. He has the privilege of spending most of his time in the Rockefeller Institute for Medical Research, as one of the scientists brought together in that Institute by Simon Flexner. There he has contemplated the phenomena of life while they were analyzed by incomparable experts such as Meltzer, Jacques Loeb, Noguchi, and many others. Owing to the genius of Flexner, the study of living things has been undertaken with a broadness of vision so far unequalled. Matter is investigated in those laboratories at every level of its organization, of its ascension towards the making of man. With the help of X-rays, physicists are unveiling the architectonic of the molecules of the simpler substances of our tissues—that is, the spatial relations of the atoms constituting those molecules. Chemists and physical chemists devote themselves to the analysis of the more complex substances encountered within the body, such as the hæmoglobin of the blood, the proteins of the tissues and the humours, and the ferments responsible for the unceasing splitting and building up of those enormous aggregates of atoms. Instead of directing their attention to the molecular edifices themselves, other chemists consider the relations of those edifices with one another when they enter the fluids of the body. In short, the physico-chemical equilibria that maintain constant the composition of blood serum in spite of the perpetual changes of the tissues. Thus are brought to light the chemical aspects of physiological phenomena. Several groups of physiologists, with the aid of the most varied techniques, are studying the larger structures resulting from the aggregation and organization of molecules, the cells of the tissues and of the blood— that is, living matter itself. They examine those cells, their ways of association, and the laws governing their relations with their surroundings; the whole made up of the organs and humours; the influence of the cosmic environment on this whole; and the effects of chemical substances on tissues and consciousness. Other specialists devote themselves to the investigation of those small beings, the viruses and bacteria, whose presence in our tissues is responsible for infectious diseases; of the marvellous methods used by the organism in its fight against them; of the degenerative diseases, such as cancer, heart lesions, nephritis. Finally, the momentous problem of individuality and of its chemical basis is being successfully attacked. The writer has had the exceptional opportunity of listening to great men specialized in these researches, and of following the results of their experiments. Thus the effort of inert matter toward organization, the properties of living beings, and the harmony of our body and our mind appeared to him in their beauty. In addition, he himself has studied the most diverse subjects, from surgery to cell physiology and to metapsychics. This was made possible by facilities which, for the first time, were put at the disposal of science for the performance of its task. It seems that the subtle inspiration of Welch and the practical idealism of Frederick T. Gates caused new conceptions of biology and new formulas for research to spring from Flexner's mind. To the pure spirit of science Flexner gave the help of new methods designed to save the workers' time, to facilitate their free co-operation, and to create better experimental techniques. Owing to these innovations, one can not only undertake extensive researches of one's own, but also acquire a first-hand knowledge of subjects whose mastery in former days necessitated the whole lifetime of several scientists.

We now possess such a large amount of information on human beings that its very immensity prevents us from using it properly. In order to be of service, our knowledge must be synthetic and concise. This book, therefore, was not intended to be a treatise on Man. For such a treatise would run into dozens of volumes. The author's intention was merely to build up an intelligible synthesis of the data which we possess about ourselves. He has attempted to describe a large number of fundamental facts in a very simple manner, and still not to be elementary, not to indulge in scientific popularization or to offer to the public a weak and childish aspect of reality. He has written for the scholar as well as for the layman. He fully understands the difficulties inherent in the temerity of his undertaking. He has tried to confine all knowledge of man within the pages of a small book. Of course, he has not succeeded. He will not satisfy the specialists, because they know far more than he does, and they will regard him as superficial. Neither will he please the general public, for this volume contains too many technical details. However, in order to acquire a synthetic knowledge of ourselves, it was indispensable to summarize the data of several sciences, and also to depict with bold and rapid strokes the physical, chemical, and physiological mechanisms hidden under the harmony of our acts and our thoughts. We must realize that an attempt, however awkward and though partly a failure, is better than no attempt at all.

The necessity of compressing a large amount of information into a short space has important drawbacks. It gives a dogmatic appearance to propositions which are nothing but conclusions of observations and experiments. Subjects that have engrossed physiologists, hygienists, physicians, educators, economists, sociologists for years have often had to be described in a few lines or a few words. Almost every sentence of this book is the expression of the long labour of a scientist, of his patient researches, sometimes of his entire lifetime spent in the study of a single problem. For the sake of conciseness, the writer has been obliged briefly to summarize gigantic masses of observations. Thus, descriptions of facts have been given the form of assertions. To a similar cause may be attributed a seeming lack of accuracy. Most organic and mental phenomena have been treated in a diagrammatic manner. Therefore, things that markedly differ appear to be grouped together, as, at a distance, houses, rocks, and trees are not distinguishable from one another. It must not be forgotten that in this book the expression of reality is only approximately accurate. A brief description of an immense subject involves inevitable defects. But the sketch of a landscape should not be expected to contain all the details of a photograph.

Before beginning this work, the author realized its difficulty, its almost impossibility. He undertook it merely because somebody had to undertake it; because men cannot follow modern civilization along its present course, because they are degenerating. They have been fascinated by the beauty of the sciences of inert matter. They have not understood that their body and consciousness are subjected to natural laws, more obscure than, but as inexorable as, the laws of the sidereal world. Neither have they understood that they cannot transgress these laws without being punished. They must, therefore, learn the necessary relations of the cosmic universe, of their fellow men, and of their inner selves, and also those of their tissues and their mind. Indeed, man stands above all things. Should he degenerate, the beauty of civilization, and even the grandeur of the physical universe, would vanish. For these reasons this book was written. It was not written in the peace of the country, but in the confusion, the noise, and the weariness of New York. The author has been urged to carry out this work by his friends, philosophers, scientists, jurists, economists, with whom he has for years discussed the great problems of our time. From Frederic R. Coudert, whose penetrating vision reaches, beyond the horizons of America, those of Europe, came the impulse responsible for this book. Indeed, the majority of the nations follow the lead of North America. Those countries that have blindly adopted the spirit and the techniques of industrial civilization, Russia as well as England, France, and Germany, are exposed to the same dangers as the United States. Humanity's attention must turn from the machines and the world of inanimate matter to the body and the soul of man, to the organic and mental processes which have created the machines and the universe of Newton and Einstein.

The only claim of this book is to put at everyone's disposal an ensemble of scientific data concerning the human beings of our time. We are beginning to realize the weakness of our civilization. Many want to shake off the dogmas imposed upon them by modern society. This book has been written for them, and also for those who are bold enough to understand the necessity, not only of mental, political, and social changes, but of the overthrow of industrial civilization and of the advent of another conception of human progress. This book is, therefore, dedicated to all whose everyday task is the rearing of children, the formation or the guidance of the individual; to school-teachers, hygienists, physicians, clergymen, social workers, professors, judges, army officers, engineers, economists, politicians, industrial leaders, etc; also to those who are interested in the mere knowledge of our body and our mind; in short, to every man and every woman. It is offered to all as a simple account of facts revealed about human beings by scientific observation.

Man, the Unknown

*

CHAPTER I

THE NEED OF A BETTER KNOWLEDGE OF MAN

1. The sciences of life have progressed more slowly than those of inert matter. Our ignorance of ourselves. 2. This ignorance is due to our ancestors' mode of existence, to the complexity of man, and to the structure of our mind. 3. How mechanical, physical, and chemical sciences have modified our environment. 4. The results of such a change. 5. This change is harmful, having been made without due consideration of our nature. 6. Need of a more complete knowledge of ourselves.

I

THERE is a strange disparity between the sciences of inert matter and those of life. Astronomy, mechanics, and physics are based on concepts which can be expressed, tersely and elegantly, in mathematical language. They have built up a universe as harmonious as the monuments of ancient Greece. They weave about it a magnificent texture of calculations and hypotheses. They search for reality beyond the realm of common thought up to unutterable abstractions consisting only of equations of symbols. Such is not the position of biological sciences. Those who investigate the phenomena of life are as if lost in an inextricable jungle, in the midst of a magic forest, whose countless trees unceasingly change their place and their shape. They are crushed under a mass of facts, which they can describe but are incapable of defining in algebraic equations. From the things encountered in the material world, whether atoms or stars, rocks or clouds, steel or water, certain qualities, such as weight and spatial dimensions, have been abstracted. These abstractions, and not the

15

concrete facts, are the matter of scientific reasoning. The observation of objects constitutes only a lower form of science,
the descriptive form. Descriptive science classifies phenomena. But the unchanging relations between variable quantities—that is, the natural laws—only appear when science
becomes more abstract. It is because physics and chemistry
are abstract and quantitative that they had such great and
rapid success. Although they do not pretend to unveil the
ultimate nature of things, they give us the power to predict
future events, and often to determine at will their occurrence.
In learning the secret of the constitution and of the properties of matter, we have gained the mastery of almost everything which exists on the surface of the earth, excepting ourselves.

The science of living beings in general, and especially
of the human individual, has not made such great progress.
It still remains in the descriptive state. Man is an indivisible
whole of extreme complexity. No simple representation of
him can be obtained. There is no method capable of apprehending him simultaneously in his entirety, his parts, and his
relations with the outer world. In order to analyze ourselves
we are obliged to seek the help of various techniques and,
therefore, to utilize several sciences. Naturally, all these
sciences arrive at a different conception of their common
object. They abstract only from *man* what is attainable by
their special methods. And those abstractions, after they
have been added together, are still less rich than the concrete
fact. They leave behind them a residue too important to be
neglected. Anatomy, chemistry, physiology, psychology,
pedagogy, history, sociology, political economy do not exhaust their subject. Man, as known to the specialists, is far
from being the concrete man, the real man. He is nothing
but a schema, consisting of other schemata built up by the
techniques of each science. He is, at the same time, the
corpse dissected by the anatomists, the consciousness observed by the psychologists and the great teachers of the

spiritual life, and the personality which introspection shows to everyone as lying in the depth of himself. He is the chemical substances constituting the tissues and humours of the body. He is the amazing community of cells and nutrient fluids whose organic laws are studied by the physiologists. He is the compound of tissues and consciousness that hygienists and educators endeavour to lead to its optimum development while it extends into time. He is the *homo œconomicus* who must ceaselessly consume manufactured products in order that the machines, of which he is made a slave, may be kept at work. But he is also the poet, the hero, and the saint. He is not only the prodigiously complex being analyzed by our scientific techniques, but also the tendencies, the conjectures, the aspirations of humanity. Our conceptions of him are imbued with metaphysics. They are founded on so many and such imprecise data that the temptation is great to choose among them those which please us. Therefore, our idea of man varies according to our feelings and our beliefs. A materialist and a spiritualist accept the same definition of a crystal of sodium chloride; but they do not agree with one another upon that of the human being. A mechanistic physiologist and a vitalistic physiologist do not consider the organism in the same light. The living being of Jacques Loeb differs profoundly from that of Hans Driesch. Indeed, mankind has made a gigantic effort to know itself. Although we possess the treasure of the observations accumulated by the scientists, the philosophers, the poets, and the great mystics of all times, we have grasped only certain aspects of ourselves. We do not apprehend man as a whole. We know him as composed of distinct parts. And even these parts are created by our methods. Each one of us is made up of a procession of phantoms, in the midst of which strides an unknowable reality.

In fact our ignorance is profound. Most of the questions put to themselves by those who study human beings remain without answer. Immense regions of our inner world are still unknown. How do the molecules of chemical substances associate in order to form the complex and temporary organs of the cell? How do the genes contained in the nucleus of a fertilized ovum determine the characteristics of the individual deriving from that ovum? How do cells organize themselves by their own efforts into societies, such as the tissues and the organs? Like the ants and the bees, they have advance knowledge of the part they are destined to play in the life of the community. And hidden mechanisms enable them to build up an organism both complex and simple. What is the nature of our duration, of psychological time, and of physiological time? We know that we are a compound of tissues, organs, fluids, and consciousness. But the relations between consciousness and cerebrum are still a mystery. We lack almost entirely a knowledge of the physiology of nervous cells. To what extent does will power modify the organism? How is the mind influenced by the state of the organs? In what manner can the organic and mental characteristics, which each individual inherits, be changed by the mode of life, the chemical substances contained in food, the climate, and the physiological and moral disciplines?

We are very far from knowing what relations exist between skeleton, muscles, and organs, and mental and spiritual activities. We are ignorant of the factors that bring about nervous equilibrium and resistance to fatigue and to diseases. We do not know how moral sense, judgment, and audacity could be augmented. What is the relative importance of intellectual, moral, and mystical activities? What is the significance of æsthetic and religious sense? What form of energy is responsible for telepathic communications? Without any doubt, certain physiological and mental factors determine happiness or misery, success or failure. But we do not know what they are. We cannot artificially give to any individual the aptitude for happiness. As yet we do not know what environment is the most favourable for the optimum development of civilized man. Is it possible to suppress struggle, effort, and suffering from our physiological and spiritual formation? How can we prevent the degeneracy of man in modern civilization? Many other questions could be asked on subjects which are to us of the utmost interest. They would also remain unanswered. It is quite evident that the accomplishments of all the sciences having man as an object remain insufficient, and that our knowledge of ourselves is still most rudimentary.

2

Our ignorance may be attributed, at the same time, to the mode of existence of our ancestors, to the complexity of our nature, and to the structure of our mind. Before all, man had to live. And that need demanded the conquest of the outer world. It was imperative to secure food and shelter, to fight wild animals and other men. For immense periods, our forefathers had neither the leisure nor the inclination to study themselves. They employed their intelligence in other ways, such as manufacturing weapons and tools, discovering fire, training cattle and horses, inventing the wheel, the culture of cereals, etc., etc. Long before becoming interested in the constitution of their body and their mind, they meditated on the sun, the moon, the stars, the tides, and the passing of the seasons. Astronomy was already far advanced at an epoch when physiology was totally unknown. Galileo reduced the earth, centre of the world, to the rank of a humble satellite of the sun, while his contemporaries had not even the most elementary notion of the structure and the functions of brain, liver, or thyroid gland. As, under the natural conditions of life, the human organism works satisfactorily and needs no attention, science progressed in the direction in which it was led by human curiosity—that is, toward the outer world.

From time to time, among the billions of human beings who have successively inhabited the earth, a few were born endowed with rare and marvellous powers, the intuition of unknown things, the imagination that creates new worlds, and the faculty of discovering the hidden relations existing between certain phenomena. These men explored the physical universe. This universe is of a simple constitution. Therefore, it rapidly gave in to the attack of the scientists and yielded the secret of certain of its laws. And the knowledge of these laws enabled us to utilize the world of matter for our own profit. The practical applications of scientific discoveries are lucrative for those who promote them. They facilitate the existence of all. They please the public, whose comfort they augment. Everyone became, of course, much more interested in the inventions that lessen human effort, lighten the burden of the toiler, accelerate the rapidity of communications, and soften the harshness of life, than in the discoveries that throw some light on the intricate problems relating to the constitution of our body and of our consciousness. The conquest of the material world, which has ceaselessly absorbed the attention and the will of men, caused the organic and the spiritual world to fall into almost complete oblivion. In fact the knowledge of our surroundings was indispensable, but that of our own nature appeared to be much less immediately useful. However, disease, pain, death, and more or less obscure aspirations toward a hidden power transcending the visible universe, drew the attention of men, in some measure, to the inner world of their body and their mind. At first medicine contented itself with the practical problem of relieving the sick by empiric recipes. It realized only in recent times that the most effective method of preventing or curing illness is to acquire a complete understanding of the normal and diseased body—that is, to construct the sciences that are called anatomy, biological chemistry, physiology, and pathology. However, the mystery of our existence, the moral sufferings, the craving for the unknown, and the metaphysical phenomena appeared to our ancestors as more important than bodily pain and diseases. The study of spiritual life and of philosophy attracted greater men than the study of medicine. The laws of mysticity became known before those of physiology. But such laws were brought to light only when mankind had acquired sufficient leisure to turn a little of his attention to other things than the conquest of the outer world.

There is another reason for the slow progress of the knowledge of ourselves. Our mind is so constructed as to delight in contemplating simple facts. We feel a kind of repugnance in attacking such a complex problem as that of the constitution of living beings and of man. The intellect, as Bergson wrote, is characterized by a natural inability to comprehend life. On the contrary, we love to discover in the cosmos the geometrical forms that exist in the depths of our consciousness. The exactitude of the proportions of our monuments and the precision of our machines express a fundamental character of our mind. Geometry does not exist in the earthly world. It has originated in ourselves. The methods of nature are never so precise as those of man. We do not find in the universe the clearness and accuracy of our thought. We attempt, therefore, to abstract from the complexity of phenomena some simple systems whose components bear to one another certain relations susceptible of being described mathematically. This power of abstraction of the human intellect is responsible for the amazing progress of physics and chemistry. A similar success has rewarded the physico-chemical study of living beings. The laws of chemistry and of physics are identical in the world of living things and in that of inanimate matter, as Claude Bernard thought long ago. This fact explains why modern physiology has discovered, for example, that the constancy of the alkalinity of the blood and of the water of the ocean is expressed by identical laws, that the energy spent by the contracting muscle is supplied by the fermentation of sugar, etc. The physico-chemical aspects of human beings are almost as easy to investigate as those of the other objects of the terrestrial world.

Such is the task which general physiology succeeds in accomplishing.

The study of the truly physiological phenomena—that is, of those resulting from the organization of living matter—meets with more important obstacles. On account of the extreme smallness of the things to be analyzed, it is impossible to use the ordinary techniques of physics and of chemistry. What method could bring to light the chemical constitution of the nucleus of the sexual cells, of its chromosomes, and of the genes that compose these chromosomes? Nevertheless, those very minute aggregates of chemicals are of capital importance, because they contain the future of the individual and of the race. The fragility of certain tissues, such as the nervous substance, is so great that to study them in the living state is almost impossible. We do not possess any technique capable of penetrating the mysteries of the brain, and of the harmonious association of its cells. Our mind, which loves the simple beauty of mathematical formulas, is bewildered when it contemplates the stupendous mass of cells, humours, and consciousness which make up the individual. We try, therefore, to apply to this compound the concepts that have proved useful in the realm of physics, chemistry, and mechanics, and in the philosophical and religious disciplines. Such an attempt does not meet with much success, because we can be reduced neither to a physico-chemical system nor to a spiritual entity. Of course, the science of man has to use the concepts of all the other sciences. But it must also develop its own. For it is as fundamental as the sciences of the molecules, the atoms, and the electrons.

In short, the slow progress of the knowledge of the human being, as compared with the splendid ascension of physics, astronomy, chemistry, and mechanics, is due to our ancestors' lack of leisure, to the complexity of the subject, and to the structure of our mind. Those obstacles are fundamental. There is no hope of eliminating them. They will always have to be overcome at the cost of strenuous effort. The

knowledge of ourselves will never attain the elegant simplicity, the abstractness, and the beauty of physics. The factors
that have retarded its development are not likely to vanish.
We must realize clearly that the science of man is the most
difficult of all sciences.

3

The environment which has moulded the body and the
soul of our ancestors during many millennia has now
been replaced by another. This silent revolution has taken
place almost without our noticing it. We have not realized
its importance. Nevertheless, it is one of the most dramatic
events in the history of humanity. For any modification in
their surroundings inevitably and profoundly disturbs all living beings. We must, therefore, ascertain the extent of the
transformations imposed by science upon the ancestral mode
of life, and consequently upon ourselves.

Since the advent of industry, a large part of the population
has been compelled to live in restricted areas. The workmen
are herded together, either in the suburbs of the large cities or
in villages built for them. They are occupied in the factories
during fixed hours, doing easy, monotonous, and well-paid
work. The cities are also inhabited by office workers, employees of stores, banks, and public administrations, physicians, lawyers, schoolteachers, and the multitude of those
who, directly or indirectly, draw their livelihood from com-
merce and industry. Factories and offices are large, well
lighted, clean. Their temperature is uniform. Modern heating and refrigerating appliances raise the temperature during the winter and lower it during the summer. The skyscrapers of the great cities have transformed the streets into
gloomy canyons. But inside of the buildings, the light of the
sun is replaced by electric bulbs rich in ultra-rich rays. Instead of the air of the street, polluted by petrol fumes, the

offices and workshops receive pure air drawn in from the
upper atmosphere by ventilators on the roof. The dwellers in
the modern city are protected against all inclemencies of the
weather. But they are no longer able to live as did our ancestors, near their workshops, their stores, or their offices.
The wealthier inhabit the gigantic buildings of the main
avenues. At the top of dizzy towers, the kings of the business
world possess delightful homes, surrounded by trees, grass,
and flowers. They live there, as sheltered from noise, dust,
and all disturbances, as if they dwelt on the summit of a
mountain. They are more completely isolated from the common herd than were the feudal lords behind the walls and
the moats of their fortified castles. The less wealthy, even
those with quite modest means, lodge in apartments whose
comfort surpasses that which surrounded Louis XIV or
Frederick the Great. Many have their residence far from the
city. Each evening express trains transport innumerable
crowds to suburbs, where broad roads running between
green strips of grass and rows of trees are bordered with
pretty and comfortable houses. The workmen and the hum-
blest employees live in dwellings better appointed than those
of the rich of former times. The heating appliances that
automatically regulate the temperature of the houses, the
bathrooms, the refrigerators, the electric stoves, the domestic machinery for preparing food and cleaning rooms, and
the garages for the automobiles, give to the abode of everybody, not only in the city and the suburbs, but also in the
country, a degree of comfort which previously was found
only in that of very few privileged individuals.

Simultaneously with the habitat, the mode of life has been
transformed. This transformation is due chiefly to the increase in the rapidity of communications. Indeed, it is evident that modern trains and steamers, aeroplanes, automobiles, telegraph, telephone, and wireless have modified
the relations of men and of nations all over the world. Each
individual does a great many more things than formerly. He

takes part in a much larger number of events. Every day he comes into contact with more people. Quiet and unemployed moments are exceptional in his existence. The narrow groups of the family and of the parish have been dissolved. Intimacy no longer exists. For the life of the small group has been substituted that of the herd. Solitude is looked upon as a punishment or as a rare luxury. The frequent attendance at cinema, theatrical, or athletic performances, the clubs, the meetings of all sorts, the gigantic universities, factories, department stores, and hotels have engendered in all the habit of living in common. The telephone, the radio, and the gramophone records carry unceasingly the vulgarity of the crowd, as well as its pleasures and its psychology, into everyone's house, even in the most isolated and remote villages. Each individual is always in direct or indirect communication with other human beings, and keeps himself constantly informed about the small or important events taking place in his town, or his city, or at the other end of the world. One hears the chimes of Westminster in the most retired houses of the French countryside. Any farmer in Vermont, if it pleases him to do so, may listen to orators speaking in Berlin, London, or Paris.

Everywhere, in the cities, as well as in the country, in private houses as in factories, in the workshops, on the roads, in the fields, and on the farms, machines have decreased the intensity of human effort. To-day it is not necessary to walk. Lifts have replaced stairs. Everybody rides in buses, motors, or trams, even when the distance to be covered is very short. Natural bodily exercises, such as walking and running over rough ground, mountain-climbing, tilling the land by hand, clearing forests with the axe, working while exposed to rain, sun, wind, cold, or heat, have given place to well-regulated sports that involve almost no risk, and to machines that abolish muscular effort. Everywhere there are tennis-courts, golf-links, artificial skating-rinks, heated swimming-pools, and sheltered arenas where athletes train and fight while protected against the inclemencies of the weather. In this manner all can develop their muscles without being subjected to the fatigue and the hardships involved in the exercises pertaining to a more primitive form of life.

The aliments of our ancestors, which consisted chiefly of coarse flour, meat, and alcoholic drinks, have been replaced by much more delicate and varied food. Beef and mutton are no longer the staple foods. The principal elements of modern diet are milk, cream, butter, cereals refined by the elimination of the shells of the grain, fruits of tropical as well as of temperate countries, fresh or canned vegetables, salads, large quantities of sugar in the form of pies, sweets, and puddings. Alcohol alone has kept its place. The food of children has undergone a profound change. It is now very artificial and abundant. The same may be said of the diet of adults. The regularity of the working-hours in offices and factories has entailed that of the meals. Owing to the wealth which was general until a few years ago, and to the decline in the religious spirit and in the observance of ritualistic fasts, human beings have never been fed so punctually and uninterruptedly.

It is also to the wealth of the post-war period that the enormous diffusion of education is due. Everywhere, schools, colleges, and universities have been erected, and immediately invaded by vast crowds of students. Youth has understood the rôle of science in the modern world. "Knowledge is power," wrote Bacon. All institutions of learning are devoted to the intellectual development of children and young people. At the same time, they give great attention to their physical condition. It is obvious that the main interest of these educational establishments consists in the promotion of mental and muscular strength. Science has demonstrated its usefulness in such an evident manner that it has obtained the first place in the curriculum. A great many young men and women submit themselves to its disciplines. Scientific institutions, universities, and industrial corporations have built so many laboratories that every scientific worker has a chance to make use of his particular knowledge.

The mode of life of modern men is profoundly influenced by hygiene and medicine and the principles resulting from the discoveries of Pasteur. The promulgation of the Pastorian doctrines has been an event of the highest importance to humanity. Their application rapidly led to the suppression of the great infectious diseases which periodically ravaged the civilized world, and of those endemic in each country. The necessity for cleanliness was demonstrated. Infantile mortality at once decreased. The average duration of life has augmented to an amazing extent and has reached fifty-nine years in the United States, and sixty-five years in New Zealand. People do not live longer, but more people live to be old. Hygiene has considerably increased the quantity of human beings. At the same time, medicine, by a better conception of the nature of diseases and a judicious application of surgical techniques, has extended its beneficent influence to the weak, the defective, those predisposed to microbial infections, to all who formerly could not endure the conditions of a rougher life. It has permitted civilization to multiply its human capital enormously. It has also given to each individual much greater security against pain and disease.

The intellectual and moral surroundings in which we are immersed have equally been moulded by science. There is a profound difference between the world that permeates the mind of modern men and the world wherein our ancestors lived. Before the intellectual victories that have brought us wealth and comfort, moral values have naturally given ground. Reason has swept away religious beliefs. The knowledge of the natural laws, and the power given us by this knowledge over the material world, and also over human beings, alone are of importance. Banks, universities, laboratories, medical schools, hospitals, have become as beautiful as the Greek temples, the Gothic cathedrals, and the palaces

of the Popes. Until the recent economic crisis, bank or rail-
way presidents were the ideals of youth. The principal of a
great university still occupies a very high place in the esteem
of the public because he dispenses science. And science is the
mother of wealth, comfort, and health. However, the intellectual atmosphere, in which modern men live, rapidly
changes. Financial magnates, professors, scientists, and economic experts are losing their hold over the public. The
people of to-day are sufficiently educated to read newspapers
and magazines, to listen to the speeches broadcast by politicians, business men, charlatans, and apostles. They are
saturated with commercial, political, or social propaganda,
whose techniques are becoming more and more perfect. At
the same time they read articles and books wherein science
and philosophy are popularized. Our universe, through the
great discoveries of physics and astronomy, has acquired a
marvellous grandeur. Each individual is able, if it so pleases
him, to hear about the theories of Einstein, or to read the
books of Eddington and of Jeans, the articles of Shapley and
of Millikan. The public is as interested in the cosmic rays as
in cinema stars and football players. Everyone is aware that
space is curved, that the world is composed of blind and unknown forces, that we are nothing but infinitely small particles on the surface of a grain of dust lost in the immensity
of the cosmos, and that this cosmos is totally deprived of life
and consciousness. Our universe is exclusively mechanical.
It cannot be otherwise, since it has been created from an
unknown substratum by the techniques of physics and astronomy. Just as are all the surroundings of modern men, it is
the expression of the amazing development of the sciences of
inert matter.

4

The profound changes imposed on the habits of men by the applications of science have occurred recently. In fact, we are still in the midst of the industrial revolution. It is difficult, therefore, to know exactly how the substitution of an artificial mode of existence for the natural one and a complete modification of their environment have acted upon civilized human beings. There is, however, no doubt that such an action has taken place. For every living thing depends intimately on its surroundings, and adapts itself to any modification of these surroundings by an appropriate change. We must, therefore, ascertain in what manner we have been influenced by the mode of life, the customs, the diet, the education, and the intellectual and moral habits imposed on us by modern civilization. Have we benefited by such progress? This momentous question can be answered only after a careful examination of the state of the nations which were the first to profit by the application of scientific discoveries.

It is evident that men have joyfully welcomed modern civilization. They have abandoned the countryside and flocked to the cities and the factories. They eagerly adopt the mode of life and the ways of acting and of thinking of the new era. They lay aside their old habits without hesitation, because these habits demand a greater effort. It is less fatiguing to work in a factory or an office than on a farm. But even in the country, new techniques have relieved the harshness of existence. Modern houses make life easier for everybody. By their comfort, their warmth, and their pleasant lighting, they give their inmates a feeling of rest and contentment. Their up-to-date appointments considerably decrease the labour that, in bygone days, housekeeping demanded from women. Besides the lessening of muscular effort and the possession of comfort, human beings have accepted cheerfully the privilege of never being alone, of enjoying the innumerable distractions of the city, of living among huge crowds, of never thinking. They also appreciate being released, through a purely intellectual education, from the moral restraint imposed upon them by Puritan discipline and religious principles. In truth, modern life has set them free. It incites them to acquire wealth by any and every possible means, provided that these means do not lead them to gaol. It opens to them all the countries of the earth. It has liberated them from all superstitions. It allows them the frequent excitation and the easy satisfaction of their sexual appetites. It does away with constraint, discipline, effort, everything that is inconvenient and laborious. The people, especially those belonging to the lower classes, are happier from a material standpoint than in former times. However, some of them progressively cease to appreciate the distractions and the vulgar pleasures of modern life. Occasionally their health does not permit them to continue indefinitely the alimentary, alcoholic, and sexual excesses to which they are led by the suppression of all discipline. Besides, they are haunted by the fear of losing their employment, their means of subsistence, their savings, their fortune. They are unable to satisfy the need for security that exists in the depth of each of us. In spite of social insurance, they feel uneasy about their future. Those who are capable of thinking become discontented.

It is certain, nevertheless, that health is improving. Not only has mortality decreased, but each individual is handsomer, larger, and stronger. To-day children are much taller than their parents. An abundance of good food and physical exercises have augmented the size of the body and its muscular strength. Often the best athletes at the international games come from the United States. In the athletic teams of the American universities there are many individuals who are really magnificent specimens of human beings. Under the present educational conditions, bones and muscles develop perfectly. America has succeeded in reproducing the most admirable forms of ancient beauty. However, the longevity of the men proficient in all kinds of sports and enjoying every advantage of modern life is not greater than that of their ancestors. It may even be less. Their resistance to fatigue and worry seems to have decreased. It appears that the individuals accustomed to natural bodily exercise, to hardships, and to the inclemencies of the weather, as were their fathers, are capable of harder and more sustained efforts than our athletes. We know that the products of modern education need much sleep, good food, and regular habits. Their nervous system is delicate. They do not endure the mode of existence in the large cities, the confinement in offices, the worries of business, and even the everyday difficulties and sufferings of life. They easily break down. Perhaps the triumphs of hygiene, medicine, and modern education are not so advantageous as we are led to believe.

We should also ask ourselves whether there are no inconveniences attached to the great decrease in the death rate during infancy and youth. In fact, the weak are saved as well as the strong. Natural selection no longer plays its part. No one knows what will be the future of a race so well protected by medical sciences. But we are confronted with much graver problems, which demand immediate solution. While infantile diarrhœa, tuberculosis, diphtheria, typhoid fever, etc., are being eliminated, they are replaced by degenerative diseases. There are also a large number of affections of the nervous system and of the mind. In certain states the multitude of the insane confined in the asylums exceeds that of the patients kept in all other hospitals. Like insanity, nervous disorders and intellectual weakness seem to have become more frequent. They are the most active factors of individual misery and of the destruction of families. Mental deterioration is more dangerous for civilization than the infectious diseases to which hygienists and physicians have so far exclusively devoted their attention.

In spite of the immense sums of money expended on the education of the children and the young people of the United

States, the intellectual élite does not seem to have increased. The average man and woman are, without any doubt, better educated and, superficially at least, more refined. The taste for reading is greater. More reviews and books are bought' by the public than in former times. The number of people who are interested in science, letters, and art has grown. But most of them are chiefly attracted by the lowest form of literature and by the imitations of science and of art. It seems that the excellent hygienic conditions in which children are reared, and the care lavished upon them in school, have not raised their intellectual and moral standards. There may possibly be some antagonism between their physical development and their mental size. After all, we do not know whether a larger stature in a given race expresses a state of progress, as is assumed to-day, or of degeneracy. There is no doubt that children are much happier in the schools where compulsion has been suppressed, where they are allowed exclusively to study the subjects in which they are interested, where intellectual effort and voluntary attention are not exacted. What are the results of such an education? In modern civilization the individual is characterized chiefly by a fairly great activity, entirely directed toward the practical side of life, by much ignorance, by a certain shrewdness, and by a kind of mental weakness which leaves him under the influence of the environment wherein he happens to be placed. It appears that intelligence itself gives way when character weakens. For this reason, perhaps, this quality, characteristic of France in former times, has so markedly failed in that country. In the United States the intellectual standard remains low, in spite of the increasing number of schools and universities.

Modern civilization seems to be incapable of producing people endowed with imagination, intelligence, and courage. In practically every country there is a decrease in the intellectual and moral calibre of those who carry the responsibility of public affairs. The financial, industrial, and commercial organizations have reached a gigantic size. They are influenced not only by the conditions of the country where they are established, but also by the state of the neighbouring countries and of the entire world. In all nations economic and social conditions undergo extremely rapid changes. Nearly everywhere the existing form of government is again under discussion. The great democracies find themselves face to face with formidable problems—problems concerning their very existence and demanding an immediate solution. And we realize that, despite the immense hopes which humanity has placed in modern civilization, such a civilization has failed in developing men of sufficient intelligence and audacity to guide it along the dangerous road on which it is stumbling. Human beings have not grown so rapidly as the institutions sprung from their brains. It is chiefly the intellectual and moral deficiencies of the political leaders, and their ignorance, which endanger modern nations.

Finally, we must ascertain how the new mode of life will influence the future of the race. The response of the women to the modifications brought about in the ancestral habits by industrial civilization has been immediate and decisive. The birth-rate has at once fallen. This event has been felt most precociously and seriously in the social classes and in the nations which were the first to benefit from the progress brought about, directly or indirectly, by the applications of scientific discoveries. Voluntary sterility is not a new thing in the history of the world. It has already been observed in a certain period of past civilizations. It is a classical symptom. We know its significance.

It is evident, then, that the changes produced in our environment by technology have influenced us profoundly. Their effects assume an unexpected character. They are strikingly different from those which were hoped for and which could legitimately be expected from the improvements of all kinds brought to the habitat, the mode of life, the diet, the education, and the intellectual atmosphere of

B (A181)

human beings. How has such a paradoxical result been obtained?

5

A simple answer could be given to this question. Modern civilization finds itself in a difficult position because it does not suit us. It has been erected without any knowledge of our real nature. It was born from the whims of scientific discoveries, from the appetites of men, their illusions, their theories, and their desires. Although constructed by our efforts, it is not adjusted to our size and shape.

Obviously science follows no plan. It develops at random. Its progress depends on fortuitous conditions, such as the birth of men of genius, the form of their mind, the direction taken by their curiosity. It is not at all actuated by a desire to improve the state of human beings. The discoveries responsible for industrial civilization were brought forth at the fancy of the scientists' intuitions and of the more or less casual circumstances of their careers. If Galileo, Newton, or Lavoisier had applied their intellectual powers to the study of body and consciousness, our world probably would be different to-day. Men of science do not know where they are going. They are guided by chance, by subtle reasoning, by a sort of clairvoyance. Each one of them is a world apart, governed by his own laws. From time to time, things obscure to others become clear to him. In general, discoveries are developed without any prevision of their consequences. These consequences, however, have revolutionized the world and made our civilization what it is.

From the wealth of science we have selected certain parts. And our choice has in no way been influenced by a consideration of the higher interests of humanity. It has simply followed the direction of our natural tendencies. The principles of the greatest convenience and of the least effort, the

pleasure procured by speed, change, and comfort, and also
the need of escaping from ourselves, are the determining
factors in the success of new inventions. But no one has ever
asked himself how we would stand the enormous acceleration of the rhythm of life resulting from rapid transport,
telegraph, telephone, modern business methods, machines
that write and calculate, and those that do all the housekeeping drudgery of former times. The tendency responsible for
the universal adoption of the aeroplane, the automobile, the
cinema, the telephone, the radio, and, in the near future, of
television, is as natural as that which, in the night of the ages,
led our ancestors to drink alcohol. Steam-heated houses,
electric lighting, lifts, biological morals, and chemical adulteration of foodstuffs have been accepted solely because
those innovations were agreeable and convenient. But no
account whatever has been taken of their probable effect on
human beings.

In the organization of industrial life the influence of the
factory upon the physiological and mental state of the
workers has been completely neglected. Modern industry is
based on the conception of the maximum production at lowest cost, in order that an individual or a group of individuals
may earn as much money as possible. It has expanded without any idea of the true nature of the human beings who run
the machines, and without giving any consideration to the
effects produced on the individuals and on their descendants
by the artificial mode of existence imposed by the factory.
The great cities have been built with no regard for us. The
shape and dimensions of the skyscrapers depend entirely on
the necessity of obtaining the maximum income per square
foot of ground, and of offering to the tenants offices and
apartments that please them. This caused the construction of
gigantic buildings where too large masses of human beings
are crowded together. Civilized men like such a way of living. While they enjoy the comfort and banal luxury of their
dwelling, they do not realize that they are deprived of the

necessities of life. The modern city consists of monstrous edifices and of dark, narrow streets full of petrol fumes, coal dust, and toxic gases, torn by the noise of the taxi-cabs, lorries, and buses, and thronged ceaselessly by great crowds. Obviously, it has not been planned for the good of its inhabitants.

Our life is influenced in a large measure by commercial advertising. Such publicity is undertaken only in the interest of the advertisers and not of the consumers. For example, the public has been made to believe that white bread is better than brown. Then, flour has been bolted more and more thoroughly and thus deprived of its most useful components. Such treatment permits its preservation for longer periods and facilitates the making of bread. The millers and the bakers earn more money. The consumers eat an inferior product, believing it to be a superior one. And in the countries where bread is the principal food, the population degenerates. Enormous amounts of money are spent for publicity. As a result, large quantities of alimentary and pharmaceutical products, at the least useless, and often harmful, have become a necessity for civilized men. In this manner the greediness of individuals, sufficiently shrewd to create a popular demand for the goods that they have for sale, plays a leading part in the modern world.

However, the propaganda that directs our ways of living is not always inspired by selfish motives. Instead of being prompted by the financial interests of individuals or of groups of individuals, it often aims at the common good. But its effect may also be harmful when it emanates from people having a false or incomplete conception of the human being. For example, should physicians, by prescribing special foods, as most of them do, accelerate the growth of young children? In such an instance their action is based on an incomplete knowledge of the subject. Are larger and heavier children better than smaller ones? Intelligence, alertness, audacity, and resistance to disease do not depend on the same factors as the weight of the body. The education dispensed by schools and universities consists chiefly in a training of the memory and of the muscles, in certain social manners, in a worship of athletics. Are such disciplines really suitable for modern men who need, above all other things, mental equilibrium, nervous stability, sound judgment, audacity, moral courage, and endurance? Why do hygienists behave as though human beings were exclusively liable to infectious diseases, while they are also exposed to the attacks of nervous and mental disorders, and to the weakening of the mind? Although physicians, educators, and hygienists most generously lavish their efforts for the benefit of mankind, they do not attain their goal. For they deal with schemata containing only a part of the reality. The same may be said of all those who substitute their desires, their dreams, or their doctrines for the concrete human being. These theorists build up civilizations which, although designed by them for man, fit only an incomplete or monstrous image of man. The systems of government, entirely constructed in the minds of doctrinaires, are valueless. The principles of the French Revolution, the visions of Marx and Lenin, apply only to abstract men. It must be clearly realized that the laws of human relations are still unknown. Sociology and economics are conjectural sciences—that is, pseudo-sciences.

Thus it appears that the environment, which science and technology have succeeded in developing for man, does not suit him, because it has been constructed at random, without regard for his true self.

6

To summarize. The sciences of inert matter have made immense progress, while those of living beings remain in a rudimentary state. The slow advance of biology is due to the conditions of human existence, to the intricacy of the phenomena of life, and to the form of our intelligence, which delights in mechanical constructions and mathematical abstractions. The applications of scientific discoveries have transformed the material and mental worlds. These transformations exert on us a profound influence. Their unfortunate effect comes from the fact that they have been made without consideration for our nature. Our ignorance of ourselves has given to mechanics, physics, and chemistry the power to modify at random the ancestral forms of life.

Man should be the measure of all. On the contrary, he is a stranger in the world that he has created. He has been incapable of organizing this world for himself, because he did not possess a practical knowledge of his own nature. Thus the enormous advance gained by the sciences of inanimate matter over those of living things is one of the greatest catastrophes ever suffered by humanity. The environment born of our intelligence and our inventions is adjusted neither to our stature nor to our shape. We are unhappy. We degenerate morally and mentally. The groups and the nations in which industrial civilization has attained its highest development are precisely those which are becoming weaker, and whose return to barbarism is the most rapid. But they do not realize it. They are without protection against the hostile surroundings that science has built about them. In truth, our civilization, like those preceding it, has created certain conditions of existence which, for reasons still obscure, render life itself impossible. The anxiety and the woes of the inhabitants of the modern city arise from their political, economic, and social institutions, but, above all, from their own weakness. We are the victims of the backwardness of the sciences of life over those of matter.

The only possible remedy for this evil is a much more profound knowledge of ourselves. Such a knowledge will enable us to understand by what mechanisms modern existence affects our consciousness and our body. We shall thus learn how to adapt ourselves to our surroundings, and how to change them should a revolution become indispensable. In bringing to light our true nature, our potentialities, and the way to actualize them, this science will give us the explanation of our physiological weakening, and of our moral and intellectual diseases. We have no other means of learning the inexorable rules of our organic and spiritual activities, of distinguishing the prohibited from the lawful, of realizing that we are not free to modify, according to our fancy, our environment and ourselves. Since the natural conditions of existence have been destroyed by modern civilization, the science of man has become the most necessary of all sciences.

CHAPTER II

THE SCIENCE OF MAN

1. Necessity of a choice among the heterogeneous data concerning man. The operational concept of Bridgman. Its application to living beings. Confusion of concepts. Rejection of philosophical and scientific systems. Function of conjectures. 2. The need of a complete survey. Every aspect of man to receive attention. No exaggerated importance to be given to any one part. Simple phenomena not to be preferred to complex ones. Unexplainable facts not to be ignored. Man in his entirety is within the jurisdiction of science. 3. The science of man is more important than all other sciences. Its analytic and synthetic character. 4. The analysis of man requires various techniques. Those techniques create body and soul, structure and functions, and divide the body into parts. The specialists. The need for non-specialized scientists. How to promote human biological research. 5. Technical difficulties encountered in the study of man. Utilization of animals of high intelligence. How experiments of long duration should be organized. 6. The character of a utilizable synthesis of our data about man.

I

OUR ignorance of ourselves is of a peculiar nature. It does not arise from difficulty in procuring the necessary information, from its inaccuracy, or from its scarcity. On the contrary, it is due to the extreme abundance and confusion of the data accumulated about itself by humanity during the course of the ages; also to the division of man into an almost infinite number of fragments by the sciences that have endeavoured to study his body and his consciousness. This knowledge, to a large extent, has not been utilized. In fact, it is barely utilizable. Its sterility manifests itself in the meagreness of the classical abstractions, of the schemata that are the basis of medicine, hygiene, education, sociology, and political economy. There is, however, a living and rich reality buried in the enormous mass of definitions, observations, doctrines, desires, and dreams representing man's efforts toward a knowledge of himself. In addition to the systems and speculations of scientists and philosophers, we have the positive results of the experience of past generations, and also a multitude of observations carried out with the spirit and, occasionally, with the techniques of science. But we must make a judicious choice from these heterogeneous things.

Among the numerous concepts relating to the human being, some are mere logical constructs of our mind. We do not find in the outer world any being to whom they apply. The others are purely and simply the result of experience. They have been called by Bridgman operational concepts. An operational concept is equivalent to the operation or to the set of operations involved in its acquisition. Indeed, all positive knowledge demands the use of a certain technique, of certain physical or mental operations. When we say that an object is one metre long, we mean that it has the same length as a rod of wood or of metal, whose dimension is, in its turn, equal to that of the standard metre kept at the International Bureau of Weights and Measures in Paris. It is quite evident that the things we can observe are the only ones we really know. In the foregoing example, the concept of length is synonymous with the measurement of such length. According to Bridgman, concepts dealing with things situated outside the experimental field are meaningless. Thus, a question has no signification if it is not possible to discover the operations permitting us to answer it.

The precision of any concept whatsoever depends upon that of the operations by which it is acquired. If man is defined as a being composed of matter and consciousness, such a proposition is meaningless. For the relations between consciousness and bodily matter have not, so far, been brought into the experimental field. But an operational definition is given of man when we consider him as an organism capable

B*

of manifesting physico-chemical, physiological, and psychological activities. In biology, as in physics, the concepts which will always remain real, and must be the basis of science, are linked to certain methods of observation. For example, our present idea of the cells of the cerebral cortex, their pyramidal body, their dendritic processes, and their smooth axon, results from the techniques invented by Ramon y Cajal. This is an operational concept. Such a concept will change only when new and more perfect techniques are discovered. But to say that cerebral cells are the seat of mental processes is a worthless affirmation, for there is no possibility of observing the presence of mental processes in the body of cerebral cells. Operational concepts are the only solid foundation upon which we can build. From the immense fund of knowledge we possess about ourselves, we must select the data corresponding to what exists not only in our mind, but also in nature.

We know that among the concepts relating to man, some are specific of him, others belong to all living beings, and still others are those of chemistry, physics, and mechanics. There are as many systems of concepts as of strata in the organization of living matter. At the level of the electronic, atomic, and molecular structures found in man's tissues, as well as in trees, stones, or clouds, the concepts of space-time continuum, energy, force, mass, entropy, should be used, and also those of osmotic tension, electric charge, ions, capillarity, permeability, diffusion. The concepts of micella, dispersion, adsorption, and flocculation appear at the level of the material aggregates larger than molecules. When the molecules and their combinations have erected tissue cells, and when these cells have associated together to form organs and organisms, the concepts of chromosome, gene, heredity, adaptation, physiological time, reflex, instinct, etc., must be added to those already mentioned. They are the very concepts of physiology. They exist simultaneously with the physico-chemical concepts, but cannot be reduced to them.

At the highest level of organization, in addition to electrons, atoms, molecules, cells, and tissues, we encounter a whole composed of organs, humours, and consciousness. Then physico-chemical and physiological concepts become insufficient. To them we must join the psychological concepts characteristic of man, such as intelligence, moral sense, æsthetic sense, and social sense. The principles of minimum effort and of maximum production or of maximum pleasure, the quest for liberty, for equality, etc., have to be substituted for the thermodynamic laws and those of adaptation.

Each system of concepts can only be legitimately used in the domain of the science to which it belongs. The concepts of physics, chemistry, physiology, and psychology are applicable to the superposed levels of the bodily organization. But the concepts appropriate at one level should not be mingled indiscriminately with those specific to another. For example, the second law of thermodynamics, the law of dissipation of free energy, indispensable at the molecular level, is useless at the psychological level, where the principles of least effort and of maximum pleasure are applied. The concepts of capillarity and of osmotic tension do not throw any light on problems pertaining to consciousness. It is nothing but word play to explain a psychological phenomenon in terms of cell physiology, or of quantum mechanics. However, the mechanistic physiologists of the nineteenth century, and their disciples who still linger with us, have committed such an error in endeavouring to reduce man entirely to physical chemistry. This unjustified generalization of the results of sound experiments is due to over-specialization. Concepts should not be misused. They must be kept in their place in the hierarchy of sciences.

The confusion in our knowledge of ourselves comes chiefly from the presence, among the positive facts, of the remains of scientific, philosophic, and religious systems. If our mind adheres to any system whatsoever, the aspect and the significance of concrete phenomena are changed. At all times humanity has contemplated itself through glasses coloured by doctrines, beliefs, and illusions. These false or inexact ideas must be discarded. Long ago Claude Bernard in his writings mentioned the necessity of getting rid of philosophical and scientific systems as one would break the chains of intellectual slavery. But such freedom has not yet been attained. Biologists and, above all, educators, economists, and sociologists, when facing extremely complex problems, have often yielded to the temptation to build up theories and afterwards to turn them into articles of faith, and their sciences have crystallized in formulas as rigid as the dogmas of a religion.

We meet with troublesome reminders of such mistakes in all the departments of knowledge. The quarrel of the vitalists and the mechanists, the futility of which astounds us to-day, arose from one of the most famous of these errors. The vitalists thought that the organism was a machine whose parts were integrated with one another by a factor that was not physico-chemical. According to them, the processes responsible for the unity of the living being were governed by an independent spiritual principle, an entelechy, an idea analogous to that of an engineer who designs a machine. This autonomous factor was not a form of energy and did not produce energy. It was only concerned with the management of the organism. Evidently, entelechy is not an operational concept. It is purely a mental construct. In short, the vitalists considered the body as a machine, guided by an engineer, whom they called entelechy. And they did not realize that this engineer was nothing but the intelligence of the observer. As for the mechanists, they believed that all physiological and psychological activities could be explained by the laws of physics, chemistry, and mechanics. They thus built a machine, and, like the vitalists, they were the engineer of this machine. Then, as Woodger pointed out, they forgot the existence of that engineer. Such a concept is not operational. It is evident that mechanism and vitalism should be rejected for the same reason as all other systems. At the same time we must free ourselves from the mass of illusions, errors, and badly observed facts, from the false problems investigated by the weak-minded of the realm of science, and from the pseudo-discoveries of charlatans and scientists extolled by the daily press. Also from the sadly useless investigations, the long studies of meaningless things, the inextricable jumble that has been standing mountain high ever since biological research became a profession like those of the school-teacher, the clergyman, and the bank clerk.

This elimination completed, the results of the patient labour of all sciences concerning themselves with man, the accumulated wealth of their experience, will remain as the unshakeable basis of our knowledge. In the history of humanity, the expression of all our fundamental activities can be read at a single glance. In addition to positive observations, to sure facts, there are many things neither positive nor indubitable. They should not be rejected. Of course, operational concepts are the only foundation upon which science can be solidly built. But creative imagination alone is capable of inspiring conjectures and dreams pregnant with the worlds of the future. We must continue asking questions which, from the point of view of sound, scientific criticism, are meaningless. And even if we tried to prevent our mind from pursuing the impossible and the unknowable, such an effort would be vain. Curiosity is a necessity of our nature, a blind impulse that obeys no rule. Our mind turns around all external objects and penetrates within the depths of ourselves, as instinctively and as irresistibly as a raccoon explores, with its clever little paws, the slightest details of its narrow world. Curiosity impels us to discover the universe. It inexorably draws us in its train to unknown countries. And unclimbable mountains vanish before it like smoke before the wind.

2

A thorough examination of man is indispensable. The
barrenness of classical schemata is due to the fact that, despite the great scope of our knowledge, we have never apprehended our whole being with a sufficiently penetrating effort.
Thus we must do more than consider the aspect of man at a
certain period of his history, in certain conditions of his life.
We must grasp him in all his activities, those that are ordi-
narily apparent as well as those that may remain potential.
Such information can only be obtained by looking carefully
in the present and in the past for all the manifestations of our
organic and mental powers. Also by an examination, both
analytic and synthetic, of our constitution and of our physical, chemical, and mental relations with our environment.
We should follow the wise advice that Descartes, in his *Discourse on Method*, gave to those who seek the truth, and
divide our subject into as many parts as are necessary in
order to make a complete inventory of each one of them.
But it should be clearly understood that such a division is
only a methodological expedient, created by ourselves, and
that man remains indivisible.

There is no privileged territory. In the abysses of our inner
world everything has a meaning. We cannot choose only
those things that please us, according to the dictates of our
feelings, our imagination, the scientific and philosophical
form of our mind. A difficult or obscure subject must not be
neglected just because it is difficult and obscure. All methods
should be employed. The qualitative is as true as the quantitative. The relations that can be expressed in mathematical
terms do not possess greater reality than those that cannot
be so expressed. Darwin, Claude Bernard, and Pasteur,
whose discoveries could not be described in algebraic formulas, were as great scientists as Newton and Einstein.
Reality is not necessarily clear and simple. It is not even sure
that we are always able to understand it. In addition, it as-

sumes infinitely varied aspects. A state of consciousness, the humeral bone, a wound, are equally real things. A phenomenon does not owe its importance to the facility with which scientific techniques can be applied to its study. It must be conceived in function, not of the observer and his method, but of the subject, the human being. The grief of the mother who has lost her child, the distress of the mystical soul plunged in the "dark night," the suffering of the patient tortured by cancer, are evident realities, although they are not measurable. The study of the phenomena of clairvoyance should not be neglected any more than that of the chronaxy of nerves, though clairvoyance can neither be produced at will nor measured, while it is possible to measure chronaxy exactly by a simple method. In making this inventory we should utilize all possible means and be content with observing the phenomena that cannot be measured.

It often happens that undue importance is given to some part at the expense of the others. We are obliged to consider all the different aspects of man, physico-chemical, anatomical, physiological, metaphysical, intellectual, moral, artistic, religious, economic, and social. Every specialist, owing to a well-known professional bias, believes that he understands the entire human being, while in reality he only grasps a tiny part of him. Fragmentary aspects are considered as representing the whole. And these aspects are taken at random, following the fashion of the moment, which in turn gives more importance to the individual or to society, to physiological appetites or to spiritual activities, to muscular development or to brain power, to beauty or to utility, etc. Man, therefore, appears with many different visages. We arbitrarily choose among them the one that pleases us and forget the others.

Another mistake consists in suppressing a part of reality from the inventory. There are many reasons accounting for this. We prefer to study systems that can easily be isolated and approached by simple methods. We generally neglect the more complex. Our mind has a partiality for precise and definitive solutions and for the resulting intellectual security. We have an almost irresistible tendency to select the subjects of our investigations for their technical facility and clearness rather than for their importance. Thus modern physiologists principally concern themselves with physico-chemical phenomena taking place in living animals, and pay less attention to physiological and functional processes. The same thing happens with physicians when they specialize in subjects whose techniques are easy and already known, rather than in degenerative diseases, neuroses, and psychoses, whose study would require the use of imagination and the creation of new methods. Everyone realizes, however, that the discovery of some of the laws of the organization of living matter would be more important than, for example, that of the rhythm of the cilia of tracheal cells. Without any doubt, it would be much more useful to free humanity from cancer, tuberculosis, arteriosclerosis, syphilis, and the innumerable misfortunes caused by nervous and mental diseases, than to engross oneself in the minute study of physico-chemical phenomena of secondary importance manifesting themselves in the course of diseases. On account of technical difficulties, certain matters are banished from the field of scientific research, and refused the right of making themselves known.

Important facts may be completely ignored. Our mind has a natural tendency to reject the things that do not fit into the frame of the scientific or philosophical beliefs of our time. After all, scientists are only men. They are saturated with the prejudices of their environment and of their epoch. They willingly believe that facts that cannot be explained by current theories do not exist. During the period when physiology was identified with physical chemistry, the period of Jacques Loeb and of Bayliss, the study of mental functions was neglected. No one was interested in psychology and in mind disorders. At the present time, scientists who are concerned solely in the physical, chemical, and physico-chemical aspects of physiological processes still look upon telepathy and other metapsychical phenomena as illusions. Evident facts having an unorthodox appearance are suppressed. By reason of these difficulties, the inventory of the things which could lead us to a better understanding of the human being has been left incomplete. We must, then, go back to a naïve observation of ourselves in all our aspects, reject nothing, and describe simply what we see.

At first glance the scientific method seems not to be applicable to the analysis of all our activities. It is obvious that we, the observers, are unable to follow human personality into every region where it extends. Our techniques do not grasp things having neither dimensions nor weight. They only reach those situated in space and time. They are incapable of measuring vanity, hatred, love, beauty, or the dreams of the scientist, the inspiration of the poet, the elevation of the mystical soul towards God. But they easily record the physiological aspects and the material results of these psychological states. Mental and spiritual activities, when they play an important part in our life, express themselves by a certain behaviour, certain acts, a certain attitude toward our fellow men. It is only in this manner that the moral, æsthetic, and mystic functions can be explored by scientific methods. We also have at our disposal the statements of those who have travelled in these almost unknown regions. But the verbal expression of their experiences is, in general, disconcerting. Outside the domain of intelligence nothing is clearly definable. Of course, the elusiveness of a thing does not signify its non-existence. When one sails in dense fog, the invisible rocks are none the less present. From time to time their menacing forms emerge from the white mist, and at once they are swallowed up again. To this phenomenon can be truthfully compared the evanescent visions of artists and, above all, of great mystics. Those things which our techniques are incapable of grasping nevertheless stamp the initiated with a visible mark. In such indirect ways does science know the spiritual world which, by definition, it is forbidden to enter. Man in his entirety is located within the jurisdiction of the scientific techniques.

3

The critical review of the data concerning man yields a large amount of positive information. We are thus enabled to make a complete inventory of human activities. Such an inventory will lead to the building up of new schemata, richer than the classical ones. But our knowledge will not, in this manner, progress very strikingly. We shall have to go farther and build up a real science of man—a science capable of undertaking, with the help of all known techniques, a more exhaustive examination of our inner world, and also of realizing that each part should be considered as a function of the whole. In order to develop such a science, we must, for some time, turn our attention away from mechanical inventions and even, in a certain measure, from classical hygiene and medicine, from the purely material aspects of our existence. Everybody is interested in things that increase wealth and comfort, but no one understands that the structural, functional, and mental quality of each individual has to be improved. The health of the intelligence and of the affective sense, moral discipline, and spiritual development are just as necessary as the health of the body and the prevention of infectious diseases.

No advantage is to be gained by increasing the number of mechanical inventions. It would perhaps be as well not to accord so much importance to discoveries of physics, astronomy, and chemistry. In truth, pure science never directly brings us any harm. But when its fascinating beauty dominates our mind and enslaves our thoughts in the realm of inanimate matter it becomes dangerous. Man must now turn his attention to himself, and to the cause of his moral and intellectual disability. What is the good of increasing the comfort, the luxury, the beauty, the size, and the complications of our civilization, if our weakness prevents us from guiding it to our best advantage? It is really not worth while to go on elaborating a way of living that is bringing about the demoralization and the disappearance of the noblest elements of the great races. It would be far better to pay more attention to ourselves than to construct faster steamers, more comfortable automobiles, cheaper radios, or telescopes for examining the structure of remote nebulæ. What real progress will be accomplished when aircraft take us to Europe or to China in a few hours? Is it necessary to increase production unceasingly, so that men may consume larger and larger quantities of useless things? There is not the shadow of a doubt that mechanical, physical, and chemical sciences are incapable of giving us intelligence, moral discipline, health, nervous equilibrium, security, and peace.

Our curiosity must turn aside from its present path and take another direction. It must leave the physical and physiological in order to follow the mental and the spiritual. So far, sciences concerning themselves with human beings have confined their activities to certain aspects of their subject. They have not succeeded in escaping from Cartesian dualism. They have been dominated by mechanism. In physiology, hygiene, and medicine, as well as in the study of education and of political and social economy, scientists have been chiefly absorbed by organic, humoral, and intellectual aspects of man. They have not paid any great attention to his affective and moral form, his inner life, his character, his æsthetic and religious needs, the common substratum of organic and psychological activities, the intimate relations of the individual and of his mental and spiritual environment. A radical change is indispensable. This change requires both the work of specialists devoting their efforts to the particular knowledge related to our body and our mind, and of scientists capable of integrating the discoveries of the specialists in function of man as a whole. The new science must progress, by a double effort of analysis and synthesis, towards a conception of the human individual at once sufficiently complete and sufficiently simple to serve as a basis for our action.

4

Man cannot be separated into parts. He would cease to exist if his organs were isolated from one another. Although indivisible he assumes different aspects. His aspects are the heterogeneous manifestations of his unity to our sense organs. He can be compared to an electric lamp whose presence is recorded in a different manner by a thermometer, a voltmeter, a photographic plate, or a selenium cell. We are incapable of directly apprehending him in his simplicity. We can only grasp him through our senses and our scientific instruments. According to our means of investigation, his activity appears to be physical, chemical, physiological, or psychological. The analysis of his manifoldness naturally demands the help of various techniques. As he manifests himself exclusively through the agency of these techniques, he necessarily takes on the appearance of being multiple.

The science of man makes use of all other sciences. This is one of the reasons for its slow progress and its difficulty. For example, in order to study the influence of a psychological factor on a sensitive individual, the methods of medicine, physiology, physics, and chemistry have to be employed. Let us suppose that our subject receives bad news. This psychological event may express itself simultaneously by moral suffering, nervous agitation, circulatory disturbances, lesions of the skin, physico-chemical modifications of the blood, etc. When dealing with man we are obliged to employ the methods and concepts of several sciences, even for the simplest experiment. If we study the effects of a given food, either animal or vegetable, on a group of individuals, we must first learn the chemical composition of that food, and also the physiological and psychological states, and the ancestral characteristics of the individuals who are to be the subjects of the investigation. Then we have to record accurately the changes in weight, in height, in the form of the skeleton, in muscular strength, in susceptibility to diseases, in the physical, chemical, and anatomical characteristics of the blood, in nervous equilibrium, in intelligence, courage, fertility, longevity, which take place during the course of the experiment.

Obviously no one scientist is capable of mastering all the techniques indispensable to the study of a single human problem. Therefore progress in knowledge of ourselves requires the simultaneous efforts of various specialists. Each specialist confines himself to one part of the body, or consciousness, or of their relations with the environment. He is anatomist, physiologist, chemist, psychologist, physician, hygienist, educator, clergyman, sociologist, economist. Each speciality is divided into smaller and smaller parts. There are specialists in glandular physiology, in vitamins, in diseases of the rectum, in those of the nose, in education of small children or of adults, in hygiene of factories and of prisons, in psychology of all categories of individuals, in domestic economy, rural economy, etc. Such a division of the work has made possible the development of the particular sciences. Specialization is imperative. Scientists have to devote their attention to one department of knowledge. And it is impossible for a specialist, actively engaged in the pursuit of his own task, to understand the human being as a whole. Indeed, such a state of affairs is rendered necessary by the vast extent of the field of each science. But it presents a certain danger. For example, Calmette, who had specialized in bacteriology, wished to prevent the spread of tuberculosis among the French population. He naturally prescribed the use of the vaccine he had invented. If, in addition to being a bacteriologist, he had possessed a more general knowledge of hygiene and medicine, he would have advised also the adoption of measures with regard to dwellings, food, working conditions, and the way of living of the people. A similar occurrence took place in the United States in the organization of the elementary schools. John Dewey, who is a philosopher, undertook to improve the education of American children. But his methods were suited to the schema, the abstraction, which his professional bias made him take for the concrete child.

Still more harm is caused by the extreme specialization of the physicians. Medicine has separated the sick human being into small fragments, and each fragment has its specialist. When a specialist, from the beginning of his career, confines himself to a minute part of the body, his knowledge of the rest is so rudimentary that he is incapable of thoroughly understanding even that part in which he specializes. A similar thing happens to educators, clergymen, economists, and sociologists who, before limiting themselves entirely to their particular domain, have not taken the trouble to acquire a general knowledge of man. The more eminent the specialist, the more dangerous he is. Scientists who have strikingly distinguished themselves by great discoveries or useful inventions often come to believe that their knowledge of one subject extends to all others. Edison, for example, did not hesitate to impart to the public his views on philosophy and religion, and the public listened to his words with respect, imagining them to carry as much weight on these new subjects as on the former ones. Thus, great men, in speaking about things they do not thoroughly understand, hinder human progress in one of its fields, while having contributed to its advancement in another. The daily press often gives us the dubious benefit of the sociological, economic, and scientific opinions of manufacturers, bankers, lawyers, professors, physicians, whose highly specialized minds are incapable of apprehending in their breadth the momentous problems of our time. However, modern civilization absolutely needs specialists. Without them science could not progress. But before the results of their researches is applied to man, the scattered data of their analyses must be integrated in an intelligible synthesis.

Such a synthesis cannot be obtained by a simple round-table conference of the specialists. It requires the efforts of one man, not merely those of a group. A work of art has never been produced by a committee of artists, nor a great discovery made by a committee of scholars. The syntheses needed for the progress of our knowledge of man should be elaborated in a single brain. It is impossible to make use of the mass of information accumulated by the specialists. For no one has undertaken to co-ordinate the data already obtained, and to consider the human being in his entirety. To-day there are many scientific workers, but very few real scientists. This peculiar situation is not due to lack of individuals capable of high intellectual achievements. Indeed, syntheses, as well as discoveries, demand exceptional mental power and physiological endurance. Broad and strong minds are rarer than precise and narrow ones. It is easy to become a good chemist, a good physicist, a good physiologist, a good psychologist, or a good sociologist. On the contrary, very few individuals are capable of acquiring and using knowledge of several different sciences. However, such men do exist. Some of those whom our scientific institutions and universities have forced to specialize narrowly could apprehend a complex subject both in its entirety and in its parts. So far, scientific workers devoting themselves, within a minute field, to prolonged study of a generally insignificant detail, have always been the most favoured. An original piece of work, without any real importance, is considered of greater value than a thorough knowledge of an entire science. Presidents of universities and their advisers do not realize that synthetic minds are as indispensable as analytic ones. If the superiority of this kind of intellect were recognized, and its development encouraged, specialists would cease to be dangerous. For the significance of the parts in the organization of the whole could then be correctly estimated.

At the beginning of its history more than at its zenith a science needs superior minds. To become a great physician requires more imagination, judgment, and intelligence than to become a great chemist. At the present time our knowledge of man can progress only by attracting a powerful intellectual élite. Great mental capacities should be required from the young men who desire to devote themselves to biology. It seems that the increased number of scientific workers, their being split up into groups whose studies are limited to a small subject, and over-specialization have brought about a shrinking of intelligence. There is no doubt that the quality of any human group decreases when the number of the individuals composing this group increases beyond certain limits. The Supreme Court of the United States consists of nine men whose professional value and character are truly eminent. But if it were composed of nine hundred jurists instead of nine, the public would immediately lose, and rightly, its respect for the highest court of this country.

The best way to increase the intelligence of scientists would be to decrease their number. After all, the knowledge of man could be developed by a very small group of workers, provided that they were endowed with creative imagination and given powerful means for carrying out their researches. Great sums of money are wasted every year on scientific research, in America as well as in Europe, because those who are entrusted with this work do not generally possess the qualities necessary to the conquerors of new worlds, and also because the few individuals endowed with this exceptional power live under conditions precluding intellectual creation. Neither laboratories, nor apparatus, nor organization can give to scientists the surroundings indispensable to their success. Modern life is opposed to the life of the mind. However, men of science have to be mere units of a herd whose appetites are purely material and whose habits are entirely different from theirs. They vainly exhaust their strength and spend their time in the pursuit of the conditions demanded by the elaboration of thought. No one of them is wealthy enough to procure the isolation and the silence which in former times everybody could have for nothing, even in the largest cities. No attempt has so far been made to create, in the midst of the agitation of the new city, islands of solitude where meditation would be possible. Such an innovation, however, is an obvious necessity. The construction of vast syntheses is beyond the reach of minds unceasingly dispersed in the confusion of our present modes of existence. The development of the science of man, even more than that of the other sciences, depends on immense intellectual effort. The need of such an effort demands a revision, not only of our conception of the scientist, but also of the conditions under which scientific research is carried on.

5

Human beings are not good subjects for scientific investigation. One does not easily find people with identical characteristics. It is almost impossible to verify the results of an experiment by referring the subject to a sufficiently similar control. Let us suppose, for example, that we wish to compare two methods of education. For such a study we choose two groups of children as nearly alike as possible. If these children, although of the same age and the same size, belong to different social classes, if their food is not the same, if they live in different psychological atmospheres, the results cannot be compared. In a like manner the effects of two modes of life on children belonging to one family have little value. For human races not being pure, there are often profound differences between the offspring of the same parents. On the contrary, the results will be conclusive when the children, whose behaviour is compared under different conditions, are twins from a single ovum. We are generally obliged to be content with approximate information. This is one of the factors that have impeded the progress of the science of man.

In researches dealing with physics and chemistry, and also with physiology, one always attempts to isolate relatively simple systems, and to determine their exact conditions. But when the human being has to be studied as an entirety, and in his relations with his environment, such a limitation of the subject is impossible. The observer must be endowed with sound judgment in order not to lose his way in the complexity of the facts. The difficulties become almost insurmountable in retrospective investigations. Such studies require a very experienced mind. Of course, we should as rarely as possible utilize the conjectural science which is called history. But there have been in the past certain events revealing the existence in man of extraordinary potentialities. A knowledge of the genesis of these qualities would be of great importance. What factors caused, during the epoch of Pericles, the simultaneous appearance of so many geniuses? A similar event occurred at the time of the Renaissance. Whence sprang the immense expansion, not only of intelligence, scientific imagination, and æsthetic intuition, but also of physical vigour, audacity, and the spirit of adventure in the men of this period? Why did they possess such mighty physiological and mental activities? One easily realizes how useful would be precise information regarding the mode of life, the food, the education, the intellectual, moral, æsthetic, and religious surroundings of the people who lived during the time immediately preceding the appearance of a pleiad of great men.

Another cause of the difficulties in experimenting on human beings is the fact that the observer and his subject live at about the same rhythm. The effects of a certain diet, of an intellectual or moral discipline, of political or social changes, are felt but slowly. It is only after a lapse of thirty or forty

years that the value of an educational method can be estimated. The influence of a given mode of living upon the
physiological and mental activities of a human group does
not manifest itself before a generation has passed. Inventors
of new systems of diet, physical culture, hygiene, education,
morals, social economy, are always too early in publishing
the success of their own inventions. It is only now that the
result of the Montessori system, or of the educational principles of John Dewey, could be profitably analyzed. We
should wait another quarter of a century to know the significance of the intelligence tests which psychologists have
made in the schools during these past years. The only way to
ascertain the effect of a given factor on man is to follow a
great number of individuals through the vicissitudes of their
life right up to their death. And even then the knowledge
thus obtained will be grossly approximate.

The progress of humanity appears to us to be very slow
because we, the observers, are units of the herd. Each one of
us can make but few observations. Our life is too short.
Many experiments should be conducted for a century at the
least. Institutions should be established in such a way that
observations and experiments commenced by one scientist
would not be interrupted by his death. Such organizations
are still unknown in the realm of science. But they already
exist in other lines of endeavour. In the monastery of
Solesmes three successive generations of Benedictine monks
have devoted themselves, over a period of about fifty-five
years, to the reconstruction of Gregorian music. A similar
method should be applied to the investigation of certain
problems of human biology. Institutions, in some measure
immortal, like religious orders, which would allow the uninterrupted continuation of an experiment as long as might
be necessary, should compensate for the too short duration
of the existence of individual observers.

Certain data, urgently needed, can be procured with the
help of short-lived animals. For this purpose mice and rats

have been chiefly used. Colonies consisting of many thousands of these animals have been employed to study different diets, their influence on the rapidity of growth, on size, disease, longevity, etc. Unfortunately, rats and mice have only very remote analogies with man. It is dangerous, for example, to apply to children, whose constitution is so different, conclusions of researches made on these animals. Besides, the mental states accompanying anatomical and functional changes in bones, tissues, and humours under the influence of food and mode of life, cannot be properly investigated on such low types of animals. By observing more intelligent animals, such as monkeys and dogs, one would obtain more detailed and important information.

Monkeys, despite their cerebral development, are not good subjects for experimentation. Their pedigree is not available. They cannot be bred easily or in sufficiently large numbers. They are difficult to handle. On the contrary, intelligent dogs can be procured readily. Their ancestral characteristics are easily traced. Such animals propagate rapidly. They mature in a year. Generally, they do not live beyond fifteen years. Detailed psychological observations can be made without trouble, especially on sheep-dogs, which are sensitive, intelligent, alert, and attentive. With the aid of these animals of pure breed, and in sufficient number, the complex and important problem of the influence of environment on the individual could be elucidated. For example, we should ascertain whether the increase in stature, which is taking place in the population of the United States, is an advantage or a disadvantage. It is also imperative to know what effect modern life and food have on the nervous system of children, and on their intelligence, alertness, and audacity. An extensive experiment carried out on several hundred dogs over a period of twenty years would give some precise information on these subjects, which are of paramount importance to millions of people. It would indicate, more rapidly than the observation of human beings, in what direction the diet and mode of living of the population should be changed. Such study would effectively supplement the incomplete and brief experiments which now appear to satisfy nutrition specialists. However, the observation of even the highest type of animal cannot entirely replace that of man. In order to develop definitive knowledge, experiments on groups of human beings should be started under such conditions that they could be continued by several generations of scientists.

6

A better knowledge of ourselves cannot be acquired merely by selecting positive facts in the mass of information concerning man, and by making a complete inventory of his activities. Neither would the completion of these data by new observations and experiments, and the building up of a true science of man be sufficient. Above all, we need a synthesis that can be utilized. The purpose of this knowledge is not to satisfy our curiosity, but to rebuild ourselves and our surroundings. Such a purpose is essentially practical. The acquisition of a large quantity of new data, if these data remain scattered in the brains and in the books of specialists, is absolutely useless. A dictionary does not confer a literary or philosophical culture upon its owner. Our ideas must be assembled as a living whole, within the intelligence and the memory of a few superior individuals. Thus the efforts which humanity has made, and is ceaselessly making, to attain a better knowledge of itself would become productive.

The science of man will be the task of the future. We must now be content with an initiation, both analytic and synthetic, into those characteristics of the human being which scientific criticism has demonstrated to be true. In the following pages man will appear to us as naïvely as to the observer and to his techniques. We shall view him in the form of fragments carved by these techniques. But as far as is

possible these fragments will be replaced in the whole. Such
knowledge is, of course, most inadequate. But it is certain.
It contains no metaphysical elements. It is also empirical,
because no principle governs the choice and the order of the
observations. We do not seek to prove or to disprove any
theory. The different aspects of man are considered as
simply as, when ascending a mountain, one considers the
rocks, torrents, meadows, and pines, and even, above the
shadows of the valley, the light of the peaks. In both cases,
the observations are made as the chances of the way decide.
These observations are, however, scientific. They constitute
a more or less systematized body of knowledge. Naturally,
they have not the precision of those of astronomers and
physicists. But they are as exact as is permitted by the techniques employed, and the nature of the object to which the
techniques are applied. For instance, we know that men are
endowed with memory and æsthetic sense. Also that the pancreas secretes insulin, that certain mental diseases depend on
lesions of the brain, that some individuals manifest phenomena of clairvoyance. Memory and the activity of insulin
can be measured, but not æsthetic emotion or moral sense.
The characteristics of telepathy, or the relations between
mental diseases and the brain, lend themselves still less to
exact study. Nevertheless, all these data, although approximate, are sure.

This knowledge may be reproached with being commonplace and incomplete. It is commonplace because body and
consciousness, duration, adaptation, and individuality are
well known to specialists in anatomy, physiology, psychology, metapsychics, hygiene, medicine, education, religion,
and sociology. It is incomplete because a choice had to be
made among an immense number of facts. And such a
choice is bound to be arbitrary. It is limited to what appears
to be most important. The rest is neglected, for a synthesis
should be short and understandable at a single glance.
Human intelligence is capable of retaining only a certain

number of details. It would, then, seem that our knowledge of man, in order to be useful, must be incomplete. The likeness of a portrait is due to the selection of details, and not to their number. A drawing more forcibly expresses the character of an individual than a photograph does. We are going to trace only rough sketches of ourselves, similar to anatomical figures chalked on a blackboard. Our sketches will be true, in spite of the intentional suppression of details. They will be based on positive data and not on theories and dreams. They will ignore vitalism and mechanism, realism and nominalism, soul and body, mind and matter. But they will contain all that can be observed. Even the inexplicable facts left out by classical conceptions of man, those facts that stubbornly refuse to enter the frame of conventional thought, and therefore may lead to unknown realms. Thus our inventory will include all actual and potential activities of the human being.

In this manner we shall become initiated into a knowledge of ourselves, which is only descriptive and still not far from the concrete. Such knowledge does not claim definitiveness or infallibility. It is empirical, approximative, commonplace, and incomplete, but also scientific and intelligible to everybody.

CHAPTER III

BODY AND PHYSIOLOGICAL ACTIVITIES

1. *Man. His dual aspect. Human activities and their substratum. 2. The dimensions of the body. Its form. 3. Its outer and inner surfaces. 4. Its constitution. Cells and their societies. Their structure. Cell types. 5. Blood and organic medium. 6. Nutrition of tissues. Metabolism. 7. Circulatory apparatus, lungs, and kidneys. 8. Chemical relations of the body with its environment. Digestion. Nature of food. 9. Sexual functions. 10. Physical relations of the body with its environment. Voluntary nervous system. Skeletal and muscular systems. 11. Visceral nervous system. Sympathetic and parasympathetic. Automatism of the organs. 12. Complexity and simplicity of the body. Structural and functional limits of organs. Anatomical heterogeneity and physiological homogeneity. 13. Mode of organization of the body. Mechanical analogy. Antitheses and illusions. 14. Fragility and robustness of the body. Silence of the body during health. Factors which weaken the body. 15. The causes of disease. Infectious and degenerative diseases.*

I

WE are conscious of existing, of possessing an activity of our own, a personality. We know that we are different from all other individuals. We believe that our will is free. We feel happy or unhappy. These intuitions constitute for each of us the ultimate reality.

Our states of consciousness glide through time as a river through a valley. Like the river we are both change and permanence. We are independent of our environment, much more so than are the other animals. Our intelligence has set us free. Man is, above all, the inventor of tools, arms, and machines. With the aid of these inventions he was able to manifest his specific characteristics, and to distinguish himself from all other living beings. He has expressed his inner tendencies in an objective manner by erecting statues, temples, theatres, cathedrals, hospitals, universities, laboratories, and factories. He has, in this way, stamped the surface of the earth with the mark of his fundamental activities —that is, of his æsthetic and religious feelings, his moral sense, his intelligence, and his scientific curiosity.

This focus of mighty activities can be observed from within or from without. Seen from within, it shows to the lone observer, who is our self, his own thoughts, tendencies, desires, joys, and sorrows. Seen from without, it appears as the human body, our own, and also that of all our fellow creatures. Thus man assumes two totally different aspects. For this reason he has been looked upon as being made up of two parts, the body and the soul. However, no one has ever observed a soul without a body, or a body without a soul. Only the outer surface of our body is visible to us. We perceive our functional activities as a vague sense of well-being. But we are not conscious of any of our organs. The body obeys mechanisms entirely hidden from us. It discloses its constitution only through the techniques of anatomy and physiology. Then a stupendous complexity appears under its seeming simplicity. Man never allows himself to be observed simultaneously in his outer and public aspect, and in his inner and private one. Even if we penetrate the inextricable maze of the brain and the nervous functions, nowhere do we meet with consciousness. Soul and body are creations of our methods of observation. They are carved by those methods from an indivisible whole.

This whole consists of tissues, organic fluids, and consciousness. It extends simultaneously in space and in time. It fills the three dimensions of space, and that of time with its heterogeneous mass. However, it is not comprised fully within these four dimensions. For consciousness is located both within the cerebral matter and outside the physical continuum. The human being is too complex to be apprehended in his entirety. We have to divide him into small parts by our methods of observation. Technological necessity obliges us, therefore, to describe him as being composed of a corporal substratum and of various activities, and also to consider separately the temporal, adaptive, and individual aspects of these activities. At the same time we must avoid making the classical errors of reducing him to a body, or a consciousness, or an association of both, and of believing in the concrete existence of the parts abstracted from him by our mind.

2

The human body is placed, on the scale of magnitudes, halfway between the atom and the star. According to the size of the objects selected for comparison, it appears either large or small. Its length is equivalent to that of two hundred thousand tissue cells, or of two millions of ordinary microbes, or of two thousand millions of albumin molecules, placed end to end. Man is gigantic in comparison with an electron, an atom, a molecule, or a microbe. But when compared with a mountain, or with the earth, he is tiny. More than four thousand individuals would have to stand one upon the other in order to equal the height of Mount Everest. A terrestrial meridian is approximately equivalent to twenty millions of them placed end to end. Light, as is well known, travels about one hundred and fifty million times the length of our body in one second. The interstellar distances are such that they have to be measured in light years. Our stature, in relation to such a system of reference, becomes inconceivably small. For this reason, Eddington and Jeans, in their books of popular astronomy, always succeed in impressing their readers with the complete insignificance of man in the universe. In reality, our spatial greatness or smallness is without importance. For what is specific of man has no physical dimensions. The meaning of our presence in this world assuredly does not depend upon our size.

Our stature seems to be appropriate to the character of the tissue cells, and to the nature of the chemical exchanges, or metabolism, of the organism. As nerve impulses propagate in everybody at the same speed, men of a very much larger frame than ours would have too slow a perception of external things, and their muscular reactions would be too sluggish. At the same time the rate of their chemical exchanges would be profoundly modified. It is well known that the metabolism of large animals is lower than that of small ones. The horse, for instance, has a lesser metabolic activity than the mouse. A great increase in our stature would diminish the intensity of our exchanges, and probably deprive us of our agility and of the rapidity of our perceptions. Such an accident will not happen because the size of human beings varies only within narrow limits. The dimensions of our body are determined simultaneously by heredity and developmental conditions. In a given race, one observes tall and short individuals. These differences in the length of the skeleton come from the state of the endocrine glands and from the correlation of their activities in space and time. They are of profound significance. It is possible, by means of proper diet and mode of living, to augment or diminish the stature of the individuals composing a nation. Likewise, to modify the quality of their tissues and probably also of their mind. We must not blindly change the dimensions of the human body in order to give it more beauty and muscular strength. In fact, seemingly unimportant alterations of our size and form could cause profound modifications of our physiological and mental activities. There is no advantage in increasing man's stature by artificial means. Alertness, endurance, and audacity do not grow with the volume of the body. Men of genius are not tall. Mussolini is of medium size, and Napoleon was short.

Each man is characterized by his figure, his way of carrying himself, the aspect of his face. Our outward form expresses the qualities, the powers, of our body and our mind. In a given race it varies according to the mode of life of the individuals. The man of the Renaissance, whose life was a constant fight, who was exposed continuously to dangers and to inclemencies, who was capable of as great an enthusiasm for the discoveries of Galileo as for the masterpieces of Leonardo da Vinci or Michelangelo, did not resemble modern man who lives in a steam-heated apartment, an air-conditioned office, a closed car, who contemplates absurd films, listens to his radio, and plays golf and bridge. Each epoch puts its seal on human beings. We begin to observe the new types created by motor cars, cinemas, and athletics. Some, more frequent in Latin countries, are characterized by an adipose aspect, flabby tissues, discoloured skin, protruding abdomen, thin legs, awkward posture, unintelligent and brutal face. Others appear, especially among Anglo-Saxons, and show broad shoulders, narrow waist, and birdlike cranium. Our form is moulded by our physiological habits, and even by our usual thoughts. Its characteristics are partly due to the muscles running under the skin or along the bones. The size of these muscles depends on the exercise to which they are submitted. The beauty of the body comes from the harmonious development of the muscles and the skeleton. It reached the height of perfection at the epoch of Pericles, in the Greek athletes whom Phidias and his disciples immortalized in their statues. The shape of the face, the mouth, the cheeks, the eyelids, and the lines of the visage are determined by the habitual condition of the flat muscles, which move in the adipose tissues underlying the skin. And the state of these muscles depends on that of our mind. Indeed, each individual can give his face the expression that he chooses. But he does not keep such a mask permanently. Unwittingly, our visage progressively models itself upon our states of consciousness. With the advance of age it becomes more and more pregnant with the feelings, the appetites, and the aspirations of the whole being. The beauty of youth comes from the natural harmony of the lineaments of the human face ; that, so rare, of an old man, from his soul.

The visage expresses still deeper things than the hidden activities of consciousness. In this open book one can read not only the vices, the virtues, the intelligence, the stupidity, the feelings, the most carefully concealed habits, of an individual, but also the constitution of his body, and his tendencies to organic and mental diseases. In fact the aspect of bones, muscles, fat, skin, and hair depends on the nutrition of tissues, and the nutrition of tissues is regulated by the composition of blood plasma—that is, by the activity of the glandular and digestive systems. The state of the organs is revealed by the aspect of the body. The surface of the skin reflects the functional conditions of the endocrine glands, the stomach, the intestines, and the nervous system. It points out the morbid tendencies of the individual. In fact people who belong to different morphological classes—for instance, to the cerebral, digestive, muscular, or respiratory types— are not liable to the same organic or mental diseases. There are great functional disparities between tall and spare men, and broad and short ones. The tall type, either asthenic or athletic, is predisposed to tuberculosis and to dementia præcox ; the short, pyknic type, to cyclic mania, diabetes, rheumatism, and gout. In the diagnosis and prognosis of diseases, ancient physicians quite rightly attributed great importance to temperament, idiosyncrasies, and diatheses. Each man bears on his face the description of his body and his soul.

3

The skin which covers the outer surface of the body is impermeable to water and to gases. It does not allow the microbes living on its surface to enter the organism. It is capable of destroying them with the aid of substances secreted by its glands. But it can be crossed by the minute and deadly beings, which we call viruses. Its external face is exposed to light, wind, humidity, dryness, heat, and cold. Its internal face is in contact with an aquatic world, warm and deprived of light, where cells live like marine animals. Despite its thinness, the skin effectively protects the organic fluids against the unceasing variations of cosmic surroundings. It is moist, supple, extensible, elastic, durable. Its durability is due to its mode of constitution, to its several layers of cells, which slowly and endlessly multiply. These cells die while remaining united to one another like the slates of a roof— like slates ceaselessly blown away by the wind and continually replaced by new slates. The skin, nevertheless, retains its moistness and suppleness, because small glands secrete on its surface both water and fatty substances. At the nostrils, mouth, anus, urethra, and vagina, it joins the mucosas, those membranes that cover the inner surface of the body. All its orifices, with the exception of the nostrils, are closed by elastic and contractile rings, the sphincters. Thus it is the almost perfectly fortified frontier of a closed world.

Through its outer surface the body enters into communication with all the things of the cosmic universe. In fact the skin is the dwelling-place of an immense quantity of small receptor organs, each of which registers, according to its own structure, the changes taking place in the environment. Tactile corpuscles scattered all over its surface are sensitive to pressure, to pain, to heat, or to cold. Those situated in the mucosa of the tongue are affected by certain qualities of food, and also by temperature. Air vibrations act on the extremely complex apparatus of the internal ear by the medium of the tympanic membrane and the bones of the middle ear. The network of olfactory nerves, which extends into the nasal mucous membrane, is sensitive to odours. A strange phenomenon occurs in the embryo. The brain causes a part of itself, the optic nerve and the retina, to shoot out toward the surface of the body. The part of the skin overlying the young retina undergoes an astonishing modification. It becomes transparent, forms the cornea and the crystalline lens, and unites with other tissues to build up the prodigious optical system which we call the eye. The brain is thus enabled to record the electromagnetic waves comprised between red and violet.

Innumerable nerve fibres radiate from all these organs and connect them with the spinal cord and the brain. Through the agency of these nerves the central nervous system spreads like a web over the entire surface of the body where it enters into contact with the outer world. The aspect of the universe depends on the constitution of the sense organs, and on their degree of sensitiveness. For instance, should the retina record infra-red rays of great wave-length, nature would take on a different visage. The colour of water, rocks, and trees would vary with the seasons because of the changes in the temperature. July's clear days, when the smallest details of the landscape stand out sharply against dark shadows, would be obscured by a reddish haze. Heat rays, being visible, would conceal all objects. In winter the atmosphere would become clear and the contours of things precise. The aspect of men, however, would remain very different, their outline vague, their face hidden by a red mist issuing from their mouth and nostrils. After violent exercise the body would seem to increase in size, on account of the heat released by the skin and surrounding the figure with a larger aura. In a like manner, the cosmic world would assume another appearance if the retina became sensitive to ultra-violet rays and the skin to light rays. Or if the acuteness of all our sense organs were considerably augmented.

We ignore things which have no action on the nerve endings of the surface of the skin. Therefore, we do not perceive cosmic rays, although they pass right through our body. It seems that everything reaching the brain has to enter the sensory organs—that is, to influence the nervous layer enveloping our body. The unknown agent of telepathic communications is perhaps the only exception to this rule. In clairvoyance it looks as though the subject directly grasps the external reality without the help of the usual nerve channels. But such phenomena are rare. As a rule, the senses are the gateway through which the physical and psychological universe penetrates our organism. Thus the quality of an individual partly depends on that of his surface. For the brain is moulded by the continual messages it receives from the outer world. Therefore, the state of our envelope should not be modified thoughtlessly by new habits of life. For instance, we are far from knowing completely what effect exposure to sun rays has upon the development of the entire body. Until the exact nature of this effect has been ascertained, nudism and exaggerated tanning of the skin by natural light, or by ultra-violet rays, should not be blindly accepted by the white races. The skin and its appendages play the part of a faithful keeper of our organs and our blood. They allow certain things to enter our inner world and exclude others. They are the ever open, though carefully watched, door to our central nervous system. They must be looked upon as being an essential part of ourselves.

Our internal frontier begins at the mouth and the nose, and ends at the anus. Through these openings the outside world penetrates into the respiratory and digestive systems. While the skin is impervious to water and to gas, the mucous membranes of the lungs and of the intestines allow these substances to pass. They are responsible for the chemical continuity of our body with its surroundings. Our inner surface is far larger than that of the skin. The area covered by the flat cells of the pulmonary alveoli is immense. It is approximately equal to five hundred square metres. The thin membrane formed by these cells is traversed by oxygen from the air and by carbon dioxide from the venous blood. It is easily affected by poisonous gases and by bacteria, and more particularly by pneumococci. Atmospheric air, before reaching the pulmonary alveoli, passes through the nose, the pharnyx, the larynx, the trachea, and the bronchi, where it is moistened and freed from dust and microbes. But this natural protection is now insufficient because the air of cities has been polluted by coal dust, petrol fumes, and bacteria set free by the multitude of human beings. Respiratory mucosa is much more delicate than skin. It is defenceless against strong irritants. Its fragility may cause entire populations to be exterminated by toxic gases in the great wars of the future.

From mouth to anus the body is traversed by a stream of nutritive substances. The digestive membranes determine the nature of the chemical relations between the external world and the inner world of our tissues and organic fluids. But their functions are far more complex than those of the respiratory ones. They must profoundly transform the foodstuffs which reach their surface. They are not only a filter but also a chemical factory. The ferments secreted by their glands collaborate with those of the pancreas in decomposing the aliments into substances capable of being absorbed by the intestinal cells. The digestive surface is extraordinarily vast. The mucosas secrete and absorb large quantities of fluids. Their cells allow the foodstuffs, when digested, to enter the body. But they resist the penetration of the bacteria that swarm in the digestive tract. These dangerous enemies are generally held in control by the thin intestinal membrane, and the leucocytes defending it. But they are always a menace. Viruses thrive in the pharynx and the nose. Streptococci, staphylococci, and microbes of diphtheria in the tonsils. The bacilli of typhoid fever and of dysentery multiply with ease in the intestines. The soundness of the respiratory and digestive membranes governs, in a large measure, the resistance of the organism to infectious diseases, its strength, its equilibrium, its effectiveness, its intellectual attitude.

Thus our body constitutes a closed universe, limited on one side by the skin, and on the other by the mucosas covering our inner surfaces. If these membranes are impaired at

c*

any point, the existence of the individual is endangered. Even a superficial burn, when extending over a large area of the skin, results in death. This covering separates our organs and humours from the cosmic environment, and yet allows most extensive physical and chemical communications between these two worlds. It accomplishes the miracle of being a barrier at once closed and open. For it does not protect our nervous system against our mental surroundings. We may be wounded, and even killed, by subtle enemies which, ignoring our anatomical frontiers, invade our consciousness, like aviators bombarding a city without taking any notice of its fortifications.

4

The inside of our body does not resemble the descriptions of classical anatomy. This science has constructed a schema of the human being that is purely structural and quite unreal. It is not merely by opening a corpse that one may learn how man is constituted. Of course, we can observe in this way his framework, the skeleton and the muscles, which are the scaffold of the organs. In a cage formed by the spinal column, the ribs, and the sternum, are suspended the heart and the lungs. The liver, spleen, kidneys, stomach, intestines, and sexual glands are attached, by the folds of the peritoneum, to the inner surface of a large cavity whose bottom is formed by the pelvis, the sides by the abdominal muscles, and the roof by the diaphragm. The most fragile of all the organs, the brain and the cord, are enclosed in osseous boxes, the cranium and the spine. They are protected against the hardness of the walls of their lodgings by a system of membranes and a cushion of liquid.

One cannot understand the living being by studying a dead body. For the tissues of a corpse have been deprived of their circulating blood and of their functions. In reality, an organ separated from its nutritive medium no longer exists. In the living body, blood is present everywhere. It pulsates in the arteries, glides through the veins, fills the capillary vessels, bathes all tissues in transparent lymph. In order to apprehend this inner world as it is, more delicate techniques than those of anatomy and of histology are indispensable. We must study organs of living animals and of men, as they are seen in the course of surgical operations, and not simply those of corpses prepared for dissection. Their structure should be learned, both from microscopical sections of dead tissues more or less modified by fixatives and dyes, and from living tissues while functioning; also from cinematographic films on which their movements have been recorded. We must not separate cells from medium and function from structure, as anatomy has done.

Within the body, the cells behave like small organisms plunged in an aerated and nutritive medium. This medium is analogous to sea water. However, it contains a smaller quantity of salts, and its composition is much richer and more varied. The leucocytes of the blood and the cells covering the walls of blood vessels and lymphatics are like fish swimming freely in the depth of the ocean or lying flat on the sandy bottom. But the cells forming the tissues do not float in a fluid. They are comparable, not to fish, but to amphibia inhabiting marshes or moist sand. All living cells depend absolutely on the medium in which they are immersed. They modify this medium unceasingly, and are modified by it. In fact, they are inseparable from it; as inseparable as their body is from its nucleus. Their structure and functions are entirely subordinated to the physical, physico-chemical, and chemical conditions of the surrounding fluid. This fluid is the interstitial lymph which at once produces, and is produced by, blood plasma. Cells and medium, structure and function, cannot be separated from one another. The isolation of cells from their natural environment is altogether unwarranted. However, methodological necessity forces us to divide this ensemble into fragments, and to describe, on one side, the cells and tissues, and, on the other, the organic medium—that is, the blood and the humours.

The cells congregate in societies, which are called tissues and organs. But the analogy of these societies to human and insect communities is quite superficial. For the individuality of cells is much less definite than that of men and even of insects. The rules of these associations are merely the expression of the inherent properties of the individuals. The characteristics of human beings are more easily learned than those of their societies. Physiology is a science : human sociology is not. On the contrary, cell sociology is more advanced than the science of the structure and functions of the cell as an individual. Anatomists and physiologists have long since known the characteristics of tissues and organs—that is, of cell societies. Only recently have they succeeded in analyzing the properties of the cells themselves, of the individuals making up the organic associations. Owing to the new procedures for the cultivation of tissues, it has been possible to study living cells in a flask as easily as bees in a hive. Those cells have revealed themselves as endowed with unsuspected powers with astounding properties. Virtual in the normal conditions of life, these properties actualize under the influence of diseases, when the organic medium undergoes certain physico-chemical changes. These functional characteristics, far more than their structure, give to tissues the power of building up the living body.

Despite its minuteness, each cell is a very complex organism. It does not in any way resemble the favourite abstraction of chemists, a drop of gelatine surrounded by a semipermeable membrane. The substance, which biologists call protoplasm, is found neither in its nucleus nor in its body. Protoplasm is a concept deprived of objective meaning, just as the concept anthropoplasm would be, if by such a concept one attempted to define the content of the human body. Cells can now be filmed and magnified to such an extent that, when thrown on the screen, they are larger than a man. All their organs are then visible. In the middle of their body floats a kind of ovoid, elastic-walled balloon, the nucleus, which appears to be full of an inert and transparent jelly. In this jelly are seen two nucleoli, which slowly and unceasingly change their shape. Around the nucleus there is a great agitation of small particles. The movements are particularly active around a cluster of vesicles, corresponding to the organ called by anatomists the apparatus of Golgi or of Renaut, whose functions are connected with the nutrition of the cell. Small and indistinct granules form a kind of whirlpool in that same district. Larger globules endlessly zigzag through the cell, going as far as the extremities of its mobile and transitory arms. But the most remarkable organs are long filaments, the mitochondrias, which resemble snakes or, in certain cells, short bacteria. Vesicles, granulations, globules, and filaments glide, dance, and undulate perpetually in the free spaces of the cell body.

This structural complexity of the living cell is disconcerting, but its chemical constitution is still more intricate. The nucleus, which, with the exception of the nucleoli, appears to be completely empty, contains substances of a truly marvellous nature. The simplicity attributed by chemists to its constituent nucleoproteins is an illusion. In fact, the nuclear substance comprises the genes, those mysterious beings of which we know nothing except that they are the hereditary tendencies of cells and of men. Instead of being simple, the chemical composition of the nucleus must be of bewildering complexity. The genes are generally invisible. However, we know that they dwell in the chromosomes, those elongated bodies seen in the clear fluid of the nucleus when the cell is going to divide. At this moment the chromosomes form in a more or less distinct manner two groups. These groups move away from each other. At the same time the entire cell shakes violently, tosses its contents in all directions, and divides into two parts. These parts, the daughter cells, withdraw from each other while still united by some elastic filaments. These filaments stretch and finally give way. Thus two new elements of the organism have become individualized.

Cells, like animals, belong to many different races. These races, or types, are defined by both their structural and their functional characteristics. They spring from different fields, such as the thyroid gland, the spleen, the skin, the liver, etc. But, strange to say, cells originating from the same region may assume different types at successive periods of time. The organism is as heterogeneous in time as in space. The cell types that build up the body may be roughly divided into two classes. The fixed cells, whose associations form the tissues and the organs, and the mobile cells, which travel throughout the entire organism. The connective and epithelial types of cells belong to the fixed category. Epithelial cells are the noblest elements of the body. They constitute the brain, the skin, the endocrine glands, etc. Connective cells build up the framework of the organs. They are truly ubiquitous. Around them appear various substances, such as cartilage. calcium, fibrous tissue, elastic fibres, which give skeleton, muscles, blood vessels, and organs the solidity and elasticity indispensable to their functions. In addition, they metamorphose, into contractile elements. These are the muscles of the heart, of the vessels, of the digestive apparatus, and also of the locomotive system. Although connective and epithelial cells seem to be immobile and are still called by their old name of fixed cells, nevertheless they move, as cinematography has shown. But their movements are slow. They glide in their medium like oil spreading over the surface of water. They drag with them their nucleus, suspended in the fluid mass of their body. They differ markedly from the mobile cells. Those cells include the different types of leucocytes of the blood and of the tissues. Their motion is rapid. The leucocytes, characterized by the presence of several nuclei, resemble amœbæ. The lymphocytes crawl more slowly, like small worms. The larger ones, the monocytes, have the appearance of an octopus. They extrude long tentacles from their substance, and also surround themselves with a thin, undulating membrane. After having enveloped dead cells and microbes in the folds of this membrane, they voraciously devour them.

When these different cell types are bred in flasks their characteristics become just as apparent as those of the various kinds of microbes. Each type has its own inherent properties, which remain specific, even when several years have elapsed since its separation from the organism. Cell types are characterized by their mode of locomotion, their way of associating with one another, the aspect of their colonies, the rate of their growth, their response to various chemicals, the substances they secrete, the food they require, as well as by their shape and structure. This broader conception is taking the place of the purely morphological definitions of classical anatomy. The laws of organization of each cell community —that is, of each organ—derive from these elementary properties. Tissue cells, possessing only the characteristics ascribed to them by anatomy, would be incapable of building up a living organism. But they are endowed with much higher powers. They do not manifest all of them. Besides the activities which they usually display, they possess others, generally hidden, but capable of becoming actual in response to certain changes of the medium. They are thus enabled to deal with the unforeseeable events taking place in the course of normal life and during illnesses.

Cells unite in dense masses, the tissues and organs, whose architectonic depends on the structural and functional needs of the organism in its totality. The human body is a compact and mobile unit. And its harmony is assured by both the blood and the nerves which integrate all cell communities. The existence of tissues cannot be conceived without that of a fluid medium. The necessary relations of the anatomical elements and of the vessels carrying this nutritive medium determine the shape of the organs. Such shape also is influenced by the presence of the ducts through which glandular products are secreted. All spatial ordering of bodily structures is commanded by their food requirements. The architectural plan of each organ is inspired by the need of the cells to be immersed in a medium always rich in foodstuffs and never encumbered by waste products.

5

The organic medium is a part of the tissues. Should it be removed, the body would cease to exist. Every manifestation of the life of our organs and nervous centres, our thoughts, our affections, the cruelty, the ugliness, and the beauty of the universe, its very existence, depend on the physico-chemical state of our humours. The organic medium is composed of blood, flowing in the vessels, and of fluids, plasma or lymph, which filter through the walls of the capillaries into the tissues. There is a general organic medium, the blood, and regional media, consisting of the interstitial lymph of each organ. An organ may be compared to a pond completely filled with aquatic plants and fed by a small brook. The almost stagnant water is polluted by waste products, dead fragments of plants, and chemical substances set free by them. The degree of stagnation and of pollution of the water depends on the rapidity and the volume of the brook. Such is the case with interstitial lymph. In short, the composition of the regional media inhabited by the various cells of the body rests, directly or indirectly, on blood.

The blood is a tissue, like all the other tissues. It is composed of about twenty-five or thirty billions of red cells, and of fifty thousand millions of white cells. But these cells are not, like those of the other tissues, immobilized in a framework. They are suspended in a viscous liquid, the plasma. Blood is a moving tissue, finding its way into all parts of the body. It carries to each cell the proper nourishment, acting, at the same time, as a main sewer that takes away the waste products set free by living tissues. It also contains chemical substances and cells capable of repairing organs wherever necessary. These properties are indeed strange. When carrying out such astonishing duties, the blood stream behaves like a torrent which, with the help of the mud and the trees drifting in its stream, would set about repairing the houses situated on its banks.

Blood plasma is not exactly what chemists believe it to be. It is incomparably richer than the classical abstractions. Without any doubt plasma really is the solution of bases, acids, salts, and proteins, whose physico-chemical equilibria are expressed in the laws discovered by Van Slyke and Henderson. Owing to this particular composition, its ionic alkalinity is maintained near the neutral point, in spite of the acids ceaselessly liberated by the tissues. In this manner it supplies all the cells of the entire organism with an unvarying medium, neither too acid nor too alkaline. But it also contains proteins, polypeptides, amino acids, sugars, fats, enzymes, metals in infinitesimal quantities, and the secretions of all glands and tissues. The nature of the majority of these substances is still very imperfectly known. We are scarcely beginning to understand the immense complexity of their functions. Each cell type finds in the blood plasma the foodstuffs indispensable to its maintenance, and also substances accelerating or retarding its activity. Thus certain fatty compounds linked to the proteins of serum are capable of curbing cellular proliferation, and even of preventing it completely. The serum also contains substances opposing the multiplication of bacteria, the antibodies. These antibodies appear when the tissues have to defend themselves against invading microbes. In addition, there is in blood plasma a protein, fibrinogen, father of fibrin, whose shreds spontaneously adhere to the wounds of blood vessels and stop hæmorrhages.

Red and white corpuscles play an important part in the

constitution of the organic medium. We know that blood plasma dissolves only a small amount of atmospheric oxygen. Without the help of the red corpuscles, it would, therefore, be incapable of supplying the immense population of body cells with the oxygen they require. These red corpuscles are not living cells. They are tiny sacks full of hæmoglobin. During their passage through the lungs they take on a load of oxygen which, a few instants later, they hand over to the greedy tissue cells. When taking delivery of the oxygen these cells simultaneously get rid of their carbon dioxide and other waste products by passing them on to the blood. The white corpuscles, on the contrary, are living organisms. Sometimes they float in the blood stream, sometimes they escape from the capillary vessels by slipping through their walls into the tissues, and creep on the surface of the cells of the mucous membranes, of the intestines, of the glands, and of all the organs. Owing to these microscopic elements, the blood acts as a mobile tissue, a repairing agent, a medium both solid and fluid, capable of going wherever its presence may be necessary. It can rapidly surround microbes attacking a region of the organism with a great mass of leucocytes, which fight the infection. It also brings to the surface of a wound of the skin, or of any organ, white corpuscles of the larger type, virtual material for the reconstruction of tissues. Such leucocytes have the power of transforming themselves into fixed cells. And those cells call connective fibres into being, and repair the injured tissues by means of a scar.

The fluids that escape from the capillary vessels constitute the local medium of tissues and organs. It is practically impossible to study the composition of this medium. However, when dyes, whose colour changes with the ionic acidity of the tissues, are injected into the organism, as was done by Rous, the organs take on different hues. The diversity of the local media can be visualized. In reality, such diversity is much more profound than is shown by this procedure. But we are not able to detect all its characteristics. In the vast world of the human organism there are most varied countries. Although these countries are irrigated by branches of the same stream, the quality of the water in their lakes and their ponds also depends on the constitution of the soil and the nature of the vegetation. Each organ, each tissue, creates its own medium at the expense of blood plasma. On the reciprocal adjustment of the cells and their medium are based the health or disease, strength or weakness, happiness or misery, of each one of us.

6

Between the liquids composing the organic medium, and the world of tissues and organs, there are perpetual chemical exchanges. Nutritive activity is a mode of being of the cells, as fundamental as structure and form. As soon as their chemical exchanges, or metabolism, cease, the organs come into equilibrium with their medium and die. Nutrition is synonymous with existence. Living tissues crave oxygen and take it from blood. This means, in physico-chemical terms, that they possess a high reducing potential, that a complex system of chemical substances and of ferments enables them to use atmospheric oxygen for energy-producing reactions. From the oxygen, hydrogen, and carbon supplied by sugars and fats, living cells procure the mechanical energy necessary for the maintenance of their structure and for their movements, the electrical energy manifesting itself in every change of the organic conditions, and the heat indispensable to chemical reactions and physiological processes. They also find in blood plasma the nitrogen, sulphur, phosphorus, etc., which they utilize for the construction of new cells and in the processes of growth and repair. With the help of their ferments they divide the proteins, sugars, and fats contained in their medium into smaller and smaller fragments, and make use of the energy so liberated. They simultaneously build up, by means of energy-absorbing reactions, certain compounds, more complex and having a higher energy potential, and they incorporate them in their own substance.

The intensity of chemical exchanges in the cell communities, or in the entire being, expresses the intensity of organic life. Metabolism is measured by the quantity of oxygen absorbed and that of carbonic acid produced when the body is in a state of complete repose. This is called basal metabolism. There is a great increase in the activity of the exchanges as soon as muscles contract and perform mechanical work. Metabolism is higher in a child than in an adult, in a mouse than in a dog. Any very large increase in the stature of human beings would, as mentioned heretofore, probably be followed by a decline of basal metabolism. Brain, liver, and endocrine glands need a great deal of chemical energy. But muscular exercise raises the intensity of the exchanges in the most marked manner. Nevertheless, all our activities cannot be expressed in chemical terms. Intellectual work, strange to say, does not increase metabolism. It seems to require no energy, or to consume a quantity of it too small to be detected by our present techniques. It is, indeed, an astonishing fact that human thought, which has transformed the surface of the earth, destroyed and built nations, discovered new universes in the immensity of the sidereal spaces, is elaborated without demanding a measurable amount of energy. The mightiest effort of our intelligence has incomparably less effect on metabolism than the contraction of the biceps when this muscle lifts a weight of a few grams. The ambition of Cæsar, the meditation of Newton, the inspiration of Beethoven, the passionate contemplation of Pasteur, did not modify the chemical exchanges of these great men as much as a few bacteria or a slight stimulation of the thyroid gland would easily have done.

Basal metabolism is remarkably constant. The organism maintains the normal activity of its chemical exchanges under the most adverse conditions. Exposure to intense cold does not decrease the rhythm of nutrition. The temperature of the body falls only on the approach of death. On the contrary, bears and raccoons lower their metabolism in winter and fall into a state of slower life. Certain arthropodous animals, *Tardigrada*, completely stop their metabolism when they are dried. A condition of latent life is thus induced. After a lapse of several weeks, if one moistens these desiccated animals, they revive, and the rhythm of their life again becomes normal. We have not yet discovered the secret of producing such a suspension of nutrition in domestic animals and in man. It would be an evident advantage in cold countries if a state of latent life could be induced in sheep and cows for the duration of the winter. It might be possible, perhaps, to prolong life, cure certain diseases, and give higher opportunities to exceptionally gifted individuals, if human beings could be made to hibernate from time to time. But we are not capable of decreasing the rate of metabolism, except by the barbarous method that consists of removing the thyroid gland. And even that method is quite insufficient. As far as man is concerned, latent life, for the moment, is an impossible form of existence.

7

In the course of the chemical exchanges, waste products or catabolites are set free by tissues and organs. They tend to accumulate in the regional medium and to render it uninhabitable for the cells. The phenomenon of nutrition, therefore, requires the existence of apparatuses capable of assuring, through a rapid circulation of lymph and blood, the replacement of the nutritive substances used by the tissues, and the elimination of waste products. The volume of the circulating fluids, compared with that of the organs, is very small. The weight of blood of a human being is hardly equal to one-tenth of his total weight. However, living tissues consume large amounts of oxygen and glucose. They also liberate into the inner medium considerable quantities of carbonic, lactic, hydrochloric, phosphoric acids, etc. A fragment of living tissue, cultivated in a flask, must be given a volume of liquid equal to two thousand times its own volume, in order not to be poisoned within a few days by its waste products. In addition, it requires a gaseous atmosphere at least ten times larger than its fluid medium. Consequently, a human body reduced to pulp and cultivated *in vitro* would demand about two hundred thousand litres of nutritive fluid. It is on account of the marvellous perfection of the mechanisms responsible for the circulation of the blood, its wealth of nutritive substances, and the constant elimination of the waste products, that our tissues can live in six or seven litres of fluid, instead of two hundred thousand.

The speed of circulation is sufficiently great to prevent the composition of blood from being modified by the catabolites of tissues. The acidity of plasma increases only after violent exercise. Each organ regulates the volume and the rapidity of its blood flow by means of vasomotor nerves. The interstitial lymph becomes acid as soon as circulation slackens or stops. The more or less injurious effects of such acid poisoning on the viscera depend on the type of their constituent cells. If we remove a dog's kidney, leave it on a table for an hour, and then replant it in the animal, the kidney is not disturbed by the temporary deprivation of blood, but resumes its functions and works indefinitely in a normal manner. Neither does the suspension of the circulation in a limb, for three or four hours, have any ill effects. The brain, however, is much more sensitive to lack of oxygen. When circulation is stopped and anæmia complete in this organ for about twenty minutes, death always takes place. After only ten minutes, anæmia produces serious and often irreparable disorders. Thus it is impossible to bring back to normal life an individual whose brain has been completely deprived of circulation for a very short time. Lowering of the blood pressure is also dangerous. Brain and other organs demand a certain tension of the blood. Our conduct and the quality of our thoughts depend, in a large measure, on the state of our circulatory apparatus. All human activities are regulated by the physical and chemical conditions of the inner medium and, ultimately, by the heart and the arteries.

Blood maintains its composition constant by perpetually passing through apparatuses where it is purified and recuperates the nutritive substances removed by the tissues. When venous blood returns from the muscles and the organs it is full of carbonic acid and waste products of nutrition. The pulsations of the heart then drive it into the immense network of the lung capillaries, where each red corpuscle comes into contact with atmospheric oxygen. This gas, in conformity with certain simple physico-chemical laws, penetrates the blood and is taken up by the hæmoglobin of the red cells. Carbon dioxide simultaneously escapes into the bronchi, whence it is expelled into the outside atmosphere by the respiratory movements. The more rapid the respiration the more active are the chemical exchanges between air and blood. But during its passage through the lungs blood gets rid of carbonic acid only. It still contains non-volatile acids, and all other waste products of metabolism. Its purification is completed during its passage through the kidneys. The kidneys separate from the blood certain substances that are eliminated in the urine. They also regulate the quantity of salts indispensable to plasma in order that its osmotic tension may remain constant. The functioning of the kidneys and of the lungs is of a prodigious efficiency. It is the intense activity of these viscera that permits the fluid medium required by living tissues to be so limited, and the human body to possess such compactness and agility.

8

The nutritive material carried by the blood to the tissues derives from three sources: from atmospheric air by the agency of the lungs, from the intestinal surface, and, finally, from the endocrine glands. All substances used by the organism, with the exception of oxygen, are supplied by the intestines, either directly or indirectly. The food is successively treated by the saliva, the gastric juice, and the secretions of pancreas, liver, and intestinal mucosa. Digestive ferments divide the molecules of proteins, carbohydrates, and fats into smaller fragments. These fragments are capable of traversing the mucous membranes which defend our inner frontier. They are then absorbed by the blood and lymph vessels of the intestinal mucosa, and penetrate the organic medium. Certain fats and sugars are the only substances to enter the body without previously undergoing modification. For this reason the consistency of adipose parts varies in conformity with the nature of the animal or vegetable fats included in the diet. By feeding a dog with fats of a high melting-point or with oils fluid at body temperature, we can render its adipose tissue either hard or soft. Proteins are broken up by digestive ferments into their constituent amino acids. They thus lose their individuality, their racial specificity. In this way, amino acids, and groups of amino acids derived from proteins of beef, mutton, wheat, etc., retain no evidence of their various origins. They build up in the body new proteins specific for the human race and for the individual. The intestinal wall almost completely protects the organism from invasion by molecules belonging to the tissues of other beings, by opposing the penetration of animal or vegetal proteins into the blood. However, it sometimes allows such proteins to enter. So the body may silently become sensitive, or resistant, to many foreign substances. The barrier raised by the intestines against the outer world is not impassable.

The intestinal mucosa is not always capable of digesting or

absorbing certain indispensable elements of the food. In such an instance, even if these substances are present in the intestinal lumen, they cannot enter our tissues. In fact, the chemical elements of the outer world act on each individual in different ways, according to the specific constitution of his intestinal mucosa. From these elements are built our tissues and our humours. Man is literally made from the dust of the earth. For this reason his physiological and mental activities are profoundly influenced by the geological constitution of the country where he lives, by the nature of the animals and plants on which he generally feeds. His structure and his functions depend also on the selection he makes of certain elements among the vegetal and animal foods at his disposal. The chiefs always had a diet quite different from that of their slaves. Those who fought, commanded, and conquered used chiefly meats and fermented drinks, whereas the peaceful, the weak, and the submissive were satisfied with milk, vegetables, fruits, and cereals. Our aptitudes and our destiny come, in some measure, from the nature of the chemical substances that construct our tissues. It seems as though human beings, like animals, could be artificially given certain bodily and mental characteristics if subjected from childhood to appropriate diets.

The third kind of nutritive substances contained in blood, in addition to atmospheric oxygen and to products of intestinal digestion, consists, as already mentioned, of the secretions of the endocrine glands. The organism has the peculiar property of being its own builder, of manufacturing new compounds from the chemical substances of the blood. These compounds serve to feed certain tissues and to stimulate certain functions. This sort of creation of itself by itself is analogous to the training of the will by an effort of the will. Glands, such as the thyroid, the suprarenal, the pancreas, etc., synthetize from the chemicals in solution in the organic medium a number of new compounds, thyroxin, adrenalin, insulin, etc. They are true chemical transformers. In this way substances indispensable for the nutrition of cells and organs, and for physiological and mental activities, are produced. Such a phenomenon is as strange as if certain parts of a motor should create the oil used by other parts of the machine, the substances accelerating the combustion of the fuel, and even the thoughts of the engineer. Obviously, tissues are unable to feed exclusively on the compounds supplied by the diet after their passage through the intestinal mucosa. These compounds have to be remoulded by the glands. To these glands is due the existence of the body with its manifold activities.

Man is, first of all, a nutritive process. He consists of a ceaseless motion of chemical substances. One can compare him to the flame of a candle, or to the fountains playing in the gardens of Versailles. Those beings, made of burning gases or of water, are both permanent and transitory. Their existence depends on a stream of gas or of liquid. Like ourselves they change according to the quality and the quantity of the substances which animate them. As a large river coming from the external world and returning to it, matter perpetually flows through all the cells of the body. During its passing it yields to tissues the energy they need, and also the chemicals which build the temporary and fragile structures of our organs and humours. The corporeal substratum of all human activities originates from the inanimate world and, sooner or later, goes back to it. Our organism is made from the same elements as lifeless things. Therefore, we should not be surprised, as some modern physiologists still are, to find at work within our own self the usual laws of physics and of chemistry as they exist in the cosmic world. Since we are parts of the material universe, the absence of those laws is unthinkable.

9

The sexual glands have other functions than that of impelling man to the gesture which, in primitive life, perpetuated the race. They also intensify all physiological, mental, and spiritual activities. No eunuch has ever become a great philosopher, a great scientist, or even a great criminal. Testicles and ovaries possess functions of overwhelming importance. They generate male or female cells. Simultaneously they secrete into the blood certain substances which impress the male or female characteristics on our tissues, humours, and consciousness, and give to all our functions their character of intensity. The testicle engenders audacity, violence, and brutality, the qualities distinguishing the fighting bull from the ox drawing the plough along the furrow. The ovary affects the organism of the woman in an analogous manner. But its action lasts only during a part of her life. At the menopause the gland atrophies somewhat. The shorter life of the ovaries gives the ageing woman great inferiority to man, whose testicles remain active until extreme old age.

The differences existing between man and woman do not come from the particular form of the sexual organs, the presence of the uterus, from gestation, or from the mode of education. They are of a more fundamental nature. They are caused by the very structure of the tissues and by the impregnation of the entire organism with specific chemical substances secreted by the ovary. Ignorance of these fundamental facts has led promoters of feminism to believe that both sexes should have the same education, the same powers and the same responsibilities. In reality woman differs profoundly from man. Every one of the cells of her body bears the mark of her sex. The same is true of her organs and, above all, of her nervous system. Physiological laws are as inexorable as those of the sidereal world. They cannot be replaced by human wishes. We are obliged to accept them just as they are. Women should develop their aptitudes in accordance with their own nature, without trying to imitate the males. Their part in the progress of civilization is higher than that of men. They should not abandon their specific functions.

With regard to the propagation of the race, the importance of the two sexes is unequal. Testicle cells unceasingly produce, during the entire course of life, animalcules endowed with very active movements, the spermatozoa. These spermatozoa swim in the mucus covering the vagina and uterus, and meet the ovum at the surface of the uterine mucosa. The ovum results from the slow ripening of the germinal cells of the ovary. In the ovary of a young woman there are about three hundred thousand ova. About four hundred of them reach maturity. At the time of menstruation the cyst containing the ovum bursts. Then the ovum is projected upon the membrane of the Fallopian tube and is transported by the vibrating cilia of this membrane into the uterus. Its nucleus has already undergone an important change. It has ejected half of its substance—that is, half of each chromosome. A spermatozoon then penetrates its surface. And its chromosomes, which have also lost half of their substance, unite with those of the ovum. A human being is born. He is composed of a single cell, grafted on the uterine mucosa. This cell separates into two parts and the development of the embryo begins.

The father and the mother contribute in equal proportions to the formation of the nucleus of the ovum, which engenders every cell of the new organism. But the mother gives also, in addition to half its nuclear substance, all the protoplasm surrounding the nucleus. She thus plays a more important part in the genesis of the embryo than the father does. Indeed, parental characteristics are transmitted to the offspring by the nucleus. But the remaining part of the cell also has some influence. The laws of heredity and the present theories of the geneticists do not entirely elucidate these complex phenomena. When discussing the relative importance of the father and the mother in reproduction, we should never forget the experiments of Bataillon and of Jacques Loeb. From an unfertilized egg, and without the intervention of the male element, a normal frog was obtained through an appropriate technique. The spermatozoon can be replaced by a chemical or physical agent. Only the female element is essential.

Man's part in reproduction is short. That of the woman lasts nine months. During this time the fœtus is nourished by chemicals which filter from the maternal blood through the membranes of the placenta. While the mother supplies her child with the elements from which its tissues are constructed, she receives certain substances secreted by the embryonic organs. Such substances may be beneficial or dangerous. The fœtus, in fact, originates almost as much from the father as from the mother. Therefore, a being of partly foreign origin has taken up its abode in the woman's body. The latter is subjected to its influence during the entire pregnancy. In some instances she may be poisoned by her child. Her physiological and psychological conditions are always modified by it. But females, at any rate among mammals, seem only to attain their full development after one or more pregnancies. Women who have no children are not so well balanced and become more nervous than the others. In short, the presence of the fœtus, whose tissues greatly differ from hers because they are young and are, in part, those of her husband, acts profoundly on the woman. The importance to her of the generative function has not been sufficiently recognized. Such function is indispensable to her optimum development. It is, therefore, absurd to turn women against maternity. The same intellectual and physical training, and the same ambitions, should not be given to young girls as to boys. Educators should pay very close attention to the organic and mental peculiarities of the male and the female and to their natural functions. Between the two sexes there are irrevocable differences. And it is imperative to take them into account in constructing the civilized world.

10

Through his nervous system man records the stimuli impinging upon him from his environment. His organs and muscles supply the appropriate answer. He struggles for existence with his mind still more than with his body. In this ceaseless fight, his heart, lungs, liver, and endocrine glands are as indispensable as his muscles, hands, tools, machines, and weapons. Seemingly for this purpose he possesses two nervous systems. The central or cerebrospinal system, conscious and voluntary, commands the muscles. The sympathetic system, autonomous and unconscious, controls the organs. The second system depends on the first. This double apparatus gives to the complexity of our body the simplicity required for its action on the outside world.

The central system consists of the brain, the cerebellum, and the spinal cord. It acts directly on the nerves of the muscles, and indirectly on those of the organs. It is composed of a soft, whitish, extremely fragile substance, filling the skull and the spinal column. This substance, by the agency of the sensitive nerves, receives the messages emanating from the surface of the body and from the sensory organs. In this way the nervous centres are in constant touch with the cosmic world. Simultaneously, they send their orders to all the muscles through the motor nerves, and to all the organs through the sympathetic system. An immense number of nervous fibres intersect the organism in every direction. Their microscopic endings creep between the cells of the skin, around the acini of the glands and their excretory ducts, in the coat of the arteries and the veins, into the contractile envelopes of the stomach and the intestines, on the surface of the muscular fibres, etc. They spread their delicate network through the whole body. They all originate from cells inhabiting the central nervous system, the double chain of the sympathetic ganglia, and the small ganglia disseminated through the organs.

These cells are the noblest and most elaborate of the epithelial cells. Owing to the techniques of Ramon y Cajal, they appear in all their structural beauty. They possess a large body which, in the varieties found on the surface of the brain, resembles a pyramid, and also most complex organs whose functions still remain unknown. They extend in the form of extremely slender filaments, the dendrites, and the axons. Certain axons cover the long distance separating the cerebral surface from the lower part of the cord. Axons, dendrites, and their mother cell constitute a distinct individual, the neuron. The fibrils of one cell never unite with those of another. Their extremities form a cluster of very tiny bulbs, which are in constant motion on their almost invisible stems, as is shown by cinematographic films. They articulate with the corresponding terminals of another cell by means of a membrane, known as the synaptic membrane. In each neuron the nervous influx always diffuses in the same direction in relation to the cellular body. This direction is centripetal for the dendrites and centrifugal for the axons. It passes from one neuron to the other by crossing the synaptic membrane. Likewise it penetrates muscular fibres from the bulbs in contact with their surface. But its passage is subject to a strange condition. The value of time, or chronaxy, must be identical in the contiguous neurons, or in the neuron and the muscular fibre. The propagation of nervous influx does not take place between two neurons having different time standards. Thus a muscle and its nerve must be isochronic. If the chronaxy of the nerve or the muscle be modified by a poison, such as curare or strychnine, the influx no longer reaches the muscle. Paralysis occurs although the muscle is normal. These temporal relations of nerve and muscle are as indispensable to normal function as is their spatial continuity. We do not yet know what takes place within the nerves during pain or voluntary motion. But we are aware that a variation of electric potential travels along the nerve during its activity. In fact, Adrian has shown, in isolated fibrils, the progress of negative waves, whose arrival in the brain is expressed by a sensation of pain.

Neurons articulate with each other in a system of relays, like electrical relays. They are divided into two groups. One group is composed of receptor and motor neurons, receiving stimuli from the outside world or from the organs, and controlling the voluntary muscles ; the other group, of the neurons of association, whose vast number gives to our nervous centres their elaborate complexity. Our intelligence can no more realize the immensity of the brain than the extent of the sidereal universe. The cerebral substance contains more than twelve thousand millions of cells. These cells are connected with one another by fibrils, and each fibril possesses several branches. By means of these fibrils they associate several billions of times. And this prodigious crowd of tiny individuals and invisible fibrils, despite its undreamed-of complexity, works as if it were essentially one. To observers accustomed to the simplicity of the molecular and atomic worlds the brain appears as an unintelligible and marvellous phenomenon.

One of the principal functions of the nervous centres is to respond in an appropriate manner to stimuli coming from the environment, or, in other words, to produce reflex reactions. A beheaded frog is suspended with its legs hanging. If one of its toes is pinched, the leg moves, pulling away from the painful stimulus. This phenomenon is due to the presence of a reflex arc—that is, of two neurons, one sensitive and the other motive, articulated with one another within the cord. Generally, a reflex arc is not so simple and includes one or several associating neurons interposed between sensitive and motive neurons. The neuronic systems are responsible for reflexes such as respiration, swallowing, standing upright, walking, as well as for most of the acts of our every-day life. These movements are automatic. But some of them are influenced by consciousness. For example, when we think about our respiratory motion its rhythm is at once modified. On the contrary, heart, stomach, and intestines are quite independent of our will. However, if we pay too much attention to them their automatism may be disturbed. Although the muscles that permit standing, walking, and running receive their orders from the spinal cord, they depend for their co-ordination upon the cerebellum. Like the cord the cerebellum does not concern itself with mental processes.

The cerebral surface, or cortex of the brain, is a mosaic of distinct nervous organs connected with the different parts of the body. For instance, the lateral part of the brain, known as the region of Rolando, controls the movements of prehension and locomotion, and also articulate language. Farther back on the cortex are the visual centres. Wounds, tumours, and hæmorrhages located in these different districts result in disturbances of the corresponding functions. Similar disorders appear when the lesions are situated in the fibres uniting the cerebral centres to the lower parts of the spinal cord. The reflexes called by Pavlov conditional reflexes take place in the cerebral cortex. A dog secretes saliva when food is placed in his mouth. This is an innate reflex. But he also secretes saliva when he sees the person who usually brings him his nourishment. This is an acquired, or conditional, reflex. This property of the nervous system of animals and man renders education possible. If the surface of the brain is removed, the building up of new reflexes is quite impossible. Our knowledge of this intricate subject is still rudimentary. We do not know the relations between consciousness and nervous processes, between the mental and the cerebral. Neither do we know how events taking place in the pyramidal cells are influenced by previous or even future events, or how excitations are changed into inhibitions, and vice

D (A181)

versa. We understand still less how unpredictable phenomena spring from the brain, how thought is born.

Brain and spinal cord, with nerves and muscles, constitute
an indivisible system. Muscles, from a functional point of
view, are only a part of the brain. It is with their help and
that of the bones that human intelligence has put its mark on
the world. Man has been given power over his environment
by the shape of his skeleton. The limbs consist of articulated
levers composed of three segments. The upper limb is
mounted upon a mobile plate, the shoulder blade, while the
osseous girdle, the pelvis, to which the lower limb is jointed,
is entirely rigid and immobile. The motive muscles lie along
the bones. Near the extremity of the arm these muscles resolve into tendons, which move the fingers and the hand itself. The hand is a masterpiece. Simultaneously, it feels and
it acts. It acts as if endowed with sight. Owing to the unique
properties of its skin, its tactile nerves, its muscles, and its
bones, the hand is capable of manufacturing arms and tools.
We would never have acquired our mastery over matter without the aid of our fingers, those five small levers, each composed of three articulated segments, which are mounted
upon the metacarpus and the bones of the wrist. The hand
adapts itself to the roughest work as well as to the most delicate. It has wielded with equal skill the flint knife of the
primitive hunter, the blacksmith's hammer, the woodcutter's
axe, the farmer's plough, the sword of the mediæval knight,
the controls of the modern aviator, the artist's brush, the
journalist's pen, the threads of the silk-weaver. It is able to
kill and to bless, to steal and to give, to sow grain on the surface of the fields and to throw grenades in the trenches. The
elasticity, strength, and adaptiveness of the lower limbs,
whose pendulum-like oscillations determine walking and
running, have never been equalled by our machines, which
only make use of the principle of the wheel. The three levers,
articulated on the pelvis, adapt themselves with marvellous
suppleness to all postures, efforts, and movements. They

carry us on the polished floor of a ballroom and in the chaos of the ice-fields, upon the sidewalks of Park Avenue and on the slopes of the Rocky Mountains. They enable us to walk, to run, to fall, to climb, to swim, to wander all over the earth under all conditions.

There is another organic system composed of cerebral substance, nerves, muscles, and cartilages, which, to the same degree as the hand, has determined the superiority of man over all living beings. It consists of the tongue and the larynx and their nervous apparatus. Owing to this system we are capable of expressing our thoughts, of communicating with our fellow men by means of sounds. Were it not for language civilization would not exist. The use of speech, like that of the hand, has greatly aided the development of the brain. The cerebral parts of the hand, the tongue, and the larynx extend over a large area of the brain surface. At the same time that the nervous centres control writing, speaking, and the grasping and handling of objects, they are, in return, stimulated by these acts. Simultaneously, they are determining and determined. It seems that the work of the mind is helped by the rhythmic contractions of the muscles. Certain exercises appear to stimulate thought. For this reason, perhaps, Aristotle and his disciples were in the habit of walking while discussing the fundamental problems of philosophy and science. No part of the nervous centres seems to act separately. Viscera, muscles, spinal cord, cerebrum, are functionally one. Skeletal muscles, for their co-ordinated action, depend on brain and spinal cord, and also on many organs. They receive their orders from the central nervous system, and their energy from the heart, the lungs, the endocrine glands, and the blood. To carry out the directions of the brain they demand the help of the whole body.

II

The autonomous nervous system enables each viscus to co-operate with the entire organism in our dealings with the outside world. Organs such as the stomach, liver, heart, etc., are not subject to our will. We are incapable of decreasing or increasing the calibre of our arteries, the rhythm of our pulse or of the contractions of our intestines. The automatism of these functions is due to the presence of reflex arcs within the organs. These regional brains are made up of small clusters of nervous cells scattered in the tissues, under the skin, around the blood vessels, etc. There are numerous reflex centres responsible for the independence of the viscera. For example, an intestinal loop, when removed from the organism and provided with artificial circulation, displays normal movements. A grafted kidney, although its nerves are cut, starts to work at once. Most organs are endowed with a certain freedom. They are thus able to function, even when isolated from the body. However, they are bound by innumerable nervous fibres to the double chain of sympathetic ganglia situated in front of the spinal column, and to other ganglia surrounding the abdominal vessels. These ganglia integrate all the organs and regulate their work. Moreover, through their relations with the spinal cord and the brain they co-ordinate the activity of the viscera with that of the muscles in the acts which demand an effort of the entire body.

The viscera, although dependent on the central nervous system, are, in some measure, independent of it. It is possible to remove, in a single mass, the lungs, heart, stomach, liver, pancreas, intestines, spleen, kidneys, and bladder, with their blood vessels and nerves, from the body of a cat or a dog, without the heart ceasing to beat, or the blood to circulate. If this visceral entity is placed in a warm bath and oxygen supplied to its lungs, life continues. The heart pulsates, the stomach and the intestines move and digest their food. The viscera can be effectively isolated from the central nervous system in a simpler way, as Cannon has done, by extirpating the double sympathetic chain from living cats. The animals which have undergone this operation continue to live in good health as long as they remain in their cage. But they are not capable of a free existence. In the struggle for life they can no longer call their heart, lungs, and glands to the help of their muscles, claws, and teeth.

The double chain of the sympathetic ganglia is connected with the cerebrospinal system by branches communicating with the cranial, dorsal, and pelvic regions of the nervous substance. The sympathetic or autonomous nerves of the cranial and pelvic regions are called parasympathetic. Those of the dorsal region are the sympathetic. In their action the parasympathetic and the sympathetic are antagonistic to one another. Each organ receives its nerves simultaneously from these two systems. The parasympathetic slows the heart, and the sympathetic accelerates it. The former dilates the pupil, while the latter causes its contraction. The movements of the intestines are, on the contrary, decreased by the sympathetic and increased by the parasympathetic. According to the predominance of the one or the other of these systems, human beings are endowed with different temperaments. The circulation of each organ is regulated by these nerves. The sympathetic brings about constriction of the arteries and pallor of the face, such as are observed in emotion and certain diseases. Its section is followed by redness of the skin and contraction of the pupil. Some glands, such as the hypophysis and the suprarenals, are made up of both glandular and nervous cells. They enter into activity under the influence of the sympathetic. The chemical substances secreted by these cells have the same effect upon blood vessels as the stimulation of the nerve. They increase the power of the sympathetic. Like the sympathetic, adrenalin causes the vessels to contract. In fact the autonomous nervous system, by means of its sympathetic and parasympathetic fibres, dominates the entire world of the viscera, and unifies their action.

We shall describe later how the adaptive functions, those which enable the organism to endure, depend mostly on the sympathetic system.

The autonomous apparatus is linked, as we know, to the central nervous system, supreme co-ordinator of all organic activities. It is represented by a centre situated at the base of the brain. This centre determines the manifestation of emotions. Wounds or tumours in this region bring about certain disorders of the affective functions. In fact,' it is by the agency of the endocrine glands that our emotions express themselves. Shame, fear, and anger modify the cutaneous circulation. They cause pallor or flushing of the face, contraction or dilatation of the pupils, protrusion of the eye, discharge of adrenalin into the circulation, interruption of the gastric secretions, etc. Our states of consciousness have a marked effect upon the functions of the viscera. Many diseases of the stomach and of the heart originate in nervous troubles. The independence of the sympathetic system from the brain is not sufficient to protect our organs against the disturbances of our mind.

Organs are provided with sensitive nerves. They send frequent messages to the nervous centres and, more particularly, to the centre of visceral consciousness. When, in the daily struggle for existence, our attention is attracted by the outside world, the stimuli coming from the organs do not pass the threshold of consciousness. However, they do give a certain colour to our thoughts, our emotions, our actions, to all our life, though we do not clearly realize their hidden power. One sometimes experiences, without any reason, a feeling of imminent misfortune, or an impression of joy, of unexplainable happiness. The state of our organic system obscurely acts on consciousness. A diseased viscus may, in this manner, sound an alarm. When a man, in either good or bad health, feels that he is in danger, that death approaches, such warning probably comes to him from the centre of visceral consciousness. And visceral consciousness is rarely mistaken. Of course, in the inhabitants of the new city, sympathetic functions are often as ill balanced as mental activities. The autonomous system seems to become less capable of protecting the heart, stomach, intestines, and glands from the worries of existence. Against the dangers and brutality of primitive life it effectively defended the organs. But it is not strong enough to resist the constant shocks of modern life.

12

The body thus appears as an extremely complex thing, a stupendous association of different cell races, each race comprising millions of individuals. These individuals live immersed in humours made of chemical substances, which are manufactured by the organs, and of other substances derived from food. From one end of the body to the other they communicate by chemical messengers—that is, by the agency of their secretions. Moreover, they are united by the nervous system. Their associations, as revealed by scientific techniques, are of an enormous complexity. Nevertheless, these immense crowds of individuals behave like a perfectly integrated being. Our acts are simple : for example, the act of accurately estimating a minute weight, or of selecting a given number of objects, without counting them and without making a mistake. However, such gestures appear to our mind to be composed of a multitude of elements. They require the harmonious functioning of muscular and tactile senses, of the retina, of the eye and hand muscles, of innumerable nervous and muscular cells. Their simplicity is probably real, their complexity artificial—that is, created by our techniques of observation. No object seems to be simpler, more homogeneous, than the water of the ocean. But if we could examine this water through a microscope having a magnifying power of about one million diameters, its simplicity would vanish. The clear drop would become a heterogeneous population of molecules of different dimensions and shapes, moving at various speeds in an inextricable chaos. Thus the things of our world are simple or complex, according to the techniques that we select for studying them. In fact, functional simplicity always corresponds to a complex substratum. This is a primary datum of observation which must be accepted just as it is.

Our tissues are of great structural heterogeneity. They are composed of many disparate elements. Liver, spleen, heart, kidneys are societies of specific cells. They are individuals definitely limited in space. For anatomists and surgeons the organic heterogeneity of the body is unquestionable. Nevertheless, it may be more apparent than real. Functions are much less precisely located than organs. The skeleton, for example, is not merely the framework of the body. It also constitutes a part of the circulatory, respiratory, and nutritive systems, since, with the aid of the bone marrow, it manufactures leucocytes and red cells. The liver secretes bile, destroys poisons and microbes, stores glycogen, regulates sugar metabolism in the entire organism, and produces heparin. In a like manner, the pancreas, the suprarenals, the spleen, etc., do not confine themselves to one function. Each viscus possesses multiple activities and takes part in almost all the events of the body. Its structural frontiers are narrower than its functional ones. Its physiological individuality is far more comprehensive than its anatomical individuality. A cell community, by means of its manufactured products, penetrates all other communities. The vast cellular associations called viscera are placed, as we know, under the command of a single nervous centre. This centre sends its silent orders to every region of the organic world. In this way, heart, blood vessels, lungs, digestive apparatus, and endocrine glands become a functional whole in which all organic individualities blend.

The heterogeneity of the organism is, in fact, created by the fancy of the observer. Should an organ be defined by its histological elements or by the chemical substances it constantly fabricates? The kidneys appear to the anatomist as two distinct glands. From a physiological point of view, however, they are a single being. If one of them is removed, the size of the other at once increases. An organ is not limited by its surface. It reaches as far as the substances it secretes. In reality, its structural and functional condition depends on the rate of elimination of these substances or of their absorption by other organs. Each gland extends, by means of its internal secretions, over the whole organism. Let us suppose the substances set free in the blood by testicles to be blue. The entire body of the male would be blue. The testicles themselves would be more intensely coloured. But their specific hue would be diffused in all tissues and organs, even in the cartilages at the extremity of the bones. The body would then appear to be formed of an immense testicle. The spatial and temporal dimensions of each gland are, in fact, equal to those of the entire organism. An organ consists of its inner medium as much as of its anatomical elements. It is constituted both by specific cells and specific fluid or medium. And this fluid, this inner medium, greatly transcends the anatomical frontier. When the concept of a gland is reduced to that of its fibrous framework, epithelial cells, blood vessels, and nerves, the existence of the living organism becomes incomprehensible. In short, the body is an anatomical heterogeneity and a physiological homogeneity. It acts as if it were simple. But it shows us a complex structure. Such an antithesis is created by our mind. We always delight in picturing man as being constructed like one of our machines.

13

Indeed, both a machine and our body are organisms. But the organization of our body is not similar to that of the machine. A machine is composed of many parts, originally

D*

separate. Once these parts are put together, its manifoldness becomes unity. Like the human individual, it is assembled for a specific purpose. Like him, it is both simple and complex. But it is primarily complex and secondarily simple. On the contrary, man is primarily simple and secondarily complex. He originates from a single cell. This cell divides into two others, which divide in their turn, and such division continues indefinitely. In the course of this process of structural elaboration, the embryo retains the functional simplicity of the egg. The cells seem to remember their original unity, even when they have become the elements of an innumerable multitude. They know spontaneously the functions attributed to them in the organized whole. If we cultivate epithelial cells over a period of several months, quite apart from the animal to which they belong, they arrange themselves in a mosaic, exactly as if to protect a surface. Yet the surface to be protected is lacking. Leucocytes, living in flasks, industriously devour microbes and red corpuscles, although there is no organism to be defended against the incursions of these enemies. The innate knowledge of the part they must play in the whole is a mode of being of all the elements of the body.

Isolated cells have the singular power of reproducing, without direction or purpose, the edifices characterizing each organ. If a few red corpuscles, impelled by gravity, flow from a drop of blood placed in liquid plasma and form a tiny stream, banks are soon built up. Then, these banks cover themselves with filaments of fibrin, and the stream becomes a pipe, through which the red cells glide just as in a blood vessel. Next, leucocytes come, adhere to the surface of the pipe, and surround it with their undulating membrane. The blood stream now assumes the appearance of a capillary vessel enveloped in a layer of contractile cells. Thus isolated red and white corpuscles manage to construct a segment of circulatory apparatus, although there is neither heart, circulation, nor tissues to be irrigated. Cells are like bees erecting their geometrical alveoli, synthetizing honey, feeding their embryos, as though each one of them understood mathematics, chemistry, and biology, and unselfishly acted for the interests of the entire community. The spontaneous tendency toward formation of the organs by their constitutive cells, like the social aptitude of the insects, is a primary datum of observation. It cannot be explained in the light of our present concepts.

An organ builds itself by techniques very foreign to the human mind. It is not made of extraneous material, like a house. Neither is it a cellular construction, a mere assemblage of cells. It is, of course, composed of cells, as a house is of bricks. But it is born from a cell, as if the house originated from one brick, a magic brick that would set about manufacturing other bricks. Those bricks, without waiting for the architect's drawings or the coming of the bricklayers, would assemble themselves and form the walls. They would also metamorphose into window-panes, roofing-slates, coal for heating, and water for the kitchen and the bathroom. An organ develops by means such as those attributed to fairies in the tales told to children in bygone times. It is engendered by cells which, to all appearances, have a knowledge of the future edifice, and synthetize from substances contained in blood plasma the building material and even the workers.

These methods used by the organism have not the simplicity of ours. They appear strange to us. Our intelligence does not encounter itself in the intra-organic world. It is modelled on the simplicity of the cosmic universe, and not on the complexity of the inner mechanisms of living beings. For the moment we cannot understand the mode of organization of our body and its nutritive, nervous, and mental activities. The laws of mechanics, physics, and chemistry are completely applicable to inert matter; partly, to man. The illusions of the mechanicists of the nineteenth century, the dogmas of Jacques Loeb, the childish physico-chemical conceptions of the human being, in which so many physiologists and physicians still believe, have to be definitely abandoned.

We must also dismiss the philosophical and humanistic dreams of physicists and astronomers. Following many others, Jeans believes and teaches that God, creator of the sidereal universe, is a mathematician. If that is so, the material world, the living beings, and man have been created, obviously, by different Gods. How naïve our speculations! Our knowledge of the human body is, in truth, most rudimentary. It is impossible, for the present, to grasp its constitution. We must, then, be content with the scientific observation of our organic and mental activities, and, without any other guide, march forward into the unknown.

14

Our body is extremely robust. It adapts itself to all climates, arctic cold as well as tropical heat. It also resists starvation, weather inclemencies, fatigue, hardships, overwork. Man is the hardiest of all animals, and the white races, builders of our civilization, the hardiest of all races. However, our organs are fragile. They are damaged by the slightest shock. They disintegrate as soon as blood circulation stops. Such contrast between the strength and the fragility of the organism is, like most of the antitheses encountered in biology, an illusion of our mind. We always unconsciously compare our body with a machine. The strength of a machine depends on the metal used in its construction, and on the perfection of the assembling of its parts. But that of man is due to other causes. His endurance comes more especially from the elasticity of his tissues, their tenacity, their property of growing instead of wearing out, from the strange power displayed by the organism in meeting a new situation by adaptive changes. Resistance to disease, work, and worries, capacity for effort, and nervous equilibrium are the signs of the superiority of a man. Such qualities characterized the founders of our civilization in the United States as well as in

Europe. The great white races owe their success to the perfection of their nervous system—a nervous system which, although very delicate and excitable, can, however, be disciplined. To the exceptional qualities of their tissues and consciousness is due the predominance over the rest of the world of the peoples of western Europe, and of their swarms in the United States.

We are ignorant of the nature of this organic robustness, of this nervous and mental superiority. Must they be attributed to the structure of the cells, to the chemical substances they synthetize, to the mode of integration of the organs by the humours and nerves? We do not know. These qualities are hereditary. They have existed in our people for many centuries. But even in the greatest and richest nations they may disappear. The history of past civilizations shows that such a calamity is possible. But it does not explain clearly its genesis. Obviously, the resistance of the body and the mind must be conserved at all costs in a great nation. Mental and nervous strength is infinitely more important than muscular strength. The descendant of a great race, if he has not degenerated, is endowed with natural immunity to fatigue and to fear. He does not think about his health or his security. He is not interested in medicine, and ignores physicians. He does not believe that the Golden Age will arrive when physiological chemists have obtained in a pure state all vitamins and secretory products of endocrine glands. He looks upon himself as destined to fight, to love, to think, and to conquer. He knows that safety should not be first. His action on his environment is as essentially simple as the leap of a wild animal upon its prey. No more than the animal does he feel his structural complexity.

The sound body lives in silence. We do not hear, we do not feel, its working. The rhythms of our existence are expressed by cenesthesic impressions which, like the soft whirring of a sixteen-cylinder motor, fill the depths of our consciousness when we are in silence and meditation. The harmony of organic functions gives a feeling of peace. When an organ begins to deteriorate, this peace may be disturbed. Pain is a signal of distress. Many people, although they are not ill, are not in good health. Perhaps the quality of some of their tissues is defective. The secretions of such a gland, or such a mucosa, may be insufficient or too abundant; the excitability of their nervous system exaggerated; their organic functions not exactly correlated in space or in time; or their tissues not as capable of resisting infections as they should be. Such individuals feel profoundly these organic deficiencies, which bring them much misery. The future discoverer of a method for inducing tissues and organs to develop harmoniously will be a greater benefactor of humanity than Pasteur himself. For he will present man with the most precious of all gifts, with an almost divine offering, the aptitude for happiness.

The weakening of the body has many causes. It is well known that the quality of tissues is lowered by too poor or too rich a diet, by alcoholism, syphilis, consanguineous unions, and also by prosperity and leisure. Wealth is as dangerous as ignorance and poverty. Civilized men degenerate in tropical climates. On the contrary, they thrive in temperate or cold countries. They need a way of life involving constant struggle, mental and muscular effort, physiological and moral discipline, and some privations. Such conditions inure the body to fatigue and to sorrows. They protect it against disease and especially against nervous diseases. They irresistibly drive humanity to the conquest of the external world.

15

Disease consists of a functional and structural disorder. Its aspects are as numerous as our organic activities. There are diseases of the stomach, of the heart, of the nervous system, etc. But in illness the body preserves the same unity as in health. It is sick as a whole. No disturbance remains strictly confined to a single organ. Physicians have been led to consider each disease as a specialty by the old anatomical conception of the human being. Only those who know man both in his parts and in his entirety, simultaneously under his anatomical, physiological, and mental aspects, are capable of understanding him when he is sick.

There are two great classes of disease—infectious, or microbian, diseases, and degenerative diseases. The first are caused by viruses or bacteria penetrating into the body. Viruses are invisible beings, extremely small, hardly larger than a molecule of albumin. They live within the cells themselves. They are fond of the nervous substance, and also of the skin and the glands. They destroy those tissues in men and animals or modify their functions. They produce infantile paralysis, grippe, encephalitis lethargica, etc., as also measles, typhus, yellow fever, and perhaps cancer. They can transform inoffensive cells, the leucocytes of the hen, for instance, into ferocious beasts which invade muscles and organs and, in a few days, kill the animal affected with the disease. These formidable beings are unknown to us. Nobody has ever seen them. They only manifest themselves by their effects upon tissues. Before their onslaught cells stand defenceless. They resist viruses no more than the leaves of a tree resist smoke. In comparison with viruses bacteria are veritable giants. However, they easily penetrate into our body through the mucosas of the intestines, those of the nose, the eyes, the throat, or through the surface of a wound. They do not instal themselves within the cells, but around them. They invade the loose tissues separating the organs. They multiply under the skin, between the muscles, in the abdominal cavity, in the membranes enveloping the brain and the cord. They secrete toxic substances in the interstitial lymph. They may also migrate into the blood. They throw into confusion all organic functions.

Degenerative diseases are often the consequence of bacterial infections, as in certain maladies of the heart and of the kidneys. They are also caused by the presence in the organism of toxic substances issuing from the tissues themselves. When the secretions of the thyroid gland become too abundant, or poisonous, the symptoms of exophthalmic goitre make their appearance. Certain disorders are due to lack of secretions indispensable to nutrition. The deficiency of endocrine glands, of thyroid, pancreas, liver, of gastric mucosa, brings on diseases such as myxœdema, diabetes, pernicious anæmia, etc. Other disorders are determined by the absence of elements required for the construction and maintenance of tissues, such as vitamins, mineral salts, iodine, metals. When the organs do not receive from the cosmic world through the intestine the building substances which they need, they lose their power of resistance to infection, develop structural lesions, manufacture poisons, etc. There are also diseases which have so far baffled all the scientists and the institutes for medical research of America, Europe, Africa, Asia, and Australia; among them, cancer and a multitude of nervous and mental affections.

Great gains in health have been achieved since the beginning of this century. Tuberculosis is being vanquished. Deaths from infantile diarrhœa, diphtheria, typhoid fever, etc., are being eliminated. All diseases of bacterial origin have decreased in a striking manner. The average length of life—that is, the expectation of life at birth—was only forty-nine years in 1900. To-day it has gained more than eleven years. The chances of survival for each age up to maturity have notably augmented. Nevertheless, in spite of the triumphs of medical science, the problem of disease is very far from solved. Modern man is delicate. Eleven hundred thousand persons have to attend the medical needs of 120,000,000 other persons. Every year, among the population of the United States, there are about 100,000,000 illnesses, serious or slight. In the hospitals, 700,000 beds are occupied every day of the year. The care of these patients requires the efforts of 145,000 doctors, 280,000 nurses or student nurses, 60,000 dentists, and 150,000 pharmacists. It also necessitates 7,000 hospitals, 8,000 clinics, and 60,000 pharmacies. The public spends annually $715,000,000 in medicines. Medical care, under all its forms, costs about $3,500,000,000 yearly. Obviously, disease is still a heavy economic burden. Its importance in modern life is incalculable.

Medicine is far from having decreased human sufferings as much as it endeavours to make us believe. Indeed, the number of deaths from infectious diseases has greatly diminished. But we still must die, and we die in a much larger proportion from degenerative diseases. The years of life which we have gained by the suppression of diphtheria, smallpox, typhoid fever, etc., are paid for by the long sufferings and the lingering deaths caused by chronic affections, and especially by cancer, diabetes, and heart disease. In addition, man is liable, as he was in former times, to chronic nephritis, brain tumours, arteriosclerosis, syphilis, cerebral hæmorrhages, hypertension, and also to the intellectual, moral and physiological decay determined by these maladies. He is equally subject to the organic and functional disorders brought in their train by excess of food, insufficient physical exercise, and overwork. The lack of equilibrium and the neuroses of the visceral nervous system bring about many affections of the stomach and the intestines. Heart diseases become more frequent. And also diabetes. The maladies of the central nervous system are innumerable. In the course of his life, every individual suffers from some attack of neurasthenia, of nervous depression, engendered by constant agitation, noise, and worries. Although modern hygiene has made human existence far safer, longer, and more pleasant, diseases have not been mastered. They have simply changed in nature.

This change comes undoubtedly from the elimination of infections. But it may be due also to modifications in the constitution of tissues under the influence of the new modes of life. The organism seems to have become more susceptible to degenerative diseases. It is continually subjected to nervous and mental shocks, to toxic substances manufactured by disturbed organs, to those contained in food and air. It is also affected by the deficiencies of the essential physiological and mental functions. The staple foods may not contain the same nutritive substances as in former times. Mass production has modified the composition of wheat, eggs, milk, fruit, and butter, although these articles have retained their familiar appearance. Chemical fertilizers, by increasing the abundance of the crops without replacing all the exhausted elements of the soil, have indirectly contributed to change the nutritive value of cereal grains and of vegetables. Hens have been compelled, by artificial diet and mode of living, to enter the ranks of mass producers. Has not the quality of their eggs been modified? The same question may be asked about milk, because cows are now confined to the stable all the year round, and are fed on manufactured provender. Hygienists have not paid sufficient attention to the genesis of diseases. Their studies of conditions of life and diet, and of their effects on the physiological and mental state of modern man, are superficial, incomplete, and of too short duration. They have, thus, contributed to the weakening of our body and our soul. And they leave us without protection against the degenerative diseases, the diseases resulting from civilization. We cannot understand the characteristics of these affections before having considered the nature of our mental activities. In disease as in health, body and consciousness, although distinct, are inseparable.

CHAPTER IV

MENTAL ACTIVITIES

*1. Operational concept of consciousness. Body and soul.
Meaningless questions. Man consists of all his manifested activities. 2. Intellectual activities. Their measurement. Conditions of their development. Scientific certainty. Intuition.
Logical and intuitive minds. Clairvoyance and telepathy.
3. Moral activities. Metabolism and emotion. Moral constitution. Moral beauty. 4. Æsthetic activities. Popular art.
Beauty and its practical importance. 5. Mystic activities.
Asceticism and contemplation. Operational concept of mystic
experience. 6. Correlation of the activities of consciousness.
Intelligence and moral sense. Intelligence, æsthetic, and mystic
activities. 7. Effects of physiological on mental activities.
8. Effects of mental on organic activities. Meditation and
Action. Prayer. Miracles. 9. Effects of social environment
on mental activities. Atrophy of consciousness. 10. Mental
diseases. Feeble-minded and insane. Organic basis of mental
diseases. Feeble-mindedness in dogs. Social environment and
mental diseases.*

I

SIMULTANEOUSLY with physiological activities, the body
manifests other activities, which are called mental. The organs express themselves by mechanical work, heat, electrical
phenomena, and chemical transformations, measurable by
the techniques of physics and chemistry. The existence of
the mind, of consciousness, is detected by other procedures,
such as those employed in introspection and in the study of
human behaviour. The concept of consciousness is equivalent to the analysis made by ourself of our own self, and of
the expression of the self of our fellow men. It is convenient
to divide the mental activities into intellectual, moral,
æsthetic, and religious, although such classification is nothing but an artefact. In reality, the body and the soul are

115

views taken of the same object by different methods, abstractions obtained by our reason from the concrete unity of our being. The antithesis of matter and mind represents merely the opposition of two kinds of techniques. The error of Descartes was to believe in the reality of these abstractions and to consider the material and the mental as heterogeneous, as two different things. This dualism has weighed heavily upon the entire history of our knowledge of man. For it has engendered the false problem of the relations of the soul and the body.

There are no such relations. Neither the soul nor the body can be investigated separately. We observe merely a complex being, whose activities have been arbitrarily divided into physiological and mental. Of course, one will always continue to speak of the soul as an entity. Just as one speaks of the setting and the rising of the sun, although everybody knows, since Galileo's time, that the sun is relatively immobile. The soul is the aspect of ourselves that is specific of our nature and distinguishes man from all other animals. We are not capable of defining this familiar and profoundly mysterious entity. What is thought, that strange being, which lives in the depths of ourselves without consuming a measurable quantity of chemical energy? Is it related to the known forms of energy? Could it be a constituent of our universe, ignored by the physicists, but infinitely more important than light? The mind is hidden within the living matter, completely neglected by physiologists and economists, almost unnoticed by physicians. And yet it is the most colossal power of this world. Is it produced by the cerebral cells, like insulin by the pancreas and bile by the liver? From what substances is it elaborated? Does it come from a pre-existing element, as glucose from glycogen, or fibrin from fibrinogen? Does it consist of a kind of energy differing from that studied by physics, expressing itself by other laws, and generated by the cells of the cerebral cortex? Or should it be considered as an immaterial being, located outside space and time, outside the dimensions of the cosmic universe, and inserting itself by an unknown procedure into our brain, which would be the indispensable condition of its manifestations and the determining agent of its characteristics?

At all times, and in all countries, great philosophers have devoted their lives to the investigation of these problems. They have not found their solution. We cannot refrain from asking the same questions. But those questions will remain unanswered until new methods for penetrating more deeply into consciousness are discovered. Meanwhile, we feel the urge to know, and not merely to speculate or to dream. If our understanding of this essential, specific aspect of the human being is to progress, we must make a careful study of the phenomena attainable by our present methods of observation, and of their relations with physiological activities. We must also have the courage to explore those regions of the self whose horizons, on every side, are shrouded in dense mist.

Man consists of all his actual and potential activities. The functions which, at certain epochs and in certain environments, remain virtual, are as real as those which constantly express themselves. The writings of Ruysbroeck the Admirable contain as many truths as those of Claude Bernard. *The Adornment of the Spiritual Marriage* and the *Introduction to the Study of Experimental Medicine* describe two aspects, the former less frequent and the latter more usual, of the same being. The forms of human activity considered by Plato are more specific of our nature than hunger, thirst, sexual appetite, and greed. Since the Renaissance a privileged position has arbitrarily been given to certain aspects of man. Matter has been separated from mind. To matter has been attributed a greater reality than to mind. Physiology and medicine have directed their attention to the chemical manifestations of the body's activities and to the organic disorders expressed by microscopical lesions of the tissues. Sociology has envisaged man almost uniquely from the point of view of his ability to run machines, of his output of work, of his capacity as a consumer, of his economic value. Hygiene has concerned itself with his health, the means of increasing the population, prevention of infectious diseases, and with every possible addition to our physiological welfare. Pedagogy has directed its efforts toward the intellectual and muscular development of the children. But these sciences have neglected the study of the various aspects of consciousness. They should have examined man in the converging light of physiology and psychology. They should have utilized equitably the data supplied by introspection and by the study of behaviour. Both these techniques attain the same object. But one considers man from inside, and the other from outside. There is no reason to give to one a greater value than to the other.

2

The existence of intelligence is a primary datum of observation. This power of discerning the relations between things assumes a certain value and a certain form in each individual. Intelligence is measurable by appropriate techniques. These measurements deal only with a conventional aspect of the mind. They do not give an accurate idea of intellectual value. But they permit a rough classification of human beings. They are useful in selecting suitable men for unimportant positions, such as those open to factory hands and minor bank or store clerks. In addition, they have brought to light an important fact, the weakness of the mind of most individuals. There is, indeed, an enormous diversity in the quantity and the quality of the intelligence possessed by each one. In this respect certain men are giants, and many, dwarfs. Every human being is born with different intellectual capacities. But, great or small, these potentialities require, in order to be actualized, constant exercise and certain ill-defined environmental conditions. Intellectual power is augmented by the habit of precise reasoning, the study of logic, the use of mathematical language, mental discipline, and complete and deep observation of things. On the contrary, incomplete and superficial observations, a rapid succession of impressions, multiplicity of images, and lack of intellectual discipline hinder the development of mind. We know how unintelligent the children are who live in a crowded city, among multitudes of people and events, in trains and automobiles, in the confusion of the streets, among the absurdities of the cinemas, in schools where intellectual concentration is not required. There are other factors capable of facilitating or hampering the growth of intelligence. They consist of certain habits of living and of eating. But their effect is not clearly known. It seems that over-abundance of food and excess of athletics prevent intellectual progress. Athletes are not, in general, very intelligent. In order to reach its highest development the mind probably demands an ensemble of conditions, which has occurred only at certain epochs and in certain countries. What were the mode of existence, the diet, and the education of the men of the great periods of the history of civilization? We are almost totally ignorant of the genesis of intelligence. And we believe that the mind of children can be developed by the mere training of their memory and by the exercises practised in modern schools!

Intelligence alone is not capable of engendering science. But it is an indispensable factor in its creation. Science, in its turn, fortifies intelligence. It has brought to humanity a new intellectual attitude, the certainty given by observation, experimentation, and logical reasoning. Certainty derived from science is very different from that derived from faith. The latter is more profound. It cannot be shaken by arguments. It resembles the certainty given by clairvoyance. But, strange to say, it is not completely foreign to science. Obviously, great discoveries are not the product of intelligence alone. Men of genius, in addition to their powers of observation and comprehension, possess other qualities, such as intuition and creative imagination. Through intuition they learn things ignored by other men, they perceive relations between seemingly isolated phenomena, they unconsciously feel the presence of the unknown treasure. All great men are endowed with intuition. They know, without analysis, without reasoning, what is important for them to know. A true leader of men does not need psychological tests, or reference cards, when choosing his subordinates. A good judge, without going into the details of legal arguments, and even, according to Cardozo, starting from erroneous premises, is capable of rendering a just sentence. A great scientist instinctively takes the path leading to a discovery. This phenomenon, in former times, was called inspiration.

Men of science belong to two different types—the logical and the intuitive. Science owes its progress to both forms of minds. Mathematics, although a purely logical structure, nevertheless makes use of intuition. Among the mathematicians there are intuitives and logicians, analysts and geometricians. Hermitte and Weierstrass were intuitives; Riemann and Bertrand logicians. The discoveries of intuition have always to be developed by logic. In ordinary life, as in science, intuition is a powerful but dangerous means of acquiring knowledge. Sometimes it can hardly be distinguished from illusion. Those who rely upon it entirely are liable to mistakes. It is far from being always trustworthy. But the great man, or the simple whose heart is pure, can be led by it to the summits of mental and spiritual life. It is a strange quality. To apprehend reality without the help of intelligence appears inexplicable. One of the aspects of intuition resembles a very rapid deduction from an instantaneous observation. The knowledge that great physicians sometimes possess concerning the present and the future state of their patients is of such a nature. A similar phenomenon occurs when one appraises in a flash a man's value, or senses his virtues and his vices. But under another aspect, intuition takes place quite independently of observation and reasoning. We may be led by it to our goal when we do not know how to attain this goal and even where it is located. This mode of knowledge is closely analogous to clairvoyance, to the sixth sense of Charles Richet.

Clairvoyance and telepathy are a primary datum of scientific observation.* Those endowed with this power grasp the secret thoughts of other individuals without using their sense organs. They also perceive events more or less remote in space and time. This quality is exceptional. It develops in only a small number of human beings. But many possess it in a rudimentary state. They use it without effort and in a spontaneous fashion. Clairvoyance appears quite commonplace to those having it. It brings to them a knowledge which is more certain than that gained through the sense organs. A clairvoyant reads the thoughts of other people as easily as he examines the expression of their faces. But the words to see and to feel do not accurately express the phenomena taking place in his consciousness. He does not observe, he does not think. He knows. The reading of thoughts seems to be related simultaneously to scientific, æsthetic, and religious in-

* The existence of telepathic phenomena, as well as other metapsychic phenomena, is not accepted by most biologists and physicians. The attitude of these scientists should not be blamed. For these phenomena are exceptional and elusive. They cannot be reproduced at will. Besides they are hidden in the enormous mass of the superstitions, lies, and illusions accumulated for centuries by mankind. Although they have been mentioned in every country and at every epoch, they have not been investigated scientifically. It is, neverthless, a fact that they are a normal, although rare, activity of the human being. The author began their study when he was a young medical student. He was interested in this subject in the same manner as in physiology, chemistry, and pathology. He realized long ago the deficiencies of the methods used by the specialists of psychical research, of the séances where professional mediums often utilize the amateurism of the experimenters. He has made his own observations and experiments. He has used in this chapter the knowledge that he has acquired himself, and not the opinion of others. The study of metapsychics does not differ from that of psychology and physiology. Scientists should not be alarmed by its unorthodox appearance. Several attempts, as is well known, have already been

spiration, and to telepathy. Telepathic communications occur frequently. In many instances, at the time of death or of great danger, an individual is brought into a certain kind of relation with another. The dying man, or the victim of an accident, even when such accident is not followed by death, appears to a friend in his usual aspect. The phantom generally remains silent. Sometimes he speaks and announces his death. The clairvoyant may also perceive at a great distance a scene, an individual, a landscape, which he is capable of describing minutely and exactly. There are many forms of telepathy. A number of persons, although not endowed with the gift of clairvoyance, have received, once or twice in their lifetime, a telepathic communication.

Thus knowledge of the external world may come to man through other channels than sense organs. It is certain that thought may be transmitted from one individual to another, even if they are separated by long distance. These facts, which belong to the new science of metapsychics, must be accepted just as they are. They constitute a part of the reality. They express a rare and almost unknown aspect of ourselves. They are possibly responsible for the uncanny mental acuteness observed in certain individuals. What extraordinary

---

made to apply scientific techniques to clairvoyance and telepathy, and have met with moderate success. The Society for Psychical Research was founded in London in 1882, under the presidency of Henry Sidgwick, Professor of Moral Philosophy at the University of Cambridge. In 1919, an International Institute of Metapsychics was established in Paris with the approval of the French Government, and under the auspices of the great physiologist, Richet, the discoverer of anaphylaxis, and of a learned physician, Joseph Teissier, Professor of Medicine at the University of Lyons. Among the members of its Committee of Administration are a professor at the Medical School of the University of Paris, and several physicians. Its president, Charles Richet, has written a treatise on Metapsychics. The Institute publishes the *Revue Métapsychique*. In the United States this branch of human psychology has hardly attracted the attention of the scientific institutions. However, the Department of Psychology of Duke University has undertaken some valuable metaphysical researches under the direction of Dr. J. B. Rhine.

penetration would result from the union of disciplined intelligence and of telepathic aptitude! Indeed, intelligence, which has given us mastery over the physical world, is not a simple thing. We know only one of its aspects. We endeavour to develop it in the schools and universities. This aspect is but a small part of a marvellous activity consisting of reason, judgment, voluntary attention, intuition, and perhaps clairvoyance. To such a function, man is indebted for his power to apprehend reality, and to understand his environment, his fellow creatures, and himself.

3

Intellectual activity is, at the same time, distinct and indistinct from the flowing mass of our other states of consciousness. It is a mode of our being and changes as we do. We may compare it to a cinematographic film, which would record the successive phases of a story on a surface varying in sensitiveness from one point to another. It is even more analogous to the valleys and the hills of the long billows of the ocean, which reflect in a different manner the clouds passing in the sky. Intelligence projects its visions on the perpetually changing screen of our affective states, of our sorrows or our joys, of our love or our hatred. To study this aspect of ourselves we separate it artificially from an indivisible wholeness. In reality, the man who thinks, observes, and reasons is, at the same time, happy or unhappy, disturbed or serene, stimulated or depressed by his appetites, his aversions, and his desires. The world, therefore, assumes a different visage, according to the affective and physiological states, which are the moving background of consciousness during intellectual activity. Everyone knows that love, hate, anger, and fear are capable of bringing confusion even to logic. In order to manifest themselves, these states of consciousness require certain modifications of the chemical exchanges. The more intense the emotional disturbances, the more active become these exchanges. We know that, on the contrary, metabolism is not modified by intellectual work. Affective functions are very near the physiological. They give to each human being his temperament. Temperament changes from one individual to the other, from one race to the other. It is a mixture of mental, physiological, and structural characteristics. It is man himself. It is responsible for his narrowness, his mediocrity, or his strength. What factors bring about the weakening of temperament in certain social groups and in certain nations? It seems that the violence of the emotional moods diminishes when wealth increases, when education is generalized, when diet becomes more elaborate. At the same time, affective functions are observed to separate from intelligence, and to exaggerate unduly certain of their aspects. The forms of life, of education, or of food brought by modern civilization perhaps tend to give us the qualities of cattle, or to develop our emotional impulses inharmoniously.

Moral activity is equivalent to the aptitude possessed by man to impose upon himself a rule of conduct, to choose between several possible acts those which he considers to be good, to get rid of his own selfishness and maliciousness. It creates in him the feeling of obligation, of duty. This peculiar sense is observed only in a small number of individuals. In most of them it remains virtual. But the fact of its existence cannot be denied. If moral sense did not exist, Socrates would not have drunk the hemlock. To-day it may be observed, even in a state of high development, in certain social groups and in certain countries. It has manifested itself at all epochs. In the course of the history of mankind its importance has been demonstrated to be fundamental. It is related both to intelligence and to æsthetic and religious senses. It impels us to distinguish right from wrong and to choose right in preference to wrong. In highly civilized beings, will and intelligence are one and the same function. From will and intelligence come all moral values.

Moral sense, like intellectual activity, apparently depends on certain structural and functional states of the body. These states result from the immanent constitution of our tissues and our minds, and also from factors which have acted upon us during our development. In his essay on the *Foundation of Ethics*, presented at the Royal Society of Sciences of Copenhagen, Schopenhauer expressed the opinion that the moral principle has its basis in our nature. In other terms, human beings possess innate tendencies to selfishness, meanness, or pity. These tendencies appear very early in life. They are obvious to any careful observer. There are, writes Gallavardin, the pure egoists, completely indifferent to the happiness or misery of their fellow men. There are the malicious, who take pleasure in witnessing the misfortunes or sufferings of others, and even in causing them. There are those who suffer themselves from the sufferings of any human being. This power of sympathy engenders kindness and charity, and the acts inspired by those virtues. The capacity of feeling the pain of others is the essential characteristic of the human being who endeavours to alleviate, among his brothers, the burden and the misery of existence. Each one, in a certain measure, is born good, mediocre, or bad. But, like intelligence, moral sense can be developed by education, discipline, and will power.

The definition of good and evil is based both on reason and on the immemorial experience of humanity. It is related to basic necessities of individual and social life. However, it is somewhat arbitrary. But at each epoch and in each country it should be very clearly defined and identical for all classes of individuals. The good is equivalent to justice, charity, beauty; the evil, to selfishness, meanness, ugliness. In modern civilization the theoretical rules of conduct are based upon the remains of Christian morals. No one obeys them. Modern man has rejected all discipline of his appetites. However, biological and industrial morals have no practical value, because they are artificial and take into consideration only one aspect of the human being. They ignore some of our most essential activities. They do not give to man an armour strong enough to protect him against his own inherent vices.

In order to keep his mental and organic balance, man must impose upon himself an inner rule. The State can thrust legality upon people by force, but not morality. Everyone should realize the necessity of selecting the right and avoiding the wrong, of submitting himself to such necessity by an effort of his own will. The Roman Catholic Church, in its deep understanding of human psychology, has given to moral activities a far higher place than to intellectual ones. The men honoured by her above all others, are neither the leaders of nations, the men of science, nor the philosophers. They are the saints—that is, those who are virtuous in a heroic manner. When we watch the inhabitants of the new city, we fully understand the practical necessity of moral sense. Intelligence, will power, and morality are very closely related. But moral sense is more important than intelligence. When it disappears from a nation the whole social structure slowly commences to crumble away. In biological research we have not given so far to moral activities the importance that they deserve. Moral sense must be studied in as positive a manner as intelligence. Such a study is certainly difficult. But the many aspects of this sense in individuals and groups of individuals can easily be discerned. It is also possible to analyze the physiological, psychological, and social effects of morals. Of course, such researches cannot be undertaken in a laboratory. Field work is indispensable. There are still to-day many human communities which show the various characteristics of moral sense, and the results of its absence or of its presence in different degrees. Without any doubt, moral activities are located within the domain of scientific observation.

In modern civilization individuals whose conduct is inspired by a moral ideal are very seldom encountered. However, such individuals still exist. We cannot help noticing their aspect when we meet them. Moral beauty is an exceptional and very striking phenomenon. He who has contemplated it but once never forgets its aspect. This form of beauty is far more impressive than the beauty of nature and of science. It gives to those who possess its divine gifts, a strange, an inexplicable power. It increases the strength of intellect. It establishes peace among men. Much more than science, art, and religious rites, moral beauty is the basis of civilization.

4

Æsthetic sense exists in the most primitive human beings as in the most civilized. It even survives the disappearance of intelligence. For the idiot and the insane are capable of artistic productions. The creation of forms, or of series of sounds, capable of awakening an æsthetic emotion, is an elementary need of our nature. Man has always contemplated with delight animals, flowers, trees, sky, ocean, and mountains. Before the dawn of civilization he used his rough tools to reproduce the profile of living beings on wood, ivory, and stone. To-day, when his æsthetic sense is not dulled by his education, his habits of life, and the stupidity of factory work, he takes pleasure in making objects after his own inspiration. He enjoys an æsthetic feeling in concentrating on such work. In Europe, and especially in France, there are still cooks, butchers, stone-cutters, sabot-makers, carpenters, blacksmiths, cutlers, and mechanics who are artists. Those who make pastry of beautiful shape and delicate taste, who sculpture in lard houses, men, and animals, who forge majestic iron gates, who build handsome pieces of furniture, who carve a rough statue from stone or wood, who weave beautiful wool or silk materials, experience, as much as great sculptors, painters, musicians, or architects, the divine pleasure of creation.

Æsthetic activity remains potential in most individuals because industrial civilization has surrounded them with coarse, vulgar, and ugly sights; because we have been transformed into machines. The worker spends his life repeating the same gesture thousands of times each day. He manufactures only single parts. He never makes the complete object. He is not allowed to use his intelligence. He is the blind horse plodding round and round the whole day long to draw water from a well. Industrialism forbids man the very mental activities which could bring him every day some joy. In sacrificing mind to matter, modern civilization has perpetrated a momentous error—an error all the more dangerous because nobody revolts against it, because it is accepted as easily as the unhealthy life of great cities and the confinement in factories. However, those who experience even a rudimentary æsthetic feeling in their work are far happier than those who produce merely in order to be able to consume. In its present form, industry has deprived the worker of originality and beauty. The vulgarity and the gloom of our civilization are due, at least partly, to the suppression from our daily life of the simpler forms of æsthetic pleasure.

Æsthetic activity manifests itself in both the creation and the contemplation of beauty. It is completely disinterested. In the joy of creation, consciousness escapes from itself and becomes absorbed in another being. Beauty is an inexhaustible source of happiness for those who discover its abode. It is hidden everywhere. It springs up from the hands which model or decorate home-made earthenware, which carve wood, which weave silk, which chisel marble, which open and repair human flesh. It animates the bloody art of the surgeons, as well as that of the painters, the musicians, and the poets. It is present also in the calculations of Galileo, in the visions of Dante, in the experiments of Pasteur, in the rising of the sun on the ocean, in the winter storms on the high mountains. It becomes still more poignant in the immensity of the sidereal and atomic worlds, in the prodigious harmony of the brain cells, or in the silent sacrifice of the man who gives his life for the salvation of others. Under its multiple forms it is always the noblest and most important guest of the human cerebrum, creator of our universe.

The sense of beauty does not develop spontaneously. It exists in our consciousness in a potential state. At certain epochs, in certain circumstances, it remains virtual. It may even vanish in nations which formerly were proud of their great artists and their masterpieces. To-day, France despises the majestic remnants of her past and even destroys her natural beauties. The descendants of the men who conceived and erected the monastery of Mont Saint-Michel no longer understand its splendour. They cheerfully accept the indescribable ugliness of the modern houses in Normandy and Brittany, and especially in the Paris suburbs. Like Mont Saint-Michel and the majority of French cities and villages, Paris has been disgraced by a hideous commercialism. During the history of a civilization, the sense of beauty, like moral sense, grows, reaches its optimum, declines, and disappears.

5

In modern men we seldom observe the manifestations of mystical activity or religious sense.* The tendency to mysti-

* Although religious activity has played an important part in the history of humanity, one cannot acquire easily even a superficial knowledge of this form, now so rare, of our mental functions. Indeed, the literature concerning asceticism and mysticity is immense. The writings of the great Christian mystics are at our disposal. One may meet also, even in the new city, men and women who are centres of true religious activity. Generally, however, the mystics are out of our reach in monasteries. Or they occupy humble positions and are completely ignored.

city, even in its most rudimentary form, is exceptional. Much more exceptional than moral sense. Nevertheless, it remains one of the essential human activities. Humanity has been more thoroughly impregnated with religious inspiration than with philosophical thought. In the ancient city religion was the basis of family and social life. The cathedrals and the ruins of the temples erected by our ancestors still cover the soil of Europe. Indeed, their meaning is to-day scarcely understood. To the majority of modern men the churches are only museums for dead religions. The attitude of the tourists visiting the cathedrals of Europe clearly shows how completely religious sense has been eliminated from modern life. Mystical activity has been banished from most religions. Even its meaning has been forgotten. Such ignorance is probably responsible for the decadence of the churches. The strength of a religion depends upon the focuses of mystical activity where its life constantly grows. However, religious sense remains to-day an indispensable activity of the con-sciousness of a number of individuals. It is again manifest-ing itself among people of high culture. And, strange to say, the monasteries of the great religious orders are too small to receive all the young men and women who crave to enter the spiritual world through asceticism and mysticity.

Religious activity assumes various aspects as does moral activity. In its more elementary state it consists of a vague aspiration toward a power transcending the material and mental forms of our world, a kind of unformulated prayer, a

---

The author became interested in asceticism and mysticity at the same time as in metapsychical phenomena. He has known a few genuine mystics and saints. He does not hesitate to mention mysticity in this book, because he has observed its manifestations. But he realizes that his description of this aspect of mental activity will please neither men of science nor men of religion. Scientists will consider such an attempt as puerile or insane; ecclesiastics, as improper and aborted, because mystical phenomena belong only in an indirect way to the domain of science. Both these criticisms will be justified. Nevertheless, it is im-possible not to count mysticism among fundamental human activities.

quest for more absolute beauty than that of art or science. It is akin to æsthetic activity. The love of beauty leads to mysticism. In addition, religious rites are associated with various forms of art. Song easily becomes transformed into prayer. The beauty pursued by the mystic is still richer and more indefinable than the ideal of the artist. It has no form. It cannot be expressed in any language. It hides within the things of the visible world. It manifests itself rarely. It requires an elevation of the mind toward a being who is the source of all things, toward a power, a centre of forces, whom the mystic calls God. At each period of history in each nation there have been individuals possessing to a high degree this particular sense. Christian mysticism constitutes the highest form of religious activity. It is more integrated with the other activities of consciousness than are Hindu and Tibetan mysticisms. Over Asiatic religions it has the advantage of having received, in its very infancy, the lessons of Greece and of Rome. Greece gave it intelligence, and Rome, order and measure.

Mysticism, in its highest state, comprises a very elaborate technique, a strict discipline. First, the practice of asceticism. It is as impossible to enter the realm of mysticity without ascetic preparation as to become an athlete without submitting to physical training. Initiation to asceticism is hard. Therefore, very few men have the courage to venture upon the mystic way. He who wants to undertake this rough and difficult journey must renounce all the things of this world and, finally, himself. Then he may have to dwell for a long time in the shadows of spiritual night. While asking for the grace of God and deploring his degradation and undeservedness, he undergoes the purification of his senses. It is the first and dark stage of mystic life. He progressively weans himself from himself. His prayer becomes contemplation. He enters into illuminative life. He is not capable of describing his experiences. When he attempts to express what he feels, he sometimes borrows, as did St. John of the Cross, the language of carnal love. His mind escapes from space and time. He apprehends an ineffable being. He reaches the stage of unitive life. He is in God and acts with Him.

The life of all great mystics consists of the same steps. We must accept their experiences as described by them. Only those who themselves have led the life of prayer are capable of understanding its peculiarities. The search for God is, indeed, an entirely personal undertaking. By the exercise of the normal activities of his consciousness, man may endeavour to reach an invisible reality both immanent in and transcending the material world. Thus he throws himself into the most audacious adventure that one can dare. He may be looked upon as a hero or a lunatic. But nobody should ask whether mystical experience is true or false, whether it is auto-suggestion, hallucination, or a journey of the soul beyond the dimensions of our world and its union with a higher reality. One must be content with having an operational concept of such an experience. Mysticism is splendidly generous. It brings to man the fulfilment of his highest desires : inner strength, spiritual light, divine love, ineffable peace. Religious intuition is as real as æsthetic inspiration. Through the contemplation of superhuman beauty, mystics and poets may reach the ultimate truth.

6

These fundamental activities are not distinct from one another. Their limits are convenient but artificial. They may be compared to an amœba whose multiple and transitory limbs, the pseudopods, consist of a single substance. They are also analogous to the unrolling of superposed films which remain indecipherable unless separated from one another. Everything happens as if the bodily substratum, while flowing in time, showed several simultaneous aspects of its unity ; aspects, which our techniques divide into physiologi cal and mental. Under its mental aspect, human activity ceaselessly modifies its form, its quality, and its intensity. This essentially simple phenomenon is described as an association of different functions. The plurality of the manifestations of the mind is born from a methodological necessity. In order to describe consciousness we are obliged to separate it into parts. As the pseudopods of the amœba are the amœba itself, the aspects of consciousness are man himself, and blend in his oneness.

Intelligence is almost useless to those who possess nothing else. The pure intellectual is an incomplete human being. He is unhappy because he is not capable of entering the world that he understands. The ability to grasp the relations between phenomena remains sterile unless associated with other activities, such as moral sense, affectivity, will power, judgment, imagination, and some organic strength. It can only be utilized at the cost of an effort. Those who want to conquer real knowledge have to endure a long and hard preparation. They submit themselves to a kind of asceticism. In the absence of concentration, intelligence is unproductive. Once disciplined it becomes capable of pursuing truth. But to reach its goal it requires the help of moral sense. Great scientists always have profound intellectual honesty. They follow reality wherever led by it. They never seek to substitute their own desires for facts, or to hide these facts when they become troublesome. The man who longs for the contemplation of truth has to establish peace within him. His mind should be like the still water of a lake. Affective activities, however, are indispensable to the progress of intelligence. But they should consist only of enthusiasm, that passion which Pasteur called the inner god. Thought grows only within those who are capable of love and hate. It requires the aid of the whole body, besides that of the other mental functions. When intelligence ascends the highest summits and is illuminated by intuition and creative imagination, it still needs a moral and organic frame.

The exclusive development of the affective, æsthetic, or mystic activities brings into being inferior individuals, idle dreamers, narrow, unsound minds. Such types are often encountered, although intellectual education is given nowadays to everybody. However, high culture is not necessary to fertilize æsthetic and religious senses and to bring forth artists, poets, and mystics, all those who disinterestedly contemplate the various aspects of beauty. The same is true of moral sense and judgment. These activities are almost sufficient within themselves. They do not require to be associated with great intelligence to supply man with an aptitude for happiness. They seem to strengthen organic functions. Their development must be the supreme goal of education because they give equilibrium to the individual. They make him a solid building-stone of the social edifice. To those who constitute the multitudes of industrial civilization moral sense is far more necessary than intelligence.

The distribution of mental activities varies greatly in the different social groups. Most civilized men manifest only an elementary form of consciousness. They are capable of the easy work which, in modern society, ensures the survival of the individual. They produce, they consume, they satisfy their physiological appetites. They also take pleasure in watching, among great crowds, athletic spectacles, in seeing childish and vulgar moving pictures, in being rapidly transported without effort, or in looking at swiftly moving objects. They are soft, sentimental, lascivious, and violent. They have no moral, æsthetic, or religious sense. They are extremely numerous. They have engendered a vast herd of children whose intelligence remains rudimentary. They constitute a part of the population of the three million criminals living in freedom, of those inhabiting the jails, and of the feeble-minded, the morons, the insane, who overflow from asylums and specialized hospitals.

The majority of criminals, who are not in penitentiaries, belong to a higher class. They are marked, however, by the atrophy of certain activities of consciousness. The born criminal, invented by Lombroso, does not exist. But there are born defectives who become criminals. In reality many criminals are normal. They are often more clever than policemen and judges. Sociologists and social workers do not meet them during their survey of prisons. The gangsters and crooks, heroes of the cinema and the daily papers, some-times display normal and even high mental, affective, and æsthetic activities. But their moral sense has not developed. This disharmony in the world of consciousness is a pheno-menon characteristic of our time. We have succeeded in giv-ing organic health to the inhabitants of the modern city. But despite the immense sums spent on education, we have failed to develop completely their intellectual and moral activities. Even in the élite of the population consciousness often lacks harmony and strength. The elementary functions are dis-persed, of poor quality, and of low intensity. Some of them may be quite deficient. The mind of most people can be com-pared to a reservoir containing a small quantity of water of doubtful composition and under low pressure, and that of only a few individuals to a reservoir containing a large volume of pure water under high pressure.

The happiest and most useful men consist of a well-integrated whole of intellectual, moral, and organic activities. The quality of these activities, and their equilibrium, gives to such a type its superiority over the others. Their intensity determines the social level of a given individual. It makes of him a tradesman or a bank president, a little physician or a celebrated professor, a village mayor or a president of the United States. The development of complete human beings must be the aim of our efforts. It is only with such thoroughly developed individuals that a real civilization can be con-structed. There is also a class of men who, although as dis-harmonious as the criminal and the insane, are indispensable to modern society. They are the men of genius. These are characterized by a monstrous growth of some of their psychological activities. A great artist, a great scientist, a great philosopher, is rarely a great man. He is generally a man of common type with one side over-developed. Genius can be compared to a tumour growing upon a normal organism. These ill-balanced beings are often unhappy. But they give to the entire community the benefit of their mighty impulses. Their disharmony results in the progress of civilization. Humanity has never gained anything from the efforts of the crowd. It is driven onward by the passion of a few abnormal individuals, by the flame of their intelligence, by their ideal of science, of charity, and of beauty.

7

Mental activities evidently depend on physiological activities. Organic modifications are observed to correspond to the succession of the states of consciousness. Inversely, psychological phenomena are determined by certain functional states of the organs. The whole consisting of body and consciousness is modifiable by organic as well as by mental factors. Mind and organism commune in man like form and marble in a statue. One cannot change the form without breaking the marble. The brain is supposed to be the seat of the psychological functions, because its lesions are followed by immediate and profound disorders of consciousness. It is probably by means of the cerebral cells that mind inserts itself in matter. Brain and intelligence develop simultaneously in children. When senile atrophy occurs intelligence decreases. The presence of the spirochætes of syphilis around the pyramidal cells brings about delusions of grandeur. When the virus of lethargic encephalitis attacks the brain substance, profound disturbances of personality appear. Mental activity suffers temporary changes under the influence of alcohol carried by blood from the stomach to the nervous cells. The fall of blood pressure due to a hæmorrhage suppresses all manifestations of consciousness. In short, mental life is observed to depend on the state of the cerebrum.

These observations do not suffice to demonstrate that the brain alone is the organ of consciousness. In fact the cerebral centres are not composed exclusively of nervous matter. They also consist of fluids in which the cells are immersed and whose composition is regulated by blood serum. And blood serum contains the gland and tissue secretions that diffuse through the entire body. Every organ is present in the cerebral cortex by the agency of blood and lymph. Therefore, our states of consciousness are linked to the chemical constitution of the humours of the brain as much as to the structural state of its cells. When the organic medium is deprived of the secretions of the suprarenal glands, the patient falls into a profound depression. He resembles a cold-blooded animal. The functional disorders of the thyroid gland bring about either nervous and mental excitation or apathy. Moral idiots, feeble-minded, and criminals are found in families where lesions of this gland are hereditary. Everyone knows how human personality is modified by diseases of the liver, the stomach, and the intestines. Obviously, the cells of the organs discharge into the bodily fluids certain substances that react upon our mental and spiritual functions.

The testicle, more than any other gland, exerts a profound influence upon the strength and quality of the mind. In general, great poets, artists, and saints, as well as conquerors, are strongly sexed. The removal of the genital glands, even in adult individuals, produces some modifications of the mental state. After extirpation of the ovaries, women become apathetic and lose part of their intellectual activity or moral sense. The personality of men who have undergone castration is altered in a more or less marked way. The historical cowardice of Abélard in face of the passionate love and sacrifice of Héloïse was probably due to the brutal mutilation imposed upon him. Almost all great artists were great

F*

lovers. Inspiration seems to depend on a certain condition of the sexual glands. Love stimulates mind when it does not attain its object. If Beatrice had been the mistress of Dante, there would perhaps be no *Divine Comedy*. The great mystics often used the expressions of Solomon's Song. It seems that their unassuaged sexual appetites urged them more forcibly along the path of renunciation and complete sacrifice. A workman's wife can request the services of her husband every day. But the wife of an artist or of a philosopher has not the right to do so as often. It is well known that sexual excesses impede intellectual activity. In order to reach its full power, intelligence seems to require both the presence of well-developed sexual glands and the temporary repression of the sexual appetite. Freud has rightly emphasized the capital importance of sexual impulses in the activities of consciousness. However, his observations refer chiefly to sick people. His conclusions should not be generalized to include normal individuals, especially those who are endowed with a strong nervous system and mastery over themselves. While the weak, the nervous, and the unbalanced become more abnormal when their sexual appetites are repressed, the strong are rendered still stronger by practising such a form of asceticism.

The dependence of mental activities and physiological functions does not agree with the classical conception that places the soul exclusively in the brain. In fact the entire body appears to be the substratum of mental and spiritual energies. Thought is the offspring of the endocrine glands as well as of the cerebral cortex. The integrity of the organism is indispensable to the manifestations of consciousness. Man thinks, invents, loves, suffers, admires, and prays with his brain and all his organs.

8

Each state of consciousness probably has a corresponding organic expression. Emotions, as is well known, determine the dilatation or the contraction of the small arteries through the vasomotor nerves. They are, therefore, accompanied by changes in the circulation of the blood in tissues and organs. Pleasure causes the skin of the face to flush. Anger and fear turn it white. In certain individuals, bad news may bring about a spasm of the coronary arteries, anæmia of the heart, and sudden death. The affective states act on all the glands by increasing or decreasing their circulation. They stimulate or stop the secretions or modify their chemical constitution. The desire for food causes salivation, even in the absence of any aliment. In Pavlov's dogs, salivation followed the sound of a bell, if the bell had previously rung while the animal was being fed. An emotion may set in activity complex mechanisms. When one induces a sentiment of fear in a cat, as Cannon did in a famous experiment, the vessels of the suprarenal glands become dilated, the glands secrete adrenalin, adrenalin increases the pressure of the blood and the rapidity of its circulation, and prepares the whole organism for attack or defence.

Thus envy, hate, fear, when these sentiments are habitual, are capable of starting organic changes and genuine diseases. Moral suffering profoundly disturbs health. Business men who do not know how to fight worry die young. The old clinicians thought that protracted sorrows and constant anxiety prepare the way for the development of cancer. Emotions induce, in especially sensitive individuals, striking modifications of the tissues and humours. The hair of a Belgian woman condemned to death by the Germans became white during the night preceding the execution. On the arm of another woman an eruption appeared during a bombardment. After the explosion of each shell the eruption became redder and larger. Such phenomena are far from being exceptional. Joltrain has proved that a moral shock may cause marked changes in the blood. A patient, after having experienced great fright, showed a drop in arterial pressure, and a decrease in the number of the white corpuscles, and in the coagulation time of blood plasma. The French expression, *se faire du mauvais sang*, is literally true. Thought can generate organic lesions. The instability of modern life, the ceaseless agitation, and the lack of security create states of consciousness which bring about nervous and organic disorders of the stomach and of the intestines, defective nutrition, and passage of intestinal microbes into the circulatory apparatus. Colitis and the accompanying infections of the kidneys and of the bladder are the remote results of mental and moral unbalance. Such diseases are almost unknown in social groups where life is simpler and not so agitated, where anxiety is less constant. In a like manner, those who keep the peace of their inner self in the midst of the tumult of the modern city are immune from nervous and organic disorders.

Physiological activities must remain outside the field of consciousness. They are disturbed when we turn our attention towards them. Thus psycho-analysis, in directing the mind of the patient upon himself, may aggravate his state of unbalance. Instead of indulging in self-analysis it is better to escape from oneself through an effort that does not scatter the mind. When our activity is set toward a precise end, our mental and organic functions become completely harmonized. The unification of the desires, the application of the mind to a single purpose, produce a sort of inner peace. Man integrates himself by meditation just as by action. But he should not be content with contemplating the beauty of the ocean, of the mountains, and of the clouds, the masterpieces of the artists and the poets, the majestic constructions of philosophical thought, the mathematical formulas which express natural laws. He must also be the soul which strives to attain a moral ideal, searches for light in the darkness of this world, marches forward along the mystic way, and renounces itself in order to apprehend the invisible substratum of the universe.

The unification of the activities of consciousness leads to greater harmony of organic and mental functions. In the communities where moral sense and intelligence are simultaneously developed, nervous and nutritive diseases, criminality, and insanity are rare. In such groups the individual is happier. But when psychological activities become more intense and specialized, they may bring about certain disturbances of the health. Those who pursue moral, scientific, or religious ideals do not seek physiological security or longevity. To those ideals they sacrifice themselves. It seems also that certain states of consciousness determine true pathological changes. Most of the great mystics have endured physiological and mental suffering, at least during a part of their life. Moreover, contemplation may be accompanied by nervous phenomena resembling those of hysteria and clairvoyance. In the history of the saints one reads descriptions of ecstasies, thought transmission, visions of events happening at a distance, and even of levitations. According to the testimony of their companions, several of the Christian mystics have manifested this strange phenomenon. The subject, absorbed in his prayer, totally unconscious of the outside world, gently rises above the ground. But it has not been possible so far to bring these extraordinary facts into the field of scientific observation.

Certain spiritual activities may cause anatomical as well as functional modifications of the tissues and the organs. These organic phenomena are observed in various circumstances, among them being the state of prayer. Prayer should be understood, not as a mere mechanical recitation of formulas, but as a mystical elevation, an absorption of consciousness in the contemplation of a principle both permeating and transcending our world. Such a psychological state is not intellectual. It is incomprehensible to philosophers and scientists, and inaccessible to them. But the simple seem to feel God as easily as the heat of the sun or the kindness of a friend. The prayer which is followed by organic effects is of a special nature. First, it is entirely disinterested. Man offers himself to God. He stands before Him like the canvas before the painter or the marble before the sculptor. At the same time, he asks for His grace, exposes his needs and those of his brothers in suffering. Generally, the patient who is cured is not praying for himself, but for another. Such a type of prayer demands complete renunciation—that is, a higher form of asceticism. The modest, the ignorant, and the poor are more capable of this self-denial than the rich and the intellectual. When it possesses such characteristics, prayer may set in motion a strange phenomenon, the miracle.

In all countries, at all times, people have believed in the existence of miracles, in the more or less rapid healing of the sick at places of pilgrimage, at certain sanctuaries.* But after the great impetus of science during the nineteenth century

* Miraculous cures seldom occur. Despite their small number, they prove the existence of organic and mental processes that we do not know. They show that certain mystic states, such as that of prayer, have definite effects. They are stubborn, irreducible facts, which must be taken into account. The author knows that miracles are as far from scientific orthodoxy as mysticity. The investigation of such phenomena is still more delicate than that of telepathy and clairvoyance. But science has to explore the entire field of reality. He has attempted to learn the characteristics of this mode of healing, as well as of the ordinary modes. He began this study in 1902, at a time when the documents were scarce, when it was difficult for a young doctor, and dangerous for his future career, to become interested in such a subject. To-day, any physician can observe the patients brought to Lourdes, and examine the records kept in the Medical Bureau. Lourdes is the centre of an International Medical Association, composed of many members. There is a slowly growing literature about miraculous healing. Physicians are becoming more interested in these extraordinary facts. Several cases have been reported at the Medical Society of Bordeaux by professors of the medical school of the university and other eminent physicians. The Committee on Medicine and Religion of the New York Academy of Medicine, presided over by Dr. F. Peterson, has recently sent to Lourdes one of its members in order to begin a study of this important subject.

such belief completely disappeared. It was generally admitted, not only that miracles did not exist, but that they could not exist. As the laws of thermodynamics make perpetual motion impossible, physiological laws oppose miracles. Such is still the attitude of most physiologists and physicians. However, in view of the facts observed during the last fifty years this attitude cannot be sustained. The most important cases of miraculous healing have been recorded by the Medical Bureau of Lourdes. Our present conception of the influence of prayer upon pathological lesions is based upon the observation of patients who have been cured almost instantaneously of various affections, such as peritoneal tuberculosis, cold abscesses, osteitis, suppurating wounds, lupus, cancer, etc. The process of healing changes little from one individual to another. Often, an acute pain. Then a sudden sensation of being cured. In a few seconds, a few minutes, at the most a few hours, wounds are cicatrized, pathological symptoms disappear, appetite returns. Sometimes functional disorders vanish before the anatomical lesions are repaired. The skeletal deformations of Pott's disease, the cancerous glands, may still persist two or three days after the healing of the main lesions. The miracle is chiefly characterized by an extreme acceleration of the processes of organic repair. There is no doubt that the rate of cicatrization of the anatomical defects is much greater than the normal one. The only condition indispensable to the occurrence of the phenomenon is prayer. But there is no need for the patient himself to pray, or even to have any religious faith. It is sufficient that some one around him be in a state of prayer. Such facts are of profound significance. They show the reality of certain relations, of still unknown nature, between psychological and organic processes. They prove the objective importance of the spiritual activities, which hygienists, physicians, educators, and sociologists have almost always neglected to study. They open to man a new world.

9

Mental activities are influenced by social environment as profoundly as by the fluids of the body. Like physiological activities they improve with exercise. Driven by the ordinary necessities of life, organs, bones, and muscles work without interruption. Thus they are compelled to develop. But according to the mode of existence of the individual, they become more or less harmonious and strong. The constitution of an Alpine guide is much superior to that of an inhabitant of New York. Nevertheless, the organs and muscles of the latter suffice for sedentary life. Mind, on the contrary, does not unfold spontaneously. The son of a scholar inherits no knowledge from his father. If left alone on a desert island he would be no better than Cro-Magnon men. The powers of the mind remain virtual in the absence of education and of an environment bearing the stamp of the intellectual, moral, æsthetic, and religious accomplishments of our ancestors. The psychological state of the social group determines, in a large measure, the number, the quality, and the intensity of the manifestations of individual consciousness. If the social environment is mediocre intelligence and moral sense fail to develop. These activities may become thoroughly vitiated by bad surroundings. We are immersed in the habits of our epoch, like tissue cells in the organic fluids. Like these cells, we are incapable of defending ourselves against the influence of the community. The body more effectively resists the cosmic than the psychological world. It is guarded against the incursions of its physical and chemical enemies by the skin, and the digestive and respiratory mucosas. On the contrary, the frontiers of the mind are entirely open. Consciousness is thus exposed to the attacks of its intellectual and spiritual surroundings. According to the nature of these attacks, it develops in a normal or defective manner.

Intelligence depends largely on education and environment. Also, on inner discipline, on the current ideas of one's time and one's group. It has to be moulded by the habit of logical thinking, by that of mathematical language, and by a methodical study of humanities and sciences. School-teachers and university professors, as well as libraries, laboratories, books, and reviews, are adequate means for developing the mind. Even in the absence of professors, books could suffice for this task. One may live in an unintelligent social environment and yet acquire a high culture. The education of the intelligence is relatively easy. But the formation of the moral, æsthetic, and religious activities is very difficult. The influence of environment on these aspects of consciousness is much more subtle. No one can learn to distinguish right from wrong, and beauty from vulgarity, by taking a course of lectures. Morality, art, and religion are not taught like grammar, mathematics, and history. To feel and to know are two profoundly different mental states. Formal teaching reaches intelligence alone. Moral sense, beauty, and mysticity are learned only when present in our surroundings and part of our daily life. We have mentioned that the growth of intelligence is obtained by training and exercise, whereas the other activities of consciousness demand a group with whose existence they are identified.

Civilization has not succeeded, so far, in creating an environment suitable to mental activities. The low intellectual and spiritual value of most human beings is due largely to deficiencies of their psychological atmosphere. The supremacy of matter and the dogmas of industrial religion have destroyed culture, beauty, and morals, as they were understood by the Christian civilization, mother of modern science. The small social groups, possessing their own individuality and traditions, have also been broken up by the changes in their habits. The intellectual classes have been debased by the immense spread of newspapers, cheap literature, radios, and cinemas. Unintelligence is becoming more and more general, in spite of the excellence of the courses given in schools, colleges, and universities. Strange to say, it often exists with advanced scientific knowledge. School children and students form their minds on the silly programmes of public entertainments. Social environment, instead of favouring the growth of intelligence, opposes it with all its might. However, it is more propitious to the development of the appreciation of beauty. America has imported the greatest musicians of Europe. Its museums are organized with a magnificence so far unequalled. Industrial art is growing rapidly. Architecture has entered into a period of triumph. Buildings of extraordinary splendour have transformed the aspect of large cities. Each individual, if he wishes, may cultivate his æsthetic sense in a certain measure.

Moral sense is almost completely ignored by modern society. We have, in fact, suppressed its manifestations. All are imbued with irresponsibility. Those who discern good and evil, who are industrious and provident, remain poor and are looked upon as morons. The woman who has several children, who devotes herself to their education, instead of to her own career, is considered weak-minded. If a man saves a little money for his wife and the education of his children, this money is stolen from him by enterprising financiers, or taken by the Government and distributed to those who have been reduced to want by their own improvidence and the short-sightedness of manufacturers, bankers, and economists. Artists and men of science supply the community with beauty, health, and wealth. They live and die in poverty. Robbers enjoy prosperity in peace. Gangsters are protected by politicians and respected by judges. They are the heroes whom children admire at the cinema and imitate in their games. A rich man has every right. He may discard his ageing wife, abandon his old mother to penury, rob those who have entrusted their money to him, without losing the consideration of his friends. Homosexuality flourishes. Sexual morals have been cast aside. Psycho-analysts supervise men and women in their conjugal relations. There is no difference between wrong and right, just and unjust. Criminals thrive at liberty among the rest of the population. No one makes any objection to their presence. Ministers have rationalized religion. They have destroyed its mystical basis. But they do not succeed in attracting modern men. In their half-empty churches they vainly preach a weak morality. They are content with the part of policemen, helping in the interest of the wealthy to preserve the framework of present society. Or, like politicians, they flatter the appetites of the crowd.

Man is powerless against such psychological attacks. He necessarily yields to the influence of his group. If one lives in the company of criminals or fools, one becomes a criminal or a fool. Isolation is the only hope of salvation. But where will the inhabitants of the new city find solitude? "Thou canst retire within thyself when thou wouldst," said Marcus Aurelius. "No retreat is more peaceful or less troubled than that encountered by man in his own soul." But we are not capable of such an effort. We cannot fight our social surroundings victoriously.

10

The mind is not as robust as the body. It is remarkable that mental diseases by themselves are more numerous than all the other diseases put together. Hospitals for the insane are full to overflowing, and unable to receive all those who should be restrained. In the State of New York, according to C. W. Beers, one person out of every twenty-two has to be placed in an asylum at some time or other. In the whole of the United States the hospitals care for almost eight times more feeble-minded or lunatics than consumptives. Each year about sixty-eight thousand new cases are admitted to insane asylums and similar institutions. If the admissions continue at such a rate, about one million of the children and young people who are to-day attending schools and colleges will, sooner or later, be confined in asylums. In the state hospitals there were, in 1932, 340,000 insane. There were also in special institutions 81,580 feeble-minded and epileptics, and 10,930 on parole. These statistics do not include the mental cases treated in private hospitals. In the whole country, besides the insane, there are 500,000 feeble-minded. And in addition, surveys made under the auspices of the National Committee for Mental Hygiene have revealed that at least 400,000 children are so unintelligent that they cannot profitably follow the courses of the public schools. In fact the individuals who are mentally deranged are far more numerous. It is estimated that several hundred thousand persons, not mentioned in any statistics, are affected with psychoneuroses. These figures show how great is the fragility of the consciousness of civilized men, and how important for modern society is the problem of mental health. The diseases of the mind are a serious menace. They are more dangerous than tuberculosis, cancer, heart and kidney diseases, and even typhus, plague, and cholera. They are to be feared, not only because they increase the number of criminals, but chiefly because they profoundly weaken the dominant white races. It should be realized that there are not many more feeble-minded and insane among the criminals than in the rest of the nation. Indeed, a large number of defectives are found in the prisons. But we must not forget that most intelligent criminals are at large. The frequency of neurosis and psychosis is doubtless the expression of a very grave defect of modern civilization. The new habits of existence have certainly not improved our mental health.

Modern medicine has failed in its endeavour to assure to everyone the possession of the activities which are truly specific to the human being. Physicians are utterly incapable of protecting consciousness against its unknown enemies. The symptoms of mental diseases and the different types of feeble-mindedness have been well classified. But we are completely ignorant of the nature of these disorders. We have not ascertained whether they are due to structural lesions of the brain or to changes in the composition of blood-plasma, or to both these causes. It is probable that our nervous and psychological activities depend simultaneously on the anatomical conditions of the cerebral cells, on the substances set free in the blood by endocrine glands and other tissues, and on our mental states themselves. Functional disorders of the glands, as well as structural lesions of the brain, may be responsible for neuroses and psychoses. Even a complete knowledge of these phenomena would not bring about great progress. The pathology of the mind depends on psychology, as the pathology of the organs on physiology. But physiology is a science, while psychology is not. Psychology awaits its Claude Bernard or its Pasteur. It is in the state of surgery when surgeons were barbers, of chemistry before Lavoisier, at the epoch of the alchemists. However, it would be unjust to incriminate modern psychologists and their methods for the rudimentary condition of their science. The extreme complexity of the subject is the main cause of their ignorance. There are no techniques permitting the exploration of the unknown world of the nervous cells, of their association and projection fibres, and of the cerebral and mental processes.

It has not been possible to bring to light any precise relations between schizophrenic manifestations, for example, and structural alterations of the cerebral cortex. The hopes of Kroepelin, the famous pioneer in the maladies of the mind, have not materialized. The anatomical study of these diseases has not thrown much light on their nature. Mental disorders are perhaps not localized in space. Some symptoms can be attributed to a lack of harmony in the temporal succession of nervous phenomena, to changes in the value of time for cells constituting a functional system. We know also that the lesions produced in certain regions of the cerebrum, either by the spirochætes of syphilis or by the mysterious agent of encephalitis lethargica, bring about definite modifications of the personality. This knowledge is vague, uncertain, in process of formation. However, it is imperative not to wait for a complete understanding of the nature of insanity before developing a truly effective hygiene of the mind.

The discovery of the causes of mental diseases would be more important than that of their nature. Such knowledge could lead to the prevention of these maladies. Feeble-mindedness and insanity are perhaps the price of industrial civilization, and of the resulting changes in our ways of life. However, these affections are often part of the inheritance received from his parents by each individual. They manifest themselves among people whose nervous system is already unbalanced. In the families which have already produced neurotic, queer, over-sensitive individuals, the insane and the feeble-minded suddenly appear. However, they also spring up from lineages which have so far been free from mental disorders. There are certainly other causes of insanity than hereditary factors. We must, therefore, ascertain how modern life acts upon consciousness.

In successive generations of pure-bred dogs nervousness is often observed to increase. We find among these animals individuals closely resembling the feeble-minded and the insane. This phenomenon occurs in subjects brought up under artificial conditions, living in comfortable kennels, and provided with choice food quite different from that of their ancestors, the sheep-dogs, which fought and defeated the wolves. It seems that the new conditions of existence, imposed upon dogs, as well as upon men, tend to modify the nervous system unfavourably. But experiments of long duration are necessary in order to obtain a precise knowledge of the mechanism of this degeneration. The factors promoting the development of idiocy and insanity are of great complexity. Dementia præcox and circular insanity manifest themselves more especially in the social groups where life is restless and disordered, food too elaborate or too poor, and syphilis frequent; and also when the nervous system is hereditarily unstable, when moral discipline has been suppressed, when selfishness, irresponsibility, and dispersion are customary. There are probably some relations between these factors and the genesis of psychoses. The modern habits of living hide a fundamental defect. In the environment created by technology our most specific functions develop incompletely. Despite the marvels of scientific civilization human personality tends to dissolve.

CHAPTER V

INWARD TIME

1. *Duration. Its measurement by a clock. Extension of things in space and time. Mathematical, or abstract, time. Operational concept of concrete, or physical, time.* **2.** *Definition of inward time. Physiological and psychological times. Measurement of physiological time. Growth index of blood plasma. Its variations according to chronological age.* **3.** *Characteristics of physiological time. Recording of the past by tissues and humours. Irregularity and irreversibility of physiological time.* **4.** *Substratum of physiological time. Reciprocal alterations of tissues and their medium. Progressive changes of blood plasma in the course of life.* **5.** *Longevity. The span of life has not increased. Causes of this phenomenon. Possibility of increasing the span of life. Should it be done?* **6.** *Artificial rejuvenation. Is rejuvenation possible?* **7.** *Operational concept of inward time. The true value of physical time during youth and old age.* **8.** *Utilization of the concept of inward time. Respective durations of man and civilization. Physiological time and society. Physiological time and the individual.* **9.** *Rhythm of physiological time and artificial moulding of man.*

I

THE duration of man, just as his size, varies according to the unit used for its measurement. It is long when related to that of mice or butterflies, short in comparison with the life of an oak, insignificant if placed in the frame of the earth's history. We measure it by the motion of the hands of a clock around the dial. We liken it to the passage of those hands over equal intervals, the seconds, the minutes, the hours. The time of a clock corresponds to certain rhythmic events, such as the earth's rotation on its axis and around the sun. Our duration is, then, expressed in units of solar time and consists of about twenty-five thousand days. For the clock which measures it a child's day is equal to that of its parents. In

152

reality, those twenty-four hours represent a very small part of the child's future life, and a much larger fraction of that of its parents. But they may also be looked upon as a minute fragment of an old man's past existence and a far more important part of that of a nursling. Thus the value of physical time seems to differ according to whether we look back to the past or forward to the future.

We have to refer our duration to a clock because we are immersed in the physical continuum. And the clock measures one of the dimensions of this continuum. On the surface of our planet, those dimensions are discerned through particular characteristics. The vertical is identified by the phenomenon of gravity. We are unable to make any distinction between the two horizontal dimensions. We could, however, separate them from each other if our nervous system were endowed with the properties of a magnetic needle. As for the fourth dimension, or time, it takes on a strange aspect. While the other three dimensions of things are short and almost motionless, it appears as ceaselessly extending and very long. We travel quite easily over the two horizontal dimensions. But in order to move in the vertical one, we must use a staircase or an elevator, an aircraft or a balloon, for we have to contend with gravity. To travel in time is absolutely impossible. Wells has not divulged the secrets of construction of the machine which enabled one of his heroes to leave his room by the fourth dimension and to escape into the future. For concrete man time is very different from space. But the four dimensions would seem identical to an abstract man inhabiting the sidereal spaces. Although distinct from space, time is inseparable from it, at the surface of the earth as in the rest of the universe, when considered by the biologist as well as by the physicist.

In nature time is always found united to space. It is a necessary aspect of material beings. No concrete thing has only three spatial dimensions. A rock, a tree, an animal cannot be instantaneous. Indeed, we are capable of building up in our minds beings entirely described within three dimensions. But all concrete objects have four. And man extends both in time and in space. To an observer living far more slowly than we do he would appear as something narrow and elongated, analogous to the incandescent trail of a meteor. Besides, he possesses another aspect, impossible to define clearly. For he is not wholly comprised within the physical continuum. Thought is not confined within time and space. Moral, æsthetic, and religious activities do not inhabit the physical continuum exclusively. Moreover, we know that clairvoyants may detect hidden things at great distances. Some of them perceive events which have already happened or which will take place in the future. It should be noted that they apprehend the future in the same way as the past. They are sometimes incapable of distinguishing the one from the other. For example, they may speak, at two different epochs, of the same fact, without suspecting that the first vision relates to the future, and the second to the past. Certain activities of consciousness seem to travel over space and time.

The nature of time varies according to the objects considered by our mind. The time that we observe in nature has no separate existence. It is only a mode of being of concrete objects. We ourselves create mathematical time. It is a mental construct, an abstraction indispensable to the building up of science. We conveniently compare it to a straight line, each successive instant being represented by a point. Since Galileo's day this abstraction has been substituted for the concrete data resulting from the direct observation of things. The philosophers of the Middle Ages considered time as an agent concretizing abstractions. Such a conception resembled more closely that of Minkowski than that of Galileo. To them, as to Minkowski, to Einstein, and to modern physicists, time, in nature, appeared as completely inseparable from space. In reducing objects to their primary qualities—that is, to what can be measured and is susceptible of mathematical treatment—Galileo deprived them of their secondary qualities, and of duration. This arbitrary simplification made possible the development of physics. At the same time, it led to an unwarrantably schematic conception of the world, especially of the biological world. We must listen to Bergson and attribute to time a reality of its own, and give back their secondary qualities and duration to inanimate and living beings.

The concept of time is equivalent to the operation required to estimate duration in the objects of our universe. Duration consists of the superposition of the different aspects of an identity. It is a kind of intrinsic movement of things. The earth revolves on its axis and, without losing its primary qualities, shows a surface which is sometimes lighted and sometimes darkened. Mountains may progressively change their shape under the action of snow, rain, and erosion, although they remain themselves. A tree grows, and does not lose its identity. The human individual retains his personality throughout the flux of the organic and mental processes that make up his life. Each inanimate or living being comprises an inner motion, a succession of states, a rhythm, which is his very own. Such motion is inherent time. It can be measured by reference to the motion of another being. Thus we measure our duration by comparing it with solar time. As we inhabit the surface of the earth, we find it convenient to place in its frame the spatial and temporal dimensions of everything found thereon. We estimate our height with the aid of the metre, which is approximately the forty-millionth part of the meridian of our planet. In a like manner, the rotation of the earth, or the number of hours ticked off by a clock, is the standard to which we refer our temporal dimensions or the flow of our time. It is natural for human beings to use the intervals separating the rising of the sun from its setting as the means to measure their duration and organize their lives. However, the moon could serve the same purpose. In fact, to fishermen dwelling on shores where the tides are very high, lunar time is more important than solar time. Their way of living, and the hours reserved for sleeping and eating, are determined by the rhythm of the tides. In such circumstances human duration is fitted into the frame of the daily variations of the sea-level. In short, time is a specific character of things. Its nature varies according to the constitution of each object. Human beings have acquired the habit of identifying their duration, and that of all other beings, with the time shown by clocks. Nevertheless, our inner time is as distinct from, and independent of, this extrinsic time, as our body is, in space, distinct from, and independent of, the earth and the sun.

2

Inner time is the expression of the changes of the body and its activities during the course of life. It is equivalent to the uninterrupted succession of the structural, humoral, physiological, and mental states which constitute our personality. It is truly a dimension of ourselves. Imaginary slices carved from our body and soul through such dimension would be as heterogeneous as the sections made by anatomists perpendicularly to the three spatial axes. As Wells says in *The Time Machine*, a man's portraits at eight years, fifteen years, seventeen years, twenty-three years, and so on, are sections, or rather images, in three dimensions of a being of four dimensions, who is a fixed and unalterable thing. The differences between these sections express changes progressively occurring in the constitution of the individual. These changes are organic and mental. Thus inward time has to be divided into physiological and psychological times.

Physiological time is a fixed dimension, consisting of the series of all organic changes undergone by a human being from the beginning of his embryonic life to his death. It may also be considered as a movement, as the successive states which build up our fourth dimension under the eyes of the observer. Some of these states are rhythmic and reversible, such as the pulsations of the heart, the contractions of the muscles, the movements of the stomach and those of the intestines, the secretions of the glands of the digestive apparatus, and the phenomena of menstruation. Others are progressive and irreversible, such as the loss of the skin's elasticity, the increase in the quantity of the red blood cells, the sclerosis of the tissues and the arteries. But the rhythmic and reversible movements are likewise altered during the course of life. They themselves also undergo a progressive and irreversible change. Simultaneously, the constitution of the tissues and the humours becomes modified. This complex movement is physiological time.

The other aspect of inner time is psychological time. Consciousness, under the influence of the stimuli coming from the outside world, records its own motion, the series of its states. Time, according to Bergson, is the very stuff of psychological life. "Duration is not one instant replacing another. . . . Duration is the continuous progress of the past which gnaws into the future and which swells as it advances. . . . The piling up of the past upon the past goes on without relaxation. In reality, the past is preserved by itself, automatically. In its entirety, probably, it follows us at every instant. . . . Doubtless we think with only a small part of our past, but it is with our entire past, including the original bent of our soul, that we desire, will and act."* We are a history. And the length of that history, rather than the number of our years, expresses the wealth of our inner life. We obscurely feel that we are not to-day identical with what we were yesterday. The days seem to fly more and more rapidly. But none of these changes is sufficiently precise or constant to be measured. The intrinsic motion of our consciousness is indefinable. Certain of our psychological activities are not

* Henri Bergson, *Creative Evolution*, pp. 4–5. Translation by Arthur Mitchell. New York, Henry Holt and Company, Inc.

modified by duration. They deteriorate only when the brain succumbs to illness or to senility.

Inward time cannot be properly measured in units of solar time. However, it is generally expressed in days and years because these units are convenient and applicable to the classification of terrestrial events. But such a procedure gives no information about the rhythm of the inner processes constituting our intrinsic time. Obviously, chronological age does not correspond to physiological age. Puberty occurs at different epochs in different individuals. It is the same with menopause. True age is an organic and functional state. It has to be measured by the rhythm of the changes of this state. Such rhythm varies according to individuals. Some remain young for many years. On the contrary, the organs of others wear out early in life. The value of physical time in a Norwegian, whose life is long, is far from being identical with that in an Eskimo, whose life is short. To estimate true, or physiological, age, we must discover, either in the tissues or in the humours, a measurable phenomenon, which progresses without interruption during the whole lifetime.

Man is constituted, in his fourth dimension, by a series of forms following, and blending into, each other. He is egg, embryo, infant, adolescent, adult, mature and old man. These morphological aspects are the expression of chemical, organic, and psychological events. Most of these variations cannot be measured. When measurable they are generally found to take place only during a certain period of the existence of the individual. But physiological duration is equivalent to our fourth dimension in its entire length. The progressive slackening of growth during infancy and youth, the phenomena of puberty and of menopause, the diminution of basal metabolism, the whitening of the hair, etc., are the manifestations of different stages of our duration. The rate at which tissues grow also declines with age. Such growth activity may be roughly estimated in fragments of tissues extirpated from the body and cultivated in flasks. But as far as the age of the organism itself is concerned, the information thus obtained is far from being reliable. Indeed, some tissues grow more active, others less active, at certain periods of physiological life. Each organ changes at its own rhythm, which differs from that of the body as a whole. Certain phenomena, however, express a general modification of the organism. For example, the rate of healing of a superficial wound varies in function of the age of the patient. It is well known that the progress of cicatrization can be calculated with two equations set up by Lecomte du Noüy. The first of these equations gives a coefficient, called index of cicatrization, which depends on the surface and the age of the wound. By introducing this index in a second equation, one may, from two measurements of the wound taken at an interval of several days, predict the future progress of repair. The smaller the wound and the younger the man, the greater is the index. With the help of this index, Lecomte du Noüy has discovered a constant that expresses the regenerative activity characteristic of a given age. This constant is equal to the product of the index by the square root of the surface of the wound. The curve of its variations shows that a twenty-year-old patient heals twice as quickly as a forty-year-old one. Through these equations, the physiological age of a man can be deduced from the rate of healing of a wound. From ten to about forty-five years, the information thus obtained is very definite. But later the variations of the index of cicatrization are so small that they lose all significance.

Blood plasma alone displays, throughout the entire lifetime, progressive modifications characterizing the senescence of the body as a whole. We know that it contains the secretions of all tissues and organs. Plasma and tissues being a closed system, any alteration in the tissues reacts on the plasma, and vice versa. During the course of life this system undergoes continuous changes. Some of these changes may be detected both by chemical analysis and by physiological reactions. The plasma or the serum of an ageing animal has been found to increase its restraining effect on the growth of cell colonies. The ratio of the area of a colony living in serum, to that of an identical colony living in a saline solution and acting as a control, is called the growth index. The older the animal to which the serum belongs, the smaller is this index. Thus the rhythm of physiological time can be measured. During the first days of life, blood serum does not inhibit the growth of cell colonies any more than does the control solution. At this moment the value of the index approaches unity. As the animal becomes older its serum restrains cell multiplication more effectively. And the index decreases. During the last years of life it is generally equal to zero.

Although very imperfect, this method gives some precise information on the rhythm of physiological time at the beginning of life, when ageing is rapid. But in the final period of maturity, when ageing is slow, it becomes quite insufficient. By the variations of the growth index the life of a dog can be divided into ten units of physiological time. The duration of this animal may roughly be expressed in these units instead of in years. Thus it has become possible to compare physiological time with solar time. And their rhythms appear to be very different. The curve showing the decrease of the index value in function of chronological age falls sharply during the first year. During the second and third years its slope becomes less and less pronounced. The segment of the curve corresponding to the mature years has a tendency to become a straight line. And the portion representing old age does not deviate from the horizontal. Obviously, ageing progresses much more rapidly at the beginning than at the end of life. When infancy and old age are expressed in solar years, infancy appears to be very short and old age very long. On the contrary, measured in units of physiological time, infancy is very long and old age very short.

3

We have mentioned that physiological time is quite different from physical time. If all the clocks accelerated or retarded their motion, and if the earth correspondingly modified the rhythm of its rotation, our duration would remain unchanged. But it would seem to decrease or to increase. In this manner the alteration undergone by solar time would become apparent. While we are swept onward upon the stream of physical time, we move at the rhythm of the inner processes constituting physiological duration. Indeed, we are not mere grains of dust floating on a river, but also drops of oil spreading out over the surface of the water with a motion of their own, while being borne along by the current. Physical time is foreign to us, whereas inner time is ourself. Our present does not drop into nothingness as does the present of a pendulum. It is recorded simultaneously in mind, tissues, and blood. We keep within ourselves the organic, humoral, and psychological marks of all the events of our life. Like a nation, like an old country, like the cities, the factories, the farms, the cultivated fields, the Gothic cathedrals, the feudal castles, the Roman monuments of Europe, we are the result of a history. Our personality is enriched by each new experience of our organs, humours, and consciousness. Each thought, each action, each illness, has definitive consequences, inasmuch as we never separate ourselves from our past. We may completely recover from a disease or from a wrong deed. But we bear forever the scar of those events.

Solar time flows at a uniform rate. It consists of equal intervals. Its pace never changes. On the contrary, physiological time differs from one man to another. In the races enjoying long life it is slower, and more rapid in those whose life is short. It also varies within a single individual at the different periods of his life. A year is richer in physiological and mental events during infancy than during old age. The rhythm of these events decreases rapidly at first, and later on much more slowly. The number of units of physical time corresponding to a unit of physiological time becomes progressively greater. In short, the body is an ensemble of organic movements, whose rhythm is very fast during infancy, much less rapid during youth, and very slow in maturity and old age. It is when our physiological activities begin to weaken that our mind attains the summit of its development.

Physiological time is far from having the precision of a clock. Organic processes undergo certain fluctuations. Their rhythm is not constant. Their slackening in the course of life is expressed by an irregular curve. These irregularities are due to accidents in the concatenation of the physiological phenomena constituting our duration. At some moments the progress of age seems to cease. At other periods it accelerates. There are also phases in which personality concentrates and grows, and phases in which it dissipates. As stated above, inner time and its organic and psychological substratum do not possess the regularity of solar time. A sort of rejuvenation may be brought about by a happy event, or a better equilibrium of the physiological and psychological functions. Possibly, certain states of mental and bodily well-being are accompanied by modifications of the humours characteristic of a true rejuvenation. Moral suffering, business worries, infectious and degenerative diseases accelerate organic decay. The appearance of senescence may be induced in a dog by injections of sterile pus. The animal grows thin, becomes tired and depressed. At the same time, his blood and tissues display physiological reactions analogous to those of old age. But those reactions are reversible and, later, the organic functions re-establish their normal rhythm. An old man's aspect changes but slightly from one year to another. In the absence of disease senescence is a very slow process. When it becomes rapid the intervention of factors other than physiological ones is to be suspected. In general such a phenomenon may be accounted for by anxiety and sorrow, by substances deriving from bacterial infections, by a degenerating organ, or by cancer. The speeding up of senescence always expresses the presence of an organic or moral lesion in the ageing body.

Like physical time, physiological time is irreversible. In fact, it is as irreversible as the processes responsible for its existence. In the higher animals duration never changes its direction. However, in hibernating mammals it becomes partly suspended. In a dried rotifer its flow comes to a complete standstill. The organic rhythm of cold-blooded animals accelerates when their environment becomes warmer. The flies kept by Jacques Loeb at an abnormally high temperature aged much more rapidly and died sooner. Likewise, the value of the physiological time of an alligator changes if the surrounding temperature goes up from 20° to 40° C. In this instance, the index of cicatrization of a superficial wound rises and falls with the temperature. But, in using such simple procedures, it is not possible to induce in men any profound change of the tissues. The rhythm of physiological time is not modifiable except by interference with certain fundamental processes and their mode of association. We cannot retard senescence, or reverse its direction, unless we know the nature of the mechanisms which are the substratum of duration.

4

Physiological duration owes its existence and its characteristics to a certain type of organization of animate matter. It appears as soon as a portion of space containing living cells becomes relatively isolated from the cosmic world. At all levels of organization in the body of a cell or in that of a man physiological time depends on modifications of the medium produced by nutrition, and on the response of the cells to those modifications. A cell colony begins to record time as soon as its waste products are allowed to stagnate, and thus to alter its surroundings. The simplest system where the phenomenon of senescence is observed consists of a group of tissue cells cultivated in a small volume of nutritive medium. In such a system the medium is progressively modified by the products of nutrition and, in its turn, modifies the cells. Then appear senescence and death. The rhythm of physiological time depends on the relations between the tissues and their medium. It varies according to the volume, the metabolic activity, the nature of the cell colony, and the quantity and the chemical composition of the fluid and gaseous media. The technique used in the preparation of a culture accounts for the rhythm of life of such culture. For example, a fragment of heart fed with a single drop of plasma in the confined atmosphere of a hollow slide, and another one immersed in a flask containing a large volume of nutritive fluids and gases, have quite different fates. The rate of accumulation of the waste products in the medium, and the nature of these products, determine the characteristics of the duration of the tissues. When the composition of the medium is maintained constant, the cell colonies remain indefinitely in the same state of activity. They record time by quantitative, and not by qualitative, changes. If, by an appropriate technique, their volume is prevented from increasing, they never grow old. Colonies obtained from a heart fragment removed in January, 1912, from a chick embryo, are growing as actively to-day as twenty-three years ago. In fact they are immortal.

Within the body the relations of the tissues and of their medium are incomparably more complex than in the artificial system represented by a culture of cells. Although the lymph and the blood, which constitute the organic medium, are continually modified by the waste products of cell nutrition, their composition is maintained constant by the lungs, kidneys, liver, etc. However, in spite of these regulatory mechanisms, very slow changes do take place in humour and tissues. They are detected by variations in the growth

index of plasma, and in the constant that expresses the regenerative activity of skin. They correspond to successive
states in the chemical composition of the humours. The proteins of blood serum become more abundant and their characters are modified. It is chiefly the fats which give to serum
the property of acting upon certain cell types and of dimin-
ishing the rapidity of their multiplication. These fats increase
in quantity and change in nature during life. The modifications of serum are not the result of a progressive accumulation, of a sort of retention of fats and proteins in the organic
medium. It is quite easy to remove from a dog the greater
part of its blood, to separate the plasma from the corpuscles,
and to replace it by a saline solution. The blood cells, thus
freed from the proteins and fatty substances of plasma, are
reinjected into the animal. In less than a fortnight, plasma is
observed to be regenerated by the tissues, without any change
in its composition. Its state is, therefore, due to the condition of the tissues, and not to an accumulation of harmful
substances. And this state is specific of each age. Even if
blood serum is removed several times, it always regenerates
with the characteristics corresponding to the age of the animal. The state of the humours during senescence thus appears to be determined by substances contained in the organs
as in almost inexhaustible reservoirs.

In the course of life, the tissues undergo important alterations. They lose much water. They are encumbered with
non-living elements and connective fibres, which are neither
elastic nor extensible. The organs acquire more rigidity.
Arteries become hard. Circulation is less active. Profound
modifications take place in the structure of the glands. Epithelial cells lose their qualities little by little. They regenerate
more slowly, or not at all. Their secretions are less rich.
Such changes occur at various rates, according to the organs.
Certain organs grow old more rapidly than others. But we
do not know as yet the reason for this phenomenon. Such
regional senescence may attack the arteries, the heart, the

brain, the kidneys, or any other organ. The ageing of a single system of tissues is dangerous. Longevity is much greater when the elements of the body grow old in a uniform way. If the skeletal muscles remain active when the heart and the vessels are already worn out, they become a danger to the entire body. Abnormally vigorous organs in a senile organism are almost as harmful as senile organs in a young organism. The youthful functioning of any anatomical system, either sexual glands, digestive apparatus, or muscles, is very dangerous for old men. Obviously, the value of time is not the same for all tissues. This heterochronism shortens the duration of life. If excessive work is imposed on any part of the body, even in individuals whose tissues are isochronic, ageing is also accelerated. An organ which is submitted to over-activity, toxic influences, and abnormal stimulations, wears out more quickly than the others. And its premature senility brings on the death of the organism.

We know that physiological time, like physical time, is not an entity. Physical time depends on the constitution of clocks and of the solar system ; physiological time, on that of tissues and humours, and on their reciprocal relations. The characteristics of duration are those of the structural and functional processes specific of a certain type of organization. The length of life is conditioned by the very mechanisms that make man independent of the cosmic environment and give him his spatial mobility, by the small volume of the blood, by the activity of the systems responsible for the purification of the humours. These systems do not succeed in preventing certain progressive modifications of the serum and the tissues from occurring. Perhaps the tissues are not completely freed of waste products by the blood stream. Perhaps they are insufficiently fed. If the volume of the organic medium were much greater, and the elimination of waste products more complete, human life might last longer. But our body would be far larger, softer, less compact. It would resemble the gigantic prehistoric animals. We certainly would be deprived of the agility, the speed, and the skill that we now possess.

Like physiological time, psychological time is only an aspect of ourselves. Its nature, like that of memory, is unknown. Memory is responsible for our awareness of the passage of time. However, psychological duration is composed of other elements. Personality is partly made up of recollections. But it also comes from the impression left upon all our organs by every physical, chemical, physiological, or psychological event of our life. We obscurely feel the passing of duration. We are capable of estimating such duration, in a grossly approximative manner, in terms of physical time. We perceive its flux as, perhaps, do muscular or nervous elements. Each cell type records physical time in its own way. The value of time for nerves and muscles is expressed, as already mentioned, in chronaxies. All anatomical elements are far from having the same chronaxy. The isochronism and heterochronism of cells play a capital part in their work. This estimation of time by the tissues may possibly reach the threshold of consciousness, and be responsible for the indefinable feeling in the depths of our self of silently flowing waters, on which float our states of consciousness, like the spots of a searchlight on the dark surface of an immense river. We realize that we change, that we are not identical with our former self, but that we are the same being. The distance from which we look back upon the small child, who was ourself, is precisely the dimension of our organism and of our consciousness which we compare to a spatial dimension. Of this aspect of inward time we know nothing, except that it is both dependent and independent of the rhythm of organic life, and moves more and more rapidly as we grow older.

5

The greatest desire of men is for eternal youth. From Merlin down to Cagliostro, Brown-Séquard, and Voronoff, charlatans and scientists have pursued the same dream and suffered the same defeat. No one has discovered the supreme secret. Meanwhile, our need of it is becoming more and more urgent. Scientific civilization has destroyed the world of the soul. But the realm of matter is widely opened to man. He must, then, keep intact the vigour of his body and of his intelligence. Only the strength of youth gives him the power to satisfy his physiological appetites and to conquer the outer world. In some measure, however, we have realized the ancestral dream. We enjoy youth, or its appearance, for a much longer time than our fathers did. But we have not succeeded in increasing the duration of our existence. A man of forty-five has no more chance of dying at the age of eighty years now than in the last century.

This failure of hygiene and medicine is a strange fact. In spite of the progress achieved in the heating, ventilation, and lighting of houses, of dietary hygiene, bathrooms, and sports, of periodical medical examinations, and increasing numbers of medical specialists, not even one day has been added to the span of human life. Are we to believe that hygienists, chemists, and physicians are mistaken in their ruling of the existence of the individual, like politicians, economists and financiers in the organization of the life of the nation? After all, it may be that modern comfort and habits imposed upon the dwellers of the new city do not agree with natural laws. However, a marked change has taken place in the appearance of men and women. Owing to hygiene, athletics, alimentary restrictions, beauty parlours, and to the superficial activity engendered by telephone and automobile, all are more alert than in former times. At fifty, women are still young. Modern progress, however, has brought in its train counterfeit money as well as gold. When their visages, lifted and smoothed by the beauty surgeon, again become flabby, when massage no longer prevails against invading fat, those women whose appearance has been girlish for so many years look older than their grandmothers did at the same age. The pseudo-young men, who play tennis and dance as at twenty years, who discard their old wife and marry a young woman, are liable to softening of the brain, and to diseases of the heart and the kidneys. Sometimes they die suddenly in their bed, in their office, on the golf-links, at an age when their ancestors were still tilling their land or managing their business with a firm hand. The causes of this failure of modern life are not exactly known. Indeed, hygienists and physicians cannot be held responsible for it. The premature wearing out of modern men is probably due to worries, lack of economic security, overwork, absence of moral discipline, and excesses of all sorts.

A better knowledge of the mechanisms of physiological duration could bring a solution of the problem of longevity. But the science of man is still too rudimentary to be useful. We must, then, ascertain, in a purely empirical manner, whether life can be made longer. The presence of a few centenarians in every country demonstrates the extent of our temporal potentialities. No practical conclusions, however, have resulted so far from the observation of these centenarians. Obviously, longevity is hereditary. But it depends also on the conditions of development. When descendants of families where longevity is usual come to dwell in large cities, they generally lose, in one or two generations, the capacity of living to be old. A study of animals of pure stock and of well-known ancestral constitution would probably show in what measure environment may augment the span of existence. In certain races of mice, mated between brothers and sisters over many generations, the duration of life remains quite constant. However, if one places the animals in large pens, in a state of semi-liberty, instead of keeping them in cages, and allows them to burrow and return to more primi-

F*

tive conditions of existence, they die much earlier. When certain substances are removed from the diet, longevity is also found to decrease. On the contrary, life lengthens if the animals are given certain food or subjected to fasting during certain fixed periods for several generations. It is evident that simple changes in the mode of existence are capable of influencing the duration of life. Man's longevity could probably be augmented by analogous, or other, procedures.

We must not yield to the temptation to use blindly for this purpose the means placed at our disposal by medicine. Longevity is only desirable if it increases the duration of youth, and not that of old age. The lengthening of the senescent period would be a calamity. The ageing individual, when not capable of providing for himself, is an encumbrance to his family and to the community. If all men lived to be one hundred years old, the younger members of the population could not support such a heavy burden. Before attempting to prolong life we must discover methods for conserving organic and mental activities to the eve of death. It is imperative that the number of the diseased, the paralyzed, the weak, and the insane should not be augmented. Besides, it would not be wise to give everybody a long existence. The danger of increasing the quantity of human beings without regard to their quality is well known. Why should more years be added to the life of persons who are unhappy, selfish, stupid, and useless? The number of centenarians must not be augmented until we can prevent intellectual and moral decay, and also the lingering diseases of old age.

6

It would be more useful to discover a method for rejuvenating individuals whose physiological and mental qualities justify such a measure. Rejuvenation can be conceived as a complete reversal of inward time. The subject would be carried back to a previous stage of his life by some operation. One would amputate a part of his fourth dimension. However, for practical purposes, rejuvenation should be given a more restricted meaning and be considered as an incomplete reversal of duration. The direction of psychological time would not be changed. Memory would persist. Tissues and humours would be rejuvenated. With the help of organs in possession of their youthful vigour, the subject could utilize the experience acquired in the course of a long life. The word rejuvenation, when used in connection with the experiments and operations carried out by Steinach, Voronoff, and others, refers to an improvement in the general condition of the patients, to a feeling of strength and of sprightliness, to a revival of the sexual functions. But such changes occurring in an old man after the treatment do not mean that rejuvenation has taken place. Studies of the chemical composition of the blood serum, and of its physiological reactions, are the only means of detecting a reversal of physiological age. A permanent increase in the growth index of serum would demonstrate the reality of results claimed by the surgeons. For rejuvenation is equivalent to certain physiological and chemical modifications measurable in blood plasma. Nevertheless, the absence of such findings does not necessarily mean that the age of the subject has not decreased. Our techniques are still far from perfect. They cannot reveal, in an old individual, a reversal of physiological time of less than several years. If a fourteen-year-old dog were brought back to the age of ten, the change in the growth index of his serum would be hardly discernible.

Among the ancient medical superstitions, there was a persistent belief in the virtue of young blood, in its power to impart youth to an old and worn-out body. Pope Innocent VIII had the blood of three young men transfused into his veins. But after this operation he died. As it is quite likely that death was due to a technical accident, perhaps the idea deserves reconsideration. The introduction of young blood into an old organism might bring about favourable changes. It is strange that such an operation has not been tried again. This omission is due, possibly, to the fact that endocrine glands have gained the favour of the physicians. Brown-Séquard, after having injected into himself a fresh extract of testicle, believed that he was rejuvenated. This discovery brought him very great fame. However, he died shortly afterwards. But faith in the testicle as an agent of rejuvenation survived. Steinach attempted to demonstrate that the ligature of its duct stimulates the gland. He performed this operation on many old men. But the results were doubtful. Brown-Séquard's idea was taken up again and extended by Voronoff. The latter, instead of simply injecting testicular extracts, grafted in old men, or men prematurely aged, testicles from chimpanzees. It is incontestable that the operation was followed by an improvement in the general condition and the sexual functions of the patients. But the testicle of a chimpanzee does not live long in a man. During the process of degeneration, it may set free certain secretory products, and these substances, passing into the circulating blood, probably activate the sexual and other endocrine glands of the subject. Such operations do not give lasting results. Old age, as we know, is due to profound modifications of all the tissues and humours, and not to the deficiency of a single gland. The loss of activity of the sexual glands is not the cause of senescence, but one of its consequences. It is probable that neither Steinach nor Voronoff has ever observed true rejuvenation. But their failure does not by any means signify that rejuvenation is forever impossible to obtain.

We can believe that a partial reversal of physiological time will become realizable. Duration, as already mentioned, consists of certain structural and functional processes. True age depends on progressive changes of the tissues and humours. Tissues and humours are one and the same system. If an old man were given the glands of a still-born infant and the blood of a young man, he would possibly be rejuvenated. Many technical difficulties remain to be overcome before such an operation can be undertaken. We have no way of selecting organs suitable to a given individual. There is no procedure for rendering tissues capable of adapting themselves to the body of their host in a definitive manner. But the progress of science is swift. With the aid of the methods already existing, and of those which will be discovered, we must pursue the search for the great secret.

Man will never tire of seeking immortality. He will not attain it because he is bound by certain laws of his organic constitution. He may succeed in retarding, perhaps even in reversing in some measure, the inexorable advance of physiological time. Never will he vanquish death. Death is the price he has to pay for his brain and his personality. But some day medicine will teach him that old age, free from diseases of the body and the soul, is not to be feared. To illness, and not to senescence, are due most of our woes.

7

The human significance of physical time is bound naturally to the nature of inner time. We have already mentioned that physiological time is a flux of irreversible changes of the tissues and humours. It may be approximately measured in special units, each unit being equivalent to a certain functional modification of blood serum. Its characteristics depend on the structure of the organism and on the physiological processes connected with such structure. They are specific of each species, of each individual, and of the age of each individual.

Physiological time is generally referred to physical time, to the time of a clock, inasmuch as we are part of the material world. The natural periods of our life are measured in days or years. Infancy, childhood, and adolescence last about eighteen years; maturity and old age, fifty or sixty years. Thus man consists of a brief period of development and of a long period of completion and decay. On the contrary, physical time may be referred to physiological time, and the time of a clock expressed in terms of human duration. Then a strange phenomenon occurs. Physical time loses the uniformity of its value. The content of a year in units of physiological time becomes variable. It is different for each individual, and for each period of an individual's life.

One perceives, more or less clearly, the changes in the value of physical time, which occur in the course of one's life. The days of our childhood seemed very slow, and those of our maturity are disconcertingly rapid. Possibly we experience this feeling because we unconsciously place physical time in the frame of our duration. And, naturally, physical time seems to vary inversely to it. The rhythm of our duration slows down progressively. Physical time glides along at a uniform rate. It is like a large river flowing through a plain. At the dawn of his life, man briskly runs along the bank, and he goes faster than the stream. Toward midday, his pace slackens. The waters now glide as speedily as he walks. When night falls, man is tired. The stream accelerates the swiftness of its flow. Man drops far behind. Then he stops, and lies down forever. And the river inexorably continues on its course. In fact, the river never accelerates its flow. Only the progressive slackening of our pace is responsible for this illusion. The seeming length of the first part of our existence and the brevity of the last may also be due to the well-known fact that, for the child and for the old man, a year represents quite different proportions of the past. It is more probable, however, that our consciousness vaguely perceives the slowing down of our time—that is, of our physiological processes, and that each one of us runs along the bank and looks at the streaming waters of physical time.

The value of the days of early childhood is very great. Every moment should be utilized for education. The waste of this period of life can never be compensated. Instead of being allowed to grow like plants or little animals, children should be the object of the most enlightened training. But this training calls for a profound knowledge of physiology and psychology, which modern educators have not yet been given the opportunity of acquiring. The declining years of maturity and senescence have little physiological value. They are almost empty of organic and mental changes. They have to be filled with artificial activities. The ageing man should neither stop working nor retire. Inaction further impoverishes the content of time. Leisure is even more dangerous for the old than for the young. To those whose forces are declining, appropriate work should be given, but not rest. Neither should physiological processes be stimulated at this moment. It is preferable to hide their slowness under a number of psychological events. If our days are filled with mental and spiritual adventures, they glide much less rapidly. They may even recover the plenitude of those of youth.

8

Duration is wedded to man, like the shape to the marble of the statue. Man refers all the events of his world to himself. He uses his span of life as a time unit in his estimation of the age of the earth, of the human race, of civilization, of the length of his own undertakings. Nevertheless, an individual and a nation cannot be placed in the same temporal scale. Social problems should not be considered in the same light as individual ones. They evolve very slowly. Our observations and our experiences are always too short. For this reason they have little significance. The results of a modification in the material and mental conditions of the existence of a population rarely manifest themselves in less than a century. However, the investigation of the great biological questions is confined to isolated individuals. There is no provision for the continuation of their work when they die. In a like manner, scientific and political institutions are conceived in terms of individual duration. The Roman Catholic Church is the only organization to have realized that the progress of humanity is very slow, that the passing of a generation is an insignificant event in the history of the world. In the evolution of mankind the duration of the individual is inadequate as a unit of temporal measure. The advent of scientific civilization necessitates a fresh discussion of all fundamental subjects. We are witnessing our own moral, intellectual, and social failure. We have been living under the delusion that democracies would survive through the weak and short-sighted efforts of the ignorant. We begin to understand that they are decaying. Problems involving the future of the great races demand a solution. It is now imperative to prepare for distant events, to mould young generations with a different ideal. The government of nations by men who estimate time in function of their own duration leads, as we well know, to confusion and to failure. We have to stretch our temporal outlook beyond ourselves.

On the contrary, in the organization of transitory social groups, such as a class of children, or a gang of workmen, individual time alone must be taken into account. The members of a group are obliged to work at the same rhythm. The intellectual activity of school children composing a class must be of practically the same standard. In factories, banks, stores, universities, etc., the workers are supposed to accomplish a certain task in a certain time. Those whose strength declines on account of age or illness impede the progress of the whole. So far, human beings are classified according to their chronological age. Children of the same age are placed in the same class. The date of retirement is also determined by the age of the worker. It is known, however, that the true condition of an individual does not depend on his chronological age. In certain types of occupation, individuals should be grouped according to physiological age. Puberty has been used as a way of classifying children in some New York schools. But there are still no means of ascertaining at what time a man should be pensioned. Neither is there any general method of measuring the rate of the organic and mental decline of a given individual. However, physiological tests have been developed by which the condition of a flyer can be accurately estimated. Pilots are retired according to their physiological, and not their chronological, age.

Young and old people, although in the same region of space, live in different temporal worlds. We are inexorably separated by age from one another. A mother never succeeds in being a sister to her daughter. It is impossible for children to understand their parents, and still less their grandparents. Obviously, the individuals belonging to four successive generations are profoundly heterochronic. An old man and his great-grandson are complete strangers. The shorter the temporal distance separating two generations, the stronger may be the moral influence of the older over the younger. Women should be mothers when they are still very young. Thus they would not be isolated from their children by a temporal gap too great to be bridged, even by love.

9

From the concept of physiological time derive certain rules of our action on human beings. Organic and mental developments are not inexorable. They can be modified, in some measure, according to our will, because we are a movement, a succession of superposed patterns in the frame of our identity. Although man is a closed world, his outside and inside frontiers are open to many physical, chemical, and psychological agents. And those agents are capable of modifying our tissues and our mind. The moment, the mode, and the rhythm of our interventions depend on the structure of physiological time. Our temporal dimension extends chiefly during childhood, when functional processes are most active. Then, organs and mind are plastic. Their formation can effectively be aided. As organic events happen each day in great numbers, their growing mass can receive such shape as it seems proper to impress permanently upon the individual. The moulding of the organism according to a selected pattern must take into account the nature of duration, the constitution of our temporal dimension. Our interventions have to be made in the cadence of inner time. Man is like a viscous liquid flowing into the physical continuum. He cannot instantaneously change his direction. We should not endeavour to modify his mental and structural form by rough procedures, as one shapes a statue of marble by blows of the hammer. Surgical operations alone produce in tissues sudden alterations which are beneficial. And still, recovery from the quick work of the knife is slow. No profound changes of the body as a whole can be obtained rapidly. Our action must blend with the physiological processes, substratum of inner time, by following their own rhythm. For instance, it is useless to administer to a child a large quantity of cod-liver oil in a single dose. But a small amount of this remedy, given each day for several months, modifies the dimensions and the form of the skeleton. Likewise, the mental factors act only in a progressive manner. Our interventions in the building up of body and consciousness have their full effects only when they conform to the laws of our duration.

A child may be compared to a brook, which follows any change in its bed. The brook persists in its identity, in spite of the diversity of its forms. It may become a lake or a torrent. Under the influence of environment personality may spread and become very thin, or concentrate and acquire great strength. The growth of personality involves a constant trimming of our self. At the beginning of life man is endowed with vast potentialities. He is limited in his development only by the extensible frontiers of his ancestral predispositions. But at each instant he has to make a choice. And each choice throws into nothingness one of his potentialities. He has of necessity to select one of the several roads open to the wanderings of his existence, to the exclusion of all others. Thus he deprives himself of seeing the countries wherein he could have travelled along the other roads. In our infancy we carry within ourselves numerous virtual beings, who die one by one. In our old age we are surrounded by an escort of those we could have been, of all our aborted potentialities. Every man is a fluid that becomes solid, a treasure that grows poorer, a history in the making, a personality that is being created. And our progress, or our disintegration, depends on physical, chemical, and physiological factors, on viruses and bacteria, on psychological influences, and, finally, on our own will. We are constantly being made by our environment and by our self. And duration is the very material of organic and mental life, as it means "invention, creation of forms, continual elaboration of the absolutely new." *

* Henri Bergson, *op. cit.* p. 11.

CHAPTER VI

ADAPTIVE FUNCTIONS

1. *Adaptive functions are responsible for duration.* 2. *Intra-organic adaptation. Automatic regulation of the volume and composition of blood and humours. Its physico-chemical and physiological nature.* 3. *Organic correlations. Teleological aspect of the phenomenon. Adaptation to future events. Adaptation to hæmorrhage. Correlation of the structures of the eye.* 4. *Repair of tissues.* 5. *Adaptive phenomena and modern surgery.* 6. *Significance of diseases. Natural and acquired immunities.* 7. *Infectious and degenerative diseases. Artificial and natural health.* 8. *Extra-organic adaptation. Adaptation to physical environment.* 9. *Permanent changes imposed upon body and consciousness by adaptation.* 10. *Adaptation to social environment. Effort, conquest, flight. Lack of adaptation.* 11. *Characteristics of adaptive functions. Principle of Le Chatelier. Steady states. The law of effort.* 12. *Disuse of adaptive functions in modern civilization.* 13. *Activity of adaptive mechanisms necessary for the optimum development of man.* 14. *Practical significance of adaptive functions.*

I

THERE is a striking contrast between the durability of our body and the transitory character of its elements. Man is composed of a soft, alterable matter, susceptible of disintegrating in a few hours. However, he lasts longer than if made of steel. Not only does he last, but he ceaselessly overcomes the difficulties and dangers of the outside world. He accommodates himself, much better than the other animals do, to the changing conditions of his environment. He persists in living, despite physical, economic, and social upheavals. Such endurance is due to a very particular mode of activity of his tissues and humours. The body seems to mould itself on events. Instead of wearing out it changes. Our organs always improvise means of meeting every new situation. And these means are such that they tend to give us a maximum duration. The physiological processes, which are the substratum of inner time, always incline in the direction leading to the longest survival of the individual. This strange function, this watchful automatism, makes possible human existence with its specific characters. It is called adaptation.

All physiological activities are endowed with the property of being adaptive. Adaptation, therefore, assumes innumerable forms. However, its aspects may be grouped into two categories, intra-organic and extra-organic. Intra-organic adaptation is responsible for the constancy of the organic medium and of the relations of tissues and humours. It determines the correlation of the organs. It brings about the automatic repair of tissues and the cure of diseases. Extra-organic adaptation adjusts the individual to the physical, psychological, and economic world. It allows him to survive in spite of the unfavourable conditions of his environment. Under these two aspects the adaptive functions are at work during each instant of our whole life. They are the indispensable basis of our duration.

2

Whatever our sufferings, our joys, and the agitation of the world may be, our organs do not modify their inward rhythm to any great extent. The chemical exchanges of the cells and the humours continue imperturbably. The blood pulsates in the arteries and flows at an almost constant speed in the innumerable capillaries of the tissues. There is an impressive difference between the regularity of the phenomena taking place within our body and the extreme variability of our environment. Our organic states are very steady. But this stability is not equivalent to a condition of rest or equilibrium. It is due, on the contrary, to the unceasing activity of the entire organism. To maintain the constancy of the blood's composition and the regularity of its circulation, an immense number of physiological processes are required. The tranquillity of the tissues is assured by the converging efforts of all the functional systems. And the more irregular and violent our life, the greater are these efforts. For the brutality of our relations with the cosmic world must never trouble the peace of the cells and humours of our inner world.

The blood is not subjected to large variations of pressure and volume. However, it receives and loses a great deal of water in an irregular manner. After each meal it takes in the fluids absorbed by the intestinal mucosa from the food and the digestive juices. At other moments its volume tends to decrease. In the course of digestion, it loses several litres of water, which are used by the stomach, intestines, liver, and pancreas for manufacturing their secretions. An analogous phenomenon occurs during violent muscular exercise, a boxing-match for example, if the perspiration glands work actively. Blood also diminishes in volume in the course of certain diseases, such as dysentery or cholera, when a great deal of liquid passes from the capillary vessels into the lumen of the intestine. The administration of a purgative is followed by a similar waste of water. The gains and losses are exactly counterbalanced by mechanisms regulating the blood volume.

These mechanisms extend over the whole body. They maintain constant both the pressure and the volume of the blood. The pressure does not depend on the absolute amount of the blood, but on the relation of this amount to the capacity of the circulatory apparatus. This apparatus, however, is not comparable to a system of pipes fed by a pump. It has no analogy with the machines constructed by man. Arteries and veins automatically modify their calibre. They contract or dilate under the influence of the nerves of their muscular envelope. In addition, the walls of the capillaries are permeable. The water of the blood is thus free to enter or to leave the circulatory apparatus. It also escapes from the body through the kidneys, the pores of the skin, the intestinal mucosa, and evaporates in the lungs. The heart realizes the miracle of maintaining constant the pressure of the blood in a system of vessels whose capacity and permeability ceaselessly vary. When blood tends to accumulate in too large a quantity in the heart, a reflex, starting from the right auricle, increases the rate of cardiac pulsations, and blood escapes more rapidly from the heart into the vessels. Moreover, serum traverses the wall of the capillaries and inundates connective tissue and muscles. In this manner the circulatory system automatically ejects all excess of fluid. If, on the contrary, the volume and the pressure of the blood diminish, the change is recorded by nerve endings hidden in the wall of the sinus of the carotid artery. This reflex determines a contraction of the vessels and a reduction in the capacity of the circulatory apparatus. At the same time, the fluids of the tissues and those contained in the stomach pass into the vascular system by filtering through the wall of the capillaries. Such are the mechanisms responsible for the nearly perfect constancy of the amount and the tension of the blood.

The composition of the blood is also very stable. Under normal conditions, the quantity of red cells, plasma, salts, proteins, fats, and sugars varies only in a small measure. It always remains higher than is really necessary for the usual requirements of the tissues. Consequently, unforeseen events, such as privation of food, hæmorrhages, or intense and prolonged muscular efforts do not modify in a dangerous manner the state of the organic fluids. The tissues contain abundant reserves of water, salts, fats, proteins, and sugar. Oxygen, however, is not stored anywhere. It must be unceasingly supplied to the blood by the lungs. The organism needs variable quantities of this gas, according to the activity of its chemical exchanges. At the same time it produces more or less carbon dioxide. However, the tension of these gases in the blood remains constant. This phenomenon is due to a mechanism both physico-chemical and physiological. A physico-chemical equilibrium determines the amount of oxygen taken up by the red corpuscles during their passage through the lungs, and carried by those corpuscles to the tissues. During its journey through the peripheral capillary vessels, the blood absorbs the carbon dioxide set free by the tissues. This acid decreases the affinity of hæmoglobin for oxygen. It promotes the passing of the gas from the red corpuscles to the cells of the organs. The exchange of oxygen and carbon dioxide between tissues and blood is due exclusively to the chemical properties of the hæmoglobin, the proteins, and the salts of blood plasma.

A physiological process is responsible for the quantity of oxygen carried by the blood to the tissues. The activity of the respiratory muscles, which give a more or less rapid motion to the thorax and control the penetration of air into the lungs, depends on nervous cells situated in the upper part of the spinal cord. The activity of this centre is regulated by the tension of carbon dioxide in the blood. And also by the temperature of the body and by the excess or insufficiency of oxygen in the circulation. A similar mechanism, both physico-chemical and physiological, regulates the ionic alkalinity of blood plasma. The intra-organic medium never becomes acid. This fact is all the more surprising as tissues unceasingly produce large quantities of carbonic, lactic, sulphuric acid, etc., which are set free into the lymph. These acids do not modify the reaction of blood plasma, because they are neutralized, or rather buffered, by the presence of bicarbonates and phosphates. Although blood plasma can accept a large quantity of acids without increasing its actual acidity, it must, nevertheless, get rid of them. Carbon dioxide escapes from the body by the lungs. Non-volatile acids are eliminated through the kidneys. The discharge of carbon dioxide by the pulmonary mucosa is a mere physico-chemical phenomenon, while the secretion of urine and the motion of the thorax and the lungs require the intervention of physiological processes. The physico-chemical equilibria, which assure the constancy of the organic medium, ultimately depend on the automatic intervention of the nervous system.

3

The organs are correlated by the organic fluids and the nervous system. Each element of the body adjusts itself to the others, and the others to it. This mode of adaptation is essentially teleological. If we attribute to tissues an intelligence of the same kind as ours, as mechanists and vitalists do, the physiological processes appear to associate together in view of the end to be attained. The existence of finality within the organism is undeniable. Each part seems to know the present and future needs of the whole, and acts accordingly. The significance of time and space is not the same for our tissues as for our mind. The body perceives the remote as well as the near, the future as well as the present. When pregnancy is nearly completed the tissues of the vulva and vagina are invaded by fluids. They become soft and extensible. Such a change in their consistency renders the passage of the fœtus possible a few days later. At the same time, the mammary glands multiply their cells. Before confinement, they begin to function. They are ready and waiting to feed the child. All these processes are obviously a preparation for a future event.

When one half of the thyroid gland is removed, the remaining half increases in volume. Generally, it even increases more than is necessary. The organism, as Meltzer has shown, is abundantly provided with factors of safety. In the same way, the extirpation of a kidney is followed by the enlargement of the other one, although the secretion of urine is amply assured by a single normal kidney. If at any time the organism calls upon the thyroid or the kidney for an exceptional effort, these organs will be capable of satisfying the unforeseen demand. During the entire history of the embryo the tissues seem to prepare for the future. Organic correlations take place as easily between different periods of time as between different regions of space. These facts are a primary datum of observation. But they cannot be interpreted with the help of our naïve mechanistic and vitalistic concepts. The teleological correlation of organic processes is evident in the regeneration of blood after a hæmorrhage. First, all the vessels contract. The relative volume of the remaining blood automatically increases. Thus arterial pressure is sufficiently restored for blood circulation to continue. The fluids of the tissues and the muscles pass through the wall of the capillary vessels and invade the circulatory system. The patient feels intense thirst. The blood immediately absorbs the fluids that enter the stomach and re-establishes its normal volume. The reserves of red cells escape from the organs where they were stored. Finally, the bone marrow begins manufacturing red corpuscles, which will complete the regeneration of the blood. In sum, all parts of the body contribute a concatenation of physiological, physico-chemical, and structural phenomena. These phenomena constitute the adaptation of the whole to hæmorrhage.

The component parts of an organ, of the eye, for example, appear to associate for a definite, although future, purpose. The skin covering the young retina becomes transparent, as already mentioned, and metamorphoses into cornea and lens. This transformation is considered as due to substances set free by the cerebral part of the eye, the optic vesicle. But the solution of the problem is not given by this explanation. How does it happen that the optic vesicle secretes a substance endowed with the property of rendering the skin translucid? By what means does the future retina induce the skin to manufacture a lens capable of projecting upon its nerve endings the image of the outer world? In front of the lens the iris shapes itself into a diaphragm. This diaphragm dilates or contracts according to the intensity of the light. At the same time, the sensitivity of the retina increases or decreases. In addition, the form of the lens automatically adjusts itself to near or distant vision. These correlations are obvious facts. But, as yet, they cannot be explained. Possibly they are not what they seem to be. The phenomena may be fundamentally simple. We may miss their oneness. In fact, we divide a whole into parts. And we are astonished that the parts, thus separated, exactly fit each other when they are put together again by our mind. We probably give to things an artificial individuality. Perhaps the frontiers of the organs and of the body are not where we believe them to be located. Neither do we understand the correlations between different individuals, for example, the corresponding existence of the penis and the vagina. Nor the co-operation of two individuals in the same physiological process, such as the fecundation of the egg by the spermatozoon. Those phenomena are not intelligible by the light of our present concepts of individuality, organization, space, and time.

4

When skin, muscles, blood vessels, or bones are injured by a blow, a flame, or a projectile, the organism immediately adapts itself to such a new situation. Everything happens as if a series of measures, some immediate, some delayed, were taken by the body in order to repair the lesions of the tissues. As in blood regeneration, heterogeneous and converging mechanisms come into play. They all turn toward the end to be attained, the reconstruction of the destroyed structures. An artery is cut. Blood gushes in abundance. Arterial pressure is lowered. The patient has a syncope. The hæmorrhage decreases. A clot forms in the wound. Fibrin occludes the opening of the vessel. Then the hæmorrhage definitely stops.

During the following days, leucocytes and tissues cells invade the clot of fibrin and progressively regenerate the wall of the artery. Likewise, the organism may heal a small wound of the intestines by its own means. The wounded loop first becomes immobile. It is temporarily paralyzed, and fæcal matter is thus prevented from running into the abdomen. At the same time, some other intestinal loop, or the surface of the omentum, approaches the wound and, owing to a known property of peritoneum, adheres to it. Within four or five hours the opening is occluded. Even if the surgeon's needle has drawn the edges of the wound together, healing is due to spontaneous adhesion of the peritoneal surfaces.

When a limb is broken by a blow, the sharp ends of the fractured bones tear muscles and blood vessels. They are soon surrounded by a bloody clot of fibrin, and by osseous and muscular debris. Then circulation becomes more active. The limb swells. The nutritive substances necessary for the regeneration of the tissues are brought into the wounded area by the blood. At the seat of the fracture and around it, all structural and functional processes are directed toward repair. Tissues become what they have to be in order to accomplish the common task. For example, a shred of muscle close to the focus of fracture metamorphoses into cartilage. Cartilage, as is well known, is the forerunner of bone in the soft mass temporarily uniting the broken ends. Later, cartilage transforms into osseous tissue. The skeleton is thus regenerated by a substance of exactly the same nature as its own. During the few weeks necessary for the completion of repair, an immense number of chemical, nervous, circulatory, and structural phenomena take place. They are all concatenated. The blood flowing from the vessels at the time of the accident, and the juices from the bone marrow and lacerated muscles, set in motion the physiological processes of regeneration. Each phenomenon results from the preceding one. To the physico-chemical conditions and to the chemical composition of the fluids set free in the tissues must be attributed the actualization within the cells of certain potential properties. And these potential properties give to anatomical structures the power to regenerate. Each tissue is capable of responding, at any moment of the unpredictable future, to all physico-chemical or chemical changes of the intra-organic medium in a manner consistent with the interests of the whole body.

The adaptive aspect of cicatrization is evident in superficial wounds. These wounds are exactly measurable. Their rate of healing can be calculated by Lecomte du Noüy's formulas, and the process of cicatrization thus analyzed. First, we observe that a wound cicatrizes only if cicatrization is advantageous to the body. When the tissues uncovered by the extirpation of the skin are completely protected against microbes, air, and other causes of irritation, regeneration does not take place. In fact, under such conditions it is useless. The wound, therefore, does not heal and remains in its initial state. Such a state is maintained as long as the tissues are guarded against the attacks of the outer world as perfectly as they would be by the regenerated skin. As soon as some blood, a few microbes, or an ordinary dressing is allowed to come in contact with the damaged surface and to irritate it, the process of healing starts and continues irresistibly until cicatrization is complete.

Skin, as we know, consists of superposed sheets of flat cells, the epithelial cells. These cells lie on the dermis—that is, on a soft and elastic layer of connective tissue containing many small blood vessels. When a piece of skin is removed, the bottom of the wound is seen to consist of fatty tissue and muscles. After three or four days its surface becomes smooth, glistening, and red. Then it abruptly begins to decrease with great rapidity. This phenomenon is due to a sort of contraction of the new tissue covering the wound. At the same time the skin cells commence to glide over the red surface as a white edge. Finally, they cover its entire area. A definitive scar is formed. This scar is due to the collaboration of two types of tissue, the connective tissue filling the wound, and the epithelial cells, which advance over its surface from the borders. Connective tissue is responsible for the contraction of the wound; epithelial tissue, for the membrane that ultimately covers it. The progressive decrease of the wounded area in the course of repair is expressed by an exponential curve. However, if one prevents either the epithelial tissue or the connective tissue from accomplishing their respective tasks, the curve does not change. It does not change because the deficiency of one of the factors of repair is compensated by the acceleration of the other. Obviously, the progress of the phenomenon depends on the end to be attained. If one of the regenerating mechanisms fails, it is replaced by the other. The result alone is invariable, and not the procedure. In a like manner, after a hæmorrhage, arterial pressure and blood volume are re-established by two converging mechanisms: on one side, by contraction of the blood vessels and by diminution of their capacity; on the other side, by the bringing of a quantity of liquid from the tissues and the digestive apparatus. But each of these mechanisms is capable of compensating the failure of the other.

5

The knowledge of the processes of healing has brought modern surgery into being. Surgeons would not be able to treat wounds if adaptation did not exist. They have no influence on the healing mechanisms. They content themselves with guiding the spontaneous activity of those mechanisms. For example, they manage to bring the edges of a wound, or the ends of a broken bone, into such a position that regeneration takes place without defective scar and deformity. In order to open a deep abscess, treat an infected fracture, perform a Cæsarean operation, extirpate a uterus, a portion of the stomach ôr of the intestines, or raise the roof of the skull and remove a tumour from the brain, they have to make long incisions and extensive wounds. The most accurate sutures would not suffice definitely to close such openings if the organism were not capable of making its own repairs. Surgery is based on the existence of this phenomenon. It has learned to turn adaptation to account. Owing to the extreme ingeniousness and audacity of its methods, it has surpassed the most ambitious hopes of medicine of former times. Its attainments are the purest triumph of biology. He who has completely mastered its techniques, who understands its spirit, who has acquired the knowledge of human beings and the science of their diseases, truly becomes like God. He possesses the power to open the body, explore the organs, and repair their lesions, almost without risk to the patient. To many people he restores strength, health, and the joy of living. Even to those tortured by incurable diseases, he is always capable of bringing some relief. Men of such type are rare. But their number could easily be increased by a better technical, moral, and scientific education.

The reason behind such success is simple. Surgery has merely learned that the normal processes of healing must not be hindered. It has succeeded in preventing microbes from getting into wounds. Operations, before the discoveries of Pasteur and Lister, were always followed by invasion of bacteria. Such attacks caused suppuration, gaseous gangrene, and infection of the whole body. They often ended in death. Modern techniques have practically eliminated microbes from operative wounds. In this manner they save the life of the patient and lead him to a rapid recovery, For microbes have the power to obstruct or delay adaptive processes and repair. As soon as wounds were protected against bacteria surgery began to grow. Its methods rapidly developed in the hands of Ollier, Billroth, Kocher, and their contemporaries. In a quarter of a century of stupendous progress they blossomed into the mighty art of Halsted, Tuffier, Harvey Cushing, the Mayos and of all the great modern surgeons.

This success came from the clear understanding of certain adaptive phenomena. It is indispensable, not only to preserve the wounds from infection, but also to respect, in the course of operative handling, their structural and functional conditions. Tissues are endangered by most antiseptic substances. They must not be crushed by forceps, compressed by appliances, or pulled about by the fingers of a brutal operator. Halsted and the surgeons of his school have shown how delicately wounds must be treated if they are to keep intact their regenerative power. The result of an operation depends both on the state of the tissues and on that of the patient. Modern techniques take into consideration every factor capable of modifying physiological and mental activities. The patient is protected against the dangers of fear, cold, and anæsthesia, as well as against infection, nervous shock, and hæmorrhages. And if, through some mistake, infection sets in, it can be effectively dealt with. Some day, perhaps, when the nature of healing processes is better known, it will become possible to increase their rapidity. The rate of repair, as we know, varies according to definite qualities of the humours, and especially to their youthfulness. If such qualities could temporarily be given to the blood and the tissues of the patient, recovery from surgical operations would be made much easier. Certain chemical substances are known to accelerate cell multiplication. Possibly, they will be utilized for this purpose. Each step forward in the knowledge of the mechanisms of regeneration will bring about a corresponding progress in surgery. But in the best hospital, as in the desert or the primitive forest, the healing of wounds depends, above all, on the efficiency of the adaptive functions.

6

All organic functions are modified as soon as microbes or viruses cross the frontiers of the body and invade the tissues. Illness sets in. Its characteristics depend on the mode of adjustment of the tissues to the pathological changes of their medium. For instance, fever is the reply of the body to the presence of bacteria and viruses. Other adaptive reactions are determined by the production of poisons by the organism itself, the lack of certain substances indispensable to nutrition, and the disturbances in the activities of various glands. The symptoms of Bright's disease, of scurvy, of exophthalmic goitre, express the accommodation of the organism to substances which diseased kidneys are no longer able to eliminate, to the absence of a vitamin, to the secretion of toxic products by the thyroid gland. The accommodation to pathogenic agents assumes two different aspects. On one side, it opposes their invasion of the body and tends to bring about their destruction. On the other, it repairs the lesions the organism has suffered, and causes the poisons generated by the bacteria or by the tissues themselves to disappear. Disease is nothing but the development of these processes. It is equivalent to the struggle of the body against a disturbing agent and to its effort to persist in time. But it may be, as in cancer or insanity, the expression of the passive decay of an organ, or of consciousness.

Microbes and viruses are to be found everywhere, in the air, in water, in our food. They are always present at the surface of the skin, and of the digestive and respiratory mucosas. Nevertheless, in many people they remain inoffensive. Among human beings, some are subject to diseases, and others are immune. Such a state of resistance is due to the individual constitution of the tissues and the humours, which oppose the penetration of pathogenic agents or destroy them when they have invaded our body. This is natural immunity. This form of immunity may preserve certain individuals from

almost any disease. It is one of the most precious qualities
for which man could wish. We are still ignorant of its nature.
It appears to depend on some properties of ancestral origin,
as well as on others acquired in the course of development.
Certain families are observed to be susceptible to tuberculosis, appendicitis, cancer, or mental disorders. Others
resist all diseases except the degenerative ones occurring during old age. But natural immunity does not exclusively derive from our ancestral constitution. It may come also from
the mode of life and alimentation, as Reid Hunt showed long
ago. Some diets were found to increase the susceptibility of
mice to experimental typhoid fever. The frequency of pneumonia may also be modified by food. The mice belonging to
one of the strains kept in the mousery of the Rockefeller Institute died of pneumonia in the proportion of fifty-two per
cent while subjected to the standard diet. Several groups of
these animals were given different diets. The mortality from
pneumonia fell to thirty-two per cent, fourteen per cent,
and even zero, according to the food. We should ascertain
whether natural resistance to infections could be conferred on
man by definite conditions of life. Injections of specific vaccine or serum for each disease, repeated medical examinations of the whole population, construction of gigantic
hospitals, are expensive and not very effective means of preventing diseases and of developing a nation's health. Good
health should be natural. Such innate resistance gives the
individual a strength, a boldness, which he does not possess
when his survival depends on physicians.

In addition to an inherent resistance to maladies there is
also an acquired resistance. The latter may be spontaneous
or artificial. The organism is known to adapt itself to bacteria and viruses by the production of substances capable of
directly or indirectly destroying the invaders. Thus diphtheria, typhoid fever, smallpox, measles, etc., render their
victims immune to a second attack of the disease, at least for
some time. This spontaneous immunity expresses the adap-

tation of the organism to a new situation. If a fowl is injected with the serum of a rabbit, the serum of the fowl acquires, after a few days, the property of bringing about an abundant precipitate in the serum of the rabbit. In this way the fowl has been rendered immune to the albumins of the rabbit. Likewise, when bacterial toxins are injected into an animal, this animal produces antitoxins. The phenomenon becomes more complex if the bacteria themselves are injected. These bacteria compel the animal to manufacture substances by which they are agglutinated and destroyed. At the same time, the leucocytes of blood and tissues acquire the power of devouring them, as was discovered by Metchnikoff. Independent phenomena, whose effects are converging, take place under the influence of the pathogenic agent and bring about the destruction of the invading microbes. These processes are endowed with the same characteristics of simplicity, complexity, and finality as other physiological processes.

The adaptive responses of the organism are due to definite chemical substances. Certain polysaccharids, present in the bodies of bacteria, determine specific reactions of the cells and the humours when they are united with a protein. Instead of the polysaccharids of the bacteria, the tissues of our body manufacture some carbohydrates and lipoids, which possess similar properties. These substances give to the organism the power to attack foreign proteins or foreign cells. In the same way as the microbes, the cells of an animal determine in the organism of another animal the appearance of antibodies, and those cells are finally destroyed by their antibodies. For this reason the transplantation into a man of a chimpanzee's testicles is not successful. The existence of these adaptive reactions has led to vaccination and to the use of therapeutic serums; ultimately, to artificial immunity. A great quantity of antibodies develops in the blood of an animal injected with dead or attenuated microbes, viruses, or bacterial poisons. The serum of the animal rendered immune to a disease may sometimes cure patients suffering from the disease in question. It supplies their blood with the antitoxic antibacterial substances which are lacking. Thus it gives them the power, which most individuals do not possess, to overcome the infection.

7

Either alone or with the aid of specific serums and of nonspecific chemical and physical medications, the patient fights against the invading microbes. Meanwhile, lymph and blood are modified by poisons set free by the bacteria and by the waste products of the diseased organism. Profound alterations take place in the whole body. Fever, delirium, and acceleration of the chemical exchanges occur. In dangerous infections, in typhoid fever, pneumonia, and septicæmias, for instance, lesions develop in various organs, such as heart, lungs, and liver. The cells then actualize certain properties which, in ordinary life, remain potential. They tend to render the humours deleterious to bacteria, and to stimulate all organic activities. The leucocytes multiply, secrete new substances, undergo precisely such metamorphoses as are needed by the tissues, adapt themselves to the unforeseen conditions created by the pathogenic factors, the defection of organs, the virulence of bacteria, and their local accumulation. They form abscesses in the infected regions, and the ferments contained in the pus of the abscesses digest the microbes. These ferments also possess the power of dissolving living tissues. They thus open a way for the abscess, either toward the skin or some hollow organ. In this manner, pus is eliminated from the body. The symptoms of bacterial diseases express the effort made by tissues and humours to adapt themselves to the new conditions, to resist them, and to return to a normal state.

In degenerative diseases, such as arteriosclerosis, myocarditis, nephritis, diabetes, and cancer, and those due to alimentary deficiencies, the adaptive functions likewise enter into play. The physiological processes become modified in the manner best suited to the survival of the organism. If the secretion of a gland is insufficient, some other glands augment their activity and volume in order to supplement its work. When the valve protecting the orifice of communication of the left auricle and ventricle allows the blood to flow back, the heart increases in size and strength. Thus, it succeeds in pumping into the aorta an almost normal quantity of blood. This adaptive phenomenon enables the patient to continue to lead a normal existence for several years. When the kidneys are impaired, the arterial pressure rises in order that a larger volume of blood may pass through the defective filter. During the first stage of diabetes, the organism endeavours to compensate the decrease in the quantity of insulin secreted by the pancreas. These diseases generally represent an attempt made by the body to adapt itself to a defective function.

There are pathogenic agents against which the tissues do not react, which do not elicit any response from the adaptive mechanisms. Such is, for instance, *Treponema pallidum*, the agent of syphilis. Once *Treponema* has penetrated the body, it never spontaneously leaves its victim. It takes up its abode in the skin, the blood vessels, the brain, or the bones. Neither the cells nor the humours are able to destroy it. Syphilis yields only to prolonged treatment. Likewise, cancer meets with no opposition from the organism. Tumours, whether benign or malignant, are so much like normal tissues that the body is not aware of their presence. They often develop in individuals who for a long time show no evidence of being affected. The symptoms, when they appear, are not the expression of a reaction of the organism. They are the direct result of the misdoings of the tumour, of its toxic products, of the destruction of an essential organ, or of the compression of a nerve. The progress of cancer is inexorable, because tissues and humours do not react against the invasion of the diseased cells.

In the course of an illness, the body meets with situations never previously encountered. It tends, nevertheless, to adapt itself to these new conditions by eliminating the pathogenic agents and repairing the lesions they have caused. In the absence of such adaptive power, living beings could not endure, because they are ceaselessly exposed to the attacks of viruses or bacteria, and to the structural failure of innumerable elements of the organic systems. An individual's survival was formerly wholly due to his adaptive capacity. Modern civilization, with the help of hygiene, comfort, good food, soft living, hospitals, physicians, and nurses, has kept alive many human beings of poor quality. These weaklings and their descendants contribute, in a large measure, to the enfeeblement of the white races. We should perhaps renounce this artificial form of health and exclusively pursue natural health, which results from the excellence of the adaptive functions and from the inherent resistance to disease.

8

Extra-organic adaption consists in the adjustment of the inner state of the body to the variations of the environment. This adjustment is brought about by the mechanisms responsible for stabilizing physiological and mental activities, and for giving the body its unity. To each change of the surroundings the adaptive functions furnish an appropriate reply. Man can, therefore, stand the modifications of the outside world. The atmosphere is always either warmer or colder than the skin. Nevertheless, the temperature of the humours bathing the tissues, and of the blood circulating in the vessels, remains unchanged. Such a phenomenon depends on the continuous work of the entire organism. Our temperature has a tendency to rise with that of the atmosphere, or when our chemical exchanges become more active, as, for instance, in fever. Pulmonary circulation and respiratory movements then accelerate. A larger quantity of water is evaporated from the pulmonary alveoli. Consequently, the temperature of the blood in the lungs is lowered. At the same time, the subcutaneous vessels dilate and the skin becomes red. The blood rushes to the surface of the body and cools by contact with atmospheric air. If the air is too warm, the skin becomes covered by thin streams of perspiration produced by the sweat glands. This perspiration, in evaporating, brings about a fall in the temperature. The central nervous system and the sympathetic nerves come into play. They increase the rapidity of cardiac pulsations, dilate blood-vessels, bring on the sensation of thirst, etc. On the contrary, when the outer temperature falls, the vessels of the skin contract, and the skin itself becomes white. The blood circulates sluggishly in the capillaries. It takes refuge in the inner organs whose circulation and chemical exchange are accelerated. Thus we fight external cold, as we fight heat, by nervous, circulatory, and nutritive changes of our whole body. All the organs, as well as the skin, are maintained in constant activity by exposure to heat, cold, wind, sun, and rain. When we spend our life sheltered from the inclemencies of the weather, the processes regulating the temperature of the blood, its volume, its alkalinity, etc., are rendered useless.

We become adapted to excitations emanating from the outer world, even when their violence or their weakness modifies, in an exaggerated or insufficient manner, the nerve endings of the sense organs. Excessive light is dangerous. In primitive surroundings men instinctively hide from it. There is a large number of mechanisms capable of protecting the organism from sun rays. The eye is defended by the eyelids and the diaphragm of the iris against any increase in light intensity. Simultaneously, the retina becomes less sensible. The skin opposes the penetration of solar radiations by manufacturing pigment. When these natural defences are insufficient, lesions of the retina or of the skin occur, and also certain disorders of the viscera and the nervous system. It is possible that lessened reactivity of the nervous system and of the intelligence may eventually result from too strong a light. We must not forget that the most highly civilized races—the Scandinavians, for example—are white, and have lived for many generations in a country where the atmospheric luminosity is weak during a great part of the year. In France the populations of the north are far superior to those of the Mediterranean shores. The lower races generally inhabit countries where light is violent and temperature equal and warm. It seems that the adaptation of white men to light and to heat takes place at the expense of their nervous and mental development.

In addition to light rays, the nervous system receives from the cosmic world various excitations. These stimuli are sometimes strong, sometimes weak. Man may be compared to a photographic plate, which must record different intensities of light in the same way. The effect of light on the plate is regulated by a diaphragm and a proper duration of exposure. The organism uses another method. Its adaptation to the unequal intensity of the excitations is obtained by an increase or a decrease of its receptivity. It is well known that the retina becomes much less sensitive when exposed to intense light. Likewise, the mucosa of the nose, after a short time, no longer perceives a bad odour. An intense noise, if produced continuously or at a uniform rhythm, causes little inconvenience. The roaring of the ocean as it pounds the rocks, or the rumbling of a train, does not disturb our sleep. We chiefly notice variations in the intensity of the excitations. Weber thought that, when stimulus increases in geometrical progression, sensation increases only in arithmetical progression. The intensity of sensation augments, therefore, much more slowly than that of excitation. Since we are affected, not by the absolute intensity of a stimulus, but by the difference in intensity of two successive excitations, such mechanism effectively protects our nervous system. Weber's law, although not exact, approximately expresses what takes place. However, the adaptive mechanisms of our nervous systems are not as developed as those of the other organic apparatuses. Civilization has created new stimuli against which we have no defence. Our organism tries in vain to adapt itself to the noises of the large cities and factories, to the agitation of modern life, the worries and the crowding of our days. We do not get used to lack of sleep. We are incapable of resisting hypnotic poisons, such as opium or cocaine. Strange to say, we adjust ourselves without suffering to most of these conditions. But such adjustment is far from being a victorious adaptation. It brings about organic and mental changes, which are equivalent to a degradation of civilized man.

9

Permanent modifications of body and consciousness may be produced by adaptation. In this manner environment stamps human beings with its mark. When young people are subjected to its influence over lengthy periods, they may be indelibly modified by it. Thus new structural and mental aspects appear in the individual and also in the race. It seems that environment gradually affects the cells of the sexual glands. Such modifications are naturally hereditary. Indeed, the individual does not transmit his acquired characteristics to his descendants. But when in the course of life his humours are modified by the environment, his sexual tissues may adapt themselves, by corresponding structural changes, to the state of their humoral medium. For instance, the plants, trees, animals, and men of Normandy differ greatly from those of Brittany. They bear the specific mark of the soil. In former times, when the food of the inhabitants of a village consisted exclusively of local products, the aspect of

G*

the population showed still greater differences from one province to another.

Adaptation of animals to thirst and to hunger is easily noticeable. The cattle of the Arizona deserts can go three or four days without water. A dog may remain fat and in perfect health, although eating only twice a week. Animals unable to quench their thirst except at rare intervals learn to drink abundantly. They adapt their tissues to store large quantities of water over lengthy periods. Likewise, those subjected to fasting become accustomed to absorbing in one or two days enough food for the rest of the week. It is the same with sleep. We can train ourselves to do without sleep or to sleep very little during some periods, and a great deal during others. We indulge quite easily in an excess of nourishment and of drink. If a child is given as much food as he can absorb, he rapidly gets used to eating exaggerated quantities. Later on he finds it very difficult to break himself of the habit. All the organic and mental consequences of alimentary excesses are not yet exactly understood. They seem to be manifested by an increase in the volume and the height of the body, and by a decrease in its general activity. A similar phenomenon occurs in wild rabbits when they become transformed into domestic rabbits. It is not certain that the standardized habits of modern life lead to the optimum development of human beings. The present ways of living have been adopted because they are easy and pleasant. Indeed, they differ profoundly from those of our ancestors and of the human groups which have so far resisted industrial civilization. We do not know, as yet, whether they are better or worse.

Man becomes acclimatized to high altitudes through certain modifications of his blood and of his circulatory, respiratory, skeletal, and muscular systems. The red corpuscles respond to the lowering of the barometric pressure by multiplying. Adaptation rapidly takes place. In a few weeks, soldiers transported to the summits of the Alps walk, climb, and run as actively as at lower altitudes. At the same time, the skin produces a great deal of pigment as a protection against the glare of the snow. The thorax and the muscles of the chest develop markedly. After some months in the high mountains, the muscular system is inured to the greater efforts required for active life. The shape and the posture of the body become modified. The circulatory apparatus and the heart accustom themselves to the ceaseless work they are called upon to do. The processes that regulate the temperature of the blood improve. The organism learns to resist cold and to support easily all inclemencies of the weather. When mountaineers descend to the plains, the number of their blood corpuscles becomes normal. But the adaptation of the thorax, lungs, heart, and vessels to a rarefied atmosphere, to the effects of cold, to the exertions made in the daily ascent of mountains, leaves its mark forever on the body. Intense muscular activity also brings about permanent changes. For example, on the Western ranches, the cowpunchers acquire strength, resistance, and litheness such as no athlete ever attains in the comfort of a modern university. It is the same with intellectual work. Man is indelibly marked by prolonged and intense mental struggle. This type of activity is almost impossible in the state of mechanization reached by education. It can only take place in small groups, such as that of the first disciples of Pasteur, inspired by an ardent ideal, by the will to know. The young men who gathered around Welch, at the beginning of his career at the Johns Hopkins University, have been strengthened during their whole lives and made greater by the intellectual discipline into which they were initiated under his guidance.

There is also a more subtle, less known aspect of the adaptation of organic and mental activities to environment. It consists of the response of the body to the chemical substances contained in the food. We know that in countries where water is rich in calcium, the skeleton becomes heavier than it does in regions where the water is quite pure. We also know that individuals fed on milk, eggs, vegetables, and cereals differ from those fed mostly on meat, that many substances may influence the shape of the body and consciousness. But we ignore the mechanism of this adaptation. Endocrine glands and nervous system probably become modified according to the forms of alimentation. Mental activities seem to vary with the constitution of the tissues. It is not wise to follow blindly the doctrines of physicians and hygienists, whose horizon is limited to their specialty—that is, to one aspect of the individual. The progress of man certainly will not come from an increase in weight, or in longevity.

It seems that the work of the adaptive mechanisms stimulates all organic functions. A temporary change of climate is of benefit to debilitated individuals and to convalescents. Some variations in the mode of life, in food, sleep, and habitat, are useful. The accommodation to new conditions of existence momentarily increases the activity of physiological and mental processes. The rate of adaptation to any factor depends on the rhythm of physiological time. Children respond immediately to a change of climate; adults, much more slowly. In order to produce lasting results, the action of the environment must be prolonged. During youth, a new country and new habits are able to determine permanent adaptive changes. For this reason, conscription greatly helps the development of the body by imposing on each individual a new type of life, certain exercises, and a certain discipline. Rougher conditions of existence and more responsibility would restore moral energy and audacity to the majority of those who have lost them. More virile habits should be substituted for the uniformity and softness of life in schools and universities. The adaptation of the individual to a physiological, intellectual, and moral discipline determines definite changes in the nervous system, the endocrine glands, and the mind. The organism acquires, in this way, a better integration, greater vigour, and more ability to overcome the difficulties and dangers of existence.

10

Man adapts himself to social environment as to physical environment. Mental activities, like physiological activities, tend to become modified in the way best suited to the survival of the body. They determine our adjustment to our surroundings. The individual does not generally get without effort the position he covets in the group of which he is a member. He wants wealth, knowledge, power, pleasures. He is driven by his greed, his ambition, his curiosity, his sexual appetite. But he finds himself in an environment always indifferent, sometimes hostile. He quickly realizes that he must fight for what he wants. His mode of reaction to his social surroundings depends on his specific constitution. Some people become accommodated to the world by conquering it, others by escaping from it. Still others refuse to accept its rules. The natural attitude of the individual toward his fellow men is one of strife. Consciousness responds to the enmity of the environment by an effort directed against it. Intelligence and cunning then develop, as well as the desire to learn, the will to work, to possess, and to dominate. The passion for conquest assumes diverse aspects according to individuals and circumstances. It inspires all great adventures. Such passion led Pasteur to the renovation of medicine, Mussolini to the building up of a great nation, Einstein to the creation of a universe. The same spirit drives the modern human being to robbery, to murder, and to the great financial and economic enterprises characterizing our civilization. But its impulse also builds hospitals, laboratories, universities, and churches. It impels men to fortune and to death, to heroism and to crime; but never to happiness.

The second mode of adaptation is flight. Some abandon the struggle and descend to a social level where competition is no longer necessary. They become factory workers, proletarians. Others take refuge within their own self. At the same time they can adapt themselves, in some measure, to the social group, and even conquer it through the superiority of their intelligence. But they do not fight. They are members of the community only in appearance. In fact, they live in an inner world of their own. Still others forget their surroundings in ceaseless toil. Those who are obliged to work uninterruptedly accommodate themselves to all events. A woman whose child dies, and who has to look after several other children, has no time to brood over her grief. Work is more effective than alcohol and morphine in helping people to bear adverse conditions. Certain individuals spend their lives in dreaming, in hoping for fortune, health, and happiness. Illusions and hope are also a powerful means of adaptation. Hope generates action. It is rightly looked upon by Christian morals as a great virtue. It contributes in a powerful manner to the adjustment of the individual to unfavourable circumstances. Habit is another aspect of adaptation. Sorrows are more quickly forgotten than joys. But inaction augments all sufferings.

Many people never adjust themselves to the social group. Among those unadapted are the feeble-minded. Except in special institutions they have no place in modern society. A number of normal children are born in the families of degenerates and criminals. In such a mould they shape their body and their consciousness. They become unadaptable to normal life. They supply the prisons with most of their inmates. They also constitute the far larger population that remains free to live by burglary and murder. These human beings are the fatal result of physiological and moral degradation brought about by industrial civilization. They are irresponsible. Irresponsible, also, is the youth brought up in modern schools by teachers ignorant of the necessity for effort, for intellectual concentration, for moral discipline. Later on in life, when these young men and women encounter the indifference of the world, the material and mental difficulties of existence, they are incapable of adaptation, save by asking for relief, for protection, for doles, and, if relief cannot thus be obtained, by crime. Although having strong muscles, they are deprived of nervous and moral resistance. They shrink from effort and privation. In periods of stress they demand food and shelter from their parents or from the community. Like the offspring of the wretched and the criminals, they are unfit to have a place in the new city.

Certain forms of modern life lead directly to degeneration. There are social conditions as fatal to white men as are warm and humid climates. We react to poverty, anxieties, and sorrows by working and struggling. We can stand tyranny, revolution, and war, but we are not able to fight successfully against misery or prosperity. The individual and the race are weakened by extreme poverty. Wealth is just as dangerous. Nevertheless, there are still families which, in spite of having had money and power for centuries, have kept their strength. But, in former times, power and money derived from the ownership of land. To hold the land required struggle, administrative ability, and leadership. This indispensable effort prevented degeneration. To-day, wealth does not bring in its train any responsibility toward the community. Irresponsibility, even in the absence of wealth, is harmful. In the poor, as well as in the rich, leisure engenders degeneration. Cinemas, concerts, radios, automobiles, and athletics are no substitutes for intelligent work. We are far from having solved this momentous problem of idleness created by prosperity, modern machinery, or unemployment. By imposing leisure upon man, scientific civilization has brought him great misfortune. We are as incapable of fighting the consequences of indolence and irresponsibility as cancer and mental diseases.

II

Adaptive functions assume as many different aspects as tissues and humours encounter new situations. They are not the particular expression of any organic system. They are definable only by their end. Their means vary, but their end always remains the same. Such an end is the survival of the individual. Adaptation, considered in its various manifestations and its oneness, appears as an agent of stabilization and organic repair, as the cause of the moulding of organs by function, as the link that integrates tissues and humours in a whole enduring in spite of the attacks of the outer world. Thus it appears as an entity. This abstraction is convenient for describing its characteristics. In fact, adaptation is an aspect of all physiological processes and of their physicochemical components.

When a system is in equilibrium, and a factor tends to modify the equilibrium, there occurs a reaction that opposes this factor. If sugar is dissolved in water, the temperature falls, and the lowering of the temperature diminishes the solubility of sugar. Such is the principle of Le Chatelier. When violent muscular exercise greatly increases the quantity of venous blood flowing into the heart, the central nervous system is informed of this event by the nerves of the right auricle. At once it determines an acceleration of the cardiac pulsations. The excess of venous blood is thus carried away. There is only a superficial analogy between the principle of Le Chatelier and such physiological adaptation. In the first case, an equilibrium is maintained by physical means. In the second case, a steady state, and not an equilibrium, persists with the help of physiological processes. If, instead of blood, a tissue modifies its state, a similar phenomenon occurs. The extirpation of a fragment of skin sets in motion a complex reaction which, through converging mechanisms, brings about the repair of the lesion. In both instances, the excess of venous blood and the wound are the factors tending to modify the state of the organism. These factors are opposed by a concatenation of physiological processes leading, in the first case, to acceleration of the heart and, in the second case, to cicatrization.

The more a muscle works, the more it develops. Activity

strengthens it, instead of wearing it out. An organ atrophies when not used. It is a primary datum of observation that physiological and mental functions are improved by work, also that effort is indispensable to the optimum development of the individual. Like muscles and organs, intelligence and moral sense become atrophied for want of exercise. The law of effort is still more important than the law of the constancy of the organic states. Steadiness of the inner medium is, without any doubt, indispensable to the survival of the organism. But the physiological and mental progress of the individual depends on his functional activity and on his efforts. We become adapted to the lack of use of our organic and mental systems by degenerating.

Adaptation employs multiple processes to attain its end. It never localizes in one region or one organ. It mobilizes the entire body. For example, anger profoundly modifies all the organic apparatus. The muscles contract. The sympathetic nerves and the suprarenal glands come into action. Their intervention brings about an increase of the blood pressure, an acceleration of the heart pulsations, the setting free by the liver of glucose, which will be used by the muscles as fuel. In a like manner, when the body strives against outside cold, its circulatory, respiratory, digestive, muscular, and nervous apparatuses are forced to act. In sum, the organism responds to changes in the outer world by setting in motion all its activities. The exercise of adaptive functions is as necessary to the development of body and consciousness as physical effort to that of the muscles. Accommodation to inclemency of the weather, to lack of sleep, to fatigue, and to hunger stimulates every physiological process. In order to reach his optimum state, the human being must actualize all his potentialities.

Adaptive phenomena always tend toward a certain end. But they do not always attain their goal. They do not work accurately. They operate within certain limits. Each individual withstands only a given number of bacteria and a given virulence of these bacteria. Beyond such number and virulence, the adaptive functions become insufficient to protect the body. Disease breaks out. It is the same with resistance to fatigue, to heat, or to cold. There is no doubt that adaptive power, as well as other physiological activities, increases with exercise. Like these activities, it is perfectible. Instead of preventing diseases only by protecting the individual against their agents, we must, by artificially increasing the efficiency of his adaptive functions, render each man capable of protecting himself.

To summarize. We have considered adaptation as an expression of fundamental properties of the tissues, as an aspect of nutrition. Physiological processes are modified in as many different ways as new and unforeseen situations occur. Strange to say, they shape themselves for the goal to be attained. They do not seem to estimate time and space in the same manner as our intelligence does. The tissues organize with equal ease relative to spatial configurations already existing and to those which do not as yet exist. During embryonic growth the retina and the lens associate for the benefit of the still potential eye. Adaptability is a property of the components of tissues, as well as of the tissues themselves and of the entire organism. Individual cells appear to act in the interest of the whole, just as bees work for the good of the hive. They seem to know the future. And they prepare for this future by anticipated changes of their structure and functions.

12

We utilize our adaptive functions much less than our ancestors did. For a quarter of a century, especially, we have accommodated ourselves to our environment through mechanisms created by our intelligence, and no longer through physiological mechanisms. Science has supplied us with means for keeping our intra-organic equilibrium, which are more agreeable and less laborious than the natural processes. We have mentioned how the physical conditions of our daily life are prevented from varying; how muscular exercise, food, and sleep are standardized; how modern civilization has done away with effort and moral responsibility, and transformed the modes of activity of our muscular, nervous, circulatory, and glandular systems.

We have also drawn attention to the fact that the inhabitants of the modern city no longer suffer from changes of atmospheric temperature, that they are protected by modern houses, clothes, and automobiles, that during the winter they are not subjected, as their ancestors were, to alternatives of prolonged cold and of brutal heat from stoves and open fireplaces. The organism does not have to fight cold by setting in motion the chain of the associated physiological processes, which increase the chemical exchanges and modify the circulation of all the tissues. When an individual, insufficiently clothed, has to maintain his inner temperature by violent exercise, all his organic systems work with great intensity. On the contrary, these systems remain in a condition of repose if cold weather is fought by furs and warm clothing, by the heating apparatus of a closed car, or by the walls of a steam-heated room. The skin of modern man is never whipped by the wind. It never has to defend itself for long and tiring hours against snow, rain, or sun. In former times the mechanisms responsible for regulating the temperature of blood and humours were maintained in constant activity by the struggle against the rigours of the weather. To-day they are in a state of perpetual rest. However, their work is probably indispensable to the optimum development of the body and the mind. We must realize that the adaptive functions do not correspond to a particular structure which, when not needed, could be dispensed with. They are, on the contrary, the expression of the whole body.

Muscular effort has not been completely eliminated from

modern life, but it is not frequent. It has been replaced in our daily existence by that of machines. Muscles are now used only in athletic games. Their mode of acting is standardized and subjected to arbitrary rules. It is doubtful whether these artificial exercises completely replace the hardships of a more primitive condition of life. For women, dancing and playing tennis for a few hours every week are not the equivalent of the effort required to climb up and down stairs, to carry out their domestic duties without the help of machines, to walk along the streets. Nowadays, they live in houses provided with an elevator, walk with difficulty on high heels, and almost constantly use an automobile or a trolley car. It is the same with men. Golf on Saturdays and Sundays does not compensate for the complete inaction of the rest of the week. By doing away with muscular effort in daily life, we have suppressed, without being aware of it, the ceaseless exercise required from our organic systems in order that the constancy of the inner medium be maintained. As is well known, muscles, when they work, consume sugar and oxygen, produce heat, and pour lactic acid into the circulating blood. To adapt itself to these changes, the organisms must set in action the heart, the respiratory apparatus, the liver, the pancreas, the kidneys, the sweat glands, and the cerebrospinal and sympathetic systems. In sum, the intermittent exercises of modern man, such as golf and tennis, are not equivalent to the continuous muscular activity required by the existence of our ancestors. To-day, physical effort only takes place at certain moments and on certain days. The customary state of the organic systems, of blood vessels, of sweat and endocrine glands, is that of repose.

The usage of the digestive functions has also been modified. Hard foods, such as stale bread or tough meat, are no longer permitted in our diet. Likewise, physicians have forgotten that jaws are made to grind resistant matter, and that the stomach is constructed to digest natural products. As previously mentioned, children are fed chiefly on soft, mashed, pulped food, and milk. Their jaws, their teeth, and the muscles of their face are not subjected to sufficiently hard work. It is the same with the muscles and glands of their digestive apparatus. The frequency, the regularity, and the abundance of meals render useless an adaptive function that has played an important part in the survival of human races, the adaptation to lack of food. In primitive life men were subjected to long periods of fasting. When want did not compel them to starve, they voluntarily deprived themselves of food. All religions have insisted upon the necessity of fasting. Privation of food at first brings about a sensation of hunger, occasionally some nervous stimulation, and later a feeling of weakness. But it also determines certain hidden phenomena which are far more important. The sugar of the liver, the fat of the subcutaneous deposits, are mobilized, and also the proteins of the muscles and the glands. All the organs sacrifice their own substances in order to maintain blood, heart, and brain in a normal condition. Fasting purifies and profoundly modifies our tissues.

Modern man sleeps too much or not enough. He does not easily adapt himself to too much sleep. He fares still worse if he sleeps too little during prolonged periods. It is, however, useful to accustom oneself to remain awake when one wants to sleep. The struggle against sleep sets in motion organic apparatuses whose strength develops by exercise. It also calls for an effort of the will. This effort, together with many others, has been suppressed by modern habits. In spite of the restlessness of existence, the false activity of sports and rapid transportation, the great organic systems responsible for our adaptive functions remain idle. In short, the mode of life created by scientific civilization has rendered useless a number of mechanisms whose activities had never ceased during the millennia of the existence of the human race.

13

The exercise of the adaptive functions appears to be indispensable to the optimum development of man. Our body is placed in a physical medium whose conditions are variable. The constancy of our inner states is maintained through ceaseless organic activity. Such activity is not localized in a single system. It extends to the entire body. All our anatomical apparatuses react against the outside world in the sense most favourable to our survival. Is it possible that such a fundamental property may remain virtual without inconvenience to our body? Are we not organized to live under changing and irregular conditions? Man attains his highest development when he is exposed to the rigours of the seasons, when he sometimes goes without sleep and sometimes sleeps for long hours, when his meals are sometimes abundant and sometimes scanty, when he conquers food and shelter at the price of strenuous efforts. He has also to train his muscles, to tire himself and rest, to fight, suffer, and be happy, to love and to hate. His will needs alternately to strain and to relax. He must strive against his fellow men or against himself. He is made for such an existence, just as the stomach is made for digesting food. When his adaptive processes work most intensely, he develops his virility to the fullest extent. It is a primary datum of observation that hardships make for nervous resistance and health. We know how strong physically and morally are those who, since childhood, have been submitted to intelligent discipline, who have endured some privations and adapted themselves to adverse conditions.

However, we observe human beings who develop fully even though they are not obliged by poverty to fight against their environment. But these individuals are also moulded by adaptation, although in a different way. Generally, they have imposed upon themselves, or have accepted from others, a discipline, a sort of asceticism, which has protected them against the deleterious effects of wealth and leisure. The

sons of feudal lords were subjected to a hard physical and
moral training. One of Brittany's heroes, Bertrand du
Guesclin, compelled himself every day to face the inclemencies of the weather and to fight with children of his own age.
Although small and ill-formed, he acquired such endurance
and strength as are still legendary. During the early period
of the development of the United States, the men who built
the railways, laid the foundations of the large industries,
and opened the West to civilization, triumphed over all obstacles by their will and their audacity. To-day most of the
sons of these great men possess wealth, without having had
to earn it. They have never struggled against their environment. Generally, they lack the ancestral strength. A similar
phenomenon occurred in Europe among the descendants of
the feudal aristocracy and of the great financiers and manufacturers of the nineteenth century.

The effect of the deficiencies of adaptation upon the development of man is not as yet completely known. In the
large cities there are many individuals whose adaptive activities are permanently at rest. Sometimes the consequences of
this phenomenon become obvious. They manifest themselves especially in the children of rich families, and, likewise, in those who are brought up in the same way as the
rich. From their birth, these children live under conditions
that bring about the atrophy of their adaptive systems. They
are kept in warm rooms and, when they go out, dressed like
little Eskimos. They are crammed with food, they sleep as
much as they like, have no responsibility, never make an intellectual or moral effort, learn only what amuses them, and
struggle against nothing. The result is well known. They
generally become pleasant and handsome, often strong,
easily tired, extremely selfish, without intellectual acuteness,
moral sense, and nervous resistance. These defects are not of
ancestral origin. They are observed in the descendants of the
men who built up American industries, as well as in those of
the newcomers. Obviously, a function as important as adap-

tation cannot be left in disuse with impunity. The law of the struggle for life must, above all, be obeyed. Degeneration of body and soul is the price paid by the individuals and the races who have forgotten the existence of this law.

As optimum development requires the activity of all organic systems, a decrease in the value of man necessarily follows the decay of the adaptive functions. In the process of education, these functions must be kept constantly at work. Each one of them is equally useful. Muscles are no more important than brains. They only contribute strength and harmony to the body. Instead of training athletes, we have to construct modern men. And modern men need more nervous resistance, intelligence, and moral energy than muscular power. The acquisition of these qualities calls for effort, struggle, and discipline. It also demands that human beings should not be exposed to conditions of existence to which they are unadaptable. Apparently there is no adaptation possible to ceaseless agitation, intellectual dispersion, alcoholism, precocious sexual excesses, noise, polluted air, and adulterated foods. If such is the case, we must modify our mode of life and our environment, even at the cost of a destructive revolution. After all, the purpose of civilization is not the progress of science and machines, but the progress of man.

14

In conclusion. Adaptation is a mode of being of all organic and mental processes. It is not an entity. It is equivalent to the automatic grouping of our activities in such a manner as to assure the survival of the individual. It is essentially teleological. Owing to the adaptive activities, the organic medium remains constant, the body conserves its unity and recovers from diseases. It is for the same reason we endure, in spite of the fragility and the transitory character of our tissues. Adaptation is as indispensable as nutrition. In fact it is only an aspect of nutrition. However, in the organization of modern life no account has ever been taken of such an important function. Its use has been almost completely given up. And this neglect has brought about a deterioration of the body and of the mind.

This mode of activity is necessary to the complete development of the human being. Its deficiency determines the atrophy of the nutritive and mental functions from which it is not distinct. Adaptation causes the organic processes to move simultaneously according to the rhythms of physiological time and of the unforeseeable variations of the environment. Any change in the environment elicits a response of all physiological and mental processes. Those movements of the functional systems express the apprehension by man of the outer reality. They act as a buffer for the material and psychological shocks which he unceasingly receives. They not only permit him to endure, but they also are the agents of his formation and of his progress. They are endowed with a property of capital importance: the property of being easily modified by certain chemical, physical, and psychological factors, which we know well how to handle. We can use these factors as tools, and thus successfully intervene in the development of human activities. In fact, the knowledge of the mechanisms of adaptation gives man the power of renovating and of constructing himself.

CHAPTER VII

THE INDIVIDUAL

1. *The human being and the individual. The quarrel between realists and nominalists. Confusion of symbols and concrete facts.* 2. *Individuality of tissues and humours.* 3. *Psychological individuality. Characteristics of personality.* 4. *Individuality of disease. Medicine and the reality of Universals.* 5. *Origin of individuality. The quarrel between behaviourists and geneticists. Relative importance of heredity and environment. Influence of hereditary factors on the individual.* 6. *Influence of developmental factors on the individual. Variations in the effect of these factors according to immanent characteristics of tissues.* 7. *Spatial frontiers of the individual. Anatomical and psychological limits. Extension of the individual beyond his anatomical structure.* 8. *Temporal frontiers of the individual. Links of organism and mind with the past and the future.* 9. *The individual.* 10. *Man consists of the human being and of the individual. Realism and nominalism are both indispensable.* 11. *Practical significance of such knowledge.*

I

HUMAN beings are not found anywhere in nature. There are only individuals. The individual differs from the human being because he is a concrete event. He is the one who acts, loves, suffers, fights, and dies. On the contrary, the human being is a Platonic Idea living in our minds and in our books. He consists of the abstractions studied by physiologists, psychologists, and sociologists. His characteristics are expressed by Universals. To-day we are again facing a problem which engrossed the philosophical minds of the Middle Ages, the problem of the reality of general ideas. In defence of the Universals, Anselm sustained against Abélard a historical fight, whose echoes are still heard after eight hundred years. Abélard was defeated. However, Anselm and Abélard, the realists who believed in the existence of the Universals and the nominalists who did not believe in it, were equally right.

Indeed, we need both the general and the particular, the human being and the individual. The reality of the general—that is, of the Universals—is indispensable to the construction of science, because our mind readily moves only among abstractions. For modern scientists, as for Plato, Ideas are the sole reality. This abstract reality leads our mind to the knowledge of the concrete. The general helps us to grasp the particular. Owing to the abstractions created by the sciences of the human being, each individual can be clothed in convenient schemata. Although not made to his measure, these schemata approximately fit him. At the same time, the empirical consideration of the concrete facts determines the evolution and the progress of the schemas, of the Ideas, of the Universals. It continually enriches these abstractions. The study of a multitude of individuals develops a more and more complete science of the human being. The Ideas, instead of being immutable in their beauty, Plato thought, move and expand as soon as our mind becomes immersed in the ever-flowing waters of empirical reality.

We live in two different worlds—the world of facts and that of their symbols. In order to acquire knowledge of ourselves, we utilize both observation and scientific abstractions. But the abstract may be mistaken for the concrete. In such an instance, facts are treated as symbols and the individual is likened to the human being. Most of the errors made by educators, physicians, and sociologists come from such confusion. Scientists accustomed to the techniques of mechanics, chemistry, physics, and physiology, and unfamiliar with philosophy and intellectual culture, are liable to mingle the concepts of the different disciplines and not to distinguish clearly the general from the particular. However, in the concept of man, it is important to define exactly the part of the human being and that of the individual. Education, medi-

cine, and sociology are concerned with the individual. They
are guilty of a disastrous error when they look upon him only
as a symbol, as a human being. Indeed, individuality is fundamental in man. It is not merely a certain aspect of the
organism, but it permeates our entire being. It makes the
self a unique event in the history of the world. It stamps its
mark on the whole of body and consciousness, and, although
remaining indivisible, on each component of this whole. For
the sake of convenience we will consider separately the
organic, humoral, and mental aspects of the individual,
instead of apprehending him in his oneness.

2

Individuals are easily distinguished from one another by
the lineaments of their visages, their gestures, their way of
walking, their intellectual and moral characters. Time causes
many changes in their appearance. Despite these changes,
each individual can always be identified, as Bertillon has
shown long since, by the dimensions of certain parts of his
skeleton. The lines of the finger tips are also indelible characteristics. Fingerprints are the genuine signature of man.
However, the configuration of the skin is only one of the
aspects of the individuality of tissues. In general, the latter
is not evidenced by any morphological peculiarity. The cells
of the thyroid gland, the liver, the skin, etc., of one individual
appear to be identical with those of another individual. In
every one the pulsations of the heart are nearly, although not
quite, the same. The structure and functions of organs do
not seem to be marked by individual properties. However,
their specificity would doubtless be evidenced by more subtle
methods of examination. Certain dogs are endowed with
such a sharp olfactory sense that they recognize the specific
smell of their master among a crowd of other men. Likewise,
the tissues of one individual are capable of perceiving the

specificity of his humours and the foreign character of the humours of another.

The individuality of tissues may manifest itself in the following way. Fragments of skin, some supplied by the patient himself and others by a friend or a relative, are grafted on the surface of a wound. After a few days the grafts coming from the patient are adherent to the wound and grow larger, whereas those taken from the other people loosen and grow smaller. The former survive, and the latter die. One very rarely finds two individuals so closely alike that they are able to exchange their tissues. Many years ago, Cristiani transplanted into a little girl, whose thyroid function was deficient, a few fragments of the thyroid gland of her mother. The child was cured. Some ten years later she married and became pregnant. Not only were the grafts still alive, but they increased in size, as normal thyroid glands do in like circumstances. Such a result is quite exceptional. However, between identical twins, glandular transplantation would doubtless succeed. As a rule, the tissues of one individual refuse to accept those of another individual. When, by the suture of the vessels, blood circulates again in a transplanted kidney, the organ immediately secretes urine. At first it behaves normally. After a few weeks, however, albumin, then blood, appear in the urine. And a disease similar to nephritis rapidly brings on atrophy of the kidney. However, if the grafted organ comes from the animal itself, its functions are permanently re-established. Obviously, the humours recognize, in foreign tissues, certain differences of constitution, which are not revealed by any other test. Cells are specific of the individual to whom they belong. This peculiarity of our body has so far prevented the wide use of the transplantation of organs for therapeutic purposes.

The humours possess a similar specificity. This specificity is detected by a definite effect of the blood serum of one individual upon the red corpuscles of another individual. Under the influence of serum the corpuscles often agglutinate. The accidents noticed after blood transfusion are due to such a phenomenon. It is, therefore, indispensable that the corpuscles of the donor should not be agglutinated by the serum of the patient. According to a remarkable discovery made by Landsteiner, human beings are divided into four groups, the knowledge of which is essential to the success of transfusion. The serum of the members of certain groups agglutinates the corpuscles of the members of certain other groups. One of the groups is composed of universal donors, whose cells are not agglutinated by the serum of any other group. No inconvenience results from the mingling of their blood with that of any other person. These characteristics persist during the entire life. They are transmitted from generation to generation, according to the laws of Mendel. In addition, Landsteiner discovered about thirty sub-groups, by using special serological methods. In transfusion their influence is negligible. But it is indicative of the existence of resemblances and differences between smaller groups of individuals. The test of agglutination of blood corpuscles by serum, although most useful, is still imperfect. It only brings to light certain relations between categories of individuals. It does not disclose the more subtle characteristics that single out each individual from all others in his category.

The properties specific to each animal are evidenced by the results of the transplantation of organs. There is no means by which they can easily be detected. Repeated injections of one individual's serum into the veins of another, belonging to the same blood group, bring about no reaction, no formation of antibodies in measurable amount. A patient, therefore, can be subjected without danger to several consecutive transfusions. His humours react against neither the corpuscles nor the serum of the donor. However, the differences specific of the individual, which preclude successful exchanges of organs, would probably be revealed by sufficiently delicate tests. The specificity of tissues and humours depends on proteins and chemical groups called haptens by Landsteiner.

Haptens are carbohydrates and fatty substances. The compounds resulting from the union of a hapten with a protein, when injected into an animal, determine the appearance in its serum of antibodies specifically opposed to the hapten. The specificity of the individual depends on the inner structure of the large molecules resulting from haptens and proteins. Individuals of the same race are more similar to each other than to individuals belonging to other races. The protein and carbohydrate molecules are made up of a large number of groups of atoms. The possible permutations of these groups are practically infinite. It is probable that, among the gigantic crowds of human beings who have inhabited the earth, no two individuals have ever been of identical chemical constitution. The personality of the tissues is linked in a manner still unknown with the molecules entering into the construction of the cells and the humours. Our individuality takes its roots in the very depths of ourselves.

Individuality stamps all the component parts of the body. It is present in the physiological processes, as well as in the chemical structure of the humours and cells. Everyone reacts in his own way to the events of the outside world—to noise, to danger, to food, to cold, to heat, to the attacks of microbes and viruses. When animals of pure stock are injected with equal quantities of a foreign protein, or of a suspension of bacteria, they never respond to those injections in an identical manner. A few do not respond at all. During great epidemics human beings behave according to their individual characteristics. Some fall ill and die. Some fall ill but recover. Others are entirely immune. Still others are slightly affected by the disease, but without presenting any specific symptoms. Each one manifests a different adaptivity to the infective agent. As Richet said, there is a humoral personality just as there is a mental personality.

Physiological duration bears also the mark of our individuality. Its value, as we know, is not the same for every human being. Besides, it does not remain constant during the course of our life. As each event is recorded within the body, our organic and humoral personality becomes more and more specific during the process of ageing. It is enriched by all the happenings of our inner world. For cells and humours, like mind, are endowed with memory. The body is permanently modified by each disease, each injection of serum or of vaccine, each invasion of the tissues by bacteria, viruses, or foreign chemical substances. These events determine within ourselves allergic states—that is, states in which our reactivity is modified. In this manner, tissues and humours acquire a progressively growing individuality. Old people differ from one another far more than children do. Every man is a history unlike all others.

3

Mental, structural, and humoral individualities blend in an unknown manner. They bear to one another the same relations as do psychological activities, cerebral processes, and organic functions. They give us our uniqueness. They cause every man to be himself and nobody else. Identical twins coming from the same ovum, having the same genetical constitution, are, however, two quite different persons. Mental characteristics are a more delicate reagent of individuality than organic and humoral characteristics. Everyone is defined simultaneously by the number, quality, and intensity of his psychological activities. There are no individuals of identical mentality. Indeed, those whose consciousness is rudimentary closely resemble each other. The richer the personality, the greater the individual differences. All the activities of consciousness rarely develop at the same time in one individual. In most men, some of them are weak or lacking. There is a marked difference not only in the intensity of those functions, but also in their quality. Moreover, the number of their possible combinations is infinite. No task is more difficult than to analyze the constitution of a given individual. The complexity of mental personality being extreme, and the psychological tests insufficient, it is impossible to classify individuals accurately. They can, however, be divided into categories according to their intellectual, affective, moral, æsthetic, and religious characteristics, to the combinations of these characteristics, and to their relations with the various types of physiological activities. There are also some obvious relations between psychological and morphological types. The physical aspect of an individual is an indication of the constitution of his tissues, humours, and mind. Between the more definite types there are many intermediate ones. The possible classifications are almost innumerable. They are, consequently, of little value.

Individuals have been separated into intellectual, sensitive, and voluntary types. In each category, there are the hesitating, the annoying, the impulsive, the incoherent, the weak, the dispersed, the restless, and also the reflective, the self-controlled, the honest, the well balanced. Among the intellectual, several distinct groups are observed: the broad-minded, whose ideas are numerous, who assimilate, co-ordinate, and unite a most varied knowledge; the narrow-minded, incapable of grasping vast ensembles, but who master perfectly the details of one subject. Intelligence is more frequently precise and analytical than capable of great syntheses. There are also the group of the logicians and that of the intuitives. Most of the great men belong to this latter group. There are many combinations of the intellectual and affective types. The intellectual may be emotional, passionate, enterprising, and also cowardly, irresolute, and weak. Among them, the mystical type is exceptional. The same multiplicity of combinations exists in the groups characterized by moral, æsthetic, and religious tendencies. Such a classification evidences the prodigious variety of the human

types.* The study of psychological individuality is as decep-
tive as would be that of chemistry, if the number of the elements should become infinite.

Each individual is conscious of being unique. Such uniqueness is real. But there are great differences in the degree of
individualization. Certain personalities are very rich, very
strong. Others are weak, easily modified by environment
and circumstances. Between simple weakening of the personality and psychoses, there are many intermediate states.
People suffering from certain neuroses have the feeling that
their personality is being dissolved. Other diseases really
destroy personality. Encephalitis lethargica brings about
cerebral lesions which may profoundly modify the individual.
The same may be said of dementia præcox and general paralysis. In other diseases the psychological changes are only
temporary. Hysteria engenders double personality. The
patient seems to become two different individuals. Each of
these artificial persons ignores the thoughts and acts of the
other. Likewise, one can, during hypnotic sleep, modify the
identity of the subject. If another personality is imposed
upon him by suggestion, he takes the attitudes and feels the
emotions of his second self. In addition to those who thus
become two persons, there are others whose personalities are
incompletely disassociated. In this category are many types
of neurotics, those who practise automatic writing, a number
of mediums, and also the queer, weak, unsteady beings who
are so numerous in modern society.

It is not yet possible to make a complete survey of psychological individuality, and to measure its component
parts. Neither can we exactly determine its nature, and how
one individual differs from another. We are not even capable
of discovering the essential characteristics of a given man.
And still less his potentialities. Each youth, however, should
insert himself in his social group according to his aptitudes

* Georges Dumas, *Traité de Psychologie*, 1924, t. II, livre II,
chapitre III, p. 575.

and to his specific mental and physiological activities. But he cannot do it, because he is ignorant of himself. Parents and educators share with him such ignorance. They do not know how to detect the nature of the individuality of children. And they endeavour to standardize them. Modern business methods take no account of the personality of the workers. They ignore the fact that all men are different. Most of us are unaware of our own aptitudes. However, everybody cannot do everything. According to his characteristics, each individual adjusts himself more easily to a certain type of work or a certain mode of living. His success and happiness depend on the affinity between himself and his environment. He should fit into his social group as a key fits into its lock. Parents and schoolteachers should set themselves first and foremost to acquire a knowledge of the inherent qualities and the potentialities of each child. Unfortunately, scientific psychology cannot give them very effective help. The tests applied to school children and students by inexperienced psychologists have no great significance. They give an illusive confidence to those unacquainted with psychology. In fact, they should be accorded less importance. Psychology is not yet a science. To-day, individuality and its potentialities are not measurable. But a wise observer, trained in the study of human beings, is sometimes capable of discovering the future in the present characteristics of a given individual.

4

A disease is not an entity. We observe individuals suffering from pneumonia, syphilis, diabetes, typhoid fever, etc. Then we construct in our mind certain Universals, certain abstractions, which we call diseases. Illness expresses the adaptation of the organism to a pathogenic agent, or its passive destruction by this agent. Adaptation and destruction assume the form of the sick individual and the rhythm of his inner time. The body is more rapidly destroyed by degenerative diseases during youth than during old age. It replies to all enemies in a specific manner. The form of its reply depends on the inherent properties of the tissues. Angina pectoris, for example, announces its presence by acute suffering. The heart seems to be gripped in steel claws. But the intensity of the pain varies according to the sensitiveness of the individual. When the patient is not sensitive, the disease takes another aspect. Without warning, without pain, it kills its victim. Typhoid fever, as we know, is accompanied by high temperature, headache, diarrhœa, general depression. It is a serious illness necessitating a long sojourn in the hospital. However, certain individuals, although suffering from this malady, continue to attend to their usual occupations. In the course of epidemics of influenza, diphtheria, yellow fever, etc., some patients feel only a slight fever, a little discomfort. In spite of the lack of symptoms, they are affected by the disease. Their mode of response to the infection is due to the inherent resistance of their tissues. As we know, the adaptive mechanisms which protect the body from microbes and viruses differ in each individual. When the organism is incapable of resistance, as in cancer, it is being destroyed at a rhythm and in a manner determined by its own properties. In a young woman, a cancer of the breast rapidly brings on death. On the contrary, in extreme old age, it evolves very slowly, as slowly as the body itself. Disease is a personal event. It consists of the individual himself. There are as many different diseases as patients.

However, it would have been impossible to build up a science of medicine merely by compiling a great number of individual observations. The facts had to be classified and simplified with the aid of abstractions. In this way disease was born. And medical treatises could be written. A kind of science was built up, roughly descriptive, rudimentary, imperfect, but convenient, indefinitely perfectible and easy to teach. Unfortunately, we have been content with this result

We did not understand that treatises describing pathological entities contain only a part of the knowledge indispensable to those who attend the sick. Medical knowledge should go beyond the science of diseases. The physician must clearly distinguish the sick human being described in his books from the concrete patient whom he has to treat, who must not only be studied, but, above all, relieved, encouraged, and cured. His rôle is to discover the characteristics of the sick man's individuality, his resistance to pathogenic factors, his sensibility to pain, the value of his organic activities, his past, and his future. The outcome of an illness in a given individual has to be predicted, not by a calculation of the probabilities, but by a precise analysis of the organic, humoral, and psychological personality of this individual. In fact, medicine, when confining itself to the study of diseases, amputates a part of its own body.

Many physicians still persist in pursuing abstractions exclusively. Some, however, believe that a knowledge of the patient is as important as that of the disease. The former desire to remain in the realm of symbols. The latter feel the necessity of apprehending the concrete. To-day the old quarrel of the realists and the nominalists is being revived around the schools of medicine. Scientific medicine, installed in its palaces, defends, as did the Church of the Middle Ages, the reality of the Universals. It anathematizes the nominalists who, following the example of Abélard, consider Universals and disease as creations of our mind, and the patient as the only reality. In fact, a physician has to be both realist and nominalist. He must study the individual as well as the disease. The distrust which the public feels toward medicine, the inefficiency, and sometimes the ridicule, of therapeutics, are, perhaps, due to the confusion of the symbols indispensable to the building up of medical sciences with the concrete patient who has to be treated and relieved. The physician's lack of success comes from his living in an imaginary world. Instead of his patients, he sees the diseases described in the treatises of medicine. He is a victim of the belief in Universals. Moreover, he mixes the concepts of principle and method, of science and technology. He does not realize sufficiently that the individual is a whole, that adaptive functions extend to all organic systems, and that anatomical divisions are artificial. The separation of the body into parts has so far been to his advantage. But it is dangerous and costly for the patient, and ultimately for the physician.

Medicine has to take into account the nature of man, of his unity, and of his uniqueness. Its sole purpose is to relieve the suffering of the individual and to cure him. Indeed, physicians must use the spirit and the methods of science. They have to become capable of recognizing and treating diseases and, still better, of preventing them. Medicine is not a discipline of the mind. There is no valid motive for cultivating it for itself, or for the advantage of those who practise it. The goal of all our efforts should be exclusively the healing of the sick. But medicine is the most difficult of all human attainments. It should not be likened to any science. A professor of medicine is not an ordinary teacher. He differs profoundly from other professors. While the fields covered by his colleagues specializing in the study of anatomy, physiology, chemistry, pathology, pharmacology, etc., are limited and clearly defined, he must acquire an almost universal knowledge. In addition, he needs sound judgment, great physical endurance, and ceaseless activity. He should possess higher qualities than those of a laboratory worker. He is set a task very different from that of a man of science. The latter can confine himself entirely to the world of symbols. Physicians, on the contrary, have to face both concrete reality and scientific abstractions. Their mind must simultaneously grasp the phenomena and their symbols, search into organs and consciousness, and enter, with each individual, a different world. They are asked to realize the impossible feat of building up a science of the particular. Of course, they might use the expedient of indiscriminately applying their scientific knowledge to each patient, as, for instance, a salesman trying to fit the same ready-made coat to people of different sizes. But they do not really fulfil their duty unless they discover the specific peculiarities of each patient. Their success depends not only on their knowledge, but also on their ability to grasp the characteristics which make each human being an individual.

5

The uniqueness of each man has a double origin. It comes simultaneously from the constitution of the ovum, from which he originates, and from his development and his history. We have already mentioned how, before fertilization, the ovum expels half of its nucleus, half of each chromosome —that is, half the hereditary factors, the genes, which are arranged in a linear series along the chromosomes. We know how the head of a spermatozoon penetrates the ovum, after having also lost half of its chromosomes, how the body, with all its characteristics and tendencies, derives from the union of the male and female chromosomes within the nucleus of the fertilized egg. At this moment the individual exists only in a potential state. He contains the dominant factors responsible for the visible characteristics of his parents. And also the recessive factors, which have remained hidden during their entire life. According to their relative position in the new individual's chromosomes, the recessive factors will manifest their activity or will be neutralized by dominant factors. These relations are described by the science of genetics as the laws of heredity. They merely express the origin of the inherent characteristics of each human being. But these characteristics are nothing but tendencies or potentialities. According to the circumstances encountered by the embryo, the fœtus, the child, and the adolescent during their development, these tendencies become actual or remain virtual. And each man's history is as unique as were the nature and the arrangement of his constitutive genes when he was an ovum. Thus the originality of the human being depends both on heredity and on development.

We know that individuality springs from these two sources. But not what part each of them plays in our formation. Is heredity more important than development, or vice versa? Watson and the behaviourists proclaim that education and environment are capable of giving human beings any desired form. Education would be everything, and heredity nothing. Geneticists believe, on the contrary, that heredity imposes itself on man like ancient fate, and that the salvation of the race lies, not in education, but in eugenics. Both schools forget that such a problem cannot be solved by arguments, but only by observations and experiments.

Observations and experiments teach us that the parts of heredity and of development vary in each individual, and that generally their respective values cannot be determined. However, in children conceived by the same parents, brought up together and in the same manner, there are striking differences in form, stature, nervous constitution, intellectual aptitudes, and moral qualities. It is obvious that these differences are of ancestral origin. Animals behave in a like way. Let us take as an example a litter of shepherd dogs, still being suckled by their mother. Each of the nine or ten puppies presents distinct characteristics. Some react to a sudden noise, to the report of a pistol, for example, by crouching on the ground, some by standing up on their little paws, others by advancing toward the noise. Some conquer the best teats, others let themselves be pushed out of their place. Some ramble away from their mother and explore the neighbourhood of their kennel. Others stay with her. Some growl when touched. Others remain silent. When the animals brought up together under identical conditions have grown into adults, most of their characteristics are found unchanged by development. Shy and timorous dogs remain shy and timorous all their lives. Those that were fearless and alert sometimes lose these qualities as they grow older, but, in general, they become still more fearless and active. Among the characteristics of ancestral origin, some are not utilized, the others develop. Twins originating in the same ovum possess the same inherent characteristics. At first they are quite identical. However, if they are parted right at the beginning of their lives and are brought up in different ways and in different countries, they lose such identity. After eighteen or twenty years, they show marked differences, and also great resemblances, especially from an intellectual point of view. From this it appears that, given dissimilar surroundings, identity of constitution does not determine the formation of identical individuals. It is also evident that disparity of environment does not efface identity of constitution. According to the conditions under which development takes place, some or others of the potentialities are actualized. And two beings, originally identical, become different.

What influence do the genes, those particles of nuclear substance originating from our ancestors, exert on the formation of the individual, on the building up of body and consciousness? In what measure does the constitution of the individual depend on that of the egg? Many observations and experiments have shown that certain aspects of the individual are already present in the ovum, that others are only potential. The genes, therefore, exercise their influence, either in an inexorable manner by imposing on the individual characteristics which develop fatally, or in the form of tendencies which become, or fail to become, effective, according to the circumstances of the development. Sex is inevitably determined from the time of the union of the paternal and maternal cells. The egg of the future male possesses one chromosome less than that of the female, or an atrophied chromosome. In this manner, all the cells of the body of the man differ from those of the body of the woman. Weakness of mind, insanity, hæmophilia, deafmutism, as is known, are

H*

hereditary defects. Certain diseases, such as cancer, hypertension, tuberculosis, etc., are transmitted also from parents to children, but as a tendency. The conditions of development may impede or favour their actualization. It is the same with strength, alertness, will power, intelligence, and judgment. The value of each individual is determined in a large measure by his hereditary predispositions. But as human beings are not of pure breed, the characteristics of the products of a given marriage cannot be predicted. However, it is known that children born in families of superior people are more likely to be of a superior type than those born in an inferior family. Owing to the hazards of the nuclear unions, a great man's descendants may include mediocre children, or an obscure family may give birth to a great man. The tendency to superiority is by no means irresistible, like that to insanity, for example. Eugenics succeeds in producing superior types only under certain conditions of development and education. It has no magic power, and is not capable, when unaided, of greatly improving the individuals.

6

The ancestral tendencies, transmitted according to the laws of Mendel and other laws, give a special aspect to the development of each man. In order to manifest themselves, they naturally require the co-operation of the environment. The potentialities of tissues and consciousness actualize only through the chemical, physical, physiological, and mental factors of such environment. One cannot distinguish, in general, the inherited from the acquired. Indeed, certain peculiarities, such as the colour of eyes and of hair, shortsightedness, and feeble-mindedness, are evidently of hereditary origin. But many other characteristics depend on the influence environment has upon body and mind. The development of the organism bends in different directions, in compliance with its surroundings, and its inherent properties become actual or remain virtual. It is certain that hereditary tendencies are profoundly modified by the circumstances of our formation. But we must also realize that each individual develops according to his own rules, to the specific qualities of his tissues. Moreover, the original intensity of our tendencies, their capacity for actualization, varies. The destiny of certain individuals is inexorably determined. That of others more or less depends on the conditions of their development.

It is impossible to predict in what measure a child's hereditary tendencies will be affected by his education, mode of life, and social surroundings. The genetical constitution of the tissues of a human being is always a mystery. We do not know how the genes of his parents, grandparents, and great-grandparents are grouped in the egg from which he originated. Neither do we know whether certain nuclear particles of some distant and forgotten ancestor are not present in him, nor whether spontaneous changes in the genes themselves may not cause the appearance of some unforeseen characteristics. It sometimes happens that a child, whose ancestral tendencies have been known for several generations, manifests completely new and unexpected aspects. However, the probable results of a given environment upon a given individual can be anticipated in a certain measure. A seasoned observer is able to grasp the significance of the growing characteristics of a child, as well as of a puppy, very early in its life. Developmental conditions cannot transform a weak, apathetic, dispersed, timid, inactive child into an energetic man, a powerful and audacious leader. Vitality, imagination, boldness are never entirely due to environment. Neither can they be repressed by it. Indeed, the circumstances of development are efficient only within the limits of the hereditary predispositions, of the immanent qualities of tissues and consciousness. But we never know the exact nature of these predispositions. We must, however, presume them to be favourable, and act accordingly. It is imperative that each individual should receive an education conducive to the growth of his virtual qualities, until the qualities in question are proven not to exist.

The chemical, physiological, and psychological factors of the environment favour or hinder the development of the inherent tendencies. In fact these tendencies can express themselves only by certain organic forms. If the body is deprived of the calcium and phosphorus indispensable to the building up of the skeleton, or of the vitamins and glandular secretions which permit the utilization of this material by cartilage in the formation of bones, the limbs become deformed and the pelvis narrow. Such a commonplace accident may prevent the actualization of potentialities which destined this or that woman to be a prolific mother, perhaps to beget a new Lincoln or a new Pasteur. The lack of a vitamin or an infectious disease may cause the testicles, or any other gland, to atrophy and, in this manner, stop the development of an individual who, owing to his ancestral qualities, could have become the leader of a nation. All the physical and chemical conditions of the environment are capable of affecting the actualization of our potentialities. To their moulding influence is due, in a large measure, the organic and mental aspect of each human being.

Psychological factors act still more effectively on the individual. They give to our life its intellectual and moral form. They induce discipline or dispersion. They lead us to the neglect or the mastery of ourselves. Through circulatory and glandular changes, they also transform the activities and the constitution of the body. The discipline of the mind and of the physiological appetites has a definite effect, not only on the psychological attitude of the individual, but also on his organic and humoral structure. We do not know in what measure the mental influences emanating from the environment are capable of promoting or stifling ancestral tendencies. Without any doubt, they play a leading part in the destiny of the individual. They sometimes annihilate the highest mental qualities. They develop certain individuals beyond all expectations. They help the weak and render the strong yet stronger. Young Bonaparte read Plutarch and endeavoured to think and to live as the great men of antiquity did. It is not immaterial that a child idolize Babe Ruth or George Washington, Charlie Chaplin or Lindbergh. To play at being a gangster is not the same thing as to play at being a soldier. Whatever his ancestral tendencies may be, each individual is started by his developmental conditions upon a road which may lead him either to the solitude of the mountains, to the beauty of the hills, or to the mud of the marshes where most civilized men delight in living.

The influence of environment upon individualization varies according to the state of tissues and consciousness. In other words, the same factor, acting on several individuals, or upon the same individual at different periods of his existence, does not have identical effects. It is well known that the response of a given organism to environment depends on its hereditary tendencies. For example, the obstacle that stops one man stimulates another to a greater effort, and determines in him the actualization of potentialities which so far had remained hidden. Likewise, at successive periods of life, before or after certain diseases, the organism responds to a pathogenic influence in different ways. The effect of an excess of food or sleep is not the same on a young man as on an old one. Measles are an insignificant disease in children and a serious one in adults. In addition, the reactivity of a subject varies according to his physiological age, and also to all his previous history. It depends on the nature of his individualization. In sum, the part of environment in the actualization of the hereditary tendencies of a given subject is not exactly definable. The immanent properties of the tissues and the conditions of their development are inextricably mingled in the formation of the body and the soul of each individual.

7

The individual is obviously a centre of specific activities. He appears as distinct from the inanimate world and also from other living beings. At the same time, he is linked to his environment and to his fellow men. He could not exist without them. He is characterized by being independent of, and dependent on, the cosmic universe. But we do not know how he is bound to other beings, where his spatial and temporal frontiers are. Personality is rightly believed to extend outside the physical continuum. Its limits seem to be situated beyond the surface of the skin. The definiteness of the anatomical contours is partly an illusion. Each one of us is certainly far larger and more diffuse than his body.

We know that our visible frontiers are, on one side, the skin and, on the other side, the digestive and respiratory mucosas. Our anatomical and functional integrity, as also our survival, depends on their inviolability. Their destruction and the invasion of the tissues by bacteria bring on death and disintegration of the individual. We also know that they can be crossed by cosmic rays, oxygen from the atmosphere, light, heat, and sound waves, and substances resulting from the intestinal digestion of food. Through these surfaces the inner world of our body is in continuity with the cosmic world. But this anatomical frontier is only that of one aspect of the individual. It does not enclose our mental personality. Love and hatred are realities. Through these feelings men are bound to one another in a positive manner, whatever may be the distance between them. To a woman the loss of her child causes greater suffering than the loss of a limb. The breaking of an affective bond may even bring about death. If we could visualize those immaterial links, human beings would assume new and strange aspects. Some would hardly extend beyond their anatomical limits. Others would stretch out as far as a safe in a bank, the sexual organs of another individual, certain foods or beverages, perhaps to a dog, a jewel, some object of art. Others would appear immense. They would expand in long tentacles attached to their family, to a group of friends, to an old homestead, to the sky and the mountains of their native country. Leaders of nations, great philanthropists, saints, would look like fairy-tale giants, spreading their multiple arms over a country, a continent, the entire world. There is a close relation between us and our social environment. Each human being occupies a certain place in his group. He is shackled to it by mental chains. His position may appear to him as more important than life itself. If he is deprived of it by financial losses, illness, persecution, scandal, or crime, he may prefer suicide to such a change. Obviously, the individual projects on all sides beyond his anatomical frontiers.

But man diffuses through space in a still more positive way.* In telepathic phenomena, he instantaneously sends

* The psychological frontiers of the individual in space and time are obviously suppositions. But suppositions, even when very strange, are convenient and help to group together facts that are temporarily unexplainable. Their purpose is merely to inspire new experiments. The author realizes clearly than his conjectures will be considered naïve or heretical by the layman, as well as by the scientist; that they will equally displease materialists and spiritualists, vitalists, and mechanicists; that the equilibrium of his intellect will be doubted. However, one cannot neglect facts because they are strange. On the contrary, one must investigate them. Metapsychics may bring to us more important information on the nature of man than normal psychology does. The societies of psychical research, and especially the English Society, have attracted to clairvoyance and telepathy the attention of the public. The time has come to study these phenomena as one studies physiological phenomena. But metapsychical researches must not be undertaken by amateurs, even when those amateurs are great physicists, great philosophers, or great mathematicians. To go beyond one's own field and to dabble in theology or spiritism is dangerous, even for men as illustrious as Isaac Newton, William Crookes, or Oliver Lodge. Experimenters trained in clinical medicine, having a profound knowledge of the human being, of his physiology and psychology, of his neuroses, of his aptitude to lie, of his susceptibility to suggestion, of his skill at prestidigitation, are alone qualified to investigate this subject. The author hopes that his

out a part of himself, a sort of emanation, which joins a far-away relative or friend. He thus expands to great distances. He may cross oceans and continents in a time too short to be estimated. He is capable of finding in the midst of a crowd the person whom he must meet. Then he communicates to this person certain knowledge. He can also discover in the immensity and confusion of a modern city the house, the room of the individual whom he seeks, although acquainted neither with him nor with his surroundings. Those endowed with this form of activity behave like extensible beings, amœbas of a strange kind, capable of sending pseudopods to progidious distances. The hypnotist and his subject are sometimes observed to be linked together by an invisible bond. This bond seems to emanate from the subject. When communication is established between the hypnotist and his subject, the former can, by suggestion from a distance, command the latter to perform certain acts. At this moment a telepathic relation is established between them. In such an instance, two distant individuals are in contact with each other, although both appear to be confined within their respective anatomical limits.

Thought seems to be transmitted, like electromagnetic waves, from one region of space to another. We do not know its velocity. So far it has not been possible to measure the speed of telepathic communications. Neither biologists, physicists, nor astronomers have taken into account the existence of metapsychical phenomena. Telepathy, however, is a primary datum of observation. If, some day, thought should be found to travel through space as light does, our theories about the constitution of the universe would have to be modified. But it is not sure that telepathic phenomena are due to the transmission of a physical agent. Possibly there is no spatial contact between individuals who are in communi-

suppositions about the spatial and temporal limits of the individual will possibly inspire, instead of smiles or futile discussions, experiments made with the techniques of physiology and physics.

cation. In fact, we know that mind is not entirely described within the four dimensions of the physical continuum. It is situated simultaneously within the material universe and elsewhere. It may insert itself into the cerebral cells and stretch outside space and time, like an alga, which fastens to a rock and lets its tendrils drift out into the mystery of the ocean. We are totally ignorant of the realities that lie outside space and time. We may suppose that a telepathic communication is an encounter, beyond the four dimensions of our universe, between the immaterial parts of two minds. But it is more convenient to consider these phenomena as being brought about by the expansion of the individual into space.

The spatial extensibility of personality is an exceptional fact. Nevertheless, normal individuals may sometimes read the thoughts of others as clairvoyants do. In a perhaps analogous manner some men have the power of carrying away and convincing great multitudes with seemingly commonplace words, of leading people to happiness, to battle, to sacrifice, to death. Cæsar, Napoleon, Mussolini, all great leaders of nations, grow beyond human stature. They encircle innumerable throngs of men in the net of their will and their ideas. Between certain individuals and nature there are subtle and obscure relations. Such men are able to spread across space and time and to grasp concrete reality. They seem to escape from themselves, and also from the physical continuum. Sometimes they project their tentacles in vain beyond the frontiers of the material world, and they bring back nothing of importance. But like the great prophets of science, art, and religion, they often succeed in apprehending in the abysses of the unknown, elusive and sublime beings called mathematical abstractions, Platonic Ideas, absolute beauty, God.

8

In time, as in space, the individual stretches out beyond the frontiers of his body. His temporal frontiers are neither more precise nor more fixed than his spatial ones. He is linked to the past and to the future, although his self does not extend outside the present. Our individuality, as we know, comes into being when the spermatozoon enters the egg. But before this moment, the elements of the self are already in existence, scattered in the tissues of our parents, of our parents' parents, and of our most remote ancestors. We are made of the cellular substances of our father and our mother. We depend on the past in an organic and indissoluble manner. We bear within ourselves countless fragments of our ancestors' bodies. Our qualities and defects proceed from theirs. In men, as in race-horses, strength and courage are hereditary qualities. History cannot be set aside. We must, on the contrary, make use of the past to foresee the future and to prepare our destiny.

It is well known that characteristics acquired by the individual in the course of his life are not transmitted to his descendants. However, germ-plasm is not immutable. It may change under the influence of the organic medium. It can be altered by disease, poison, food, and secretions of endocrine glands. Syphilis in parents may cause profound disorders in the body and consciousness of their children. For this reason the descent of men of genius sometimes consists of inferior beings, weak and unbalanced. *Treponema pallidum* has exterminated more great families than have all the wars of the world. Likewise, alcoholics, morphino-maniacs, and cocaine addicts may beget defectives, who pay during their entire life for the vices of their fathers. Indeed, the consequences of one's faults are easily passed on to one's descendants. But it is far more difficult to give them the benefit of one's virtues. Each individual puts his mark on his environment, his house, his family, his friends. He lives as if surrounded by himself.

Through his deeds he may transfer his qualities to his descendants. The child depends on his parents for a long period. He has time to learn all that they can teach him. He uses his innate capacity for imitation and tends to become like them. He takes on their true visage, and not the mask that they wear in social life. In general, his feeling toward his father and mother is one of indifference and of some contempt. But he willingly imitates their ignorance, vulgarity, selfishness, and cowardice. Of course, there are many types of parents. Some of them leave their offspring a heritage of intelligence, goodness, æsthetic sense, and courage. After their death their personality goes on living through their scientific discoveries, their artistic production, the political, economic, or social institutions they have founded, or more simply through the house which they have built, and the fields which they have cultivated with their own hands. It is by such people that our civilization has been created.

The influence of the individual upon the future is not equivalent to an extension of the self in time. It takes place by means of the fragments of cell substance directly transmitted by him to his children, or of his creations in the domains of art, religion, science, philosophy, etc. Sometimes, however, personality seems really to extend beyond physiological duration. There is in certain individuals a psychical element capable of travelling in time.[*] As already mentioned, clairvoyants perceive not only events spatially remote, but also past and future events. They seem to wander as easily in time as in space, or to escape from the physical continuum and contemplate the past and the future as a fly could contemplate a picture if, instead of walking on its surface, it flew at some distance above it. The facts of prediction of the future lead us to the threshold of an unknown world. They seem to point to the existence of a psychic principle capable of evolving outside the limits of our bodies. The specialists of spiritism interpret certain of these phenomena as proof of

[*] See note, p. 239.

the survival of consciousness after death. The medium believes himself to be inhabited by the spirit of the deceased. He may reveal to the experimenters some details known only to the dead man, and the exactness of which is verified later. According to Broad, these facts could be interpreted as indicating the persistence after death, not of the mind, but of a psychic factor capable of grafting itself temporarily upon the organism of the medium. This psychic factor, in uniting with a human being, would constitute a sort of consciousness belonging both to the medium and to the defunct. Its existence would be transitory. It would progressively break up and finally disappear. The results obtained by the spiritists' experiments are of great importance. But their significance is not precise. For the clairvoyant there are no secrets. At the present time, therefore, it does not seem possible to make a distinction between the survival of a psychic principle and a phenomenon of mediumistic clairvoyance.

9

To summarize. Individuality is not merely an aspect of the organism. It also constitutes an essential characteristic of each component part of this organism. It remains virtual in the fertilized ovum, and progressively unfolds its characteristics as the new being extends into time. The ancestral tendencies of this being are forced to actualize by his conflict with the environment. They incline his adaptive activities in a certain direction. In fact, the mode of utilization of its surroundings by the body is determined by its innate properties. Each individual responds to these surroundings in his own way. He chooses among the things of the outer world those which increase his individualization. He is a focus of specific activities. These activities are distinct but indivisible. The soul cannot be separated from the body, the structure from the function, the cell from its medium, the multiplicity from the unity, or the determining from the determined. We are beginning to realize that our surface is not our real frontier, that it merely sets up between us and the cosmic universe a plane of cleavage indispensable to our action. We are constructed like the castles of the Middle Ages, whose dungeons were surrounded by several lines of fortifications. Our inner defences are numerous and entangled one with another. The skin is the barrier that our microscopic enemies must not traverse. But we extend much farther beyond it, beyond space and time. We know the individual's centre, yet ignore where his outer limits are located. These limits, in fact, are hypothetical. Perhaps they do not exist. Each man is bound to those who precede and follow him. He fuses in some manner into them. Humanity does not appear to be composed of separate particles, as a gas is of molecules. It resembles an intricate network of long threads extending in space-time and consisting of series of individuals. Individuality is doubtless real, but it is much less definite than we believe. And the independence of each individual from the others and from the cosmos is an illusion.

Our body is made up of the chemical substances of the environment. These substances enter it and become modified according to its individuality. They are built up into temporary edifices, tissues, humours, and organs, which ceaselessly disintegrate and are reconstructed during our whole life. After our death they return to the world of inert matter. Certain chemical compounds assume our racial and individual peculiarities. They become truly ourselves. Others only pass through the body. They participate in the existence of our tissues without taking any of their characteristics, just as wax does not modify its chemical composition when made into statues of different shapes. They flow through the organism like a large river, from which cells draw the substances required for their growth, their maintenance, and their expenditure of energy. According to Christian mystics, we receive from the outer world certain spiritual elements. The grace of God permeates soul and body, just as atmospheric oxygen, or nitrogen from the food, diffuses in our tissues.

Individual specificity persists during the entire life, although tissues and humours continually change. The organs and their medium move at the rhythm of physiological time —that is, at the rhythm of irreversible processes, towards definitive transformations and death. But they always keep their inherent qualities. They are not modified by the stream of matter in which they are immersed, any more than the spruce trees on the mountains by the clouds passing through their branches. However, individuality grows stronger or weaker according to environmental conditions. When these conditions are particularly unfavourable it dissolves. Sometimes, mental personality is less marked than organic personality. One may rightly ask whether it still exists in modern men. Some observers doubt its reality. Theodore Dreiser considers it a myth. It is certain that the inhabitants of the new city show great uniformity in their mental and moral weakness. Most of the individuals belong to the same type : a mixture of nervousness and apathy, of vanity and lack of confidence in themselves, of muscular strength and tendency to fatigue; of genesic impulses, both irresistible and not strong, sometimes homosexual. Such a state is due to profound disorders in the formation of personality. It does not consist only in an attitude of mind, a fashion which could easily change. It expresses either a degeneration of the race, or a defective development of the individual, or both these phenomena.

This debasement is, in a certain measure, of hereditary origin. The suppression of natural selection, as already mentioned, has caused the survival of children whose tissues and consciousness are defective. The race has been weakened by the preservation of such reproducers. The relative importance of this factor of degeneration is not yet known. As we have already mentioned, the influence of heredity cannot be distinguished clearly from that of environment. Feeble-mindedness and insanity surely have an ancestral cause. The intellectual weakness observed in schools and universities, and in the population in general, comes from developmental disorders, and not from hereditary defects. When these flabby, silly young people are removed from their customary environment and placed in more primitive conditions of life, they sometimes change for the better and recover their virility. The atrophic character of the products of our civilization, therefore, is not incurable. It is far from being always the expression of a racial degeneration.

Among the multitude of weak and defective there are, however, some completely developed men. These men, when closely observed, appear to be superior to the classical schemata. In fact, the individual whose potentialities are all actualized does not resemble the human being pictured by the specialists. He is not the fragments of consciousness which psychologists attempt to measure. He is not to be found in the chemical reactions, the functional processes, and the organs which physicians have divided between themselves. Neither is he the abstraction whose concrete manifestations the educators try to guide. He is almost completely wanting in the rudimentary being manufactured by social workers, prison wardens, economists, sociologists, and politicians. In fact, he never appears to a specialist unless this specialist is willing to look at him as a whole. He is much more than the sum of all the facts accumulated by the particular sciences. We never apprehend him in his entirety. He contains vast, unknown regions. His potentialities are almost inexhaustible. Like the great natural phenomena he is still unintelligible. When one contemplates him in the harmony of all his organic and spiritual activities, one experiences a profound æsthetic emotion. Such an individual is truly the creator and the centre of the universe.

10

Modern society ignores the individual. It only takes account of human beings. It believes in the reality of the Universals and treats men as abstractions. The confusion of the concepts of individual and of human being has led industrial civilization to a fundamental error, the standardization of men. If we were all identical, we could be reared and made to live and work in great herds like cattle. But each one has his own personality. He cannot be treated like a symbol. Children should not be placed, at a very early age, in schools where they are educated wholesale. As is well known, most great men have been brought up in comparative solitude, or have refused to enter the mould of the school. Of course, schools are indispensable for technical studies. They also fill, in a certain measure, the child's need of contact with other children. But education should be the object of unfailing guidance. Such guidance belongs to the parents. They alone, and more especially the mother, have observed, since their origin, the physiological and mental peculiarities whose orientation is the aim of education. Modern society has committed a serious mistake by entirely substituting the school for the familial training. The mothers abandon their children to the kindergarten in order to attend to their careers, their social ambitions, their sexual pleasures, their literary or artistic fancies, or simply to play bridge, go to the cinema, and waste their time in busy idleness. They are, thus, responsible for the disappearance of the familial group where the child was kept in contact with adults and learned a great deal from them. Young dogs brought up in kennels with others of the same age do not develop as well as puppies free to run about with their parents. It is the same with children living in a crowd of other children, and with those living in the company of intelligent adults. The child easily moulds his physiological, affective, and mental activities upon those of his surroundings. He learns little from children of his own age. When he is only a unit in a school he remains incomplete. In order to reach his full strength, the individual requires the relative isolation and the attention of the restricted social group consisting of the family.

The neglect of individuality by our social institutions is, likewise, responsible for the atrophy of the adults. Man does not stand, without damage, the mode of existence and the uniform and stupid work imposed on factory and office workers, on all those who take part in mass production. In the immensity of modern cities he is isolated and as if lost. He is an economic abstraction, a unit of the herd. He gives up his individuality. He has neither responsibility nor dignity. Above the multitude stand out the rich men, the powerful politicians, the bandits. The others are only nameless grains of dust. On the contrary, the individual remains a man when he belongs to a small group, when he inhabits a village or a small town where his relative importance is greater, when he can hope to become, in his turn, an influential citizen. The contempt for individuality has brought about its factual disappearance.

Another error, due to the confusion of the concepts of human being and individual, is democratic equality. This dogma is now breaking down under the blows of the experience of the nations. It is, therefore, unnecessary to insist upon its falseness. But its success has been astonishingly long. How could humanity accept such faith for so many years? The democratic creed does not take account of the constitution of our body and of our consciousness. It does not apply to the concrete fact which the individual is. Indeed, human beings are equal. But individuals are not. The equality of their rights is an illusion. The feeble-minded and the man of genius should not be equal before the law. The stupid, the unintelligent, those who are dispersed, incapable of attention, of effort, have no right to a higher education. It is absurd to give them the same electoral power as the fully developed individuals. Sexes are not equal. To disregard all

these inequalities is very dangerous. The democratic principle has contributed to the collapse of civilization in opposing the development of an élite. It is obvious that, on the
contrary, individual inequalities must be respected. In
modern society the great, the small, the average, and the
mediocre are needed. But we should not attempt to develop
the higher types by the same procedures as the lower. The
standardization of men by the democratic ideal has already
determined the predominance of the weak. Everywhere the
weak are preferred to the strong. They are aided and protected, often admired. Like the invalid, the criminal, and the
insane, they attract the sympathy of the public. The myth of
equality, the love of the symbol, the contempt for the concrete fact, are in a large measure guilty of the collapse of individuality. As it was impossible to raise the inferior types,
the only means of producing democratic equality among men
was to bring all to the lowest level. Thus vanished personality.

Not only has the concept of the individual been confused
with that of the human being, but the latter has been adulterated by the introduction of foreign elements, and deprived
of certain of its own elements. We have applied to man concepts belonging to the mechanical world. We have neglected
thought, moral suffering, sacrifice, beauty, and peace. We
have treated the individual as a chemical substance, a machine, or a part of a machine. We have amputated his moral,
æsthetic, and religious functions. We have also ignored certain aspects of his physiological activities. We have not asked
how tissues and consciousness would accommodate themselves to the changes in the mode of life imposed upon us.
We have totally forgotten the important rôle of the adaptive
functions and the momentous consequences of their enforced
rest. Our present weakness comes both from our unappre-
ciation of individuality and from our ignorance of the constitution of the human being.

II

Man is the the result of heredity and environment, of the habits of life and thought imposed upon him by modern society. We have described how these habits affect his body and his consciousness. We know that he cannot adapt himself to the environment created by technology, that such environment brings about his degradation. Science and machines are not responsible for his present state. We alone are guilty. We have not been capable of distinguishing the prohibited from the lawful. We have infringed natural laws. We have thus committed the supreme sin, the sin that is always punished. The dogmas of scientific religion and industrial morals have fallen under the onslaught of biological reality. Life always gives an identical answer when asked to trespass on forbidden ground. It weakens. And civilizations collapse. The sciences of inert matter have led us into a country that is not ours. We have blindly accepted all their gifts. The individual has become narrow, specialized, immoral, unintelligent, incapable of managing himself and his own institutions. But at the same time the biological sciences have revealed to us the most precious of all secrets—the laws of the development of our body and of our consciousness. This knowledge has brought to humanity the means of renovating itself. As long as the hereditary qualities of the race remain present, the strength and the audacity of his forefathers can be resurrected in modern man by his own will. But is he still capable of such an effort?

CHAPTER VIII

THE REMAKING OF MAN

1. Can the science of man lead to his renovation? 2. Necessity of a change in our intellectual outlook. The error of the Renaissance. The supremacy of the quantitative over the qualitative, of matter over spirit, to be rejected. 3. How to render utilizable our knowledge of man. How to construct a synthesis. Can any one scientist master this mass of knowledge? 4. The institutions required for the development of the science of man. 5. The task of constructing man according to the rules of his nature. Necessity of acting on the individual through his environment. 6. The selection of individuals. Social and biological classes. 7. The construction of an élite. Voluntary eugenics. Hereditary aristocracy. 8. Physical and chemical factors in the formation of the individual. 9. Physiological factors. 10. Mental factors. 11. Health. 12. Development of personality. 13. The human universe. 14. The remaking of man.

I

SCIENCE, which has transformed the material world, gives man the power of transforming himself. It has unveiled some of the secret mechanisms of his life. It has shown him how to alter their motion, how to mould his body and his soul on patterns born of his wishes. For the first time in history, humanity, helped by science, has become master of its destiny. But will we be capable of using this knowledge of ourselves to our real advantage? To progress again, man must remake himself. And he cannot remake himself without suffering. For he is both the marble and the sculptor. In order to uncover his true visage he must shatter his own substance with heavy blows of his hammer. He will not submit to such treatment unless driven by necessity. While surrounded by the comfort, the beauty, and the mechanical marvels engendered by technology, he does not understand

252

how urgent is this operation. He fails to realize that he is degenerating. Why should he strive to modify his ways of being, living, and thinking?

Fortunately, an event unforeseen by engineers, economists, and politicians took place. The superb edifice of American finance and economics suddenly collapsed. At first the public did not believe in the reality of such a catastrophe. Its faith was not disturbed. The explanations given by the economists were heard with docility. Prosperity would return. But prosperity has not returned. To-day, the more intelligent heads of the flock are beginning to doubt. Are the causes of the crisis uniquely economic and financial? Should we not also incriminate the corruption and the stupidity of the politicians and the financiers, the ignorance and the illusions of the economists? Has not modern life decreased the intelligence and the morality of the whole nation? Why must we pay several billions of dollars each year to fight criminals? Why do the gangsters continue victoriously to attack banks, kill policemen, kidnap, ransom, or assassinate children, in spite of the immense amount of money spent in opposing them? Why are there so many feeble-minded and insane among civilized people? Does not the world crisis depend on individual and social factors that are more important than the economic ones? It is to be hoped that the spectacle of civilization at this beginning of its decline will compel us to ascertain whether the causes of the catastrophe do not lie within ourselves, as well as in our institutions, and that we will fully realize the imperativeness of our renovation.

Then we will be faced by a single obstacle, our inertia, and not by the incapacity of our race to rise again. In fact, the economic crisis came before the complete destruction of our ancestral qualities by the idleness, corruption, and softness of life. We know that intellectual apathy, immorality, and criminality are not, in general, hereditary. Most children, at their birth, are endowed with the same potentialities as their parents. We can develop their innate qualities if we

wish earnestly to do so. We have at our disposal all the
might of science. There are still many men capable of using
this power unselfishly. Modern society has not stifled all the
focuses of intellectual culture, moral courage, virtue, and
audacity. The flame is still burning. The evil is not irreparable. But the remaking of the individual demands the transformation of modern life. It cannot take place without a
material and mental revolution. To understand the necessity
of a change, and to possess the scientific means of realizing
this change, are not sufficient. The spontaneous crash of
technological civilization may help to release the impulses
required for the destruction of our present habits and the
creation of new modes of life.

Do we still have enough energy and perspicacity for such
a gigantic effort? At first sight it does not seem so. Man has
sunk into indifference to almost everything except money.
There are, however, some reasons for hope. After all, the
races responsible for the construction of our world are not
extinct. The ancestral potentialities still exist in the germ-
plasm of their weak offspring. These potentialities can yet be
actualized. Indeed, the descendants of the energetic strains
are smothered in the multitude of proletarians whom industry has blindly created. They are small in number. But
they will not succumb. For they possess a marvellous, although hidden, strength. We must not forget the stupendous
task we have accomplished since the fall of the Roman Empire. In the small area of the states of western Europe, amid
unceasing wars, famines, and epidemics, we have succeeded
in keeping, throughout the Middle Ages, the relics of antique
culture. During long, dark centuries we shed our blood on
all sides in the defence of Christendom against our enemies
of the north, the east, and the south. At the cost of immense
efforts we succeeded in thrusting back the sleep of Islam.
Then a miracle happened. From the mind of men, sharp-
ened by scholastic discipline, sprang science. And, strange
to say science was cultivated by those men of the Occident

for itself, for its truth and its beauty, with complete disinterestedness. Instead of stagnating in individual egoism, as it did in the Orient and especially in China, this science, in four hundred years, has transformed the world. Our fathers have made a prodigious effort. Most of their European and American descendants have forgotten the past. History is also ignored by those who now profit from our material civilization: by the white who, in the Middle Ages, did not fight beside us on the European battlefields, by the yellow, the brown, and the black, whose mounting tide exaggeratedly alarms Spengler. What we accomplished once we are capable of accomplishing again. Should our civilization collapse, we should build up another one. But is it indispensable to suffer the agony of chaos before reaching order and peace? Can we not rise again, without undergoing the bloody regeneration of total overthrow? Are we capable of renovating ourselves, of avoiding the cataclysms which are imminent, and of continuing our ascent?

2

We cannot undertake the restoration of ourselves and of our environment before having transformed our habits of thought. Modern society has suffered, ever since its origin, from an intellectual fault—a fault which has been constantly repeated since the Renaissance. Technology has constructed man, not according to the spirit of science, but according to erroneous metaphysical conceptions. The time has come to abandon these doctrines. We should break down the fences which have been erected between the properties of concrete objects, and between the different aspects of ourselves. The error responsible for our sufferings comes from a wrong interpretation of a genial idea of Galileo. Galileo, as is well known, distinguished the primary qualities of things, dimensions and weight, which are easily measurable, from their secondary qualities, form, colour, odour, which cannot be measured. The quantitative was separated from the qualitative. The quantitative, expressed in mathematical language, brought science to humanity. The qualitative was neglected. The abstraction of the primary qualities of objects was legitimate, but the overlooking of the secondary qualities was not. This mistake had momentous consequences. In man, the things which are not measurable are more important than those which are measurable. The existence of thought is as fundamental as, for instance, the physico-chemical equilibria of blood serum. The separation of the qualitative from the quantitative grew still wider when Descartes created the dualism of the body and the soul. Then the manifestations of the mind became inexplicable. The material was definitely isolated from the spiritual. Organic structures and physiological mechanisms assumed a far greater reality than thought, pleasure, sorrow, and beauty. This error switched civilization to the road which led science to triumph and man to degradation.

In order to find again the right direction we must return in thought to the men of the Renaissance, imbue ourselves with their spirit, their passion for empiric observation, and their contempt for philosophical systems. As they did, we have to distinguish the primary and secondary qualities of things. But we must radically differ from them and attribute to secondary qualities the same importance as to primary qualities. We should also reject the dualism of Descartes. Mind will be replaced in matter. The soul will no longer be distinct from the body. Mental manifestations, as well as physiological processes, will be within our reach. Indeed, the qualitative is more difficult to study than the quantitative. Concrete facts do not satisfy our mind, which prefers the definitive aspect of abstractions. But science must not be cultivated only for itself, for the elegance of its methods, for its light and its beauty. Its goal is the material and spiritual benefit of man. As much importance should be given to feelings as to thermodynamics. It is indispensable that our thought embraces all aspects of reality. Instead of discarding the residues of scientific abstractions we will utilize those residues as fully as the abstractions. We will not accept the tyranny of the quantitative, the superiority of mechanics, physics, or chemistry. We will renounce the intellectual attitude generated by the Renaissance, and its arbitrary definition of the real. But we must retain all the conquests made since Galileo's day. The spirit and the techniques of science are our most precious possessions.

It will be difficult to get rid of a doctrine which, during more than three hundred years, has dominated the intelligence of the civilized. The majority of men of science believe in the reality of the Universals, the exclusive right to existence of the quantitative, the supremacy of matter, the separation of the mind from the body, and the subordinated position of the mind. They will not easily give up this faith. For such a change would shake pedagogy, medicine, hygiene, psychology, and sociology to their foundations. The little garden which each scientist easily cultivates would be turned into a forest, which would have to be cleared. If scientific civilization should leave the road that it has followed since the Renaissance and return to the naïve observation of the concrete, strange events would immediately take place. Matter would lose its supremacy. Mental activities would become as important as physiological ones. The study of moral, æsthetic, and religious functions would appear as indispensable as that of mathematics, physics, and chemistry. The present methods of education would seem absurd. Schools and universities would be obliged to modify their programmes. Hygienists would be asked why they concern themselves exclusively with the prevention of organic diseases, and not with that of mental and nervous disturbances; why they pay no attention to spiritual health; why they segregate people ill with infections, and not those who propagate intellectual and moral maladies; why the habits

I (A181)

responsible for organic diseases are considered dangerous, and not those which bring on corruption, criminality, and insanity. The public would refuse to be attended by physicians knowing nothing but a small part of the body. Specialists would have to learn general medicine, or work as units of a group under the direction of a general practitioner. Pathologists would be induced to study the lesions of the humours as well as those of the organs, to take into account the influence of the mental upon the tissues, and vice versa. Economists would realize that human beings think, feel, and suffer, that they should be given other things than work, food, and leisure, that they have spiritual as well as physiological needs. And also that the causes of economic and financial crises may be moral and intellectual. We should no longer be obliged to accept the barbarous conditions of life in great cities, the tyranny of factory and office, the sacrifice of moral dignity to economic interest, of mind to money, as benefactions conferred upon us by modern civilization. We should reject mechanical inventions that hinder human development. Economics would no longer appear as the ultimate reason of everything. It is obvious that the liberation of man from the materialistic creed would transform most of the aspects of our existence. Therefore, modern society will oppose with all its might this progress in our conceptions.

However, we must take care that the failure of materialism does not bring about a spiritual reaction. Since technology and worship of matter have not been a success, the temptation may be great to choose the opposite cult, the cult of mind. The primacy of psychology would be no less dangerous than that of physiology, physics, and chemistry. Freud has done more harm than the most extreme mechanicists. It would be as disastrous to reduce man to his mental aspect as to his physiological and physico-chemical mechanisms. The study of the physical properties of blood serum, of its ionic equilibria, of protoplasmic permeability, of the chemical constitution of antigens, etc., is as indispensable as that of dreams, libido, mediumistic states, psychological effects of prayer, memory of words, etc. Substitution of the spiritual for the material would not correct the error made by the Renaissance. The exclusion of matter would be still more detrimental to man than that of mind. Salvation will be found only in the relinquishing of all doctrines, in the full acceptation of the data of observation, in the realization of the fact that man is no less and no more than these data.

3

These data must be the basis of the construction of man. Our first task is to make them utilizable. Every year we hear of the progress made by eugenists, geneticists, statisticians, behaviourists, physiologists, anatomists, biological chemists, physical chemists, psychologists, physicians, hygienists, endocrinologists, psychiatrists, immunologists, educators, social workers, clergymen, sociologists, economists, etc. But the practical results of these accomplishments are surprisingly small. This immense amount of information is disseminated in technical reviews, in treatises, in the brains of men of science. No one has it in his possession. We have now to put together its disparate fragments, and to make this knowledge live within the mind of at least a few individuals. Then it will become productive.

There are great difficulties in such an undertaking. How should we proceed to build up this synthesis? Around what aspect of man should the others be grouped? What is his most important activity? The economic, the political, the sociological, the mental, or the organic? What particular science should be caused to grow and absorb the others? Obviously, the remaking of man and of his economic and social world should be inspired by a precise knowledge of his body and of his soul—that is, of physiology, psychology, and pathology.

Medicine is the most comprehensive of all the sciences concerning man, from anatomy to political economy. However, it is far from apprehending its object in its full extent. Physicians have contented themselves with studying the structure and the activities of the individual in health and in disease, and attempting to cure the sick. Their effort has met, as we know, with modest success. Their influence on modern society has been sometimes beneficial, sometimes harmful, always secondary; excepting, however, when hygiene aided industry in promoting the growth of civilized populations. Medicine has been paralyzed by the narrowness of its doctrines. But it could easily escape from its prison and help us in a more effective manner. Nearly three hundred years ago a philosopher, who dreamed of consecrating his life to the service of man, clearly conceived the high functions of which medicine is capable. "The mind," wrote Descartes in his *Discourse on Method*, "so strongly depends on temperament and the disposition of bodily organs, that if it is possible to find some means which will make men generally more wise and more clever than they have been till now, I believe that it is in medicine one should seek it. It is true that the medicine now practised contains few things having so remarkable a usefulness. But, without having any intention of scorning it, I am confident that there is no one, even among those whose profession it is, who does not admit that everything already known about it is almost nothing in comparison with what remains to be learned, and that people could be spared an infinity of diseases, both bodily and mental, and perhaps even the weakening of old age, if the causes of those troubles and all the remedies with which nature has provided us were sufficiently well known."

Medicine has received from anatomy, physiology, psychology, and pathology the more essential elements of the knowledge of ourselves. It could easily enlarge its field, embrace, in addition to body and consciousness, their relations with the material and mental world, take in sociology and economics, and become the very science of the human being. Its aim, then, would be not only to cure or prevent diseases, but also to guide the development of all our organic, mental, and sociological activities. It would become capable of building the individual according to natural laws, and of inspiring those who will have the task of leading humanity to a true civilization. At the present time, education, hygiene, religion, town planning, and social and economic organizations are entrusted to individuals who know but a single aspect of the human being. No one would ever dream of substituting politicians, well-meaning women, lawyers, literary men, or philosophers for the engineers of the steel-works or of the chemical factories. However, such people are given the incomparably heavier responsibility of the physiological, mental, and sociological guidance of civilized men, and even of the government of great nations. Medicine, aggrandized according to the conception of Descartes, and extended in such a manner as to embrace the other sciences of man, could supply modern society with engineers understanding the mechanisms of the body and the soul of the individual, and of his relations with the cosmic and social world.

This super-science will be utilizable only if, instead of being buried in libraries, it animates our intelligence. But is it possible for a single brain to assimilate such a gigantic amount of knowledge? Can any individual master anatomy, physiology, biological chemistry, psychology, metapsychics, pathology, medicine, and also have a thorough acquaintance with genetics, nutrition, development, pedagogy, æsthetics, morals, religion, sociology, and economics? It seems that such an accomplishment is not impossible. In about twenty-five years of uninterrupted study one could learn these sciences. At the age of fifty, those who have submitted themselves to this discipline could effectively direct the construction of the human being and of a civilization based on his true nature. Indeed, the few gifted individuals who dedicate themselves to this work will have to renounce the common modes of existence. They will not be able to play golf and bridge, to go to cinemas, to listen to radios, to make speeches at banquets, to serve on committees, to attend meetings of scientific societies, political conventions, and academies, or to cross the ocean and take part in international congresses. They must live like the monks of the great contemplative orders, and not like university professors, and still less like business men. In the course of the history of all great nations, many have sacrificed themselves for the salvation of the community. Sacrifice seems to be a necessary condition of progress. There are now, as in former times, men ready for the supreme renunciation. If the multitudes inhabiting the defenceless cities of the seacoast were menaced by shells and gases, no army aviator would hesitate to thrust himself, his plane, and his bombs against the invaders. Why should not some individuals sacrifice their lives to acquire the science indispensable to the making of man and of his environment? In fact the task is extremely difficult. But minds capable of undertaking it can be discovered. The weakness of many of the scientists whom we meet in universities and laboratories is due to the mediocrity of their goal and to the narrowness of their life. Men grow when inspired by a high purpose, when contemplating vast horizons. The sacrifice of oneself is not very difficult for one burning with the passion for a great adventure. And there is no more beautiful and dangerous adventure than the renovation of modern man.

4

The making of man requires the development of institutions wherein body and mind can be formed according to natural laws, and not to the prejudices of the various schools of educators. It is essential that the individual, from infancy, be liberated from the dogmas of industrial civilization and the principles which are the very basis of modern society. The science of the human being does not need costly and numerous organizations in order to start its constructive work. It can utilize those already existing, provided they are rejuvenated. The success of such an enterprise will depend, in certain countries, on the attitude of the Government and, in others, on that of the public. In Italy, Germany, or Russia, if the dictator judged it useful to condition children according to a definite type, to modify adults and their ways of life in a definite manner, appropriate institutions would spring up at once. In democratic countries progress has to come from private initiative. When the failure of most of our educational, medical, economic, and social beliefs becomes more apparent, the public will probably feel the necessity of a remedy for this situation.

In the past, the efforts of isolated individuals have caused the ascent of religion, science, and education. The development of hygiene in the United States is entirely due to the inspiration of a few men. For instance, Hermann Biggs made New York one of the most healthful cities of the world. A group of unknown young men, under the guidance of Welch, founded the Johns Hopkins Medical School, and initiated the astonishing progress of pathology, surgery, and hygiene in the United States. When bacteriology sprang from Pasteur's brain, the Pasteur Institute was created in Paris by national subscription. The Rockefeller Institute for Medical Research was founded in New York by John D. Rockefeller, because the necessity for new discoveries in the domain of medicine had become evident to Welch, Theobald Smith, T. Mitchell Prudden, Simon Flexner, Christian Herter, and a few other scientists. In many American universities, research laboratories, destined to further the progress of physiology, immunology, chemistry, etc., were established and endowed by enlightened benefactors. The great Carnegie and Rockefeller Foundations were inspired by more general ideas: to develop education, raise the scientific level of universities, promote peace among nations, prevent infectious diseases, improve the health and the welfare of everybody with the help of scientific methods. Those movements have always been started by the realization of a need, and the establishment of an institution responding to that need. The State did not help in their beginnings. But private institutions forced the progress of public institutions. In France, for example, bacteriology was at first taught exclusively at the Pasteur Institute. Later, chairs and laboratories of bacteriology were established in all state universities.

The institutions necessary for the rebuilding of man will probably develop in a similar manner. Some day, a school, a college, a university may understand the importance of the subject. Slight efforts in the right direction have already been made. For instance, Yale University has created an Institute for the study of human relations. The Macy Foundation was established for the development of integrative ideas concerning man, his health, and his education. Greater advance has been realized in Genoa by Nicola Pende in his Institute for the study of the human individual. Many American physicians begin to feel the necessity for a broader comprehension of man. However, this feeling has by no means been formulated as clearly here as in Italy. The already existing organizations have to undergo important changes in order to become fitted for the work of human renovation. They must, for instance, eliminate the remnants of the narrow mechanisticism of the last century, and understand the imperativeness of a clarification of the concepts used in biology, of a reintegration of the parts into the whole, and of the formation of true scholars, as well as of scientific workers. The direction of the institutions of learning, and of those which apply to man the results of the special sciences, from biological chemistry to political economy, should not be given to specialists, because specialists are exaggeratedly in-

terested in the progress of their own particular studies, but
to individuals capable of embracing all sciences. The specialists must be only the tools of a synthetic mind. They will be
utilized by him in the same way as the professor of medicine
of a great university utilizes the services of pathologists, bac-
teriologists, physiologists, chemists, and physicists in the
laboratories of his clinic. None of these scientists is ever
given the direction of the treatment of the patients. An economist, an endocrinologist, a social worker, a psycho-
analyst, a biological chemist, are equally ignorant of man.
They cannot be trusted beyond the limits of their own
field.

We should not forget that our knowledge of man is still
rudimentary, that most of the great problems mentioned at
the beginning of this book remain unsolved. However, an
answer must be given to the questions which concern the fate
of hundreds of millions of individuals and the future of
civilization. Such an answer can be elaborated only in research institutes dedicated to the promotion of the science of
man. Our biological and medical laboratories have so far
devoted their activities to the pursuit of health, to the discovery of the chemical and physico-chemical mechanisms
underlying physiological phenomena. The Pasteur Institute
has followed with great success the road opened by its
founder. Under the direction of Duclaux and of Roux, it has
specialized in the investigation of bacteria and viruses, in the
means of protecting human beings from their attacks, in the
discovery of vaccines, sera, and chemicals for the prevention
or the cure of diseases. The Rockefeller Institute undertook
the survey of a broader field. The study of the agents responsible for diseases, and of their effects on animals and men,
was pursued simultaneously with that of the physical, chemical, physico-chemical, and physiological activities manifested by the body. Such investigations should now progress
further. The entire man has to be brought into the domain of
biological research. Each specialist must freely continue the
I*

exploration of his own field. But no important aspect of the human being should remain ignored. The method used by Simon Flexner in the direction of the Rockefeller Institute could be profitably extended to the organization of the biological or medical institutes of to-morrow. At the Rockefeller Institute, living matter is being studied in an exhaustive manner, from the structure of the molecules to that of the human body. However, in the organization of this vast ensemble of researches, Flexner did not impose any programme on the staff of his Institute. He was content with selecting scientists who had a natural propensity for the exploration of these different fields. A similar policy could lead to the development of laboratories for the investigation of the psychological and sociological activities, as well as the chemical and physiological.

The biological institutes of the future, in order to be productive, will have to guard against the confusion of concepts, which we have mentioned as one of the causes of the sterility of medical research. The supreme science, psychology, needs the methods and the concepts of physiology, anatomy, mechanics, chemistry, physical chemistry, physics, and mathematics—that is, of all sciences occupying a lower rank in the hierarchy of knowledge. We know that the concepts of a science of higher rank cannot be reduced to those of a science of lower rank, that large-scale phenomena are no less fundamental than small-scale phenomena, that psychological events are as real as physico-chemical ones. Mathematics, physics, and chemistry are indispensable but not basic sciences in the researches concerning living organisms. They are as indispensable as, but not more basic than, speaking and writing are, for instance, to a historian. They are not capable of constructing the concepts specific to the human being. Like the universities, the research institutions entrusted with the study of man in health and disease should be led by scientists possessing a broad knowledge of physiology, chemistry, medicine, and psychology. The biological workers of to-morrow must realize that their goal is the living organism and not merely artificially isolated systems or models: that general physiology, as considered by Bayliss, is a very small part of physiology; that organismal and mental phenomena cannot be dismissed. The studies to be undertaken in the laboratories for medical research should include all the subjects pertaining to the physical, chemical, structural, functional, and psychological activities of man, and to the relations of those activities with the cosmic and social environment.

We know that the evolution of humanity is very slow, that the study of its problems demands the lifetime of several generations of scientists. We need, therefore, an institution capable of providing for the uninterrupted pursuit for at least a century of the investigations concerning man. Modern society should be given an intellectual focus, an immortal brain, capable of conceiving and planning its future, and of promoting and pushing forward fundamental researches, in spite of the death of the individual researchers, or the bankruptcy of the research institutes. Such an organization would be the salvation of the white races in their staggering advance toward civilization. This thinking centre would consist, as does the Supreme Court of the United States, of a few individuals; the latter being trained in the knowledge of man by many years of study. It should perpetuate itself automatically in such a manner as to radiate ever young ideas. Democratic rulers, as well as dictators, could receive from this source of scientific truth the information that they need in order to develop a civilization really suitable to man.

The members of this high council would be free from research and teaching. They would deliver no addresses. They would dedicate their lives to the contemplation of the economic, sociological, psychological, physiological, and pathological phenomena manifested by the civilized nations and their constitutive individuals, and to that of the develop-

ment of science and of the influence of its applications to our
habits of life and of thought. They would endeavour to discover how modern civilization could mould itself to man
without crushing any of his essential qualities. Their silent
meditation would protect the inhabitants of the new city
from the mechanical inventions which are dangerous for
their body or their mind, from the adulteration of thought as
well as food, from the whims of the specialists in education,
nutrition, morals, sociology, etc., from all progress inspired,
not by the needs of the public, but by the greed or the illusions of their inventors. An institution of this sort would acquire enough knowledge to prevent the organic and mental
deterioration of civilized nations. Its members should be
given a position as highly considered, as free from political
intrigues and from cheap publicity, as that of the justices of
the Supreme Court. Their importance would, in truth, be
much greater than that of the jurists who watch over the
Constitution. For they would be the defenders of the body
and the soul of a great race in its tragic struggle against the
blind sciences of matter.

5

We must rescue the individual from the state of intellectual, moral, and physiological atrophy brought about by
modern conditions of life: develop all his potential activities: give him health: re-establish him in his unity, in the
harmony of his personality: induce him to utilize all the
hereditary qualities of his tissues and his consciousness:
break the shell in which education and society have succeeded in enclosing him; and reject all systems. We have to
intervene in the fundamental organic and mental processes.
These processes are man himself. But man has no independent existence. He is bound to his environment. In order to
remake him, we have to transform his world.

Our social frame, our material and mental background, should be rebuilt. But society is not plastic. Its form cannot be changed in an instant. Nevertheless, the enterprise of our restoration must start immediately, in the present conditions of our existence. Each individual has the power to modify his way of life, to create around him an environment slightly different from that of the unthinking crowd. He is capable of isolating himself in some measure, of imposing upon himself certain physiological and mental disciplines, certain work, certain habits, of acquiring the mastery of his body and mind. But if he stands alone, he cannot indefinitely resist his material, mental, and economic environment. In order to combat this environment victoriously he must associate with others having the same purpose. Revolutions often start with small groups in which the new tendencies ferment and grow. During the eighteenth century such groups prepared the overthrow of absolute monarchy in France. The French Revolution was due to the encyclopædists far more than to the Jacobins. To-day, the principles of industrial civilization should be fought with the same relentless vigour as was the *ancien régime* by the encyclopædists. But the struggle will be harder because the mode of existence brought to us by technology is as pleasant as the habit of taking alcohol, opium, or cocaine. The few individuals who are animated by the spirit of revolt might organize in secret groups. At present the protection of children is almost impossible. The influence of the school, private as well as public, cannot be counterbalanced. The young who have been freed by intelligent parents from the usual medical, pedagogical, and social superstitions, relapse through the example of their comrades. All are obliged to conform to the habits of the herd. The renovation of the individual demands his affiliation with a group sufficiently numerous to separate from others and to possess its own schools. Under the impulse of the centres of new thought, some universities may perhaps be led to abandon the classical forms of education and prepare youth for the life of tomorrow with the help of disciplines based on the true nature of man.

A group, although very small, is capable of eluding the harmful influence of the society of its epoch by imposing upon its members rules of conduct modelled on military or monastic discipline. Such a method is far from being new. Humanity has already lived through periods when communities of men or women separated from others and adopted strict regulations, in order to attain their ideals. Such groups were responsible for the development of our civilization during the Middle Ages. There were the monastic orders, the orders of chivalry, and the corporations of artisans. Among the religious organizations, some took refuge in monasteries, while others remained in the world. But all submitted to strict physiological and mental discipline. The knights complied with rules varying according to the aims of the different orders. In certain circumstances they were obliged to sacrifice their lives. As for the artisans, their relations between themselves and with the public were determined by exacting legislation. Each corporation had its customs, its ceremonies, and its religious celebrations. In short, the members of these communities renounced the ordinary forms of existence. Are we not capable of repeating, in a different form, the accomplishments of the monks, the knights, and the artisans of the Middle Ages? Two essential conditions for the progress of the individual are relative isolation and discipline. Each individual, even in the new city, can submit himself to these conditions. One has the power of refusing to go to certain plays or cinemas, to send one's children to certain schools, to listen to radio programmes, to read certain newspapers, certain books, etc. But it is chiefly through intellectual and moral discipline, and the rejection of the habits of the herd, that we can reconstruct ourselves. Sufficiently large groups could lead a still more personal life. The Doukhobors of Canada have demonstrated that those whose will is strong can secure complete independence, even in the midst of modern civilization.

The dissenting groups would not need to be very numerous to bring about profound changes in modern society. It is a well-established fact that discipline gives great strength to men. An ascetic and mystic minority would rapidly acquire an irresistible power over the dissolute and degraded majority. Such a minority would be in a position to impose, by persuasion or perhaps by force, other ways of life upon the majority. None of the dogmas of modern society are immutable. Gigantic factories, office buildings rising to the sky, inhuman cities, industrial morals, faith in mass production, are not indispensable to civilization. Other modes of existence and of thought are possible. Culture without comfort, beauty without luxury, machines without enslaving factories, science without the worship of matter, would restore to man his intelligence, his moral sense, his virility, and lead him to the summit of his development.

6

A choice must be made among the multitude of civilized human beings. We have mentioned that natural selection has not played its part for a long while; that many inferior individuals have been conserved through the efforts of hygiene and medicine. But we cannot prevent the reproduction of the weak when they are neither insane nor criminal, or destroy sickly or defective children as we do the weaklings in a litter of puppies. The only way to obviate the disastrous predominance of the weak is to develop the strong. Our efforts to render normal the unfit are evidently useless. We should, then, turn our attention toward promoting the optimum growth of the fit. By making the strong still stronger, we could effectively help the weak. For the herd always profits by the ideas and inventions of the élite. Instead of levelling organic and mental inequalities, we should amplify them and construct greater men.

We must single out the children who are endowed with high potentialities, and develop them as completely as possible, and in this manner give to the nation a non-hereditary aristocracy. Such children may be found in all classes of society, although distinguished men appear more frequently in distinguished families than in others. The descendants of the founders of American civilization may still possess the ancestral qualities. These qualities are generally hidden under the cloak of degeneration. But this degeneration is often superficial. It comes chiefly from education, idleness, lack of responsibility and moral discipline. The sons of very rich men, like those of criminals, should be removed while still infants from their natural surroundings. Thus separated from their family they could manifest their hereditary strength. In the aristocratic families of Europe there are also individuals of great vitality. The issue of the Crusaders is by no means extinct. The laws of genetics indicate the probability that the legendary audacity and love of adventure can appear again in the lineage of the feudal lords. It is possible also that the offspring of the great criminals who had imagination, courage, and judgment, of the heroes of the French or Russian Revolutions, of the high-handed business men who live among us, might be excellent building-stones for an enterprising minority. As we know, criminality is not hereditary if not united with feeble-mindedness or other mental or cerebral defects. High potentialities are rarely encountered in the sons of honest, intelligent, hard-working men who have had ill luck in their careers, who have failed in business or have muddled along all their lives in inferior positions, or among peasants living on the same spot for centuries. However, from such people sometimes spring artists, poets, adventurers, saints. A brilliantly gifted and well-known New York family came from peasants who cultivated their farm in the south of France from the time of Charlemagne to that of Napoleon.

Boldness and strength suddenly appear in families where they have never before been observed. Mutations may occur in man, just as they do in other animals and in plants. Nevertheless, one should not expect to find among peasants and proletarians many subjects endowed with great developmental possibilities. In fact, the separation of the population of a free country into different classes is not due to chance or to social conventions. It rests on a solid biological basis, the physiological and mental peculiarities of the individuals. In democratic countries, such as the United States and France, for example, any man had the possibility during the last century of rising to the position his capacities enabled him to hold. To-day most of the members of the proletarian class owe their situation to the hereditary weakness of their organs and their mind. Likewise the peasants have remained attached to the soil since the Middle Ages, because they possess the courage, judgment, physical resistance, and lack of imagination and daring which render them apt for this type of life. These unknown farmers, anonymous soldiers, passionate lovers of the soil, the backbone of the European nations, were, despite their great qualities, of a weaker organic and psychological constitution than the mediæval barons who conquered the land and defended it victoriously against all invaders. Originally the serfs and the chiefs were really born serfs and chiefs. To-day the weak should not be artificially maintained in wealth and power. It is imperative that social classes should be synonymous with biological classes. Each individual must rise or sink to the level for which he is fitted by the quality of his tissues and of his soul. The social ascent of those who possess the best organs and the best minds should be aided. Each one must have his natural place. Modern nations will save themselves by developing the strong, not by protecting the weak.

7

Eugenics is indispensable for the perpetuation of the strong. A great race must propagate its best elements. However, in the most highly civilized nations reproduction is decreasing and yields inferior products. Women voluntarily deteriorate through alcohol and tobacco. They subject themselves to dangerous dietary regimens in order to obtain a conventional slenderness of their figure. Besides, they refuse to bear children. Such a defection is due to their education, to the progress of feminism, to the growth of short-sighted selfishness. It also comes from economic conditions, nervous unbalance, instability of marriage, and fear of the burden imposed upon parents by the weakness or precocious corruption of children. The women belonging to the oldest stock, whose children would, in all probability, be of good quality, and who are in a position to bring them up intelligently, are almost sterile. It is the newcomers, peasants and proletarians from primitive European countries, who beget large families. But their offspring are far from having the value of those who came from the first settlers of North America. There is no hope for an increase in the birth-rate before a revolution takes place in the habits of thinking and living, and a new ideal rises above the horizon.

Eugenics may exercise a great influence upon the destiny of the civilized races. Of course, the reproduction of human beings cannot be regulated as in animals. The propagation of the insane and the feeble-minded, nevertheless, must be prevented. A medical examination should perhaps be imposed on people about to marry, as for admission into the army or the navy, or for employees in hotels, hospitals, and department stores. However, the security given by medical examination is not at all positive. The contradictory statements made by experts before the courts of justice demonstrate that these examinations often lack any value. It seems that eugenics, to be useful, should be voluntary. By an appropriate education each one could be made to realize what wretchedness is in store for those who marry into families contaminated by syphilis, cancer, tuberculosis, insanity, or feeble-mindedness. Such families should be considered by young people at least as undesirable as those which are poor. In truth, they are more dangerous than gangsters and murderers. No criminal causes so much misery in a human group as the tendency to insanity. Voluntary eugenics is not impossible. Indeed, love is supposed to blow as freely as the wind. But the belief in this peculiarity of love is shaken by the fact that many young men fall in love only with rich girls, and vice versa. If love is capable of listening to money, it may also submit to a consideration as practical as that of health. None should marry a human being suffering from hidden hereditary defects. Most of man's misfortunes are due to his organic and mental constitution and, in a large measure, to his heredity. Obviously, those who are afflicted with a heavy ancestral burden of insanity, feeble-mindedness, or cancer should not marry. No human being has the right to bring misery to another human being; still less that of procreating children destined to misery. Thus eugenics asks for the sacrifice of many individuals. This necessity, with which we meet for the second time, seems to be the expression of a natural law. Many living beings are sacrificed at every instant by nature to other living beings. We know the social and individual importance of renunciation. Nations have always paid the highest honours to those who gave up their lives to save their country. The concept of sacrifice, of its absolute social necessity, must be introduced into the mind of modern man.

Although eugenics may prevent the weakening of the strong, it is insufficient to determine their unlimited progress. In the purest races individuals do not rise beyond a certain level. However, among men, as among thoroughbred horses, exceptional beings appear from time to time. The determining factors of genius are entirely unknown. We are incapable of inducing a progressive evolution of germ-plasm, of bringing about by appropriate mutations the appearance of superior men. We must be content with facilitating the union of the best elements of the race through education and certain economic advantages. The progress of the strong depends on the conditions of their development and the possibility left to parents of transmitting to their offspring the qualities which they have acquired in the course of their existence. Modern society must, therefore, allow to all a certain stability of life, a home, a garden, some friends. Children must be reared in contact with things which are the expression of the mind of their parents. It is imperative to stop the transformation of the farmer, the artisan, the artist, the professor, and the man of science into manual or intellectual proletarians, possessing nothing but their hands or their brains. The development of this proletariat will be the everlasting shame of industrial civilization. It has contributed to the disappearance of the family as a social unit, and to the weakening of intelligence and moral sense. It is destroying the remains of culture. All forms of the proletariat must be suppressed. Each individual should have the security and the stability required for the foundation of a family. Marriage must cease to be only a temporary union. The union of man and woman, like that of the higher anthropoids, ought to last at least until the young have no further need of protection. The laws relating to education, and especially to that of girls, to marriage, and divorce should, above all, take into account the interest of children. Women should receive a higher education, not in order to become doctors, lawyers, or professors, but to rear their offspring to be valuable human beings.

The free practice of eugenics could lead not only to the development of stronger individuals, but also of strains endowed with more endurance, intelligence, and courage. These strains should constitute an aristocracy, from which great men would probably appear. Modern society must promote, by all possible means, the formation of better human stock. No financial or moral rewards should be too great for those who, through the wisdom of their marriage, would engender geniuses. The complexity of our civilization is immense. No one can master all its mechanisms. However, these mechanisms have to be mastered. There is need to-day of men of larger mental and moral size, capable of accomplishing such a task. The establishment of a hereditary biological aristocracy through voluntary eugenics would be an important step toward the solution of our present problems.

8

Although our knowledge of man is still very incomplete, nevertheless it gives us the power to intervene in his formation, and to help him unfold all his potentialities : to shape him according to our wishes, provided these wishes conform to natural laws. Three different procedures are at our disposal. The first comprises the physical and chemical factors, which cause definite changes in the constitution of the tissues, humours, and mind. The second sets in motion, through proper modifications in the environment, the adaptive mechanisms regulating all human activities. The third makes use of psychological factors, which influence organic development or induce the individual to build himself up by his own efforts. The handling of these agencies is difficult, empirical, and uncertain. We are not as yet well acquainted with them. They do not limit their effects to a single aspect of the individual. They act slowly, even during childhood and youth. But they always produce profound modifications of the body and of the mind.

The physical and chemical peculiarities of the climate, the soil, and the food can be used as instruments for modelling the individual. Endurance and strength generally develop in the mountains, in the countries where seasons are extreme, where mists are frequent and sunlight rare, where hurricanes blow furiously, where the land is poor and sown with rocks. The schools devoted to the formation of a hard and spirited youth should be established in such countries, and not in southern climates where the sun always shines and the temperature is even and warm. Florida and the French Riviera are suitable for weaklings, invalids, and old people, or normal individuals in need of a short rest. Moral energy, nervous equilibrium, and organic resistance are increased in children when they are trained to withstand heat and cold, dryness and humidity, burning sun and chilling rain, blizzards and fog—in short, the rigours of the seasons in northern countries. The resourcefulness and hardihood of the Yankee were probably due, in a certain measure, to the harshness of a climate where, under the sun of Spain, there are Scandinavian winters. But these climatic factors have lost their efficiency since civilized men are protected from inclemencies of the weather by the comfort and the sedentariness of their life.

The effect of the chemical compounds contained in food upon physiological and mental activities is far from being thoroughly known. Medical opinion on this point is of little value, for no experiments of sufficient duration have been made upon human beings to ascertain the influence of a given diet. There is no doubt that consciousness is affected by the quantity and the quality of the food. Those who have to dare, dominate, and create should not be fed like manual workers, or like contemplative monks who, in the solitude of monasteries, endeavour to repress in their inner self the turmoil of the secular passions. We have to discover what food is suitable for human beings vegetating in offices and factories; what chemical substances could give intelligence, courage, and alertness to the inhabitants of the new city. The race will certainly not be improved merely by supplying children and adolescents with a great abundance of milk, cream, and all known vitamins. It would be most useful to search for new compounds which, instead of uselessly increasing the size and weight of the skeleton and of the muscles, would bring about nervous strength and mental agility. Perhaps some day a scientist will discover how to manufacture great men from ordinary children, in the same manner that bees transform a common larva into a queen by the special food which they know how to prepare. But it is probable that no chemical agent alone is capable of greatly improving the individual. We must assume that the superiority of any organic and mental form is due to a combination of hereditary and developmental conditions, and that, during development, chemical factors are not to be separated from psychological and functional factors.

9

We know that adaptive processes stimulate organs and functions, that the more effective way of improving tissues and mind is to maintain them in ceaseless activity. The mechanisms, which determine in certain organs a series of reactions ordered toward an end, can easily be set in motion. As is well known, a muscular group develops by appropriate drill. If we wish to strengthen not only the muscles, but also the apparatuses responsible for their nutrition and the organs which enable the body to sustain a prolonged effort, exercises more varied than classical sports are indispensable. These exercises are the same as were practised daily in a more primitive life. Specialized athletics, as taught in schools and universities, do not give real endurance. The efforts requiring the help of muscles, vessels, heart, lungs, brain, spinal cord, and mind—that is, of the entire organism—are necessary in the construction of the individual. Running over rough ground, climbing mountains, wrestling, swimming, working in the forests and in the fields, exposure to inclemencies, early moral responsibility, and a general harshness of life bring about the harmony of the muscles, bones, organs, and consciousness.

In this manner the organic systems enabling the body to adapt itself to the outside world are trained and fully developed. The climbing of trees or rocks stimulates the activity of the apparatuses regulating the composition of plasma, the circulation of the blood, and the respiration. The organs responsible for the manufacture of red cells and hæmoglobin are set in motion by life at high altitudes. Prolonged running and the necessity of eliminating acid produced by the muscles release processes extending over the entire organism. Unsatisfied thirst drains water from the tissues. Fasting mobilizes the proteins and fatty substances from the organs. Alternation from heat to cold and from cold to heat sets at work the multiple mechanisms regulating the temperature. The adaptive systems may be stimulated in many other ways. The whole body is improved when they are brought into action. Ceaseless work renders all integrating apparatuses stronger, more alert, and better fitted to carry out their many duties.

The harmony of our organic and psychological functions is one of the most important qualities that we may possess. It can be acquired by means varying according to the specific characteristics of each individual. But it always demands a voluntary effort. Equilibrium is obtained in a large measure by intelligence and self-control. Man naturally tends toward the satisfaction of his physiological appetites and artificial needs, such as a craving for alcohol, speed, and ceaseless change. But he degenerates when he satisfies these appetites completely. He must, then, accustom himself to dominate his hunger, his need of sleep, his sexual impulses, his laziness, his fondness for muscular exercise, for alcohol, etc. Too much sleep and food are as dangerous as too little. It is first by training and later by a progressive addition of intellectual motives to the habits gained by training, that individuals possessing strong and well-balanced activities may be developed.

A man's value depends on his capacity to face adverse situations rapidly and without effort. Such alertness is attained by building up many kinds of reflexes and instinctive reactions. The younger the individual, the easier is the establishment of reflexes. A child can accumulate vast treasures of unconscious knowledge. He is easily trained, incomparably more so than the most intelligent shepherd dog. He can be taught to run without tiring, to fall like a cat, to climb, to swim, to stand and walk harmoniously, to observe everything exactly, to wake quickly and completely, to speak several languages, to obey, to attack, to defend himself, to use his hands dexterously in various kinds of work, etc. Moral habits are created in an identical manner. Dogs themselves learn not to steal. Honesty, sincerity, and courage are developed by the same procedures as those used in the formation of reflexes—that is, without argument, without discussion, without explanation. In a word, children must be conditioned.

Conditioning, according to the terminology of Pavlov, is nothing but the establishment of associated reflexes. It repeats in a scientific and modern form the procedures employed for a long time by animal trainers. In the construction of these reflexes, a relation is established between an unpleasant thing and a thing desired by the subject. The ringing of a bell, the report of a gun, even the crack of a whip, become for a dog the equivalent of the food he likes. A similar phenomenon takes place in man. One does not suffer from being deprived of food and sleep in the course of an expedition into an unknown country. Physical pain and hardship are easily supported if they accompany the success of a cherished enterprise. Death itself may smile when it is associated with some great adventure, with the beauty of sacrifice, or with the illumination of the soul that becomes immersed in God.

10

The psychological factors of development have a mighty influence on the individual, as is well known. They can be used at will for giving both to the body and to the mind their ultimate shape. We have mentioned how, by constructing proper reflexes in a child, one may prepare that child to face certain situations advantageously. The individual who possesses many acquired, or conditioned, reflexes reacts successfully to a number of foreseen stimuli. For instance, if attacked, he can instantaneously draw his pistol. But he is not prepared to respond properly to unforeseen stimuli, to unpredictable circumstances. The aptitude for improvising a fitting response to all situations depends on precise qualities of the nervous system, the organs, and the mind. These qualities can be developed by definite psychological agencies. We know that mental and moral disciplines, for instance, bring about a better equilibrium of the sympathetic system, a more complete integration of all organic and mental activities. These agencies can be divided into two classes: those acting from without, and those acting from within. To the first class belong all reflexes and states of consciousness imposed on the subject by other individuals or by his social environment. Insecurity or security, poverty or wealth, effort, struggle, idleness, responsibility, create certain mental states capable of moulding human beings in an almost specific manner. The second class comprises the factors which modify the subject from within, such as meditation, concentration, will to power, asceticism, etc.

The use of mental factors in the making of man is delicate. We can, however, easily direct the intellectual shaping of a child. Proper teachers, suitable books, introduce into his inner world the ideas destined to influence the evolution of his tissues and his mind. We have already mentioned that the growth of other mental activities, such as moral, æsthetic, and religious senses, is independent of intelligence and formal teaching. The psychological factors instrumental in training these activities are parts of the social environment. The subjects, therefore, have to be placed in a proper setting. This includes the necessity of surrounding them with a certain mental atmosphere. It is extremely difficult to-day to give children the advantages resulting from privation, struggle, hardship, and real intellectual culture, and from the development of a potent psychological agency, the inner life. This private, hidden, not-to-be-shared, undemocratic thing appears to the conservatism of many educators to be a damnable sin. However, it remains the source of all originality, of all great actions. It permits the individual to retain his personality, his poise, and the stability of his nervous system in the confusion of the new city.

Mental factors influence each individual in a different manner. They must be applied only by those who fully understand the psychological and organic peculiarities which distinguish human beings. The subjects who are weak or strong, sensitive or insensitive, selfish or unselfish, intelligent or unintelligent, alert or apathetic, etc., react in their own way to every psychological agency. There is no possibility of a wholesale application of these delicate procedures for the construction of the mind and the body. However, there are certain general conditions, both social and economic, which may act in a beneficial, or harmful, way on each individual in a given community. Sociologists and economists should never plan any change in the conditions of life without taking into consideration the mental effects of this change. It is a primary datum of observation that man does not progress in complete poverty, in prosperity, in peace, in too large a community, or in isolation. He would probably reach his optimum development in the psychological atmosphere created by a moderate amount of economic security, leisure, privation, and struggle. The effects of these conditions differ according to each race and to each individual. The events that crush certain people will drive others to revolt and victory.

We have to mould on man his social and economic world; to provide him with the psychological surroundings capable of keeping his organic systems in full activity.

These factors are, of course, far more effective in children and adolescents than in adults. They should constantly be used during this plastic period. But their influence, although less marked, remains essential during the entire course of life. At the epoch of maturity, when the value of time decreases, their importance becomes greater. Their activity is most beneficial to ageing people. Senescence seems to be delayed when body and mind are kept working. In middle and old age man needs a stricter discipline than in childhood. The early deterioration of numerous individuals is due to self-indulgence. The same factors that determine the shaping of the young human being are able to prevent the deformation of the old. A wise use of these psychological influences would retard the decay of many men, and the loss of intellectual and moral treasures, which sink prematurely into the abyss of senile degeneration.

II

There are, as we know, two kinds of health, natural and artificial. Scientific medicine has given to man artificial health, and protection against most infectious diseases. It is a marvellous gift. But man is not content with health that is only lack of malady and depends on special diets, chemicals, endocrine products, vitamins, periodical medical examinations, and the expensive attention of hospitals, doctors, and nurses. He wants natural health, which comes from resistance to infectious and degenerative diseases, from equilibrium of the nervous system. He must be constructed so as to live without thinking about his health. Medicine will achieve its greatest triumph when it discovers the means of rendering the body and the mind naturally immune to

diseases, fatigue, and fear. In remaking modern human beings we must endeavour to give them the freedom and the
happiness engendered by the perfect soundness of organic
and mental activities.

This conception of natural health will meet with strong
opposition because it disturbs our habits of thought. The
present trend of medicine is toward artificial health, toward
a kind of directed physiology. Its ideal is to intervene in the
work of tissues and organs with the help of pure chemicals,
to stimulate or replace deficient functions, to increase the
resistance of the organism to infection, to accelerate the reaction of the humours and the organs to pathogenic agencies,
etc. We still consider a human being to be a poorly constructed machine, whose parts must be constantly reinforced
or repaired. In a recent address, Henry Dale has celebrated
with great candour the triumphs of chemical therapeutics
during the last forty years, the discovery of antitoxic sera and
bacterial products, hormones, insulin, adrenalin, thyroxin,
etc., of organic compounds of arsenic, vitamins, substances
controlling sexual functions, of a number of new compounds synthetized in the laboratory for the relief of pain or
the stimulation of some flagging natural activity ; and the
advent of the gigantic industrial laboratories where these
substances are manufactured. There is no doubt that those
achievements of chemistry and physiology are extremely important, that they throw much light on the hidden mechanisms of the body. But should they be hailed as great triumphs
of humanity in its striving toward health? This is far from
being certain. Physiology cannot be compared with economics. Organic, humoral, and mental processes are infinitely more complex than economic and sociological phenomena. While directed economics may ultimately be a
success, directed physiology is a failure and will probably
remain so.

Artificial health does not suffice for human happiness.
Medical examinations, medical care, are troublesome and

often ineffectual. Drugs and hospitals are expensive. Men and women are constantly in need of small repairs although they appear to be in good health. They are not well and strong enough to play their part of human beings fully. The growing dissatisfaction of the public with the medical profession is, in some measure, due to the existence of this evil. Medicine cannot give to man the kind of health he needs without taking into consideration his true nature. We have learned that organs, humours, and mind are one, that they are the result of hereditary tendencies, of the conditions of development, of the chemical, physical, physiological, and mental factors of the environment; that health depends on a definite chemical and structural constitution of each part and on certain properties of the whole. We must help this whole to perform its functions efficiently rather than intervene ourselves in the work of each organ. Some individuals are immune to infections and degenerative diseases and to the decay of senescence. We have to learn their secret. It is the knowledge of the inner mechanisms responsible for such endurance that we must acquire. The possession of natural health would enormously increase the happiness of man.

The marvellous success of hygiene in the fight against infectious diseases and great epidemics allows biological research to turn its attention partly from bacteria and viruses to physiological and mental processes. Medicine, instead of being content with masking organic lesions, must endeavour to prevent their occurrence, or to cure them. For instance, insulin brings about the disappearance of the symptoms of diabetes; but it does not cure the disease. Diabetes can be mastered only by the discovery of its causes and of the means of bringing about the repair or the replacement of the degenerated pancreatic cells. It is obvious that the mere administration to the sick of the chemicals which they need is not sufficient. The organs must be rendered capable of normally manufacturing these chemicals within the body.

But the knowledge of the mechanisms responsible for the soundness of glands is far more profound than that of the products of these glands. We have so far followed the easiest road. We now have to switch to rough ground and enter uncharted countries. The hope of humanity lies in the prevention of degenerative and mental diseases, not in the mere care of their symptoms. The progress of medicine will not come from the construction of larger and better hospitals, of larger and better factories for pharmaceutical products. It depends entirely on imagination, on observation of the sick, on meditation and experimentation in the silence of the laboratory. And, finally, on the unveiling, beyond the proscenium of chemical structures, of the organismal and mental mysteries.

12

We now have to re-establish, in the fullness of his personality, the human being weakened and standardized by modern life. Sexes have again to be clearly defined. Each individual should be either male or female, and never manifest the sexual tendencies, mental characteristics, and ambitions of the opposite sex. Instead of resembling a machine produced in series, man should, on the contrary, emphasize his uniqueness. In order to reconstruct personality we must break the frame of the school, factory, and office, and reject the very principles of technological civilization.

Such a change is by no means impracticable. The renovation of education requires chiefly a reversal of the respective values attributed to parents and to schoolteachers in the formation of the child. We know that it is impossible to bring up individuals wholesale, that the school cannot be considered as a substitute for individual education. Teachers often fulfil their intellectual function well. But effective, æsthetic, and religious activities also need to be developed.

Parents have to realize clearly that their part is indispensable. They must be fitted for it. Is it not strange that the educational programme for girls does not contain in general any detailed study of infants and children, of their physiological and mental characteristics? Her natural function, which consists not only of bearing, but also of rearing, her young, should be restored to woman.

Like the school, the factory and the office are not intangible institutions. There have been, in the past, industrial organizations which enabled the workmen to own a house and land, to work at home when and as they willed, to use their intelligence, to manufacture entire objects, to have the joy of creation. At the present time this form of industry could be resumed. Electrical power and modern machinery make it possible for the light industries to free themselves from the curse of the factory. Could not the heavy industries also be decentralized? Or would it not be possible to use all the young men of the country in those factories for a short period, just as for military service? In this or another way the proletariat could be progressively abolished. Men would live in small communities instead of in immense droves. Each would preserve his human value within his group. Instead of being merely a piece of machinery, he would become a person. To-day, the position of the proletarian is as low as was that of the feudal serf. Like the serf, he has no hope of escaping from his bondage, of being independent, of holding authority over others. The artisan, on the contrary, has the legitimate hope that some day he may become the head of his shop. Likewise, the peasant owning his land, the fisherman owning his boat, although obliged to work hard, are, nevertheless, masters of themselves and of their time. Most industrial workers could enjoy similar independence and dignity. The white-collar people lose their personality just as factory hands do. In fact, they become proletarians. It seems that modern business organization and mass production are incompatible with the full development of the human self. If such is the case, then industrial civilization, and not civilized man, must go.

In recognizing personality, modern society has to accept its disparateness. Each individual must be utilized in accordance with his special characteristics. In attempting to establish equality among men, we have suppressed individual peculiarities which were most useful. For happiness depends on one's being exactly fitted to the nature of one's work. And there are many varied tasks in a modern nation. Human types, instead of being standardized, should be diversified, and these constitutional differences maintained and exaggerated by the mode of education and the habits of life. Each type would find its place. Modern society has refused to recognize the dissimilarity of human beings and has crowded them into four classes—the rich, the proletarian, the farmer, and the middle class. The clerk, the policeman, the clergyman, the scientist, the schoolteacher, the university professor, the shopkeeper, etc., who constitute the middle class, have practically the same standard of living. Such ill-assorted types are herded together according to their financial position and not in conformity with their individual characteristics. Obviously, they have nothing in common. The best, those who could grow, who try to develop their mental potentialities, are atrophied by the narrowness of their life. In order to promote human progress, it is not enough to hire architects, to buy bricks and steel, and to build schools, universities, laboratories, libraries, art institutes, and churches. It would be far more important to provide those who devote themselves to the things of the mind with the means of developing their personality according to their innate constitution and to their spiritual purpose; just as, during the Middle Ages, the Church created a mode of existence suitable to asceticism, mysticism, and philosophical thinking.

The brutal materialism of our civilization not only opposes the soaring of intelligence, but also crushes the affec-

K   (A181)

tive, the gentle, the weak, the lonely, those who love beauty, who look for other things than money, whose sensibility does not stand the struggle of modern life. In past centuries, the many who were too refined, or too incomplete, to fight with the rest were allowed the free development of their personality. Some lived within themselves. Others took refuge in monasteries, in charitable or contemplative orders, where they found poverty and hard work, but also dignity, beauty, and peace. Individuals of this type should be given, instead of the inimical conditions of modern society, an environment more appropriate to the growth and utilization of their specific qualities.

There remains the unsolved problem of the immense number of defectives and criminals. They are an enormous burden for the part of the population that has remained normal. As already pointed out, gigantic sums are now required to maintain prisons and insane asylums, and protect the public against gangsters and lunatics. Why do we preserve these useless and harmful beings? The abnormal prevent the development of the normal. This fact must be squarely faced. Why should society not dispose of the criminals and the insane in a more economical manner? We cannot go on trying to separate the responsible from the irresponsible, punish the guilty, spare those who, although having committed a crime, are thought to be morally innocent. We are not capable of judging men. However, the community must be protected against troublesome and dangerous elements. How can this be done? Certainly not by building larger and more comfortable prisons, just as real health will not be promoted by larger and more scientific hospitals. Criminality and insanity can be prevented only by a better knowledge of man, by eugenics, by changes in education and in social conditions. Meanwhile, criminals have to be dealt with effectively. Perhaps prisons should be abolished. They could be replaced by smaller and less expensive institutions. The conditioning of petty criminals with the whip, or some more scientific procedure, followed by a short stay in hospital, would probably suffice to ensure order. Those who have murdered, robbed while armed with automatic pistol or machine gun, kidnapped children, despoiled the poor of their savings, misled the public in important matters, should be humanely and economically disposed of in small euthanasic institutions supplied with proper gases. A similar treatment could be advantageously applied to the insane, guilty of criminal acts. Modern society should not hesitate to organize itself with reference to the normal individual. Philosophical systems and sentimental prejudices must give way before such a necessity. The development of human personality is the ultimate purpose of civilization.

13

The restoration of man to the harmony of his physiological and mental self will transform his universe. We should not forget that the universe modifies its aspects according to the conditions of our body; that it is nothing but the response of our nervous system, our sensory organs, and our techniques to an unknown and probably unknowable reality. That all our states of consciousness, all our dreams, those of the mathematicians as well as those of the lovers, are equally true. The electromagnetic waves, which express a sunset to the physicist, are no more objective than the brilliant colours perceived by the painter. The æsthetic feeling engendered by those colours, and the measurement of the length of their component light-waves, are two aspects of ourselves and have the same right to existence. Joy and sorrow are as important as planets and suns. But the world of Dante, Emerson, Bergson, or G. E. Hale is larger than that of Mr. Babbitt. The beauty of the universe will necessarily grow with the strength of our organic and psychological activities.

We must liberate man from the cosmos created by the

genius of physicists and astronomers, that cosmos in which, since the Renaissance, he has been imprisoned. Despite its stupendous immensity, the world of matter is too narrow for him. Like his economic and social environment, it does not fit him. We cannot adhere to the faith in its exclusive reality. We know that we are not altogether comprised within its dimensions, that we extend somewhere else, outside the physical continuum. Man is simultaneously a material object, a living being, a focus of mental activities. His presence in the prodigious void of the intersidereal spaces is totally negligible. But he is not a stranger in the realm of inanimate matter. With the aid of mathematical abstractions his mind apprehends the electrons as well as the stars. He is made on the scale of the terrestrial mountains, oceans, and rivers. He appertains to the surface of the earth, exactly as trees, plants, and animals do. He feels at ease in their company. He is more intimately bound to the works of art, the monuments, the mechanical marvels of the new city, the small group of his friends; those whom he loves. But he also belongs to another world : a world which, although enclosed within himself, stretches beyond space and time. And of this world, if his will is indomitable, he may travel over the infinite cycles : the cycle of Beauty, contemplated by scientists, artists, and poets; the cycle of Love, that inspires heroism and renunciation; the cycle of Grace, ultimate reward of those who passionately seek the principle of all things. Such is our universe.

14

The day has come to begin the work of our renovation. We will not establish any programme. For a programme would stifle living reality in a rigid armour. It would prevent the bursting forth of the unpredictable, and imprison the future within the limits of our mind.

We must arise and move on. We must liberate ourselves from blind technology and grasp the complexity and the wealth of our own nature. The sciences of life have shown to humanity its goal and placed at its disposal the means of reaching it. But we are still immersed in the world created by the sciences of inert matter without any respect for the laws of our development: in a world that is not made for us, because it is born from an error of our reason and from the ignorance of our true self. To such a world we cannot become adapted. We will, then, revolt against it. We will transform its values and organize it with reference to our true needs. To-day, the science of man gives us the power to develop all the potentialities of our body. We know the secret mechanisms of our physiological and mental activities and the causes of our weakness. We know how we have transgressed natural laws. We know why we are punished, why we are lost in darkness. Nevertheless, we faintly perceive through the mists of dawn a path which may lead to our salvation.

For the first time in the history of humanity, a crumbling civilization is capable of discerning the causes of its decay. For the first time it has at its disposal the gigantic strength of science. Will we utilize this knowledge and this power? It is our only hope of escaping the fate common to all great civilizations of the past. Our destiny is in our hands. On the new road, we must now go forward.

INDEX

ABÉLARD, and Universals, 218, 229
cowardice of, 137
Ability, administrative, 207
Abnormal, 290
Abscesses, as adaptation to infection, 196
cured at Lourdes, 143
Abstraction (-s), 16, 41, 218–19
and concrete child, 54
body and soul as, from concrete unity, 115–16
mathematical, and universe, 292
medicine and, 228–31
modern society treats men as, 248
power of, of human intellect, 21
residues of scientific, 257
time as agent concretizing, 154
Accommodation. See Adaptation
Acid (-s), amino, 81, 88
carbonic, 84, 85, 184
hydrochloric, 85
lactic, 85, 184, 212
phosphoric, 85
sulphuric, 184
Action, integrating function of, 140
Activity (-ies), æsthetic, 128 131, 135, 287
affective, 133, 287
intellectual, 18, 135, 203
mental, 18, 115, 134, 135, 144–5, 205, 257, 293
moral, 18, 124, 135
mystical, 18, 129
organic, 39, 135, 291
physicochemical, 42, 265
physiological, 42, 44, 115–16, 140, 205, 257, 265, 293
potential, 268
psychological 42, 44, 141, 291
religious, 129, 130–1, 287
spiritual, 18, 39
unification of, 141
Acts, complexity of, 103–4
simplicity of, 103

Adaptation, and diseases, 193
and process of healing, 192
as aspect of all physiological processes, 208
automatism of, 180
definition of, 180
disuse of, 211–13
effects of deficiencies of, 215–16
extraorganic, 181, 198
individual aspect of, 227–8
intraorganic, 181
modifications of environment and, 277, 279–80
social, 205–7
Adolescent (-s), 231, 284
Adornment of the Spiritual Marriage, 117
Adrenalin, 89, 101, 139, 285
Adrian, E. D., 96
Adsorption, 42
Adults, psychological factors in development of, 284
Advertising, commercial, 36
Aeroplane (-s), 24, 35
Æsthetics, 261
Affinity between man and environment, 227
Age, chronological, 158, 176
physiological, 158, 237
Agglutination, 195, 221–2
Aggregates, material, 42
Agitation, no adaptation possible to, 201, 216
Albumin, 221
Alchemists, psychologists like, 149
Alcohol, 26, 35, 206, 269, 274
Alcoholics, 242
Alcoholism, 216
Alertness, and reflexes, 281
Alkalinity, ionic, of blood, 81, 184
Allergic, 224
Alpine guide, 144
Alps, 202–3
Altitudes, high, 202–3
Alveoli, pulmonary, 72, 199

294

America, 30, 56, 146
Amino acids. *See* Acids
Amphibia, 75
Anæmia, pernicious, 112
Anæsthesia, 192
Analysis and synthesis, 55
Anaphylaxis, 121
Anatomists, 16, 53, 76
Anatomy, 16, 20, 260–1
    classical, 74
Ancestors, 19, 24, 26, 27, 31, 144, 242
Ancien régime, 269
Anger, 139, 209
Angina pectoris, 228
Anglo-Saxons, 68
Anselm, 218
Anthropoids, 276
Anthropoplasm, 76
Antibodies, 81, 195, 222–3
Antigens, 259
Antitoxins, 195
Ants, 18
Anus, 72
Anxiety, 140
Aorta, 197
Apathy, intellectual, 253
Appetites, physiological, 47, 280
    sexual, 30, 138
Aptitudes, for happiness, 18
    insertion in social group according to, 227
Arc, reflex, 96
Architectonic, 79
Architecture, 146
Arenas, 25
Aristocracy, feudal, 215
    hereditary biological, 276–7
    non-hereditary, 272
Aristotle, 99
Arizona, 202
Arsenic, 285
Art, industrial, 146
Arteriosclerosis, 48, 196–7
Artery, carotid, 183
Artisan (-s), 270, 288
    corporations of, 270
Artists, 127, 272
Asceticism, and mysticism, 131–2
    as factor in renovation of man, 282

Asceticism, discipline, a sort of, 214
    mode of existence suitable to, 289
    of scientist, 133
Aspect (-s), morphological, 158
    of individual, 220
    of man, 16, 47, 65
    of physiological processes, 48–9
Asthenic, 69
Astronomy, 15, 19, 22, 28
Asylums, insane, 290
Athletes, 25–6, 30
    and modern men, 216
    Greek, 68
    intelligence of, 119
Athletics, 212, 279
Atmosphere, 198
    mental, 282
    psychological, 283
Atoms, 15, 22, 43, 223
Atrophy, 268
    senile, 136
Audacity, 18, 33, 36–7
Aura, 71
Auricle, left, 197
    right, 208
Automobile (-s), 24, 35, 211
Autosuggestion, 132
Axon (-s), 42, 95

BABBITT, 291
Bacon, Francis, 26
Bacteria and surgical technique, 191
    immunity against, 194–6
    individuality in response of body to, 223
    invasion of body by, 111
    investigation of, 265
    natural and acquired resistance to, 194–6
    protection of body against, 72, 73
Balance, mental, 126
    organic, 126
Bandits, 249
Barbarism, 38
Bataillon, 93
Bayliss, W. M., 48, 267

Bears, lower metabolism of, in winter, 85
Beatrice, 138
Beauty, and æsthetic activity, 129
  and vulgarity, 145
  appreciation of, 146
  moral, 127
  of old man, 68–9
  of sacrifice, 281
  of youth, 68–9
  quest for absolute, 131
  sense of, 129
Beers, C. W., 147
Bees, 18, 76, 279
Beethoven, 84
Behaviour, 118
Behaviourists, 232
Benedictine monks, 59
Bergson, Henri, 21, 155, 157, 179, 291
Bernard, Claude, 21, 44, 46, 117, 149
Bertillon, A., 220
Bertrand, 120
Bicarbonates, 184
Biggs, Hermann, 263
Bile, 104, 116
Billroth, 191
Biologists, 44
Biology, 15, 37–8, 264
  human, 59
Birth rate, and civilization, 33
Bladder, 140
Blood, 80–3, 181–5
  alkalinity of, 21, 184
  composition of, 80–3, 183
  fall of pressure, 137
  plasma, 69, 75, 159–60
  purification of, 87
  removal of, and reinjection into dog, 165
  serum, 159–60, 256, 258–9
  universal donors of, 222
  venous, 72
  vessels, 75, 104
  young, 171–2
Body, and chemical substances of environment, 245
  and soul, 256
  complexity of, 65, 103–4
  durability of, 180

Body, pyramidal, 42
  robustness of, 108–9
  transitory character of elements of, 180
  unity of, 198
  weakening of, 110
Boldness, 235, 273
Bombardment, and cutaneous eruption, 139–40
Bonaparte, 237
  See also Napoleon
Bond, affective, 238
Bones, deformation of, 236
  repair of, 188–9
Bordeaux Medical Society, 142
Brain (-s), 19, 62, 84, 141
  cortex of, 97
  immensity of, 96
  immortal, 267
  muscles and, 216
Bridgman, P. W., 41
Bright's disease, 193
Brittany, 129, 201, 215
Broad, C. D., 244
Bronchi, 87
Brown-Séquard, E., 168, 172
Burn, superficial, 74

Cæsar, 84, 241
Cæsarean operation, 190
Cagliostro, 168
Calcium, 203, 236
Calmette, 53–4
Canada, 270–1
Cancer, 48, 113, 194, 197–8, 228, 234, 275
  cured at Lourdes, 143
Cannon, W. B., 101, 139
Capillaries, 80, 187
Capillarity, 42
Carbohydrates, 195, 223
Carbon, 83
Carbon dioxide, 72, 82, 184
Carbonic acid. See Acids
Cardozo, B. N., 120
Carnegie Foundation, 263–4
Carotid artery, 183
Cartilage, 188, 236
Castration, 137
Cat, 101, 139
Catabolites, 85

Cathedrals, 130
Cattle, adaptation of, 202
Cell (-s), chromosomes of, 22
  connective, 78
  cultivation of epithelial, 106
  culture of, 76, 79
  epithelial, 78, 189–90
  fixed, 78
  genes, 22
  like bees, 106–7
  mobile, 78
  nervous, 18
  of nervous systems, 95
  nucleus of, 22
  pancreatic, 286
  pyramidal, 97
  sexual, 22
  types characterized, 79
Centenarians, 169
Centre, thinking, 267
Cerebellum, 97
Cerebrum, 18, 137
Changes, pathological, determined
    by certain states of conscious-
    ness, 141
Chaplin, Charlie, 237
Character (-s), and intelligence, 32
  intellectual, 220
  moral, 220
Characteristic (-s), 18
  acquired, 201, 234–7
  identical, 57
  inherent, 201, 234–7
  mental, 18
  organic, 18
Charlemagne, 273
Chemistry, 16, 21, 22, 38, 42, 44,
    257–8, 285
  biological, 20, 261
  physical, 43, 48
Chiefs and serfs, 273
Child (-ren), 231, 272
  of rich families, 215
  protection of, 248, 269
  standardization of, 227
  training of, 276, 281
  unintelligence of, 119
Childhood, 176
  value of, 174–5
Chimpanzee, 172
China, 255
  K*

Cholera, 182
Christendom, defence of, 254
Chromosome (-s), 22, 42, 77, 92,
    231, 233
Chronaxy (-ies), 47, 95, 167
Church (-es), 147, 289
  decadence of, 130
  Roman Catholic, 126, 176
Cicatrization, 143, 189, 208
  index of, 159
Cinema, 35
Circulation, 101
Civilization, 31, 145, 267, 271
  American, 272
  basis of, 127
  crumbling, 293
  founders of, 108–9
  industrial, 33, 38, 202, 263, 269
  modern, 19, 29, 32–3, 258, 271
  purpose of, 216
  scientific, 176, 207, 213
  technological, 287
  vulgarity of modern, 128
Clairvoyance, 47, 72, 121–3
Clairvoyant (-s), 141, 154, 239, 242
Class, middle, 289
Climate (-s), 18, 110
  adaptation to, 204
Clock (-s) and our duration, 152,
    155, 161
Cocaine, 242, 269
Cod-liver oil, 178
Cold, fight against, 199
Colitis, 140
Comfort and modern life, 24
Communications, rapidity of, 20,
    24
  telepathic, 18, 72
Communities, small, and human
    value, 288
Competition and social level,
    205–6
Complexity of body. See Body
Concentration, 282
  intellectual, 206
Concept (-s), 15, 22, 42–4
  mechanistic, 186
  of individual, 250
  operational, 41–2, 132
  vitalistic, 186
Conditioning, 281, 290–1

Conduct, theoretical rules of, 125
Configurations, spatial, 210
Conquest, 205
Consciousness, 18, 20, 34, 38, 43, 47, 65, 118, 136, 141, 144, 282
Constitution, genetical, 235
Contemplation, 131, 141
Continuity, spatial, 95–6
Continuum, physical, 153–4, 241, 292
    space-time, 42, 153–4
Contours, definiteness of anatomical, 238
Cord, spinal, 71, 97, 184
Cornea, 71, 186
Corpses, study of, 74
Corpuscles, red, 82, 106, 186, 221
    tactile, 70
    white, 82, 106
Correlations, organic, 186
    teleological, 186
Corruption, 258
Cortex, cerebral, 97, 137, 138, 149
Cosmos, 21, 28, 291–2
Countries, democratic, 263
    Latin, 68
Courage, 32, 281
    moral, 37
Cowpunchers, 203
Cows, 85
Creator of universe, 247
Criminality, 141, 253, 272, 290
Criminals, 134–5, 206, 272, 290–1
Crisis, economic, 28, 253, 258
Cristiani, 221
Cro-Magnon, 144
Crookes, William, 239
Crusaders, 272
Crystalline lens, 71
Culture, 134, 145, 283
    of cells, 76, 79
Curare, 95
Curiosity, 45
Cushing, H., 191

DALE, Henry, 285
Dante, 129, 138, 291
Darwin, 46
Datum, primary, 104, 107, 118, 121, 186, 209, 214, 240, 283
da Vinci, Leonardo, 68

Day, as measure of terrestrial events, 158
    value of a, 152–3
Deafmutism, 233
Death, rate, 31
    warning of, 102
Debasement of hereditary origins, 246
Decay, acceleration of organic, 162
Defectives, 135, 242, 290–1
Degeneracy, 19, 32
Degenerates, 206
Degeneration, 207, 216, 247, 272
Degradation, brought about by industrial civilization, 207
    due to lack of adaptation, 201
Dementia præcox, 69, 150, 226
Democracy (-ies), 33, 176
Dendrites, 95
Dermis, 189
Descartes, R., 46, 116, 256, 260
Desires, unification of, 140
Destiny, 235, 252, 293
Development, 232, 261
    defective, 247
    optimum, 17, 18, 93, 209, 214, 216, 283
Dewey, John, 54, 58
Diabetes, 69, 112–3, 197, 227, 286
Diaphragm, 187
Diarrhœa, infantile, 31, 112
Diatheses, 69
Dictators, 263
Diet (-s), 89, 194, 278
    modern, 26
    of children, 26
    special, 284
Diffusion, 42
Digestive tract, 73
Dignity, lack of, as consequence of neglect of individuality, 249
Dimension (-s), 15, 292
    four, fourth, 153, 156, 158, 171
    horizontal, 153
    spatial, 15
    temporal, 178
    vertical, 153
Diphtheria, 31, 73, 112, 194, 228
Discipline (-s), 144, 214
    intellectual, 270

Discipline, mental, 269, 282
  moral, 18, 110, 206, 270, 282
  of mind, 236
  philosophical, 22
  physiological, 18, 110, 269
  Puritan, 30
  religious, 22
Discourse on Method, 46, 260
Discoveries, without prevision of
  their consequences, 34
Diseases, 48, 193, 227–31
  change in nature of, 113–14
  decrease of infectious, 112
  degenerative, 31, 48, 111–12,
    228, 287
  genesis of, 114
  infectious, 31, 37, 111
  intellectual, 38
  mental, 48, 62, 147–8, 287
  moral, 38
  nervous, 48, 141
  organic, 257–8
  prevention of, 287
Disharmony, of consciousness,
  135–6
Disorders, mental, 37
  nervous, 37
Dispersion, 42, 236
  intellectual, 216
Divine Comedy, 138
Divorce, 276
Dog (-s), 60, 100, 160, 281
  nervousness in, 150
  shepherd, 60, 232, 281
Dogma (-s), of democratic equality, 249
  of modern society, 271
  of scientific religion and indus-
    trial morals, 251
Doles, 206
Doukhobors, 270–1
Dreams, relative value of the
  study of, 259
Dreiser, Theodore, 246
Driesch, Hans, 17
Dualism, 116
  Cartesian, 51, 256
Duclaux, 265
du Guesclin, Bertrand, 215
Dumas, G., 226
Duration, 18, 155, 163, 171

Duration, physiological, 158,
  223–4
Duty, feeling of, 124
Dysentery, 73, 182

EAR, 70
Earth, 292
Economics, 37, 258, 261
  directed, 285
Economists, 44, 258, 265
Ecstasies, 141
Eddington, A. S., 28, 66
Edison, T. A., 54
Education, 40, 91, 97, 127, 135
  144, 203, 219–20, 257, 261
  268, 275, 287–8
  diffusion of, 26
  intellectual, 134
  methods of, 57
  modern, 31
  renovation of, 287
Educators, 37, 44, 263
  and optimum development, 17
Effort, 30, 206
  intellectual, 57
  muscular, 212–3
  voluntary, 280
Egoists, pure, 125
Einstein, Albert, 28, 46, 154,
  205
Electrons, 22, 43, 292
Elevator (-s), 25, 212
Élite, 32, 56, 135, 250, 272
Emanation, 240
Embryo, 70, 91–2, 186, 231
  functional simplicity of, 106
Emerson, R. W., 291
Emotion (-s), 102, 139–40
  æsthetic, 127, 247
Empiric (-al), character of science
  of man, 62
  recipes and primitive medicine,
    20
Encephalitis lethargica, 111, 136,
  149, 226
Encyclopædists, 269
Endocrine glands, 66, 89
Endurance, 37, 180, 277
Energy, 42, 116
  dissipation of free, 43
  moral, 278

Entelechy, 44
Enthusiasm as defined by Pasteur, 133
Entity (-ies), pathological, 229
 spiritual, 22
Entropy, 42
Environment, 18, 23, 32, 37, 144, 145, 198, 201, 205, 217, 234, 236, 239, 244, 247, 251, 268
 economic, 292
 factors of, 236
 influence of, 237
 physical, 205
 power over, 98
 social, 205, 283, 292
 stimuli of, 94
 variability of, 181
Enzymes, 81
Epidemics, 223
Epoch, variation of human beings according to each, 68
Equality, 289
 dogmas of democratic, 249
Equilibrium (-ia), 134, 162, 181, 208, 280, 282, 284
 intraorganic, 211
 mental, 37
 nervous, 18, 108, 278, 284
 physicochemical, 185, 256
Eruption appearing during bombardment, 139–40
Escaping as a reaction to surroundings, 205–6
Eskimo, 158
Eugenics, 232, 234, 259, 274–7, 290
Eunuch, 91
Europe, 127, 130, 146, 254, 272, 274
Euthanasic institutions, 291
Events, visions of, 141
Examination, medical, 274, 285
Excesses, alimentary, 202
 sexual, 138, 216
Exercise (-s), 25, 279, 281
 artificial, 212
Experimentation and progress of medicine, 287
Experiments, 232, 233
 spiritualists', 244
Eye, 71, 186, 199

Fact (-s), concrete, 16
 evolution of schemas from concrete, 219
 treated as symbols, 219
Factor (-s), chemical, 279
 dominant, 231
 functional, 279
 hereditary, 231
 mental, 282–3
 physical, 277
 psychological, 279
 recessive, 231
Factory (-ies), 23, 25, 29, 35, 278, 288
Failure, intellectual, 176
 moral, 176
 of hygiene and medicine, 168
 social, 176
Faith, 119
Fallopian tube, 92
Family, disappearance of, 25, 248, 276
Farmer as class of human beings, 289
Fasting, 202, 212, 280
Fats, 81, 83
 action of, 165
Fear, 139
Fecundation, 187
Feeble-minded (-ness), 134, 137, 234, 247, 274–5
Feeling, æsthetic, 291
Feminism, 91, 274
Fertilization, 231
Fertilizers, chemical, 114
Fever, 193
 typhoid. See Typhoid fever
 yellow, 228
Fibres, nerve, 71
Fibrin, 81, 188
Fibrinogen, 81
Finality, 185
Finance, American, 253
Financiers, 215
Fingerprints, 220
Fingers and mastery over matter, 98
Flexner, Simon, 263, 266
Flight, 205
Flocculation, 42
Florida, 278

Flour, 26
Fluids, nutrient, 17
    organic, 185
Fœtus, 93, 185, 231
Food (-s), 18, 203
    adulterated, 216
    effects of, 52–3
    staple, 114
Forms, geometrical, 21
Foundation of Ethics, 125
Fowl injected with serum of rabbit, 195
Fracture, repair of, 188
Frame, social, 269, 287
France, 32, 127, 129, 264, 269, 273
Frederick the Great, 24
Freedom engendered by soundness of organs, 285
French Revolution, 37, 269
Freud, 138, 258
Frog, 93, 96
Frontier (-s), anatomical, 70, 238
    psychological, 239
    spatial, 238
    temporal, 238
Function (-s), 75, 104, 244
    adaptive, 180–217, 257
    æsthetic, 257
    affective, 124
    digestive, 212–3
    mental, 48
    moral, 257
    organic, 280
    psychological, 280
    religious, 257

GALILEO, 19, 34, 68, 116, 128, 154–5, 255–6
Gallavardin, Louis, 125
Ganglia, small, 95
    sympathetic, 95, 100–1
Gangrene, 191
Gangsters, 135, 290
Gene (-s), 18, 42, 77, 231, 233
Geneticists, theories of, 92, 232
Genetics, 261, 272
Genius (-es), 34, 120, 136, 276–7
Genoa, 264
Geometry, 21
Germany, 263
Germ-plasm, 242, 276

Gestation, 91
Gland (-s), endocrine, 84, 89, 112, 138, 172, 242
    mammary, 185
    pancreas, 89
    sexual, 91, 201
    suprarenal, 89, 101, 209
    sweat, 212
    thyroid, 18, 85, 89, 137, 185, 193, 220, 221
Glucose, 85, 116, 209
Glycogen, 104, 116
God, 131, 241
    a mathematician, 108
    grace of, 131; 246
Goitre, exophthalmic, 112, 193
Golf, 212, 262
Good definition of, and evil, 125
Gout, 69
Government, 33, 176, 263
Gramophone records, and vulgarity of crowd, 25
Greece, 15, 132
Gregorian music, 59
Groups, dissenting, 271
Growth, index, 160, 164–5, 171
    optimum, 271
Guide, Alpine, 144

HABIT (-s), as an aspect of adaptation, 206
    moral, 281
    virile, 204
Hæmoglobin, 82, 184
Hæmophilia, 233
Hæmorrhage (-s), 81, 183, 188
    cerebral, 113
Hale, G. E., 291
Hallucination, 132
Halsted, W. S., 191–2
Hand, 98
Happiness, aptitude for, 18, 110
    engendered by soundness of organs, 285
Haptens, 222–3
Hardship, advantages resulting from, 280
Harmony, of organic and psychological functions, 280
    restoration to, 291
Hatred, 238

Healing, 148, 192
Health, 30, 268
    artificial, 198, 284-5
    natural, 198, 284-5
    spiritual, 257
Heart, 112, 183, 212
    disease, 113
    fragment of chick embryo, 164
    pulsations of, 220
Heat, fight against, 199
Héloïse, 137
Henderson, L. J., 81
Heparin, 104
Herd, 25, 270, 272
Hereditary, 201, 234
Heredity, 42, 232, 246, 251
    laws of, 92
Hermitte, 120
Herter, Christian, 263
Heterochronism, 167, 177
Heterogeneity, organic, 104
Hibernation, 163
History, 16, 58, 255
Homo œconomicus, 17
Homogeneity, 105
Homosexual (-ity), 146, 246
Honesty, 281
    intellectual, 133
Hope, 206
Hormones, 285
Horse (-s), 67
    thoroughbred, 275
Hospitals, 112-3, 286-7
    for insane, 147-8
Hotels, 25
Humanity, 245, 267
Humours, 17, 43, 172, 258
    specificity of, 220-2
Hunger, 202, 280
Hunt, Reid, 194
Hydrogen, 83
Hygiene, 257, 260-1, 263, 271, 286
    and quantity of human beings, 27
    basis of, 40
    development of, in United States, 263
    subject of, 118
Hygienists, 31, 257
    and optimum development, 17
Hypertension, 113, 234

Hypnotist, 240
Hypophysis, 101
Hypotheses, 15
Hysteria, 141, 226

IDEA (-s), Platonic, 218-9, 241
Idiosyncrasies, 69
Idiots, moral, 137
Idleness, 207, 282
Illusion (-s), 120, 206
Imagination, 32, 45, 120, 133, 235, 287
Imitation, capacity for, 243
Immorality, 253
Immortality, 173
Immunity, acquired, 194
    artificial, 194-5
    natural, 109, 193-4
    spontaneous, 194-5
Impulses, genesic, 246
    nerve, 67
    sexual, 274
Inaction, and suffering, 206
    and time, 175
Independence, an illusion, 245
Index, growth, 160
    growth, of serum, 171
Individual (-s), 16, 18, 208, 218-51
    categories of, 225
    classification of, 176
    heterochronic, 177
    thoroughly developed, 135
Individuality, 187, 220-1, 223, 232, 245, 249
    anatomical, 104
    collapse of, 250
    humoral, 224
    mental, 224
    neglect of, 249
    physiological, 104
    psychological, 226-7
    structural, 224
Individualization, 237, 244
    degree of, 226
Indolence, 207
Industrialism, 150
Industry, 23, 128
Inequalities, individual, 249
    mental, 272
    organic, 272
Inertia, 253

Infection (-s), 192, 257, 286
  elimination of, 113
  microbial, 27
Influence, of individual, 243
  pathogenic, 237
Influenza, 111, 228
Infra-red rays, 71
Inhibitions, 97
Injuries, 187
Insane, 32, 253, 274
Insanity, 141, 233, 247, 275
  causes of, 150 •
  circular, 150
Insecurity, 282
Inspiration, 120, 138
  æsthetic, 122, 132
  religious, 122
  scientific, 122
Instinct, 42
Institutes, biological, 266
  research, 265
Institutions, euthanasic, 291
  political, 176
  scientific, 176
Insulin, 62, 89, 116, 197, 285–6
Insurance, social, 30
Integration, 282
Integrity, anatomical, 238
  functional, 238
Intellect, 21
Intellectual, pure, 133
  value, 118
  victories, 27
  work, 83
Intelligence, 32–3, 36, 43, 118–21,
    133, 144, 185, 205, 209, 225,
    276, 289–90
  genesis of, 119
  quality of, 118
  quantity of, 118
  tests, 59, 227
International Bureau of Weights
    and Measures, 41
International Institute of Meta-
    psychics, 121
International Medical Associa-
    tion, 142
Interventions, and cadence of in-
    ner time, 178
  full effects of our, 178
Intestines, 69, 73, 188

Intimacy, 25
Introduction to the Study of Ex-
    perimental Medicine, 117
Introspection, 17, 118
Intuition (-s), 20, 64, 120–1, 133
  religious, 132
Intuitive (-s), 120, 225
Inventions, 20
Inventor, 64
Inventory, 46–7
Inviolability of our visible fron-
    tiers, 238
Iodine, 112
Ions, 42
Iris, 187, 199
Irresponsibility, 146, 206
Islam, 254
Isochronic, 95, 166
Isochronism, 167
Isolation, 57, 147, 270, 283
Italy, 263–4

JACOBINS, 269
Jeans, J., 28, 66, 108
Johns Hopkins Medical School,
    263
Johns Hopkins University, 203
Joltrain, E., 140
Judge and intuition, 120
Judgment, 18, 37, 133

KIDNEY (-s), 104, 112, 185, 193,
    197, 212, 221
  atrophy, 221
  function of, 87
  grafted, 100
  removal and replantation of,
    86
Kindergarten, 248
Knights, 270
Knowledge, medical, 229
Kocher, 191
Kroepelin, 149

LABORATORY (-IES), 287
  industrial, 285
Landsteiner, K., 222
Language, 99
  mathematical, 15, 256
Larynx, 73, 99
Lavoisier, 34, 149

Law (-s), 16, 27, 251, 275, 293
  of adaptation, 43
  organic, 17
  thermodynamic, 43
Laziness, 280
Leaders, 239, 241
Leadership, 207
Le Chatelier, 208
Lecomte du Noüy, P., 159, 189
Legality, 126
Leisure, 175, 207
Lenin, 37
Lens, 186–7, 210
  crystalline, 71
Lesions, cerebral, 226
  organic, 286
Leucocytes, 73, 75, 78, 82, 104, 106, 195, 196
Level, molecular, 43
  psychological, 43
Levitations, 141
Libido, 259
Life, duration of, 27
  expectation of, at birth, 112
  illuminative, 131
  inner, 283
  latent, 85
  mode of, 18
  mystic, 132
  phenomena of, 15
  spiritual, 17, 21
Light, excessive, 199
  speed of, 66
  waves, 291
Limb (-s), 98, 188, 236
Lincoln, 236
Lindbergh, 237
Lipoids, 195
Lister, 191
Liver, 19, 84, 112, 212, 213, 220
Lodge, Sir O., 239
Loeb, Jacques, 17, 48, 93, 107, 163
Logicians, 120, 225
Lombroso, 135
London, 121
Longevity, 30–1, 141, 168–70, 204
Lords, feudal, 215
Louis XIV, 24
Lourdes, 142–3
  Medical Bureau, 142–3

Love, 238
Lunatics, 290
Lungs, 183, 199
  function of, 87
Lupus cured at Lourdes, 143
Lymph, 8, 85
  interstitial, 75, 80, 86
Lymphatics, 75
Lymphocytes, 78
Lyons, University of, 121

Machine (-s), 17, 25
Machinery, modern, 207, 288
Macy Foundation, 264
Maladies intellectual, 257
  moral, 257
Man, an indivisible whole, 18
  as focus of activities, 65, 244
  definition of, 16–17
  empirical character of science of, 62
  remaking of, 252–93
Mania, cyclic, 69
Manufacturers, 215
Marcus Aurelius, 147
Marriage, 276
  instability of, 274
Marrow, bone, 104, 186
Marx, 37
Mass production, effect of, 114
Material, 256
Materialism, 258, 289–90
Materialist (-s), 17, 239
Mathematics, 120, 257
Matter, 41, 128
  constitution and properties of, 16
  inanimate, 292
  inert, 17, 28, 38, 251
  separated from mind, 117, 256
  supremacy of, 145, 257
Maturity, 175, 284
Mayos, 191
Meanness, 125
Measles, 194, 237
Mechanicists, 107, 239
Mechanics, 15, 22, 38, 42, 44, 257
  quantum, 43
Mechanism, 44, 63
  adaptive, 200–1, 228, 277
  healing, 190

Mechanisticism, 264
Mechanists, 38, 185, 258
Medicine, 20, 27, 40, 148, 219–20, 228, 230, 257–8, 260–1, 271, 286
 scientific, 229, 284
Mediterranean, 200
Medium (-s), 121, 226, 244
Mediumistic states, 259
Meditation, 57, 140, 282, 287
Meltzer, S. J., 185
Membrane (-s), synaptic, 95
 tympanic, 70
Memory, 62, 167, 171
 training of, 119
Men, business, 262
 completely developed, 247
 modern, 216
 standardization of, 248
 white, 207
Mendel, 222, 234
Menopause, 91, 158
Menstruation, 92
Mentality, identical, 224
Merlin, 168
Metabolism, 67, 84–5, 158, 164
 basal, 84–5
Metacarpus, 98
Metals, 81, 112
Metaphysics, 17, 255
Metapsychic (-s), 121, 239, 261
Metchnikoff, E., 195
Mice, 59–60, 67, 169, 194
Micella, 42
Michelangelo, 68
Microbes, 69, 73, 191, 193
Middle Ages, 154, 218, 229, 254, 255, 270, 289
Millikan, R. A., 28
Mind, 19, 32, 128, 204, 256, 258
 pathology of, 149
 synthetic, 265
 weakness of, 233
Ministers, 147
Minkowski, 154
Minority, power of an ascetic and mystic, 271
Miracle, 142–3
Misery, degeneration due to prosperity or, 209
Mitochondria, 77

Mobility, spatial, and length of life, 166
Modifications, organic, and states of consciousness, 136
Molecules, 18, 22, 43
 carbohydrate, 223
 protein, 223
Monasteries, 129, 270
Monkeys, 60
Monks, 262, 278
 Benedictine, 59
Monocytes, 79–80
Montessori system, 59
Mont Saint-Michel, 129
Morality, 145
Morals, 125–6, 261
 biological, 125
 Christian, 125–6, 206
 industrial, 125, 251
 sexual, 146
Morons, 134
Morphine, 206
Morphinomaniacs, 242
Mortality, 30
 infantile, 27
Motion, perpetual, 143
Mountaineers, 203
Mount Everest, 66
Mouse. See Mice
Movements, automatic, 97
Mucosa (-s), 72–4
 digestive, 193, 238
 intestinal, 88–9
 respiratory, 193, 200, 238
Murderers, 275
Muscle (-s), 18, 21, 188, 216
 motive, 98
 skeletal, 99
Museums, 146
Music, Gregorian, 59
Mussolini, 67, 205, 241
Mutations, 273, 276
Myocarditis, 197
Mysticism, 131–2, 289
 Christian, 131, 141
 Hindu, 131
 Tibetan, 131
Mysticity, 21, 130, 145
Mystics, 17, 50, 132, 134, 138
 Christian, 129, 246
Myxœdema, 112

NAPOLEON, 67, 241, 273
  See also Bonaparte
National Committee for Mental
    Hygiene, 148
Needle, magnetic, 153
Nephritis, 113, 197, 221
Nerves, autonomous, 101
  olfactory, 70
  optic, 70
  sympathetic, 101, 199, 209
  vasomotor, 86, 139
Nervous system, 31, 69, 103, 185,
    204, 291
  autonomous, 100–3
  central, 94, 199, 208
  cerebrospinal, 94, 212
  sympathetic, 94
Neurasthenia, 113
Neuron, 95–6
Neuroses, 48, 149, 226, 239
Neurotics, 226
Newton, 34, 46, 239
New York, 144, 147, 263
  Academy of Medicine, Com-
    mittee on Medicine and
    Religion, 142
  inhabitant of, 144
  State, 147
New Zealand, 27
Nitrogen, 84
Noise, 200–1, 216
Nominalism, 63
Nominalists, 219, 229
Normal, development of the, 290
Normandy, 129, 201
North America, 274
Norwegian, 158
Nose, 72, 200
Nucleoli, 77
Nucleoproteins, 77
Nucleus, 18, 75, 77, 231
Nudism, 72
Nutrition, 85, 210, 261

OBLIGATION, 124
Observation (-s), 232, 256, 283, 287
  data of, 259
  individual, 228
Occident, 254–5
Office, 278, 288
Old man, beauty of, 68–9

Ollier, 191
Omentum, 188
Operations, surgical, 178, 191
Opium, 269
Orders, monastic, 262, 270
  of chivalry, 270
Organism (-s), 17, 72, 105–8
  heterogeneous in time and
    space, 78
Organization, 187
  modern business, 288
Organs, 18, 43, 71, 74, 104
  correlation of, 185
  fragility of, 108
  pathology of, 149
  receptor, 70
  sensory, 71, 291
  techniques of building, 107
Orient, 255
Originality, 128, 232, 283
Osteitis cured at Lourdes, 143
Ovaries, 92
  extirpation of, 137
Over-specialization, 54
Ovum, 18, 92, 231, 233, 244
Oxygen, 84, 85, 183–4, 212

PAIN, signal of distress, 110
Pancreas, 62, 73, 104, 116, 197,
    212
Paralysis, 95
  general, of the insane, 226
  infantile, 111
Parasympathetic, 101
Parents, 248, 288
  types of, 243
Paris, 129, 263
Parish, 25
Pasteur, 27, 46, 110, 129, 133, 149,
    191, 203, 205, 263
Pasteur Institute, 263–4, 265
Pathogenic agent, 193–5, 227
Pathologists, 258
Pathology, 20, 260–1, 263
Pavlov, 97, 139, 281
Peace, 283
Peasant (-s), 272–4, 288
Peculiarity (-ies), individual, 231,
    289
  morphological, 221
Pedagogy, 16, 118, 257, 261

Pedigree, 60
Pelvis, 98, 236
Pende, Nicola, 264
Penis, 187
Pericles, 58, 68
Peritoneum, 188
Permeability, 42
    protoplasmic, 258
Permutations, 223
Persistence after death, 244
Personality, 17, 64, 167, 178, 229, 268, 283
    disparateness of, 289
    dissolution of human, 151
    double, 226
    humoral, 223, 229
    mental, 225
    modification of human, 137
    organic, 229
    spatial extensibility of, 241
Perspiration, 198
Peterson, F., 142
Pharynx, 72
Phenomenon (-a), metapsychical, 20, 121, 240
    physiological, 22
    psychological, 136
    telepathic, 121, 239
Phidias, 68
Philanthropists, 239
Philosopher (-s), 17
Philosophy, 18
Phosphates, 184
Phosphorus, 84, 236
Physicians, 31, 37, 53, 229, 260
Physics, 15, 21, 28, 38, 42, 44, 257-8
Physiologists, 53
    mechanistic, 17, 43
    vitalistic, 17
Physiology, 16, 20, 43, 48, 258, 260-1, 285
    directed, 285
Pigment, 199, 203
Pilots, 177
Pity, 125
Placenta, 93
Plasma. See Blood
Plato, 117, 218
Platonic Idea (-s), 218, 241
Pleasure, 139
Plutarch, 237

Pneumococci, 73
Pneumonia, 196, 227
Poets, 17, 272
Poise of individual in confusion of new city, 283
Political economy, 16, 40
Politicians, 249
Polypeptides, 81
Polysaccharids, 195
Pope Innocent VIII, 171
Potential, electric, 96
    energy, 84
    high reducing, 83
Potentialities, 178, 209, 231, 234, 237, 293
    mental, 289
Pott's disease, 143
Poverty, 282
Power, electoral, 249
    electrical, 288
    of renovation, 217
    will, 18, 127, 282
Prayer, 130, 142, 259
Prediction of future, 243
Predispositions, ancestral, 178-9, 235
Pregnancy, 91, 185
Prestidigitation, 239
Principle (-s), moral, 125
    religious, 30
Prisons, 290
Privation (-s), 110, 283
Probabilities, calculation of, 229
Problems, social, 175
Processes, adaptive, 279
    dendritic, 42
    functional, 48
    healing, 170
    irreversible, 246
    mental, 217
    physiological, 48, 217
Production, mass, 288-9
Products, endocrine, 284
    waste, 85
Professors, university, 262
Progress, human, 289
Progression, arithmetical, 201
    geometrical, 201
Proletarian (-s), 254, 273-4, 289
    intellectual, 276
    manual, 276

Proletariat, 288
Propaganda, 36
Prosperity, 209, 253, 283
Protein (-s), 81, 88, 165, 195, 222
Protoplasm, 76
Prudden, T. Mitchell, 263
Pseudopods, 132
Psychical Research, Society for, 239
Psychoanalysis, 140
Psychologists, 16
Psychology, 16, 43. 48, 118, 149, 257–8, 260–1
  normal, 239
  scientific, 227
Psychoses, 48, 149, 151, 226
Puberty, 158, 176–7
Pulsations, cardiac, 199, 208
Purgative, 182
Purpose, spiritual, 289
Pycnic type and diseases, 69
Pyramidal body of cerebral cells, 42

QUALITATIVE, 256
  as true as quantitative, 46
Qualities, hereditary, 251, 268
  primary, 153, 256
  secondary, 153, 255–6
Quantitative, 16, 256–7
Quantum mechanics, 43
Quiet, exceptional in existence of modern man, 25

RABBIT (-s), 195, 202
Raccoons, metabolism of, in winter, 85
Race (-s), white, 72, 108, 198, 255, 267
  lower, 200
Radiations, solar. 199
Radio, 35, 207
  and vulgarity of crowd, 25
Ramon y Cajal, S., 42, 95
Ranches, Western, 203
Rats, 59–60
Rays, cosmic, 28, 71
  infra-red, 71
  light, 71
  sun, 71
  ultra-violet, 23, 71

Reactions, instinctive, 281
Reactivity, modifications of, 224
Realism, 63
Realists, 219, 229
Reality, 15, 17, 46, 219, 257
Receptivity, 200
Reflex (-es), 42, 280, 282
  conditional, 97
  innate, 97
Regeneration, 189, 255
Regimens, dietary, 274
Rejuvenation, 162, 170–3
Relations, chemical, 46
  mental, 46
  physical, 46
  temporal, 95
Religion (-s), 130, 261
  Asiatic, 131
  dogmas of industrial, 145
  scientific, 251
Religious beliefs, 27
Renaissance, 58, 68, 117, 255–6, 292
Renovation, 251, 293
Renunciation, 275
Reproduction, 93, 274
Research (-es), biological, 266–7, 286
  conclusions of, dangerous, 60
  psychical, 121
Resistance, 31, 74, 108, 112, 210
  organic, 278
  to disease, 18, 36
  to fatigue, 18
Responsibility, 204, 282
Restoration, 255, 268, 291
Retina, 71, 186–7, 199, 200
Retirement, 176
Revolts, 283
Revolution (-s), 23, 39, 269
  French, 37, 269, 272
  industrial, 29
  Russian, 272
Revue Métapsychique, 121
Rewards, financial 277
  moral, 277
Rheumatism, 69
Rhine, J. B., 121
Rhythm, 58
  inward, 181
  of life, 35

Rich, as a class of human beings, 289
  men above the multitude, 249
Richet, C., 121, 223
Riemann, 120
Right and wrong, 145
Robbers, 146
Rockefeller, John D., 263
Rockefeller Foundation, 264
Rockefeller Institute for Medical Research, 194, 263, 265–6
Rolando, region of, 97
Roman Catholic Church, 126, 176
Roman Empire, 254
Rome, 132
Rous, P., 82
Roux, E., 265
Royal Society of Sciences of Copenhagen, 125
Russia, 263
Ruth, Babe, 237
Ruysbroeck the Admirable, 117

SACRIFICE, 262, 275
St. John of the Cross, 131
Saints, 126, 272
Salivation, 139
Salts, mineral, 112
Scandinavian (-s), 200, 278
Scar, 189–90
Schema (-s), 16, 37, 40, 46, 50, 54, 74, 219, 247
School, 248, 257, 264, 278
Schizophrenia, 149
Schopenhauer, 125
Science, 19, 26, 28, 34, 254
  abstract, 16
  and intelligence, 119
  biological, 15
  descriptive form of, 16
  of inert matter, 15, 37, 293
  of life, 15, 293
  of living beings, 16
  of man, 22, 39, 40–63, 293
  of medicine, 230–1
Scientific reasoning, 16
Scientists, 17, 41, 230
Scurvy, 193
Séances in psychical research, 121
Secretions, glandular, 236

Sections, microscopical, 75
Security, 30, 282–3
Selection, natural, 246, 271
Self-indulgence, 284
Selfishness, 125
Senescence, 163–6, 284
  lengthening of, 170
  regional, 165–6
Sense (-s), æsthetic, 18, 43, 62, 125, 127, 134, 146, 276
  moral, 18, 43, 125, 146, 276
  olfactory, 220
  religious, 18, 129, 134, 276
  social, 43
Sensibility, 290
Separation of mind from body, 257
Septicæmias, 196
Sera, serum (-s), 81, 222, 265
  antitoxic, 285
  blood, 258
  injections of, 194
  therapeutic, 195
Serf (-s), 273, 288
Service, military, 202
Sex (-es), 233, 287
Sexual, appetites, 137
  excesses, 137
Shaping, intellectual, 282
Shapley, H., 28
Sheep, 85
Shocks, 217
Short-sightedness, 234
Shoulder blade, 98
Sidgwick, Henry, 121
Silence, 57
  of sound body, 109
Simplicity, functional, 104
Sincerity, 281
Skating-rinks, 25
Skeleton, 18, 67, 98, 104, 203
Skin, 69–70, 189–90, 220, 238
  extirpation of, 189, 208
  grafts, 221
Skyscrapers 35
Sleep, 202, 213
  hypnotic, 226
  need of, 274
Smallpox, 112, 195
Smith, Theobald, 263
Snow, 203

Society (-ies), modern, 248, 255, 258, 267, 289
of cells, 18, 76
Society for Psychical Research, 121
Sociologists, 44
Sociology, 16, 37, 76, 220, 257, 260
Socrates, 121
Sodium chloride, 17
Soldier, 237
Solesmes, monastery of, 59
Solitude, 25, 57, 147, 248
Solomon's Song, 138
Song, and prayer, 131
Soul, 65, 116, 138, 244
Soundness of organs engenders freedom, 285
Space, 67, 78, 116, 122, 149, 153, 163, 185, 187, 239, 240–1, 242–3, 292
dimensions of, 65
Spain, 278
Specialist (-s), 16, 53, 54–5, 247, 258, 264
Specialization, 53
Specificity, 221
individual, 246
of organs, 220
Spengler, O., 255
Spermatozoon (-a), 92, 187, 231
Sphincter, 70
Spinal cord, 71, 74, 184
Spiritualism, 239, 243–4
Spiritual, 256
Spiritualist (-s), 17, 239
Spleen, 78, 104
Sports, 25
Stability, 181–2, 283
nervous, 37
of life, 276
Stabilization, adaptation as an agent of, 208
Staphylococci, 73
State, psychological, 144
steady, 208
Statistics, on care of sick, 112–3
on insane, 147–8
Stature, 32, 67
Steamers, 24
Steel, 180
Steinach, E., 171, 172

Sterile women, 274
Sterility, voluntary, 33
Stimulus, 200–1
foreseen, 282
Stomach, 69, 212
Stores, 24
Strength, 273, 277
Streptococci, 73
Strife, 205
Structure (-s), and function, 244
atomic, 42
electronic, 42
molecular, 42
of organs, 75
Struggle, 282
Strychnine, 95
Substances, antiseptic, 192
chemical, 17, 18
chemical, of environment, 245
Substratum, 28, 104, 141, 181
bodily, 66, 90, 132, 138
organic, 162
psychological, 162
Suburbs, 23
Suffering, and inaction, 206
moral, 20, 139
Sugar (-s), 81, 104, 212
Suicide, 239
Sulphur, 84
Superscience, 261
Superstition (-s), 18
Suppuration, 191
Suprarenals, 101, 104
Supreme Court of the United States, 56, 267
Surgery, modern, 190–1, 263
Surroundings. See Environment
Survival, 198, 208, 213
Swimming-pools, 25
Symbols, 219
equations of, 15
world of, 229–30
Syncope, 187
Synthesis, 52, 55–6, 57
of knowledge, 259
Syphilis, 48, 113, 136, 197, 227, 242, 275
System (-s), adaptive, 280
autonomous, 100, 103
central nervous, 94, 99, 102, 199, 208

System (-s), cerebrospinal, 94, 101,
212
digestive, 69
glandular, 69
nervous, 31, 69, 94, 103, 204,
283, 291
organic, 102, 212, 279
parasympathetic, 101
philosophical, 256, 291
sympathetic, 94, 101-2, 212, 282

TANNING, 72
Tardigrada, 85
Technology, 33, 230, 252, 255, 258,
269
Teissier, J., 121
Telegraph, 24, 35
Teleological, 185, 216
Telepathic communications, 18, 72
Telepathy, 49, 62, 121-3, 239
Telephone, 24
Television, 35
Temperament (-s), 69, 101, 124
Temperature, 23, 198-9
Temples, 120
Tendencies, 231, 233
ancestral, 234, 244
hereditary, 234-5, 237
inherent, 128, 236
Tendons, 98
Tennis, 212
Tennis-courts, 25
Tension, osmotic, 42
Testicles, 91, 137-8, 172, 236
Tests, psychological, 120, 227
Therapeutics, 229
chemical, 285
Thermodynamics, 43, 143, 257
Thinking, philosophical, 289
Thirst, 186, 202, 280
Thorax, 185, 203
Thought, 15, 98, 116, 133, 138,
256, 268
habits of, 255
transmission, 141
Thyroid. See Gland (-s)
Thyroxin, 89, 285
Tides, 156
Time, 67, 78, 116, 122, 132, 149,
154, 185, 187, 220, 239, 241,
242, 243-4, 245, 292

Time, inner, 156-8, 161, 178, 181,
227-8
intrinsic, 156
lunar, 155-6
physical, 158, 163, 166, 174
physiological, 18, 42, 156-7,
160, 161-7, 171, 173-4, 176,
177-8, 204, 217, 246
psychological, 157, 167, 171
solar, 155, 158, 160-1
Time Traveller, 156
Tissue (-s), 18, 172
alterations, 165
connective, 190
cultivation of, 76, 86, 164
epithelial, 190
fatty, 190
human, amount of fluid needed
for, 86
nutrition of, 88
Tobacco, 274
Tongue, 70, 99
Tonsils, 73
Tourists, 130
Toxins, 195
Trachea, 73
Trainers, animal, 281
Training, familial, 248
Trains, 24
Traité de Psychologie, 226
Transformers, chemical, 89
Transfusion, blood, 171-2, 222
Transplantation, glandular, 221
of organs, 221
Treatises, medical, 228
Treponema pallidum, 197, 242
Truth, contemplation of, 133
ultimate, 132
Tube, Fallopian, 92
Tuberculosis, 31, 48, 69, 112, 194,
234, 275
peritoneal, cured at Lourdes, 143
Tuffier, T., 191
Tumours, 197
brain, 113
Twins, 233
identical, 224, 233
Type (-s), affective, 225
herding together of ill assorted,
289
intellectual, 225

Type (-s), mystical, 225
  pycnic, 69
  sensitive, 225
  voluntary, 225
Typhoid fever, 31, 73, 112, 194, 196, 227–8

ULTRAVIOLET rays, 23, 71
Unbalance, nervous, 274
Unemployment, 207
Unintelligence, more general, 145
Uniqueness, 231, 287
United States, 27, 30–2, 112, 147, 215, 263, 267, 273
Unity, 116, 216, 230, 245, 268
Universals, 218, 227, 229–30, 248, 257
Universe, 15, 20, 28, 245, 291
Universities, 25, 257, 264, 269–70
  American, 263
Urine, 185, 221
Uterus, 91

VACCINATION, 195
Vaccine, 54, 194, 265
Vagina, 185, 187
Value (-s), human, 288
  moral, 27
Van Slyke, D. D., 81
Ventricle, 197
Versailles, 90
Vesicle (-s), 77
  optic, 186
Vessels, suture of, 221
Vices, inherent, 126
Virility, 247
Virus (-es), 73, 111, 193, 194, 224, 228, 265, 286
Visions of events happening at a distance, 141
Viscera, 86, 99, 100–1, 104, 200
  removal of, 100–1
Vitalism, 44, 63
Vitalists, 44, 185, 239
Vitality, 235
Vitamins, 112, 193, 236, 284, 285
Voronoff, S., 168, 171–2
Vulgarity of modern civilization, 128
Vulva, 185

WASHINGTON, George, 237

Water, 15, 103–4
  alkalinity of ocean, 21
Watson, J. B., 232
Waves, electromagnetic, 71, 240, 291
Weak, predominance of, 250, 271
  reproduction of, 271
Weakening of body, 110
Weaklings, 198
Weakness, intellectual, 247
Wealth, 26, 110, 207, 282
Weber, 200–1
Weierstrass, 120
Welch, W. H., 203, 263
Wells, H. G., 153, 156
Whip and criminals, 290
Whole, functional, 104
Will, 125–6
  power, 18, 126
  to power, 282
Wireless, 24
Woodger, J. H., 44
Work, 206, 209, 280
Workers, industrial, 288
  manual, 278
  white-collar, 288
Workmen, 23
World (-s), 292
  aquatic, 70
  earthly, 21
  inner, 17, 20
  intraorganic, 107
  material, 15, 20, 27
  modern, 26
  new, 20
  organic, 20
  outer, 16, 19
  spiritual, 20
  temporal, 177
  terrestrial, 21
Wound (-s), rate of healing of, 159
  suppurating, cured at Lourdes, 143
Writing, automatic, 226

YALE University, 264
Yankee, 278
Years, 158
Yellow fever, 228
Youth, beauty of, 68–9
  eternal, 168

SOME
PENGUIN
PUBLICATIONS
*

PELICAN BOOKS

This comprehensive series, most of the books in which are written specially for it, ranges over subjects as diverse as architecture and psychology, law and music, botany and physiology, archaeology and philosophy. A selection of some recent and forthcoming titles is shewn here.

A28	Civilisation	*Clive Bell*
A43	Introducing Shakespeare	*G. B. Harrison*
A61	An Introduction to Modern Architecture	
		J. M. Richards
A84	The Scientific Attitude	*C. H. Waddington*
A90–2	Lives of the Great Composers	
		A. L. Bacharach
A102	Human Physiology	*Kenneth Walker*
A120	The Ancient World	*T. R. Glover*
A121	Mathematician's Delight	*W. W. Sawyer*
A165	The Personality of Man	*G. N. M. Tyrrell*
A169	John Citizen and the Law	*Ronald Rubinstein*
A170	Science and the Nation	*Association of Scientific Workers*
A178	The Inventor and his World	
		H. Stafford Hatfield
A179	Genetics	*H. Kalmus and L. Crump*
A183	British Herbs	*F. Ranson*
A185	Geology and Scenery	*A. E. Trueman*
A186	Scientist in Russia	*Eric Ashby*
A192	Greek Science 2	*Benjamin Farrington*
A193	The Size of the Universe	*F. J. Hargreaves*
A194	The Psychology of Sex	*Oswald Schwartz*

THE PENGUIN CLASSICS

A Library of New Translations

EDITED BY E. V. RIEU

1. HOMER: *The Odyssey*   E. V. Rieu
2. DE MAUPASSANT: *Boule de Suif and Other Stories*
    R. N. P. Sloman
3. SOPHOCLES: *The Theban Plays*   E. F. Watling
4. VOLTAIRE: *Candide*   John Butt
5. TACITUS: *On Britain and Germany*   R. Mattingly
6. DANTE: *The Divine Comedy*   Dorothy L. Sayers

IN PREPARATION

From the Greek

HOMER: *The Iliad*   E. V. Rieu
XENOPHON: *The Persian Expedition*   Rex Warner
PLATO: *The Last Days of Socrates*   Hugh Tredennick
PLATO: *The Symposium*   W. Hamilton
THEOCRITUS: *The Idylls*   Adeline Cook

From the Latin

LUCRETIUS: *The Nature of the Universe*   R. E. Latham
CAESAR: *The Conquest of Gaul*   S. A. Handford
VIRGIL: *The Pastoral Poems*   E. V. Rieu
APULEIUS: *The Golden Ass*   Robert Graves

From the Spanish

CERVANTES: *Don Quixote*   J. M. Cohen

From the French

PREVOST: *Manon Lescaut*   L. W. Tancock
FLAUBERT: *Madame Bovary*   C. A. Russell

From the Russian

TURGENEV: *On the Eve*   Gilbert Gardiner
TCHEHOV: *Plays*   Elisaveta Fen

From the Norwegian

IBSEN: *Pillars of Society and other Plays*   Una Ellis-Fermor

PENGUIN BOOKS

Penguin Occasionals

*

PENGUIN NEW WRITING

A collection of critical and creative writing. Its contributions are selected from the work of world known writers, artists and new authors. Each issue also contains sixteen pages of plates illustrating new work in the theatre and painting.

PENGUIN PARADE

Presents in an invigorating manner informative articles by authoritative writers on social and artistic affairs. The contents include critical essays on the arts and social problems, short stories, poems and illustrations, both in colour and photogravure, from work by contemporary artists.

NEW BIOLOGY

A miscellany of essays summarising aspects of contemporary biological research and application. Each number has a sixteen-page inset of plates and a glossary explaining the scientific terms used in the text.

PENGUIN FILM REVIEW

A regular publication devoted to up-to-the-minute film news and views, surveying, in a progressive, stimulating manner, all the activities and influences of the film, economically, socially and aesthetically. Also contains thirty-two pages of illustrations from recent British and foreign films.

PENGUIN MUSIC MAGAZINE

Issued at regular intervals, Penguin Music Magazine is intended to give the music lover information on the world of music and musicians. The articles, written by acknowledged authorities, are varied and stimulating and each issue contains thirty-two pages of illustrations.

SOME PENGUIN BOOKS

551	Peter Waring	*Forrest Reid*
*556	Beau Sabreur	*P. C. Wren*
558	A Child of the Jago	*Arthur Morrison*
568	The Ladies' Road	*Pamela Hinkson*
580	The Cardinal's Snuffbox	*Henry Harland*
582	Nordenholt's Million	*J. J. Connington*
586	The Twilight of the Gods	*Richard Garnett*
*588	A Narrow Street	*Elliot Paul*
592	The Turn of the Screw	*Henry James*
593	Kimono	*John Paris*
594	Lobster Salad	*Lynn Doyle*
595	Adam and Eve and Pinch Me	
		A. E. Coppard
*605	Antigua, Penny, Puce	*Robert Graves*
609	Winesburg, Ohio	*Sherwood Anderson*
*617	Penguin Island	*Anatole France*
618	Dew on the Grass	*Eiluned Lewis*
623	The Gilt Kid	*James Curtis*
626	A Well Full of Leaves	*Elizabeth Myers*
631	Scowle and Other Papers	*Bernard Hollowood*
632	Some Do Not	*Ford Madox Ford*
633	Mr Petre	*Hilaire Belloc*
639	No More Parades	*Ford Madox Ford*
642	Mr Fortune's Maggot	*Sylvia Townsend Warner*

* A double volume

EDUCATION IN ENGLAND (A152)

W. Kenneth Richmond

The Education Act which came into force in April 1945 has re-
awakened hope of a 'new deal' in English Education. For the
first time in our history a national and comprehensive system of
education is in sight. This book deals with the history of our educational system from medieval times to the present day, summing
up with some constructive suggestions for supplementing the new
Act.

LOCAL GOVERNMENT IN ENGLAND AND WALES (A162)

W. E. Jackson

This book will interest everyone who wants to have, without
elaborate technicalities, a plain statement of what local government is all about. It provides a simplified but authentic explanation of what the local government system is, its place in the
national scheme, what the various types of local council do and
the important public services they perform.

JUVENILE DELINQUENCY AND THE LAW (A158)

A. E. Jones

The *News Chronicle* says of this book:
What is the deep-down, basic cure for the stream of wasted youth
which pours daily through our courts? For twenty years Mr A. E.
Jones, chief clerk to the magistrates at North London Police
Court, has struggled to find the answer, probing every nook and
cranny of the complicated problem while keeping his mind de-
tached, his imagination fresh and his heart warm. In a book
packed with legal and human facts, he gives the answer.

ABBREVIATIONS

ACTH	adrenocorticotrophic hormone
AMNR	acute macular neuroretinopathy
BASHH	British Association for Sexual Health and HIV
BMI	body mass index
BNF	British National Formulary
BSCC	British Society for Clinical Cytology
CEU	Clinical Effectiveness Unit
CI	confidence interval
CIN	cervical intraepithelial neoplasia
CLE	cutaneous lupus erythematosus
COC	combined oval contraception
CSM	Committee for Safety of Medicines
CT	computed tomography
DEXA	dual energy X-ray absorptiometry
DMARDs	disease modifying anti-rheumatic drugs
DVT	deep vein thrombosis
DMPA	depot medroxyprogesterone acetate
EBM	evidence-based medicine
FFPRHC	Faculty of Family Planning and Reproductive Health Care
fpa	Family Planning Association
FSH	follicle-stimulating hormone
GBS	group B streptococcus
GnRH	gonadotrophin-releasing hormone
HAART	highly active antiretroviral therapy
hCG	human chorionic gonadotrophin
HDL	high-density lipoprotein
HIV	human immunodeficiency virus
HPV	human papillomavirus
HRT	hormone replacement therapy
IgA	immunoglobulin A
IUD	intrauterine contraceptive device
IUS	intrauterine system

kg/m^2	kilogram/square metre
LDL	low-density lipoprotein
LLETZ	large loop excision of the transformation zone
LNG-IUS	levonorgestrel-releasing intrauterine system
MCA	Medicines Control Agency
MHRA	Medicines and Healthcare products Regulatory Agency
mmHg	millimetre of mercury
MRI	magnetic resonance imaging
MRSA	methicillin-resistant *Staphylococcus aureus*
MS	multiple sclerosis
NHSCSP	NHS cervical screening programme
NICE	National Institute for Health and Clinical Excellence
NSAID	non-steroidal anti-inflammatory drugs
OR	odds ratio
PCOS	polycystic ovary syndrome
PGD	Patient group directions
PID	pelvic inflammatory disease
PMS	Premenstrual syndrome
POP	progestogen-only pil
RCOG	Royal College of Obstetricians and Gynaecologists
SIGN	Scottish Intercollegiate Guidelines Network
SLE	systemic lupus erythematosus
STI	sexually transmitted infection
TIA	transient ischaemic attack
TSH	thyroid-stimulating hormone
VSD	ventricular septal defect
VTE	venous thromboembolism
vWf	von Willebrand factor
WHO	World Health Organization

ABOUT THIS BOOK

Family Planning Masterclass is not a comprehensive textbook of contraception. Rather, it addresses questions asked by experienced family planning clinicians when answers could not readily be found in standard texts. We hope that this volume will prove useful to practitioners, who can 'enquire within' when faced with a dilemma in practice relating to a rare condition or contentious issue.

The questions and answers summarised in this book are based on the first 1000 members' enquiries received by the Aberdeen-based Clinical Effectiveness Unit of the Faculty of Family Planning and Reproductive Health Care (FFPRHC). The Unit was established in September 2002 and one of our core tasks is to provide evidence-based answers to clinical enquiries submitted by individual clinician members of the FFPRHC. Full versions of all members' enquiry responses are available within a searchable database on the FFPRHC website. This book contains abbreviated, edited and updated summaries of the first 1000 answers, grouped according to topic area. We suggest that clinicians use this volume as a first point of reference when faced with a clinical dilemma. If your question is not addressed here, it may be among the more recent enquiries included on the website. Questions that remain unanswered may be posed to the Clinical Effectiveness Unit team at ffpceu@abdn.ac.uk.

Our strategy for answering members' enquiries

The Clinical Effectiveness Unit aims to provide evidence-based answers to members' questions using the principles outlined by David Sackett and colleagues in their seminal text, *Evidence-based Medicine: How to Practice and Teach EBM.*[1]

Asking an answerable question

The first task for the Unit team is to convert the often lengthy, convoluted and highly individual problem posed by our enquirer into a generalisable clinical question. We simplify each enquiry into a three-part question using evidence-based medicine (EBM) principles, comprising: a population, intervention(s), and outcome(s).

For example, an enquirer's email to our Unit might read:

> **'Last Wednesday, I saw a 32-year-old, para 3+1 woman in the surgery, along with her 3-year-old child. She is using the combined pill for contraception but feels constantly worried about pill failure. This is because her second child, born 2 years ago, was a result of pill failure. Despite these worries, she seems even more unhappy about using any other form of contraception. She likes the reassurance of regular periods and the idea that the pill is rapidly reversible. Is there any particular pill that would be less likely to result in future failure?'**

We simplify the question using the three-part EBM approach:

Population: **Women who have experienced unintended pregnancy while using combined oral contraception.**

Interventions: **Combined oral contraceptives of different formulations.**

Outcome: **Efficacy.**

We then formulate a generalisable, answerable, clinical question: 'Which combined oral contraceptive would provide greatest efficacy for a woman with a previous unintended pregnancy while using combined oral contraception?'

Finding current best evidence

The second task for the Unit team is to search for published evidence relevant to the enquiry. Using search terms derived from the three-part EBM question, we routinely search the following electronic sources:

- existing guidance from the FFPRHC and the Royal College of Obstetricians and Gynaecologists (RCOG)
- the National Guidelines Clearing House
- the World Health Organization (WHO) publications: *Medical Eligibility Criteria for Contraceptive Use* and *Selected Practice Recommendations for Contraceptive Use*

- the Cochrane Library
- MEDLINE and EMBASE from 1996 onwards.

In addition, we frequently refer to manufacturers' Summaries of Product Characteristics for individual contraceptives and extend our MEDLINE and EMBASE searches back to 1966 if relevant evidence is not found in the more recent literature.

Appraising evidence

Titles and abstracts of publications identified from searches of our routine sources are scrutinised. Some publications are eliminated at this stage if considered to be of no direct relevance to the enquiry. For the remaining publications, we obtain the full text of the paper if it is available electronically or already in our files. We undertake basic quality appraisal of each paper using standard checklists.[2] Time constraints mean that the depth of critical appraisal is less than that applied in the development of formal FFPRHC guidance and that we sometimes rely on information available in publication abstracts only, if the full text is not readily available.

Answering the question

Our final task for each Member's enquiry is to formulate an answer to the original question based on the evidence identified. Answers provided by the Clinical Effectiveness Unit team are based on published evidence, not on personal opinion or anecdotal experience. On occasions when our literature searches identify no evidence relevant to a Member's enquiry, our response is that we cannot provide an evidence-based answer. In these circumstances, a practitioner must manage a clinical dilemma on the basis of personal experience and the advice of colleagues. The EBM approach means that good clinical practice is based on the complementary strengths of research evidence and clinical judgement and experience.

The first 1000 questions

Between September 2002 and March 2005, the Clinical Effectiveness Unit team answered 1000 Members' enquiries using the approach outlined above. The topic areas of these 1000 questions are summarised below (Table 1). Over one-

Table 1. Topic areas of 1000 questions submitted to the Clinical Effectiveness Unit by Members of the FFPRHC between September 2002 and March 2005

TOPIC	Questions (n)	Percentage of total
Contraception for women with medical disorders	339	34
Copper intrauterine devices	124	12
Injectable progestogens	96	10
Concurrent drugs with hormonal contraception	90	9
Combined hormonal contraception	76	8
Progestogen-only pills	51	5
Gynaecological problems in the family planning clinic	48	5
Levonorgestrel intrauterine system	36	4
Progestogen-only implants	31	3
Organisational aspects of family planning provision	29	3
Progestogen-only emergency contraception	25	2
Cyproterone acetate-containing pill	18	2
Barrier methods	15	1
Abortion care	13	1
Methods of contraception unavailable in the UK	5	< 1
Male and female sterilisation	3	< 1
Fertility awareness-based methods	1	< 1
TOTAL	**1000**	**100**

third of enquiries related to contraceptive choices for women with medical disorders of varying degrees of rarity and complexity. For many topics, several Members submitted identical or similar questions. In these instances, the answer summarised in this book is based on the most recent Member's enquiry (which may reflect more recent evidence than the previous versions). Throughout the book, we have indicated the number of Members who posed a similar question. Where more recent information than was available at the time of the enquiry is known, this is noted in an update to the answer.

World Health Organization categories

WHO categories, as set out in the *Medical Eligibility Criteria for Contraceptive Use*, are used throughout the book. The conditions affecting eligibility for the use of each contraceptive method are classified by the WHO under one of the following four categories:

Category 1   A condition for which there is no restriction for the use of the contraceptive method.

Category 2   A condition where the advantages of using the method generally outweigh the theoretical or proven risks.

Category 3   A condition where the theoretical or proven risks usually outweigh the advantages of using the method.

Category 4   A condition that represents an unacceptable health risk if the contraceptive method is used.

Common references

The following documents are cited throughout this book and will not be referenced within each chapter:

British Medical Association, Royal Pharmaceutical Society of Great Britain. *British National Formulary*. London: BMJ Publishing Group and Royal Pharmaceutical Society of Great Britain [www.bnf.org].

Faculty of Family Planning and Reproductive Health Care. *UK Selected Practice Recommendations for Contraceptive Use*. 2002 [www.ffprhc.org.uk]

Summaries of Product Characteristics for all drugs available in the UK are accessible via the Electronic Medicines Compendium [http://emc.medicines.org.uk].

World Health Organization. *Medical Eligibility Criteria for Contraceptive Use*. 3rd ed. Geneva: WHO; 2004 [www.who.int/reproductive-health/publications/mec/index.htm].

World Health Organization. *Selected Practice Recommendations for Contraceptive Use*. 2nd ed. 2005 [www.who.int/reproductive-health/publications/spr_2/index.html].

References

1. Sackett DL, Straus SE, Richardson WS, Rosenberg W, Haynes RB. *Evidence-based Medicine. How to Practice and Teach EBM*. Toronto: Churchill Livingstone; 2000.
2. Scottish Intercollegiate Guidelines Network. *A Guideline Developers' Handbook*. Edinburgh: SIGN; 2004.

SECTION ONE

Contraceptive methods

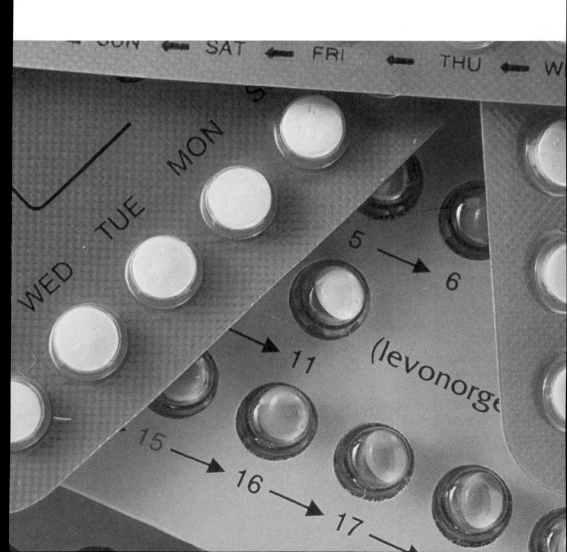

1 COMBINED HORMONAL CONTRACEPTION

Combined oral contraception

Patient selection

QUESTION

For women who wish to use the combined oral contraceptive pill, what blood pressure measurements confer eligibility to use this method?

POPULATION: Women with different levels of blood pressure.

INTERVENTION: Combined oral contraception.

OUTCOME: Safety.

ANSWER

The *WHO Medical Eligibility Criteria for Contraceptive Use* advises that for women with systolic blood pressure (on more than one reading) of 140–159 mmHg or with diastolic blood pressure of 90–99 mmHg, the risks of using the combined pill generally outweigh the benefits (WHO category 3). Women with systolic blood pressure ≥ 160 mmHg, with diastolic ≥ 100 mmHg or with 'vascular disease' (which is not defined by WHO) are advised not to use the combined pill (WHO category 4).

Guidance from the FFPRHC on first prescription of combined oral contraception supports the WHO recommendations that women with blood pressure measurements consistently higher than 140 mmHg systolic or 90 mmHg diastolic should be advised against use of the combined pill (equivalent to a WHO category 3 recommendation).[1]

The WHO *Selected Practice Recommendations* advises that clinicians may provide up to 12 months' supply of the combined pill depending on the woman's preferences and anticipated use. An annual follow-up visit is recommended, at which blood pressure may be measured again. The CEU considers that there are often benefits to following up more frequently than recommended by WHO and suggests a 3-month follow-up after initiation. In addition, women should be encouraged to return at any time to discuss adverse effects or problems, or if they wish to change their method of contraception.

Update to Answer

The FFPRHC has developed a UK version of the *WHO Medical Eligibility Criteria for Contraceptive Use* (published 2006). For use in the UK setting, the WHO advice on blood pressure levels has been modified. Systolic blood pressure (on more than one reading) of 140–159 mmHg or diastolic blood pressure of 90–94 mmHg is assigned to category 3; systolic blood pressure ≥ 160 mmHg or diastolic ≥ 95 mmHg is assigned to category 4.

QUESTION

For women with a body mass index (BMI) greater than 39 kg/m^2, is combined oral contraception a safe and effective method? (Three similar enquiries.)

POPULATION: Women with BMI greater than 39 kg/m^2
INTERVENTION: Combined oral contraception
OUTCOME: Safety and efficacy.

ANSWER

A woman with a BMI greater than 30 kg/m^2 is classified as clinically obese and with a BMI greater than 40 kg/m^2 as morbidly obese.[2] Obesity constitutes a risk factor for cardiovascular disease and venous thromboembolism (VTE). The *WHO Medical Eligibility Criteria for Contraceptive Use* categorises the use of combined oral contraceptives by women with a BMI ≥ 30 kg/m^2 as category 2, which means that the benefits of using the contraceptive method generally outweigh any risks to the individual. However, the *British National Formulary* (BNF) recommends that women with a BMI greater than 39 kg/m^2 should not use combined oral contraception.

A retrospective cohort analysis found that, after controlling for parity, women in the highest body weight quartile (≥ 70.5 kg) were at increased risk of pregnancy if prescribed low-dose (less than 35 micrograms estrogen) combined pills.[3]

The CEU advises that the WHO guidance may be followed for women with a BMI greater than $30 \, kg/m^2$ and that they may use the combined pill. However, for women with a BMI greater than $39 \, kg/m^2$, the CEU advises greater caution and suggests a progestogen-only or non-hormonal method of contraception.

QUESTION

For women who are former smokers, how long after smoking cessation can combined oral contraception safely be used? (Two similar enquiries.)

POPULATION: Women who are former smokers.
INTERVENTION: Combined oral contraception.
OUTCOME: Safety.

ANSWER

The *WHO Medical Eligibility Criteria for Contraceptive Use* does not provide guidance on former smokers but advises that non-smokers under the age of 40 years may have unrestricted use of combined oral contraception (WHO category 1). The benefits of the combined pill generally outweigh the risks (WHO category 2) for non-smokers over the age of 40 years. For women aged ≥35 years who smoke fewer than 15 cigarettes daily, the risks of the combined pill generally outweigh the benefits (WHO category 3). For women aged ≥35 years who smoke ≥15 cigarettes daily, the combined pill is **not** advised (WHO category 4).

FFPRHC guidance on contraception for women aged over 40 years[4] advises that women aged ≥35 years with no other cardiovascular risk factors who stopped smoking more than 1 year previously may consider using combined contraception (the excess risk of myocardial infarction associated with smoking falls significantly 1 year after stopping and is negligible 3–4 years later, regardless of the amount smoked).[5]

Update to Answer

The FFPRHC has developed a UK version of the *WHO Medical Eligibility Criteria for Contraceptive Use* (published 2006). For use in the UK setting, advice on former smokers has been included. This mirrors the advice in the FFPRHC guidance summarised above: a woman aged ≥35 years who stopped smoking less than 1 year ago is allocated to category 3 (risks generally outweigh benefits) whereas such a woman who stopped smoking 1 year or more ago is allocated to category 2 (benefits generally outweigh risks).

QUESTION

For women who are more than 6 months postpartum and breastfeeding, can combined oral contraception safely be used?

POPULATION: Breastfeeding women more than 6 months postpartum.

INTERVENTION: Combined oral contraception.

OUTCOME: Safety.

ANSWER

The *WHO Medical Eligibility Criteria for Contraceptive Use* provides guidance on the safe use of contraceptive methods. Using combined oral contraception in the early postpartum period can reduce the quantity and quality of breast milk. For breastfeeding women who are less than 6 weeks postpartum, the use of combined oral contraception is **not** advised (WHO category 4). For women who are primarily breastfeeding and are between 6 weeks and 6 months postpartum, the risks of combined oral contraception generally outweigh the benefits (category 3). However, for women who are still breastfeeding beyond 6 months, the benefits of the combined pill generally outweigh any risks (category 2). Similar advice is given in the WHO *Selected Practice Recommendations*.

The CEU supports the WHO recommendations that women may safely use combined oral contraception if more than 6 months postpartum and continuing to breastfeed.

References

1. Faculty of Family Planning and Reproductive Health Care Clinical Effectiveness Unit. First prescription of combined oral contraception. *J Fam Plann Reprod Health Care* 2003;29:209–22.
2. Department of Health. *Prodigy Guidance Obesity*. London: DoH; 2002 [www.prodigy.nhs.uk/guidance.asp?gt=Obesity].
3. Holt VL, Cushing-Haugen KL, Daling JR. Body weight and risk of oral contraceptive failure. *Obstet Gynecol* 2002;99:820–7.
4. Faculty of Family Planning and Reproductive Healthcare Clinical Effectiveness Unit. Contraception for Women Aged over 40 Years. *J Fam Plann Reprod Health Care* 2005;31:51–64.
5. Kawachi I, Colditz GA, Stampfer M, Willett WC, Manson JE, Rosner B, *et al.* Smoking cessation and time course of decreased risks of coronary heart disease in middle-aged women. *Arch Intern Med* 1994;154:169–75.

Choice of pill and starting regimens

QUESTION

For women who wish to use the combined oral contraceptive pill, are pills containing 20 micrograms ethinylestradiol as effective as those with higher doses of estrogen? (Three similar enquiries.)

POPULATION: Women requiring contraception.
INTERVENTION: Combined oral contraception with differing estrogen content.
OUTCOME: Efficacy.

ANSWER

The formulations of combined contraceptive pills have changed since they were originally developed. The first combined pill, in the 1960s, contained a high dose of mestranol and norethynodrel. Norethynodrel represented one of the 'first generation' of progestogens (which also includes norethisterone). A 'second generation' progestogen, levonorgestrel, was developed around 1970. From 1994, 'third generation' progestogens from the gonane class (including desogestrel, gestodene and norgestimate) were used in combined pills in an attempt to reduce androgenic and metabolic effects. Concurrent with these changes in progestogen content, the dose of estrogen in combined pills was reduced to minimise the risk of thromboembolism. The estrogen dose has been reduced stepwise from 150 micrograms to 50 micrograms and more recently to 35, 30, 20 and even 15 micrograms.[1]

Even in controlled clinical trials, it is difficult to measure the true efficacy of an oral contraceptive. Two techniques are widely used to quantify contraceptive failure rates: the Pearl index and life table analysis. The Pearl Index represents the number of failures (unintended pregnancies)/100 woman-years of exposure. A weakness of this approach is that studies of longer duration result in lower Pearl Indices, which may under-represent the true failure rate.[2-4] The CEU was unable to find any review that compared failure rates (calculated by either method) of different combined oral contraceptives.

Advice from the FFPRHC is that, when starting a combined pill for the first time, a pill containing 30–35 micrograms ethinylestradiol (with levonorgestrel or norethisterone) should generally be chosen.[5] After counselling regarding the risk of VTE, pills containing desogestrel or gestodene may be used if a woman expresses a preference. The risk of VTE does not vary with the dose of ethinylestradiol when this dose is less than 50 micrograms.

A double-blind, randomised, multicentre trial compared efficacy, cycle control and adverse effects of two combined pills (containing either 20 or 30 micrograms of ethinylestradiol with 150 micrograms desogestrel). Both formulations were found to have high contraceptive efficacy and to be well tolerated; however, cycle control was less consistent with the 20-microgram pill.[6] Another study from the same group demonstrated greater alteration in serum lipid profiles with the 30-microgram pill compared with the 20-microgram version.[7]

Thus, the CEU was unable to find any strong evidence that failure rates of combined pills increase with decreasing estrogen dose. Currently, the CEU continues to recommend a 30–35 microgram ethinylestradiol pill as a first-line choice.

QUESTION

For women using combined oral contraception, is there any evidence that certain pills are better than others in terms of certain adverse effects and sequelae? (Two similar enquiries.)

POPULATION: Women requiring contraception.

INTERVENTIONS: Combined oral contraceptives with differing formulations.

OUTCOME: Adverse-effect profile.

ANSWER

Our literature search identified very few studies that compare different types of combined pill. Based on the scant evidence identified, the following conclusions were drawn:

- Breakthrough bleeding is significantly more frequent in women using a 20-microgram ethinylestradiol pill compared with a 30-microgram pill.[6]

- There is some evidence that pills containing desogestrel or gestodene may carry a lower risk of myocardial infarction compared with pills containing levonorgestrel.[8] Nevertheless, evidence is conflicting and a 1999 case–control study did not confirm this finding.[9]

- Compared with non-users of combined contraception, women using pills containing levonorgestrel or norethisterone have a three-fold elevation in risk of VTE and women using pills containing desogestrel or gestodene have a five-fold elevation in risk.[10]

- Little evidence is available on the risk of VTE associated with pills containing norgestimate (Cilest®, Janssen-Cilag).[11,12] However, as norgestimate is metabolised to levonorgestrel such pills may carry a risk similar to that of pills containing levonorgestrel.[13,14]

- There is insufficient evidence to estimate the risk of VTE associated with pills containing drospirenone (Yasmin®, Schering Health).[15]

- Compared with users of pills containing levonorgestrel, women using pills containing cyproterone acetate (the anti-acne pill, Dianette®, Schering Health) have a four-fold elevation in risk of VTE.[16]

- Risk of VTE does not appear to be related to the dose of ethinylestradiol in the pill formulation.[17]

- Small randomised trials have shown significant reductions in acne lesions with pills containing gestodene, desogestrel or levonorgestrel.[18–20]

Considering the body of evidence as a whole, the CEU advises that, generally, a woman choosing her first pill should choose one with the lowest risk of VTE: that is, one containing levonorgestrel or norethisterone. Nevertheless, if a woman favours a different formulation for any one of a range of possible reasons, she may be offered her own choice after appropriate counselling. Experience of adverse effects differs among individuals and decisions regarding changing from one pill to another must be governed by a clinician's experience and a woman's preferences.

Update to Answer

2006 guidance from the CEU on first prescription of combined oral contraception alerts clinicians to a statement from the Committee on Safety of Medicines which suggests that the risk of VTE with drospirenone-containing combined pills does not appear to differ from that with other combined pills.

QUESTION

Which combined oral contraceptive would provide greatest efficacy, safety and acceptability for a woman with a previous 'pill failure'

POPULATION: Women who have experienced unintended pregnancy while using combined oral contraception.

INTERVENTION: Combined oral contraceptives of various formulations.

OUTCOMES: Efficacy, safety, acceptability.

ANSWER

The risk of failure of any contraceptive method, including combined oral contraception, is determined by method, user and provider factors.[21] Evidence indicates that there is little to choose between the various modern, low-dose combined pills in terms of efficacy.[22,23] Formulations containing 35 micrograms ethinylestradiol appear to be no more effective than those containing 20 micrograms.[24] Paradoxically, a 20-microgram formulation may prove more effective in practice if a lower incidence of adverse estrogenic effects improves compliance and continuation.

User factors are the most important determinants of efficacy with a user-controlled method such as combined oral contraception. A woman who has experienced unintended pregnancy while using a combined pill should therefore be counselled regarding alternative methods such as progestogen-only injectables or implants and intrauterine contraception. If such methods are unacceptable to a woman (for example due to unacceptable adverse effects) then the combined pill must be resumed.

Provider factors are important in optimising compliance and continuation for a woman with a previous 'pill failure'. Although modern low-dose pills can be as effective as their high-dose predecessors, there appears to be less margin for error in pill-taking.[25,26] Counselling, backed up by clear written information, on the importance of regular pill-taking routines is of fundamental importance.

In summary, the CEU advises that a woman who has experienced unintended pregnancy while using combined oral contraception should be re-started on a different monophasic formulation (possibly even one with a lower estrogen content to minimise adverse effects while maintaining efficacy) and should be meticulously counselled about pill-taking routines (if alternative methods are unacceptable).

QUESTION

What is the risk of ovulation for women starting hormonal contraception up to and including day 5 of the menstrual cycle, without additional contraceptive protection? (Two similar enquiries.)

POPULATION:	**Women requiring contraception.**
INTERVENTION:	**Starting hormonal contraception up to day 5 of the menstrual cycle.**
OUTCOME:	**Risk of ovulation.**

ANSWER

The WHO *Selected Practice Recommendations* advises that the combined pill and the progestogen-only pill can be started up to and including day 5 of the menstrual cycle without the need for additional contraception. Progestogen-only implants and injectables can be started up to and including day 7. The risk of ovulation was felt to be negligible with these starting regimens. Relaxing the accepted start days for hormonal methods in this way may facilitate the use of effective methods by many couples, particularly in developing countries, but may lead to unintended pregnancies in a small number of women. To minimise any risk of pregnancy, and after counselling regarding cycle length and timing of ovulation, some women may choose to use a barrier method as back up when starting hormonal contraception on any day other than day 1 or 2 of the cycle.

The CEU identified little evidence to contradict the WHO recommendations. However, we acknowledge that direct or indirect evidence is scarce. Wide variations in cycle length and timing of ovulation occur between individuals. Evidence indicates that, when a combined pill is started up to day 7 of the cycle, despite an increase in follicular size, ovulation does not ensue.[27,28] Theoretically, women with short menstrual cycles may be at risk of ovulation with 'late start' regimens; there are few data to provide an estimate of the proportion of women to whom this might apply. Clinicians should discuss the evidence to allow women, particularly those with short cycles, to make informed decisions about the use of back-up contraception.

Given the paucity of data, clinicians and women in the UK may choose to err on the side of caution. Nevertheless, women who prefer not to use a back-up method may be assured that the risk of ovulation is negligible when starting a hormonal method up to and including day 5.

QUESTION

If Microgynon 30 ED® (Schering Health) is started on a day other than day 1 of the menstrual cycle, how long would it take to become effective and is this the same for all 'every day' pills?

POPULATION: Women using 'every day' combined oral contraception.
INTERVENTION: Starting after day 1 of the menstrual cycle.
OUTCOME: Efficacy.

ANSWER

Microgynon 30 ED can be started on day 1 of the cycle without back-up contraception, since the inactive pills are taken at the end of the pack. Other brands of 'every day' pills (Femodene® ED, Schering Health, and Logynon® ED, Schering Health) are also available in the UK. Changes to packaging mean that all regimens now start with the active pills. The WHO *Selected Practice Recommendations* suggests that combined oral contraception can be started up to day 5 of the cycle without additional cover. There is limited evidence on how quickly contraceptive protection is established by combined oral contraception. A study from the 1990s showed that starting combined oral contraception up to and including day 5 was associated with a low incidence of breakthrough bleeding, good compliance and high contraceptive efficacy.[29]

Current packaging and patient information for 'every day' pills available in the UK provides for regimens that always begin with active, hormonal pills. Starting regimens can therefore be the same as for 21-day pill packs.

QUESTION

For women changing from a 30-microgram to a 35-microgram combined oral contraceptive, should the 7-day pill-free interval be omitted?

POPULATION: Women changing from a 30-microgram to a 35-microgram combined oral contraceptive.

INTERVENTION: Omission of the pill-free interval.

OUTCOME: Efficacy.

ANSWER

The UK version of the WHO *Selected Practice Recommendations* recommends that, if a woman is switching from one combined oral contraceptive to another with **the same** dose of ethinylestradiol but containing a different progestogen, she can start immediately, provided that she has been taking her previous pill consistently and correctly and that there is reasonable certainty that she is not pregnant. There is no need to omit the 7-day pill-free interval and no additional contraception is needed.

The CEU recommends that, when changing from a 30-microgram to a 35-microgram ethinylestradiol formulation (regardless of the type of progestogen), the 7-day pill-free interval need not be omitted and no back-up contraception is required. On the other hand, if changing from a 35-microgram to a 30-microgram ethinylestradiol formulation, the 7-day pill-free interval should be omitted but no back-up contraception is required.

QUESTION

Can women start hormonal contraception at the same time as receiving oral emergency contraception?

POPULATION: Women receiving progestogen-only emergency contraception.
INTERVENTION: Starting regular hormonal contraception.
OUTCOME: Safety and efficacy.

ANSWER

Giving progestogen-only emergency contraception once within a menstrual cycle will not provide protection for subsequent acts of intercourse within the same cycle. Therefore, effective contraception or abstinence is required. The CEU identified no direct evidence relating to starting regular hormonal contraception simultaneously with emergency contraception. If emergency contraception was indicated because of missed pills (either combined or progestogen-only) then the advice is to continue the regular method.

Summaries of Product Characteristics give specific advice on starting different types of hormonal contraception. Different starting regimens (which are outside the terms of product licences) have been endorsed by the WHO *Selected Practice Recommendations*. In all circumstances, it is recommended that the woman be ascertained as not pregnant at the time of starting hormonal contraception. The WHO *Selected Practice Recommendations* include criteria for being 'reasonably certain' that a woman is not pregnant:

● she has not had intercourse since last normal menses

● she has been correctly and consistently using a reliable method of contraception

● she is within the first 7 days of normal menses

● she is within 4 weeks postpartum for non-lactating women

● she is within 7 days of abortion or miscarriage

● she is fully or nearly fully breastfeeding, amenorrhoeic and less than 6 months postpartum.

Summaries of Product Characteristics state that there is a possibility of fetal abnormalities associated with continuation of hormonal contraception during pregnancy but no published evidence was identified to support this.

Ideally, following administration of progestogen-only emergency contraception, starting regular hormonal contraception should be delayed until it is certain that the woman is not pregnant. Pragmatically, if there is concern that a woman is at risk of further unprotected sex or may not reattend for contraceptive supplies, a clinician may advise starting oral hormonal contraception the day after emergency contraceptive use. A back-up barrier method would be required for 7 days (combined oral contraception) or 2 days (progestogen-only pills). The CEU advises that progestogen implants or injectables should be started at the time of the next menses.

References

1. Cerel-Suhl SL, Yeager BF. Update on oral contraceptive pills. *Am Fam Physician* 1999;60:2073–84.
2. Hatcher RA, Trussell J, Stewart F, Cates W Jr, Stewart GK, Guest F, *et al*. *Contraceptive Technology*. New York: Ardent Media; 1998.
3. Trussell J, Kost K. Contraceptive failure in the United States: a critical review of the literature. *Stud Fam Plann* 1987;18:237–83.
4. Trussell J. Methodological pitfalls in the analysis of contraceptive failure. *Stat Med* 1991;10:201–20.
5. Faculty of Family Planning and Reproductive Health Care Clinical Effectiveness Unit. First prescription of combined oral contraception. *J Fam Plann Reprod Health Care* 2003;29:209–22.
6. Akerlund M, Rode A, Westergaard J. Comparative profiles of reliability, cycle control and adverse effects of two oral contraceptive formulations containing 150 micrograms desogestrel and either 30 micrograms or 20 micrograms ethinyl oestradiol. *Br J Obstet Gynaecol* 1993;100:832–88.
7. Akerlund M, Almstrom E, Hogstedt S, Nabrink M. Oral contraceptive tablets containing 20 and 30 micrograms of ethinyl estradiol with 150 micrograms desogestrel. Their influence on lipids, lipoproteins, sex hormone binding globulin and testosterone. *Acta Obstet Gynecol Scand* 1994;73:136–43.
8. Lewis MA, Heinemann LAJ, Spitzer WO, MacRae KD, Bruppacher R. The use of oral contraceptives and the occurrence of acute myocardial infarction in young women. *Contraception* 1997;56:129–40.
9. Dunn N, Thorogood M, Faragher B, de Caestecker L, MacDonald TM, McCollum C, *et al*. Oral contraceptives and myocardial infarction; results of the MICA case–control study. *BMJ* 1999;318:1579–84.
10. Committee on Safety of Medicines. Combined oral contraceptives containing desogestrel or gestodene and the risk of venous thromboembolism. *Curr Probl Pharmacovigilance* 1999;25:1–2.
11. Lidegaard O, Edstrom B, Kreiner S. Oral contraceptives and venous thromboembolism: a five-year national case–control study. *Contraception* 2002;65:187–96.

12. Suissa S, Blais L, Spitzer WO, Cusson J, Lewis M, Heinemann L. First-time use of newer oral contraceptives and the risk of venous thromboembolism. *Contraception* 1997;56:141–6.

13. Lewis MA, Heinemann L, MacRae KD, Bruppacher R, Spitzer WO. The increased risk of venous thromboembolism and the use of third generation progestagens; role of bias in observational research. *Contraception* 1996;54:5–13.

14. Westhoff C. Oral contraceptives and venous thromboembolism: should epidemiologic associations drive clinical decision making? *Contraception* 1996;54:1–3.

15. Grootheest K, V, Vrieling T. Thromboembolism associated with the new contraceptive Yasmin. *BMJ* 2003;326:257.

16. Committee on Safety of Medicines. Cyproterone acetate (Dianette): Risk of venous thromboembolism (VTE). *Curr Probl Pharmacovigilance* 2002;28:9–10.

17. Gupta S, Hannaford P. *Combined oral contraceptives: myocardial infarction, stroke and venous thromboembolism*. London: Faculty of Family Planning and Reproductive Health Care; 1999 [www.ffprhc.org.uk/meetings/fact_coc.pdf].

18. Piérard-Franchimont C, Gaspard U, Lacante P, Rhoa M, Slachmuylders P, Piérard GE. A quantitative biometrological assessment of acne and hormonal evaluation in young women using a triphasic low-dose oral contraceptive containing gestodene. *Eur J Contracep Reprod Health Care* 2000;5:275–86.

19. Rosen MP, Breitkopf DM, Nagamani M. A randomized controlled trial of second- versus third-generation oral contraceptives in the treatment of acne vulgaris. *Am J Obstet Gynecol* 2003;188:1158–60.

20. Leyden J, Shalita A, Hordinsky M, Swinyer L, Stanczyk FZ, Weber ME. Efficacy of a low-dose oral contraceptive containing 20 mg of ethinyl estradiol and 100 mg of levonorgestrel for the treatment of moderate acne: A randomized, placebo-controlled trial. *J Am Acad Dermatol* 2002;47:399–409.

21. Potter LS. How effective are contraceptives? The determination and measurement of pregnancy rates. *Obstet Gynecol* 1996;88:13S–23S.

22. Van-Vliet HAAM, Grimes DA, Helmerhorst FM, Schulz KF. Biphasic versus monophasic oral contraceptives for contraception. *Cochrane Database Syst Rev* 2004;(2).

23. Van-Vliet HAAM, Grimes DA, Helmerhorst FM, Schulz KF. Biphasic versus triphasic oral contraceptives for contraception. *Contraception* 2002;65:321–4.

24. Rosenberg MJ, Meyers A, Roy V. Efficacy, cycle control, and side effects of low- and lower-dose oral contraceptives: a randomized trial of 20 μg and 35 μg estrogen preparations. *Contraception* 1999;60:321–9.

25. Fraser IS, Jansen RPS. Why do inadvertent pregnancies occur in oral contraceptive users? *Contraception* 1983;27:531–51.

26. Fraser IS. Forty years of combined oral contraception: the evolution of a revolution. *Med Dir Aust* 2000;173:541–4.

27. Smith SK, Kirkman RJE, Arce BB, McNeilly AS, Loudon NB, Baird DT. The effect of deliberate omission of trinordiol or microgynon on the hypothalamo-pituitary-ovarian axis. *Contraception* 1986;34:513–22.

28. Killick SR, Bancroft K, Oelbaum S, Morris J, Elstein M. Extending the duration of the pill-free interval during combined oral contraception. *Adv Contracept* 1990;6:33–40.

29. Yeshaya A, Orveito R, Kaplan B, Dicker D, Bar-Hava I, Ben-Rafael Z. Flexible starting schedule for oral contraception: effect on the incidence of breakthrough bleeding and compliance. *Eur J Contracept Reprod Health Care* 1998;3:121–23.

Risks and sequelae

QUESTION

Are women who are current or previous users of combined oral contraception at increased risk of developing breast cancer? (Four similar enquiries.)

POPULATION: Women requiring contraception.
INTERVENTION: Combined oral contraception.
OUTCOME: Risk of breast cancer.

ANSWER

The risk of developing breast cancer, for women who are current or previous users of combined oral contraception, is difficult to assess and studies provide conflicting evidence.

In 1998, the Collaborative Group on Hormonal Factors in Breast Cancer showed an increased risk of having breast cancer diagnosed while using combined oral contraception (relative risk 1.24; 95% CI 1.15–1.33).[1] Their findings suggest a 24% increase in risk of breast cancer above the background risk. The increased risk was short-term. Women had no increased risk 10 years after stopping combined oral contraception.[1]

A more recent, population-based, case–control study provided new evidence on low-dose combined oral contraception and risk of breast cancer in women aged over 35 years. Compared with never-users, current or former users of combined oral contraception did not have a significantly increased risk of breast cancer (current users: relative risk 1.0; 95% CI 0.8–1.3; former users: relative risk 0.9; 95% CI 0.8–1.0).[2]

These two large studies have shown either no increase or a very small increase in the risk of developing breast cancer associated with current or recent use of combined contraception. Any increase appears to be uninfluenced by family history of breast cancer, by duration of use, by age at first use or by dose or type of hormone. An apparent increased risk may be explained by increased health surveillance and increased detection in contraceptive users.

Until more evidence is available, women may be counselled that combined oral contraception appears to confer no, or only a very small, increase in risk of breast cancer above their background risk.

QUESTION

For women using hormonal contraception, what advice should be given regarding their risk of cervical cancer?

POPULATION: Women requiring contraception.
INTERVENTION: Hormonal contraception.
OUTCOME: Risk of cervical cancer.

ANSWER

A systematic review of case–control and cohort studies has confirmed that for women using oral contraception, the risk of cervical cancer increases with increasing duration of use.[3] The results indicate that there is little increase in the risk of developing cervical cancer with use of oral contraception for less than 5 years (relative risk 1.1; 95% CI 1.1–1.2). After 5–9 years of use, there is a 60% increase in risk of cervical cancer (relative risk 1.6; 95% CI 1.4–1.7). After 10 or more years of use, the risk of cervical cancer is doubled (relative risk 2.2; 95% CI 1.9–2.4). Results were unaltered when confounding factors such as human papilloma virus infection, sexual partners, barrier contraception and cervical screening were taken into account. The systematic review was unable to establish whether the increased risk of cervical cancer is associated with recent contraceptive use, nor how quickly (if at all) the risk diminishes.

Advice to women should be that oral contraceptive use for less than 5 years is associated with a negligible increase in risk of cervical cancer but that use beyond 5 years is associated with an increased risk. Women should be encouraged to participate in cervical screening programmes. Early detection and treatment of cervical intraepithelial neoplasia may prevent progression to malignancy.

QUESTION

For women using combined oral contraception, is there evidence that smoking increases the risk of VTE?

POPULATION: Women using combined oral contraception.
INTERVENTION: Smoking.
OUTCOME: Risk of VTE.

ANSWER

A large case–control study from Denmark investigated the risk of VTE (deep venous thrombosis or pulmonary embolism) associated with oral contraception.[4] This study showed that smoking influenced the risk of VTE in oral contraceptive users. The risk of thromboembolism increases with an increasing number of cigarettes smoked in a day, with a doubling of risk for those smoking more than 20/day. Adjusted odds ratios for VTE among users of oral contraception who smoke varying numbers of cigarettes/day (relative to oral contraceptive-using non-smokers) were:

- those smoking 1–10 cigarettes/day: odds ratio 1.3; 95% CI 1.0–1.6
- those smoking 11–20 cigarettes/day: odds ratio 1.7; 95% CI 1.4–2.1
- those smoking more than 20 cigarettes/day: odds ratio 1.9; 95% CI 1.4–2.7.

QUESTION

Do young women who are using combined oral contraception who travel to extreme altitudes have an increased risk of VTE? (Two similar enquiries.)

POPULATION: Women using combined oral contraception.
INTERVENTION: Travel to extreme altitudes.
OUTCOME: Risk of VTE.

ANSWER

The CEU was unable to find any published evidence directly relevant to this enquiry. We sought expert advice from physicians who regularly treat tourists at high altitudes.[5] Their opinion was that, at extreme altitudes, there is an increased risk of blood clotting. They therefore advise patients to stop the combined pill and use an alternative method of contraception.

A clinician should inform the woman of all other methods of contraception and of their advantages and disadvantages. Although the progestogen-only pill is not associated with an increased risk of VTE, it does not consistently inhibit ovulation and has a higher failure rate in young women. Both depot medroxy-progesterone acetate (DMPA) and the etonogestrel implant cause irregular bleeding when initiated and this may be troublesome when travelling. Used correctly and consistently, a barrier method alone or with a progestogen-only pill may be the best choice.

QUESTION

For women who deep-sea dive, is the use of the combined oral contraceptive associated with health risks?

POPULATION: Women using combined oral contraception.

INTERVENTION: Deep-sea diving.

OUTCOMES: Adverse events.

ANSWER

No evidence was identified relating to hormonal contraception and deep-sea diving. No evidence for an increased risk of thromboembolic disease in women who are deep-sea divers was found. The main health risk of diving is decompression sickness. After breathing air under increased pressure, gas bubbles form in the circulation following a too rapid return to atmospheric pressure. Gas bubbles can also form following barotrauma (to lungs, ears or stomach) due to uncontrolled expansion of gas in gas-filled cavities.[6] Diving during pregnancy is not recommended, as the fetus is at risk of decompression problems.[7]

QUESTION

For women using combined oral contraception who develop hypertension, is the incidence of pill-induced hypertension related to duration of contraceptive use?

POPULATION: Women of reproductive age.

INTERVENTION: Combined oral contraception.

OUTCOME: Risk of hypertension.

ANSWER

CEU guidance on first prescription of combined oral contraception[8] indicates that hypertensive pill users have a ten-fold increase in risk of both ischaemic and haemorrhagic stroke compared with normotensive non-users. The *WHO Medical Eligibility Criteria for Contraceptive Use* recommends that women with blood pressure consistently higher than 140 mmHg systolic or 90 mmHg diastolic should be advised against use of combined oral contraception.[9]

Pooled data from four large phase-III clinical trials suggest that combined oral contraception has a negligible effect on blood pressure itself.[9] The CEU was unable to find any published evidence relating to 'pill-induced hypertension' and duration of pill use.

QUESTION

Do women who stop the combined oral contraceptive pill and have prolonged secondary amenorrhoea have a risk of osteoporosis?

POPULATION:	**Women of reproductive age.**
INTERVENTION:	**Stopping combined oral contraception with subsequent amenorrhoea.**
OUTCOME:	**Risk of osteoporosis.**

ANSWER

Secondary amenorrhoea following discontinuation of combined oral contraception usually results from an underlying endocrine problem that has been masked by the regular withdrawal bleeds induced during combined pill use.

The most common cause of secondary amenorrhoea is pregnancy and this should always be excluded before further investigations are undertaken.[10] Polycystic ovary syndrome (PCOS) accounts for 30% of cases of secondary amenorrhoea, hyperprolactinaemia for 20%, and premature ovarian failure or weight-related amenorrhoea for most of the remainder.

Online Prodigy guidance from the Department of Health advises that women with amenorrhoea associated with low estrogen levels have an increased risk of developing osteoporosis.[11] Such women should be considered for estrogen replacement if amenorrhoea persists for longer than 6 months. The optimal estrogen dose to prevent bone loss in young women is unclear but the doses of estrogen found in combined oral contraceptives may be appropriate for women of reproductive age.

Post-pill amenorrhoea is not caused by the combined oral contraceptive itself. Amenorrhoea following cessation of combined contraception should be investigated if it persists. The risk of osteoporosis following 'post-pill amenorrhoea' will be related to the underlying cause, to the woman's peak bone density, and to the duration of low estrogen levels.

References

1. Collaborative Group on Hormonal Factors in Breast Cancer. Breast Cancer and hormonal contraceptives: reanalysis of individual data on 53,297 women with breast cancer and 100,239 controls. *Lancet* 1998;347:1713–27.
2. Marchbanks PA, McDonald JA, Wilson HGL, Folger SG, Mandel MG, Daling JR, *et al.* Oral contraceptives and the risk of breast cancer. *N Engl J Med* 2002;346:2025–32.
3. Smith JS, Green J. Cervical cancer and use of hormonal contraception: a systematic review. *Lancet* 2003;361:1159–67.

4. Lidegaard O, Edstrom B, Kreiner S. Oral contraceptives and venous thromboembolism: a five-year national case–control study. *Contraception* 2002;65:187–96.

5. CIWEC Clinic Travel Medicine Center. Trekking and the oral contraceptive pill (OCP) [www.ciwec-clinic.com/articles/pill.html].

6. Spira A. Diving and marine medicine review part ii: diving diseases. *J Travel Med* 1999;6:180–98.

7. Camporesi EM. Diving and pregnancy. *Semin Perinatol* 1996;20:292–30.

8. Faculty of Family Planning and Reproductive Health Care Clinical Effectiveness Unit. First prescription of combined oral contraception. *J Fam Plann Reprod Health Care* 2003;29:209–22.

9. Endrikat J, Gerlinger C, Cronin M, Ruebig A, Schmidt W, Dusterberg B. Blood pressure stability in a normotensive population during intake of monophasic oral contraceptive intake containing 20 microgram ethinyl oestradiol and 75 microgram desogestrel. *Eur J Contracept Reprod Health Care* 2001;6:159–66.

10. Baird D. Amenorrhoea. *Lancet* 1997;350:275–9.

11. Prodigy Guidance. Amenorrhoea. Last revised February 2005 [www.prodigy.nhs.uk/amenorrhoea].

Adverse effects

QUESTION

For women using hormonal contraception, is hair loss a recognised adverse effect? (Four similar enquiries.)

POPULATION: Women requiring contraception.
INTERVENTION: Hormonal contraception.
OUTCOME: Risk of hair loss.

ANSWER

Several types of alopecia occur. The two most common are alopecia areata and androgenic alopecia. It has been suggested that alopecia areata is an auto-immune condition where cells of an individual's own immune system prevent hair follicles from producing hair fibre. An individual's lifetime risk of alopecia areata has been estimated at 1.7%.[1] In contrast, androgenic alopecia affects 50–80% of white men and 20–40% of women. The onset of hair loss occurs much later in women than in men. The male hormone, testosterone, is converted to dihydrotestosterone by the action of 5-alpha reductase. Dihydrotestosterone causes hair shafts to narrow, producing progressively finer hairs with each new growth cycle until eventually the hairs become transparent and then stop emerging.

Some combined pill formulations contain synthetic progestogens, which have androgenic properties. Some synthetic progestogens may artificially increase a woman's testosterone levels, which may lead to an increase in dihydrotestosterone production and to androgenic alopecia. Combined pills that contain anti-androgenic progestins (such as cyproterone acetate) have been shown to reduce the rate of androgen-induced alopecia by up to 86%.[2]

Several surveys and comparative studies have reported higher rates of alopecia in women using the levonorgestrel implant (Norplant®, Hoechst Marion Roussel, now discontinued) compared with those using no contraception.[3-5] Two large US multicentre surveys reported significant discontinuation rates of levonorgestrel implants (Norplant) and of DMPA due to hair loss. Hair loss occurred most frequently in the initial months of contraceptive use.[6,7] No information was identified on hair loss associated with the progestogen-only pill, the LNG-IUS or the etonogestrel implant (Implanon®, Organon).

If a relationship is suspected between the development of alopecia and progestogen-only methods of contraception, a woman may wish to consider changing to a non-hormonal method.

QUESTION

For women using combined oral contraception, is nipple discharge a recognised adverse effect?

POPULATION: Women requiring contraception.
INTERVENTION: Hormonal contraception.
OUTCOME: Risk of nipple discharge.

ANSWER

No evidence regarding nipple discharge as an adverse effect of oral contraceptive use was identified. Guidelines for the management of women presenting with nipple discharge are available from the Scottish Intercollegiate Guidelines Network.[8] If a woman presents with nipple discharge, prolactin and thyroid-stimulating hormone (TSH) levels should be checked. Persistent, heavy or bloodstained nipple discharge in a woman aged less than 50 years requires specialist investigation.

QUESTION

For women using oral hormonal contraception, is there an increased risk of gingivitis compared with women using other methods of contraception?

POPULATION: Women requiring contraception.
INTERVENTION: Hormonal contraception.
OUTCOME: Risk of gingivitis.

ANSWER

Hormonal contraceptive use can be associated with gingivitis. There is an accepted view in the dental community that elevated hormone levels, as in pregnancy or oral contraceptive use, can predispose to gum disease. There is a biologically plausible mechanism of increased concentrations of estrogen or progestogen in the periodontal fluid providing a rich environment in which the micro-organisms responsible for plaque development can flourish.

There is observational evidence from a paper concerning Sri Lankan women[9] that use of combined oral contraception (Microgynon®, Schering Health) or progestogen-only injectable (Depo-Provera®, Pharmacia) for 2–4 years is associated with an increased incidence of gum disease compared with women not using hormonal contraception.

There is no mention of gum disease as an adverse effect of combined oral contraception in the Summaries of Product Characteristics for Microgynon, Micronor® (Janssen-Cilag) or Depo-Provera.

QUESTION

For women using combined oral contraception, is there an association with loin pain haematuria syndrome?

POPULATION: Women requiring contraception.
INTERVENTION: Hormonal contraception.
OUTCOME: Risk of loin pain haematuria syndrome.

ANSWER

The UK National Kidney Federation describes loin pain haematuria syndrome as a combination of loin (renal) pain and haematuria.[10] Several conditions may cause loin pain haematuria syndrome. These include: immunoglobulin A (IgA) nephropathy (a chronic condition in which a small amount of normal IgA antibody 'gets stuck' in the kidney as it passes through in the blood stream), thin membrane disease (the membrane that filters blood to make urine is 'too thin', allowing blood to pass across it in small amounts) and infection. Patients with no identifiable underlying cause are labelled as having 'classic loin pain haematuria syndrome'. Patients with classic loin pain haematuria syndrome may have minor abnormalities on renal biopsy; renal angiograms may show abnormal blood flow, perhaps causing a cramp-like pain. The cause is not fully understood. The condition is more common in women than in men and there may be hormonal influences. Some women find the pain worse at certain times of their menstrual cycle; sometimes the condition begins in pregnancy or during oral contraceptive use. Loin pain haematuria syndrome may persist for some years and can be lifelong; however, damage to the kidneys leading to renal failure does not occur.

Despite extensive searching, the CEU could identify no further information in the literature to support an association between loin pain haematuria syndrome and combined oral contraception.

QUESTION

For women using combined oral contraception and who develop spider naevi, is continuation of this method of contraception advisable?

POPULATION: Women using combined oral contraception who develop spider naevi.
INTERVENTION: Continuation of combined oral contraception.
OUTCOME: Safety.

ANSWER

Spider angiomas are common, benign, acquired lesions found in 10–15% of the population.[11] Rapid development of numerous spider angiomas may occur in patients with hepatic cirrhosis, malignant liver disease and other hepatic dysfunctions. However, most lesions are unrelated to systemic disease but may develop in women during pregnancy or while taking combined oral contraceptives. These usually resolve spontaneously, around 6–9 months after delivery or after discontinuing combined oral contraception.

The CEU found a German case report of a woman who developed several typical spider naevi after discontinuing combined oral contraception. She had neither acute nor chronic liver disease, was symptom-free and showed a slight increase in serum gammaglutamyl transferase.[12] The authors postulated that a 'hormone rebound' effect may have operated in this case.

Spider naevi are benign and, if unrelated to any systemic disorder, should be treated only as a cosmetic issue. Women who are disturbed by the cosmetic appearance of the spider naevi may wish to discontinue the combined pill and see if the lesions resolve.

QUESTION

Are skin striae in young women associated with use of combined oral contraception?

POPULATION: Women requiring contraception.

INTERVENTION: Combined oral contraception.

OUTCOME: Risk of skin striae.

ANSWER

Striae are lesions of the skin that resemble bands or lines. Striae can appear when there is rapid stretching of the skin. Usually, they occur as a result of abdominal enlargement in pregnancy. They may also occur during the rapid growth of puberty in males and females and can be seen in children who have become rapidly obese. Striae may also be associated with: prolonged administration of corticosteroids, diabetes mellitus, Cushing syndrome, post-pregnancy, abnormal collagen formation or the use of medicines or chemicals that interfere with collagen formation.[13]

A case report described the development of striae in a 17-year-old woman. She had undergone bilateral augmentation mammoplasty 4 months previously and developed striae on the breasts after using low-dose combined oral contraception. Discontinuation of the contraceptive pill and daily application of tretinoin cream caused the striae to mature and prevented additional lesions.[14]

Despite extensive searching, the CEU identified no further evidence of an association between combined oral contraception and development of skin striae. Thus, there is no conclusive evidence that combined oral contraception can cause skin striae. In a young teenager, development of striae is more likely to be related to rapid growth or weight gain than to concurrent use of combined oral contraception. Nevertheless, a young woman may wish to consider a non-hormonal method of contraception if her skin condition does not improve with topical treatment.

QUESTION

Is development of cutaneous lupus associated with use of combined oral contraception?

POPULATION:	Women requiring contraception.
INTERVENTION:	Combined oral contraception.
OUTCOME:	Risk of cutaneous lupus.

ANSWER

Lupus erythematosus is an autoimmune disease that causes diverse patterns of autoantibody production. Cutaneous lupus erythematosus (CLE) affects the skin and can cause disfiguring, painful skin lesions and alopecia. CLE most often affects young adult women (aged 20–50 years). A few people with CLE also have a related condition, systemic lupus erythematosus (SLE). SLE may cause more skin changes such as photosensitivity (a rash on all sun exposed skin), mouth ulcers, urticaria and diffuse hair thinning; rarely, it may cause blisters (bullous lupus erythematosus). SLE can also affect joints, kidneys, lungs, heart, liver, brain, blood vessels (vasculitis) and blood cells, and can cause renal, neurological, pulmonary and cardiovascular disease. Environmental factors such as exposure to sunlight can cause manifestations of lupus erythematosus.[15]

Some studies have found a slight increase in the development of SLE in past and current users of combined oral contraception[16,17] but, despite extensive searching, the CEU could find no information on any causal association between cutaneous lupus and combined oral contraception.

Around 20–40% of people with SLE have antiphospholipid antibodies called lupus anticoagulants. Possession of lupus anticoagulants is associated with cerebral, deep venous or renal vein thromboses, as well pulmonary emboli or arterial occlusions, particularly stroke.[18] The use of combined oral contraception is also associated with a two-fold increase in ischaemic stroke and a three- to five-fold increase in VTE.[19] The evidence is unclear as to whether or not combined oral contraception is a triggering factor for thrombosis in women with lupus erythematosus.

Owing to the increased risk of cardiovascular disease in women with lupus erythematosus and lupus anticoagulants and the possibility that combined oral contraception is a triggering factor for thrombosis in such women, the CEU advises that women with lupus erythematosus are counselled on the risks of combined oral contraception use, and consideration should be given to the use of progestogen-only or non-hormonal methods of contraception.

QUESTION

For women who have developed hirsutism while using a combined oral contraceptive (Yasmin®), what alternative contraceptive options are appropriate?

POPULATION: Women using combined oral contraception (Yasmin®) who develop hirsutism.

INTERVENTIONS: Alternative contraception.

OUTCOME: Adverse effects.

ANSWER

Guidance from the CEU advises that Dianette® (cyproterone acetate 2 mg + ethinylestradiol 35 micrograms) can be used as treatment for moderately severe hirsutism.[19] Dianette is not indicated solely as a contraceptive and therefore should be stopped 3–4 months after the hirsutism has resolved or if there is no improvement in symptoms. Dianette carries a four-fold increase in the risk of VTE compared with combined oral contraceptives containing levonorgestrel.

The Summary of Product Characteristics for Dianette states that it is licensed only for the treatment of severe acne, refractory to prolonged antibiotic therapy or moderately severe hirsutism. Dianette inhibits ovulation and thereby prevents conception; thus, women using Dianette for the treatment of hirsutism will not need to use an additional hormonal contraceptive. Treatment should be withdrawn three to four cycles after the condition has completely resolved and should not be continued solely to provide contraception.

In line with the Summary of Product Characteristics, the CEU recommends that women can use Dianette for the treatment of hirsutism and as contraception; however, it should be stopped 3–4 months after the condition has resolved or if there is no improvement in symptoms.

QUESTION

For women who wear contact lenses, which brand of combined oral contraception would have least adverse effect on tear film? (Two similar enquiries.)

POPULATION: Women who wear contact lenses.

INTERVENTIONS: Combined oral contraceptives of various formulations.

OUTCOME: Adverse effects on tear film.

ANSWER

There appears to be a complex relationship between sex hormone levels and tear function. It has been postulated that androgens are important in increasing the secretory activity of the meibomian glands, which produce the outer lipid layer of tears.[20] Data from a large prospective cohort study suggest that women who use hormone replacement therapy (HRT), particularly estrogen alone, are at increased risk of dry-eye syndrome with increasing duration of use (but this may also be influenced by age).[21]

Certain drugs are known to cause reduced tear flow; these include diuretics, antimuscarinic drugs (antihistamines, tricyclic antidepressants, antipsychotics), atropine, beta-blockers, and oral contraceptives. Reduced tear flow may cause discomfort in contact lens wearers. The CEU was unable to find any studies that have compared the effects of different brands of combined pills on tear function.

The American Optometric Association advises that, when possible, environmental factors contributing to dry eye should be identified and modified or eliminated.[22] The CEU can therefore only advise that contact lens wearers experiencing discomfort might try a different method of contraception and see if their symptoms subsequently improve.

QUESTION

For women using combined oral contraception, is vulvovaginal candidiasis a recognised adverse effect and would changing to a different pill help?

POPULATION:	**Women using combined oral contraception.**
INTERVENTIONS:	**Combined oral contraceptives of various formulations.**
OUTCOME:	**Risk of vulvovaginal candidiasis.**

ANSWER

Vulval and vaginal infections due to Candida are among the most common gynaecological conditions affecting women. Conditions of hyperestrogenaemia are associated with higher rates of yeast colonisation.[23] Recurrent vulvovaginal candidiasis is defined as four or more episodes of symptomatic vulvovaginal candidiasis during a 12-month period and affects less than 5% of healthy women. Many women who suffer from recurrent vulvovaginal candidiasis are incorrectly diagnosed by clinicians or incorrectly self-diagnosed. Any woman whose symptoms persist after using an over-the-counter preparation, or who has a recurrence of symptoms within 2 months, should seek medical care.[24]

The literature is inconsistent regarding a possible association between oral contraceptive use and vulvovaginal candidiasis. Available evidence comes from case–control and cross-sectional studies. One study reported a lower risk of vulvovaginal candidiasis in women taking 20-microgram pills compared with those on 30- or 50-microgram preparations.[25]

With the quality of evidence available, the CEU was unable to confirm that vulvovaginal candidiasis is an adverse effect of oral contraceptive use. Pragmatically, changing to a 20-microgram preparation might be appropriate.

References

1. Savafi KH, Muller SA, Suman VJ, Moshell AN, Melton LJ 3rd. Incidence of alopecia areata in Olmsted County, Minnesota, 1975 through 1989. *Mayo Clin Proc* 1995;70:628–33.
2. Raudrant D, Rabe T. Progestogens with antiandrogenic properties. *Drugs* 2003;63:463–92.
3. Molland JR, Morehead DB, Baldwin DM, Castracane VD, Lasley B, Bergquist CA. Immediate postpartum insertion of the Norplant contraceptive device. *Fertil Steril* 1996;66:43–8.
4. International Collaborative Post-Marketing Surveillance of Norplant. Post-marketing surveillance of Norplant contraceptive implants: II. Non-reproductive health. *Contraception* 2001;63:187–209.
5. Taneepanichskul S, Tanprasertkul C. Use of Norplant implants in the immediate postpartum period among asymptomatic HIV-1-positive mothers. *Contraception* 2001;64:39–41.
6. Kalmuu D, Davidson AR, Cushman LF, Heartwell S, Rulin M. Determinants of early implant discontinuation among low-income women. *Fam Plann Perspect* 1996;28:256–60.
7. Polaneczky M, Liblanc M. Long-term depot medroxyprogesterone acetate (Depo-Provera) use in inner-city adolescents. *J Adolesc Health* 1998;23:81–8.
8. Scottish Intercollegiate Guidelines Network. *Breast Cancer in Women*. Guideline 84. Edinburgh: SIGN; 1998.
9. Tilakaratne A, Soory M, Ranasinghe AW, Corea SM, Ekanayake SL, de Silva M. Effects of hormonal contraceptives on the periodontium, in a population of rural Sri-Lankan women. *J Clin Periodontol* 2000;27:753–7.
10. UK National Kidney Federation. Loin pain-haematuria syndrome [www.kidney.org.uk/Medical-Info/kidney-disease/lph.html].
11. Crowe MA. Nevus araneus (spider nevus). *eMedicine* [www.emedicine.com/derm/topic293.htm].
12. Mockenhaupt M, Schopf E. Epidemiology of drug-induced severe skin reactions. *Semin Cutan Med Surg* 1996;15:236–43.
13. MedlinePlus Medical Encyclopedia. Striae [www.nlm.nih.gov/medlineplus/ency/article/003287.htm].
14. Har-Shai Y, Barak A, Taran A, Weissman A. Striae distensae of augmented breasts after oral contraceptive therapy. *Ann Plast Surg* 1999;42:193–5.

15. American Academy of Dermatology Association. Guidelines of care for cutaneous lupus erythematosus. *J Am Acad Dermatol* 1996;34:830–6.
16. Sanchez-Guerrero J, Karlson EW, Liang MH, Hunter DJ, Speizer FE, Colditz GA. Past use of oral contraceptives and the risk of developing systemic lupus erythematosus. *Arthritis Rheum* 1997;40:804–8.
17. Cooper GS, Dooley MA, Treadwell EL, St Clair EW, Gilkeson GS. Hormonal and reproductive risk factors for development of systemic lupus erythematosus. *Arthritis Rheum* 2002;46:1830–9.
18. Bontempo FA. The lupus anticoagulant: an update. Institute for Transfusion Medicine. 2001 [www.itxm.org./tmu2001/tmu-2001.htm].
19. Faculty of Family Planning and Reproductive Health Care Clinical Effectiveness Unit. First prescription of combined oral contraception. *J Fam Plann Reprod Health Care* 2003;29:209–22.
20. Tsubota K. Tear dynamics and dry eye. *Prog Retin Eye Res* 1998;17:565–96.
21. Schaumberg DA, Buring JE, Sullivan DA, Dana MR. Hormone replacement therapy and dry eye syndrome. *JAMA* 2002;286:2114–9.
22. American Optometric Association. Care of the patient with ocular surface disorders. 2nd ed. 2002 [www.guideline.gov/summary/summary.aspx?doc_id=3549].
23. Sobel JD, Faro S, Force RW, Foxman B, Ledger WJ, Nyirjesy PR, *et al*. Vulvovaginal candidiasis; epidemiologic, diagnostic and therapeutic considerations. *Am J Obstet Gynecol* 1998;178:203–11.
24. Centers for Disease Control and Prevention. Sexually transmitted diseases treatment guidelines 2002. *MMWR Morbid Mortal Wkly Rep* 2002;51:1–80.
25. Bauters TGM, Dhont M, Temmerman M, Nelis HJ. Prevalence of vulvovaginal candidiasis and susceptibility to fluconazole in women. *Am J Obstet Gynecol* 2002;187:569–74.

Managing problems during use

QUESTION

Can smokers aged over 35 years of age use combined oral contraception for the non-contraceptive benefit of minimising intermenstrual bleeding?

POPULATION: Smokers aged over 35 years who suffer from intermenstrual bleeding.
INTERVENTION: Combined hormonal contraception.
OUTCOME: Safety.

ANSWER

The risks of myocardial infarction, stroke and VTE are increased in women who smoke and even more so in women who also use combined oral contraception.[1-5] In women who smoke more than 15 cigarettes a day, the relative risk of myocardial infarction is 20.8 (95% CI 5.2–83.1) and the relative risk of ischaemic stroke is 7.2 (95% CI 3.23–16.1) compared with non-smokers. As the risks of myocardial infarction, stroke and VTE increase with age, smokers over the age of 35 years are advised against the use of combined oral contraception. The *WHO Medical Eligibility Criteria* recommends that, for women aged 35 years and over who smoke less than 15 cigarettes a day, the risks of combined oral contraceptive use generally outweigh the benefits (WHO category 3). Women aged 35 years and over who smoke 15 or more cigarettes a day should **not** use combined oral contraceptives (WHO category 4), as this poses an unacceptable health risk. Thus, smokers who are over 35 years should be advised against combined oral contraceptive use.

Several other contraceptive options are available and may help manage menstrual problems. DMPA can be used by smokers aged over 35 years (WHO category 2). It induces amenorrhoea in 46% of women at 3 months, in 53% at 6 months and in 58% at 12 months.[6] However, irregular bleeding can occur.

The LNG-IUS is licensed for the management of idiopathic menorrhagia and as a contraceptive. Amenorrhoea can be expected in up to 25% of women after 6 months of use. However, some prospective studies have identified amenorrhoea rates of up to 44% at 6 months after insertion and of 50% at 12 and 24 months.[7] However, irregular bleeding can occur.

The CEU advises against prescribing combined oral contraception to smokers aged over 35 years. Women should be counselled on the risks associated with combined pill use in these circumstances and alternative options provided. The progestogen-only methods: in particular, DMPA and the LNG-IUS may be helpful.

Specific causes of intermenstrual bleeding should be excluded, such as missed pills, pregnancy, infection and malignancy.

QUESTION

For women using hormonal contraception, is there a relationship between the occurrence of breakthrough bleeding and loss of contraceptive efficacy?

POPULATION: Women using hormonal contraception.
INTERVENTION: Experience of breakthrough bleeding.
OUTCOME: Efficacy.

ANSWER

The CEU found little evidence in the literature of any association between breakthrough bleeding and contraceptive efficacy.

Breakthrough bleeding is common with progestogen-only forms of contraception. There is no evidence that breakthrough bleeding in that context is associated with reduced contraceptive efficacy. Indeed, there is some evidence that erratic bleeding in users of the progestogen-only pill may indicate anovulation and improved contraceptive efficacy.

One randomised trial was identified showing that in women taking a low-dose combined pill, ovulation was inhibited despite the presence of breakthrough bleeding.[8] In women using combined oral contraception with concurrent liver enzyme-inducing drugs (such as anti-epileptic medication) the presence of breakthrough bleeding is often taken to indicate that the dose of estrogen is too low. This 'marker' is commonly used in practice but the CEU identified no supporting evidence. Breakthrough bleeding may also occur if compliance with an oral preparation is poor, which is associated with loss of contraceptive efficacy.

When managing a woman who presents with unscheduled bleeding on any form of contraception, a clinician should always consider general causes of erratic vaginal bleeding, such as sexually transmitted infections (STIs) and complications of a pregnancy that has already occurred.

QUESTION

For women using 20-microgram ethinylestradiol combined oral contraceptives, is there any evidence that any one brand is better at preventing breakthrough bleeding?

POPULATION: Women using 20-microgram ethinylestradiol combined oral contraceptives.

INTERVENTION: Use of specific brands.

OUTCOME: Breakthrough bleeding.

ANSWER

The combined oral contraceptive Femodette® (Schering) contains 20 micrograms ethinylestradiol and 75 micrograms gestodene. Mercilon® (Organon) contains 20 micrograms ethinylestradiol and 150 micrograms desogestrel. Loestrin® 20 (Galen) contains 20 micrograms ethinylestradiol and 1 milligram norethisterone. It is also available in the UK but was not addressed in this enquiry.

A prospective comparative study has compared two combined pills, one containing 20 micrograms ethinylestradiol and 75 micrograms gestodene (Meliane®, Schering) and the other, 20 micrograms ethinylestradiol and 150 micrograms desogestrel (Mercilon). Over 12 cycles, women received the pills for 21 days followed by a 7-day pill-free interval. The incidence of breakthrough bleeding was 5.2% of all cycles for the Meliane group and 6.0% of all cycles for the Mercilon group (this was not a statistically significant difference).[9]

Other trials have found that the incidence of breakthrough bleeding is not significantly different when comparing different regimens of ethinylestradiol/gestodene and ethinylestradiol/desogestrel, and that breakthrough bleeding reduces over time with both combinations.[10–12]

Thus, the CEU found no evidence that any particular brand of 20-microgram ethinylestradiol combined pill is superior in terms of rate of breakthrough bleeding.

QUESTION

For women using the combined oral contraceptive, Yasmin, is there any evidence that weight gain is less than for women using other brands?

POPULATION: Women using combined oral contraceptives.
INTERVENTION: Use of Yasmin.
OUTCOME: Weight gain.

ANSWER

The combined oral contraceptive Yasmin contains 3 mg drospirenone and 30 micrograms ethinylestradiol. The Summary of Product Characteristics reports that body weight changes are uncommon in users.

A Cochrane review does not support a causal association between combined oral contraceptives in general and weight gain.[13]

Three large randomised trials compared Yasmin with a desogestrel-containing combined pill, Marvelon® (Organon).[14–16] In all three trials, Yasmin was associated with no change or a small decrease, in body weight. In comparison, the Marvelon groups showed a small rise in weight (two trials)[14,16] or a fall which was smaller than that seen in the Yasmin subjects.[15] A *Drugs & Therapeutics Bulletin* in 2002 reviewed evidence on Yasmin and found no advantages over other longer-established combined pills with regard to weight gain.[17]

The CEU supports the conclusion of the Cochrane review that there is no evidence that combined oral contraceptives cause weight gain. Randomised trials evaluating Yasmin do not strongly support significant weight loss.

QUESTION

For women using combined oral contraception who are experiencing vaginal dryness, what treatment can be offered?

POPULATION: Women using combined oral contraception who are experiencing vaginal dryness.

INTERVENTIONS: Treatments.

OUTCOME: Efficacy.

ANSWER

In postmenopausal women, topical vaginal estrogens have been shown to improve symptoms of vaginal atrophy and dryness and systemic absorption of estrogen is low. The non-hormonal, drug-free bioadhesive, Replens MD® (LDS Consumer Products), has also been shown to improve vaginal dryness in postmenopausal women.[18] Despite extensive searching, the CEU was unable to find evidence on the use of topical vaginal estrogens or Replens in the management of vaginal dryness in premenopausal women or in women using combined oral contraception. These same treatments may be used but no evidence exists on their efficacy.

QUESTION

For women undergoing neurosurgical procedures, is discontinuation of the combined oral contraceptive pill advised in order to reduce the risk of VTE?

POPULATION: Women using combined oral contraception.

INTERVENTIONS: Neurosurgical procedures.

OUTCOME: Risk of VTE.

ANSWER

The Scottish Intercollegiate Guidelines Network (SIGN) has published an evidence-based guideline on prophylaxis of VTE.[19] Neurosurgery is associated with a high risk of VTE. Asymptomatic deep vein thrombosis has been demonstrated in 20–50% of all patients following neurosurgery and autopsy studies indicate that 12% of postoperative deaths are attributable to pulmonary embolism. Risk factors for VTE include intracranial (rather than spinal) surgery, malignancy, long duration of surgery, and lower limb paralysis or weakness.[20]

Current or recent users of combined oral contraception, high-dose progestogens, HRT or raloxifene who are undergoing surgery (not specifically neurosurgery) should be counselled preoperatively regarding hormone use. Discussion should cover the balance of risks of stopping before elective surgery and arrangements should be made for alternative contraception if appropriate. The SIGN guideline included a chapter specific to oral contraceptives and HRT. SIGN recognised that the decision to discontinue combined oral contraception is controversial; the risk of postoperative VTE is increased from 0.5% to 1.0% for pill users versus non-pill users.[21] This small absolute risk must be balanced against the risk of unintended pregnancy if effective contraception is discontinued.

Ideally, when a decision is made to stop combined oral contraception, it should be stopped 4 weeks prior to the planned surgical procedure. Consideration should also be given to specific anti-thrombotic prophylaxis according to each patient's overall risk profile. Given the risks of intracranial and intraspinal bleeding, mechanical prophylaxis, rather than heparin, is generally preferred for all neurosurgery.[19]

The CEU endorses the *WHO Medical Eligibility Criteria* recommendation that combined oral contraception should not be used in women undergoing major surgery with immobilisation. This would include women undergoing neurosurgical procedures.

QUESTION

For young girls aged 13 years, can the combined oral contraceptive pill be used to treat dysmenorrhoea?

POPULATION: Adolescents with dysmenorrhoea.
INTERVENTIONS: Combined oral contraception.
OUTCOME: Safety and efficacy.

ANSWER

After the onset of menstruation, anovulation is common. By the 20th menstrual cycle, however, ovulation occurs in up to 50% of young women.[22] Ovulatory cycles tend to be associated with dysmenorrhoea.

The WHO *Medical Eligibility for Contraceptive Use* recommends that young women from the menarche onwards can use combined oral contraception. WHO does not specify a minimum age when it is safe to commence the combined pill. However, in general, in the absence of other contraindications, combined oral contraception can be used without restriction (WHO category 1) after the onset of menstruation.

Young women may use combined oral contraception to treat dysmenorrhoea or menorrhagia after the onset of menstruation (menarche).

QUESTION

For women who are postpartum and not breastfeeding, who have a history of combined oral contraceptive failure following weight loss, how can efficacy be improved?

POPULATION: **Women who are postpartum and not breastfeeding who have a history of combined oral contraceptive failure following weight loss.**

INTERVENTIONS: **Combined oral contraception.**

OUTCOME: **Efficacy.**

ANSWER

The Pearl Index for combined oral contraception has been estimated at 0.3–4.0/100 woman years. Despite perfect compliance, there may be true method failures. The 'perfect use' failure rate for combined oral contraception is quoted as 0.1% and the 'typical use' failure rate as 5%.[23]

The *WHO Medical Eligibility Criteria for Contraceptive Use* advises that, for women who are less than 21 days postpartum and not breastfeeding, the risks of combined oral contraception generally outweigh the benefits (WHO category 3). Women who are more than 21 days postpartum and not breastfeeding may have unrestricted use of combined oral contraception (WHO category 1).

The CEU found no evidence that losing weight reduces the efficacy of combined oral contraception. On the contrary, one retrospective cohort analysis suggested that obese women might be at increased risk of pregnancy if prescribed low-dose (less than 35 micrograms ethinylestradiol) combined oral contraceptives.[24] No further evidence was identified to support these findings.

CEU guidance on first prescription of combined oral contraception[1] cites one survey which showed that women are most likely to miss pills in the week following the pill-free interval.[25] Although there is some evidence of follicular activity in the 7-day pill-free interval, if combined oral contraception is restarted and taken consistently, there is no evidence of ovulation. However, this may be the time when potential for contraceptive failure is greatest. We found no evidence that compliance is improved by taking 'every day' pills; but, logically, this regimen may be easier for women who find it difficult to remember when to start their next pack. Alternatively, women may 'tricycle' conventional combined pills (take three packs consecutively without a hormone-free week) thus avoiding a pill-free interval and withdrawal bleeds. Tricycling is outside the product licence and women should be informed of this if combined oral contraception is recommended in this way.

Although not evidence-based, the pill-free interval could be shortened for women with true method failures.

QUESTION

If a woman inadvertently takes combined oral contraception during pregnancy, are there any adverse effects on the fetus?

POPULATION: Pregnant women.
INTERVENTIONS: Combined oral contraception.
OUTCOME: Teratogenicity and other adverse effects on the fetus.

ANSWER

Guidance for clinicians contained in manufacturers' Summaries of Product Characteristics indicates that combined oral contraception should be withdrawn immediately, should a pill-user become pregnant. This guidance is based on the findings of epidemiological studies, some of which have suggested a small increase in the risk of congenital malformations associated with exposure to contraceptive steroids. WHO has interpreted available evidence as showing 'no known harm if combined oral contraceptives are accidentally used during pregnancy'.

Studies reviewed by the CEU are broadly reassuring.[26–28] However, some data support associations between combined oral contraceptive exposure and risk of urinary tract anomalies[29] and preponderance of female gender.[30] Combined oral contraceptive exposure may interact with smoking in relation to risk of anomalies.[31] It has been estimated that, in the USA alone, some 70 000 babies are born annually after in-utero exposure to contraceptive steroids.[32] This fact alone is reassuring, in that any major effect would surely have become apparent.

It should be noted that there are few data relating to newer combined oral contraceptives containing new progestogens. As a general principle, long-established medicines with extensive post-marketing surveillance should be used in preference to newer agents, unless there is a definite clinical indication to do otherwise.

References

1. Faculty of Family Planning and Reproductive Health Care Clinical Effectiveness Unit. First prescription of combined oral contraception. *J Fam Plann Reprod Health Care* 2003;29:209–22.
2. World Health Organization. WHO Collaborative study of Cardiovascular Disease and Steroid Hormone Contraception. Ischaemic stroke and combined oral contraception: results of an international, multicentre, case–control study. *Lancet* 1996;348:498–505.
3. International Headache Society Task Force on Combined Oral Contraceptives and Hormone Replacement Therapy. Recommendations on the risk of ischaemic stroke associated with use of combined oral contraceptives and hormone replacement therapy in women with migraine. *Cephalagia* 2000;20:155–6.
4. Jick H, Kaye JA, Vasilakis-Scaramozza C, Jick SS. Risk of venous thromboembolism among users of third generation oral contraceptives compared with users of oral contraceptives with levonorgestrel before and after 1995: cohort and case–control analysis. *BMJ* 2000;321:1190–5.
5. Farmer RDT, Lawrenson RA, Todd JC, Williams TJ, MacRae KD, Tyrer F, *et al.* A comparison of the risks of venous thromboembolic disease in association with different combined oral contraceptives. *Br J Pharmacol* 2000;49:580–90.
6. Sangi-Haghpeykar H, Poindexter AN, Bateman L, Ditmore JR. Experiences of injectable contraceptive users in an urban setting. *Obstet Gynecol* 1996;88:227–33.
7. Hildago M, Bahamondes L, Perrotti M, Diaz J, Dantas-Monteiro C, Petta C. Bleeding patterns and clinical performance of the levonorgestrel-releasing intrauterine system (Mirena) up to two years. *Contraception* 2002;65:129–32.
8. Rossmanith WG, Wirth U, Gasser S, Thun B, Steffens D. [Comparative study on ovarian activity, cycle stability and tolerance during administration of two low-dose oral contraceptives.] *Zentralbl Gynakol* 1997;119:538–51. [German.]
9. Endrikat J, Dusterberg B, Ruebig A, Gerlinger C, Strowitzkit T. Comparison of efficacy, cycle control, and tolerability of two low-dose oral contraceptives in a multicentre clinical study. *Contraception* 1999;60:269–74.
10. Endrikat J, Cronin M, Gerlinger C, Reubig A, Schmidt W, Düsterberg B. Open, multicenter comparison of efficacy, cycle control, and tolerability of a 23-day oral contraceptive regimen with 20 mg ethinyl estradiol and 75 mg gestodene and a 21-day regimen with 20 mg ethinyl estradiol and 150 mg desogestrel. *Contraception* 2001;64:201–7.
11. Endrikat J, Cronin M, Gerlinger C, Ruebig A, Schmidt W, Düsterberg B. Double-blind, multicenter comparison of efficacy, cycle control, and tolerability of a 23-day versus a 21-day low-dose oral contraceptive regimen containing 20 mg ethinyl estradiol and 75 mg gestodene. *Contraception* 2001;64:99–105.
12. Dusterberg B, Ellman H, Muller U, Rowe E, Muhe B. A three-year clinical investigation into efficacy, cycle control and tolerability of a new low-dose monophasic oral contraceptive containing gestodene. *Gynecol Endocrinol* 196;10:33–9.

13. Gallo M, Lopez L, Grimes D, Schulz K, Helmerhorst F. Combination contraceptives: effects on weight. *Cochrane Database Syst Rev* 2006;(1):CD003987.
14. Foidart JM, Wuttke W, Bouw GM, Gerlinger C, Heithecker R. A comparative investigation of contraceptive reliability, cycle control and tolerance of two monophasic oral contraceptives containing either drospirenone or desogestrel. *Eur J Contracept Reprod Health Care* 2000;5:124–34.
15. Huber J, Foidart JM, Wuttke W, Merki-Feld GS, The HS, Gerlinger C, et al. Efficacy and tolerability of a monophasic oral contraceptive containing ethinylestradiol and drospirenone. *Eur J Contracept Reprod Health Care* 2000;5:25–34.
16. Gaspard U, Scheen A, Endrikat J, Buicu C, Lefebvre P, Gerlinger C, et al. A randomised study over 13 cycles to assess the influence of oral contraceptives containing ethinylestradiol combined with drospirenone or desogestrel on carbohydrate metabolism. *Contraception* 2003;67:423–9.
17. Yasmin a 'truly different pill'? *Drug Ther Bull* 2002;40:57–9.
18. Nachtigall LE. Comparative study: Replens versus local estrogen in menopausal women. *Fertil Steril* 1994;61:178–80.
19. Scottish Intercollegiate Guidelines Network. *Prophylaxis of Venous Thromboembolism*. Guideline 62. Edinburgh: SIGN; 2002 [www.sign.ac.uk/guidelines/fulltext/62/index.html].
20. Agnelli G. Prevention of venous thromboembolism after neurosurgery. *Thromb Haemost* 1999;82:925–30.
21. Vessey MP, Doll R, Fairbairn AS, Glober G. Postoperative thromboembolism and the use of oral contraceptives. *BMJ* 1970;3:123–6.
22. Borsos A, Lampe L, Balogh A, Csoknyay J, Ditroi F, Szekely P. Ovarian function after the menarche and hormonal contraception. *Int J Gynecol Obstet* 1988;27:249–53.
23. Hatcher RA, Trussell J, Stewart F, Cates W Jr, Stewart GK, Guest F, et al. *Contraceptive Technology*. New York: Ardent Media; 1998.
24. Holt VL, Cushing-Haugen KL, Daling JR. Body weight and risk of oral contraceptive failure. *Obstet Gynecol* 2002;99:820–7.
25. Aubeny E, Buhler M, Colau JC, Zadikian M, Childs M. Oral contraception: patterns of non-compliance. The Compliance study. *Eur J Contracept Reprod Health Care* 2002;7:155–61.
26. Savolainen E, Saksela ESL. Teratogenic hazards of oral contraceptives analyzed in a national malformation register. *Am J Obstet Gynecol* 1981;140:521–4.
27. Vessey M, Meisler L, Flavel R, Yeates D. Outcome of pregnancy in women using different methods of contraception. *Br J Obstet Gynaecol* 1979;86:548–56.
28. Pardthiasong T, Gray RH, McDaniel EB, Chandacham A. Steroid contraceptive use and pregnancy outcome. *Teratology* 1988;38:51–8.
29. Li D, Daling JR, Muller BA, Hickok DE, Fantel AG, Weiss NS. Oral contraceptive use after conception in relation to the risk of congenital urinary tract anomalies. *Teratology* 1995;51:30–6.
30. Pejsik B, Hadnagy J, Rappai G, Kobor J. [Effect of oral contraceptives on developmental anomalies and on the sex ratio of newborn infants]. *Orvosi Hetilap* 1990;131:1187–90. [In Hungarian]
31. Hill JA, Gantt PA, McDonough PG, Cunningham JJ. Ultrasound diagnosis of multiple anomalies associated with prenatal oral contraceptives. *Med Ultrasound* 1982;6:116–18.
32. Shino PH, Harlap S, Ramcharan S, Berendes H, Gupta S, Pellegrin F. Use of contraceptives prior to and after conception and exposure to other fetal hazards. *Contraception* 1979;20:105–20.

Missed pills and potential failures

In April 2005, the FFPRHC published a Faculty Statement from the CEU on the WHO *Selected Practice Recommendations* update on 'missed pills'.[1] The guidance contained in that statement on actions to be taken when women miss combined oral contraceptive pills supersedes previous Faculty recommendations. Our responses to some of our first 1000 Members' enquiries were based on recommendations that have now been superseded. These responses have been omitted from this volume. Instead, we have reproduced the summary, tables and figure from the Faculty statement in order to provide up-to-date guidance to readers.

Responses to questions about missed pills and potential contraceptive failures which are unaffected by the April 2005 Statement are included here.

Extracts from: Faculty statement from the CEU on: WHO Selected Practice Recommendations Update

The WHO *Selected Practice Recommendations for Contraceptive Use* was first published in 2002 and provides evidence-based recommendations on how to use contraception effectively. The *Selected Practice Recommendations* were adapted for UK use by the Faculty of Family Planning and Reproductive Heath Care. The UK version is available on the FFPRHC website (www.ffprhc.org). Extensive field experience with the first edition of the *Selected Practice Recommendations* highlighted to WHO the need for revised recommendations for missed combined oral contraceptive pills. The *Selected Practice Recommendations* document was updated in 2004 and revised guidance on missed pills was published. This guidance is now available on the WHO website (www.who.int/reproductive-health).

The FFPRHC endorses the new recommendations from WHO on missed combined oral contraceptive pills for the following reasons:

- There is new evidence on which to base guidance.

- The WHO *Selected Practice Recommendations* follow a published and rigorous process for assessing the available evidence.

- The recommendations were developed by an international expert panel, with UK representation.

- Field experience shows a need for simple, harmonised guidance.

This statement summarises the revised WHO *Selected Practice Recommendations* evidence-based 'missed pill rules' in formats that we hope clinicians will find useful. We recognise that different individuals favour different styles for the presentation of information. Thus, both tabular and flow chart styles of summary are provided; these convey the same information but in different ways.

The FFPRHC considers that the following statements may also serve as useful *aides memoire* for the 'missed pill rules':

- Whenever a woman realises that she has missed pills, the essential advice is 'just keep going'. She should take a pill as soon as possible and then resume her usual pill-taking schedule.

- Also, if the missed pills are in week three, she should omit the pill-free interval.

- Also, a back-up method (usually condoms) or abstinence should be used for 7 days if the following numbers of pills are missed:
  - ○ 'Two for twenty' (i.e., if two or more 20-microgram ethinylestradiol pills are missed).
  - ○ 'Three for thirty' (i.e. if three or more 30- to 35-microgram ethinylestradiol pills are missed).

The fpa has produced a revised user information sheet to reflect these changes.[2]

Advice for women missing combined oral contraceptives containing 30–35 micrograms of ethinylestradiol

Missed ONE or TWO pills:
- She should take a pill as soon as possible and then continue taking pills daily, one each day. (If a woman misses more than one pill, she can take the first missed pill and then either continue taking the rest of the missed pills or discard them to stay on schedule.)
- She does not need any additional contraceptive protection.

Missed THREE or more pills:
- She should take a pill as soon as possible and then continue taking pills daily, one each day. (Depending on when she remembers that she missed a pill or pills, she may take two pills on the same day – one at the moment of remembering, and the other at the regular time, or even at the same time.)

- She should also use condoms or abstain from sex until she has taken pills for 7 days in a row.
- If she missed the pills in the third week, she should finish the pills in her current pack and start a new pack the next day. She should not have a pill-free interval. If the pill-free interval is avoided in this way, she does not need to use emergency contraception.
- If she missed the pills in the first week (effectively extending the pill-free interval) and had unprotected sex (in week 1 or in the pill-free interval), she may wish to consider the use of emergency contraception.

For 'every day' pill regimens:
- If a woman misses any inactive pills, she should discard the missed inactive pills and then continue taking pills daily, one each day.

Advice for women missing combined oral contraceptives containing 20 micrograms or less of ethinylestradiol

Missed ONE pill:
- She should take a pill as soon as possible and then continue taking pills daily, one each day.
- She does not need any additional contraceptive protection.

Missed TWO or more pills:
- She should take a pill as soon as possible and then continue taking pills daily, one each day. (Depending on when she remembers that she missed a pill or pills, she may take two pills on the same day —one at the moment of remembering and the other at the regular time or even at the same time).
- She should also use condoms or abstain from sex until she has taken pills for 7 days in a row.
- If she missed the pills in the third week, she should finish the pills in her current pack and start a new pack the next day. She should not have a pill-free interval. If the pill-free interval is avoided in this way, she does not need to use emergency contraception.
- If she missed the pills in the first week (effectively extending the pill-free interval) and had unprotected sex (in week 1 or in the pill-free interval), she may wish to consider the use of emergency contraception.

For 'every day' pill regimens:
- If a woman misses any inactive pills, she should discard the missed inactive pills and then continue taking pills daily, one each day.

Advice for women missing combined oral contraceptives (30–35 microgram and 20-microgram ethinylestradiol formulations)	
If ONE or TWO 30–35 microgram ethinylestradiol pills have been missed at any time **OR** **ONE 20 microgram ethinylestradiol pill is missed:**	**If THREE or MORE** 30–35 microgram ethinylestradiol pills have been missed at any time **OR** **TWO or MORE 20 microgram ethinylestradiol pills are missed:**
She should take the most recent missed pill as soon she remembers.	She should take the most recent missed pill as soon as she remembers.
She should continue taking the remaining pills daily at her usual time.*	She should continue taking the remaining pills daily at her usual time.*
She does not require additional contraceptive protection.	She should be advised to use condoms or abstain from sex until she has taken pills for 7 days in a row.

	If pills are missed in week 1 (days 1–7) (because the pill-free interval has been extended):	**If pills are missed in week 3 (days 15–21) (to avoid extending the pill-free interval):**
	Emergency contraception should be considered if she had unprotected sex in the pill-free interval or in week 1.	She should finish the pills in her current pack and start a new pack the next day, thus omitting the pill-free interval.

* Depending on when she remembers her missed pill, she may take two pills on the same day (one at the moment of remembering and the other at the regular time) or even at the same time

QUESTION

For women using the combined oral contraceptive pill and who start a 'time-expired' pack, thus missing five active pills, is emergency contraception or additional barrier contraception required?

POPULATION: Women taking combined oral contraception.

INTERVENTION: Starting a 'time-expired' pack in error.

OUTCOME: Risk of pregnancy.

ANSWER

Taking five time-expired pills in the first week should be treated as missing five active pills and therefore extending the 7-day pill-free interval to 12 days. In this scenario, a woman should be instructed to start a new packet of non-expired pills and use condoms or abstain until seven consecutive pills have been taken. If unprotected sexual intercourse occurred during the pill-free week or the first 7 days of the pack, emergency contraception is indicated.

QUESTION

For a woman using the combined oral contraceptive pill who has extended her pill-free interval, on what timescale can an emergency IUD appropriately be fitted?

POPULATION: Women taking combined oral contraception with lengthening of the pill-free interval.

INTERVENTION: Emergency IUD.

OUTCOME: Risk of pregnancy.

ANSWER

The WHO and the FFPRHC advise that, when the time of ovulation can be estimated, a woman can have a copper-bearing IUD inserted for emergency contraception beyond 5 days after intercourse, as long as insertion does not occur more than 5 days after ovulation.[3] In the context of emergency contraception after a 'late pill start' (extended pill-free interval), it is difficult to estimate the time when ovulation might occur.

Published studies have identified no ovulation after as many as 11 pill-free days. However, wide variations among women are reported in the degree of follicular development.[4] Therefore, these findings must be viewed with caution.

Based on pragmatic interpretation of available research evidence, the CEU considers that an emergency IUD could appropriately be fitted up to day 15 of an extended pill-free interval (based on earliest possibility of ovulation estimated as 10 days from last pill plus the 5-day 'post-ovulation' limit for IUD insertion).

QUESTION

For a woman using the combined oral contraceptive pill who begins and completes a course of antibiotics during the pill-free interval, is additional contraception required?

POPULATION: Women taking combined oral contraception.
INTERVENTION: A course of antibiotics during the pill-free interval.
OUTCOME: Risk of pregnancy.

ANSWER

The *WHO Medical Eligibility Criteria for Contraceptive Use* advises that, for women using liver enzyme-inducing antibiotics such as rifampicin and griseo-fulvin the risks of using combined oral contraception generally outweigh the benefits (WHO category 3). Women using other antibiotics may have unrestricted use of this method (WHO category 1).

Guidance from the FFPRHC CEU on first prescription of combined oral contraception[5] advises:

- Contraception is still provided during the routine 7 hormone-free days when using the combined pill.

- Women using non-enzyme-inducing, broad-spectrum antibiotics for short courses (less than 3 weeks) should be advised to use additional contraception during the course and for 7 days afterwards.

- Women who are established users of non-enzyme-inducing antibiotics (more than 3 weeks) should be advised that, unless their antibiotic is changed, barrier contraception is not required when starting the combined pill.

- Women using short courses of the liver enzyme-inducing antibiotic rifampicin for prophylaxis are advised to use additional contraception during the course and for 4 weeks afterwards.

Women using rifampicin long-term are advised to follow the recommendations for women using other enzyme-inducing drugs. If a woman using a liver enzyme-inducing drug still chooses to use the combined pill, a regimen containing at least 50 micrograms of ethinylestradiol daily is advised, together with use of a barrier method. Additional contraception is also required for 28 days after the liver enzyme-inducer is stopped.

These recommendations are applicable regardless of when during the cycle a woman begins and completes a course of antibiotics. Thus, a woman taking non-enzyme-inducing antibiotics during her pill-free interval should be advised to use back-up contraception during the antibiotic course and for 7 days afterwards.

References

1. Faculty of Family Planning and Reproductive Health Care. Faculty statement from the CEU on a New Publication: WHO Selected Practice Recommendations for Contraceptive Use Update. Missed pills: new recommendations. *J Fam Plann Reprod Health Care* 2005;31:153–5.
2. fpa. *Your Guide to the Combined Pill* [www.fpa.org/uk/guide/contra%20PDFS/combined20%pill.pdf].
3. Faculty of Family Planning and Reproductive Health Care Clinical Effectiveness Unit. Emergency contraception: recommendations for clinical practice. *J Fam Plann Reprod Health Care* 2003;29:9–16.
4. Killick SR, Bancroft K, Oelbaum S, Morris J, Elstein M. Extending the duration of the pill-free interval during combined oral contraception. *Adv Contracept* 1990;6:33–40.
5. Faculty of Family Planning and Reproductive Health Care Clinical Effectiveness Unit. First prescription of combined oral contraception. *J Fam Plann Reprod Health Care* 2003;29:209–22.

Combined transdermal contraception

QUESTION

For women with systemic disorders or metabolic problems (such as diabetes, mild hepatic problems, thyroid disorders) are there any pharmacological reasons why transdermal contraception may be preferable to oral contraception?

POPULATION: Women with systemic disorders.

INTERVENTIONS: Combined oral contraception or combined transdermal contraception.

OUTCOMES: Safety and efficacy.

ANSWER

There have been no studies that have considered possible pharmacological benefits from transdermal administration of combined contraception for women with systemic or metabolic disorders.

In the context of HRT, oral conjugated estrogens are associated with significant changes in renin substrate, anti-thrombin III activity and hormone-binding globulins; transdermal HRT is not associated with such changes.[1,2] Similar studies are unavailable in the context of transdermal contraception. Studies that have compared plasma lipid changes in women using oral or transdermal contraception suggest that effects are similar.[3]

In the Summary of Product Characteristics for transdermal contraception it is considered that contraceptive patches will have contraindications similar to combined oral contraception. The CEU has endorsed this view in published guidance on the ethinylestradiol–norelgestromin patch (Evra®, Janssen-Cilag).[4]

QUESTION

For women using the combined contraceptive patch, is there an increased risk of VTE compared to the risk with combined oral contraception?

POPULATION: Women requiring contraception.
INTERVENTIONS: Combined oral contraception or combined transdermal contraception.
OUTCOME: Risk of VTE.

ANSWER

The 2004 edition of the *WHO Medical Eligibility Criteria for Contraceptive Use* acknowledged that epidemiological data on the long-term effects of the combined contraceptive patch were not available to the WHO Working Group. However, available evidence suggested that the patch has a similar safety and pharmacokinetic profile to combined oral contraceptives with similar hormone formulations. WHO advises that the patch should **not** be used (WHO category 4) by women:

- with a personal or family history among first-degree relatives of deep venous thrombosis or pulmonary embolism

- with current deep venous thrombosis or pulmonary embolism

- undergoing major surgery with prolonged immobilisation.

A CEU New Product Review on the combined contraceptive patch,[4] published in January 2004, cited one report of pulmonary embolism occurring in one contraceptive patch user who had used the patch up until the time of major surgery.[5]

A long-term evaluation of the patch, published in July 2004,[6] reviewed clinical data on 62 young women in the USA who started the patch between June 2002 and December 2003 and used it for a mean length of ten cycles. However, this study only found that the patch was associated with adverse effects such as skin irritation.

In September and October 2004, various newspaper reports linked use of the combined contraceptive patch to fatalities from deep vein thrombosis or pulmonary embolism. The manufacturers of the patch and the fpa both responded to these reports and stated that the role of the patch in these deaths was unclear.

It is not clear if these fatalities from VTE occurred because the women were patch users or if they would have also occurred with combined oral contraception. On the basis of available evidence, the CEU can only advise that women with the contraindications mentioned above should not use the combined patch.

References

1. Whitehead MI, Fraser D, Schenkel L, Crook D, Stevenson JC. Transdermal administration of estrogen/progestagen hormone replacement therapy. *Lancet* 1990;1990:310–12.
2. Ryszard J, Chetkowski MD, Meldrum DR, Steingold K, Randle D, Lu JK, *et al*. Biologic effects of transdermal estradiol. *N Engl J Med* 1986;314:1615–20.
3. Creasy GW, Fisher AC, Hall N, Shangold GA. Transdermal contraceptive patch delivering norelgestromin and ethinyl estradiol. Effects on the lipid profile. *J Reprod Med* 2003;48:179–86.
4. Faculty of Family Planning and Reproductive Healthcare Clinical Effectiveness Unit. *New product review. Norelgestromin/ethinyl oestradiol transdermal contraceptive system (Evra)*. London: FFPRHC; 2004.
5. Smallwood GH, Meador M, Lenihan JP, Shangold G, Fisher A, Creasy GW. Efficacy and safety of a transdermal contraceptive system. *Obstet Gynecol* 2001;98:799–805.
6. Longsdon S, Richards J, Omar HA. Long-term evaluation of the use of the transdermal contraceptive patch in adolescents. *ScientificWorldJournal* 2004;4:512–16.

The cyproterone acetate-containing pill

Dianette contains 35 micrograms ethinylestradiol and 2 mg cyproterone acetate. Cyproterone acetate has anti-androgen effects resulting in part from blockade of androgen receptors. The Summary of Product Characteristics states that it is recommended for use in women only for the treatment of androgen-sensitive skin conditions, including severe acne refractory to prolonged oral antibiotic therapy, and moderately severe hirsutism. It recommends that Dianette should not be used solely for contraception.

QUESTION

For women using Dianette, what is the incidence rate of VTE? (Five similar enquiries.)

POPULATION: Women requiring contraception.

INTERVENTION: Dianette.

OUTCOMES: Risk of VTE.

ANSWER

The Medicines and Healthcare products Regulatory Agency (MHRA) has reviewed epidemiological studies and concluded that the risk of VTE in Dianette users is higher than in users of conventional low-dose combined pills.[1]

Subsequently, a Danish study found that the absolute risk of VTE was 3.4/10 000 women-years (range 3.1–3.8) among women on any combined oral contraceptive; 4.2/10 000 women-years (range 3.2–5.2) among women on levonorgestrel-containing combined pills and 3.1/10 000 women-years (range 1.3–4.9) among women on Dianette.[2] Furthermore, a review (consistent with criteria for 'best evidence synthesis') of six peer-reviewed, controlled epidemiological studies, found that (except for one study exhibiting a small statistically significant benefit) there was no difference in the incidence rates of VTE among Dianette users and among conventional COC users. Absolute incidence rates of VTE among Dianette users ranged from 1.2/10 000 to 9.9/10 000 woman-years.[3] In addition, a 2004 analysis of data from the General Practice Research Database found (using exposure to conventional combined pills as the reference) odds ratios for VTE in Dianette-users of 1.45 (95% CI 0.80–2.64) for all women and 1.71 (95% CI 0.31–9.49) in women with acne, hirsutism or PCOS.[4]

Thus, data on the risk of VTE associated with Dianette use are conflicting. Evidence suggests that the risk is similar to that for women using conventional combined pills, with an absolute rate of the order of 30/100 000 woman years.

QUESTION

For how long can women who require contraception use Dianette safely? (Seven similar enquiries.)

POPULATION: Women requiring contraception.
INTERVENTION: Dianette.
OUTCOMES: Safety.

ANSWER

An international, multicentre study of 2506 women evaluated long-term adverse effects of cyproterone acetate-containing therapies in gynaecology. Around 32% of participants reported adverse effects including weight gain, headache, gastrointestinal disorders, mood changes, ankle oedema, skin changes and breast tenderness. Importantly, no benign or malignant liver tumours were observed. The authors concluded that 2 mg cyproterone acetate daily is not associated with serious adverse effects or with an increase in liver tumours.[5]

In recent years, it has emerged that differences in VTE risk with different combined oral contraceptives appear to be related to the type of progestogen used; with 'third generation' pills (containing gestodene or desogestrel) having a two-fold increase in risk compared with 'second generation' pills (containing norethisterone and levonorgestrel).

An important case–control study identified that combined oral contraceptive pills containing cyproterone acetate (which combine an estrogen with an anti-androgen) are associated with a four-fold increase in risk of VTE compared to a second generation pill.[6] Duration of pill use did not seem to affect risk of VTE. However, a more recent case–control study found no difference in risk of VTE in Dianette users compared to users of other combined pills containing levonorgestrel.[2,7]

However, the MHRA[1] currently advises that:

● Dianette is indicated for severe acne that has not responded to oral antibiotics or for moderately severe hirsutism but is not indicated for use just as a contraceptive.

● Treatment with Dianette should be stopped three to four cycles after the acne or hirsutism has completely resolved.

● The incidence of VTE is higher in Dianette users than in users of other low-dose estrogen combined oral contraceptives, so Dianette is contraindicated in women with current venous thrombotic or embolic disorders or with a history (or family history) of idiopathic VTE.

● Women with severe acne or hirsutism may have an inherent increase in cardiovascular risk.

In line with the Summary of Product Characteristics for Dianette, the CEU recommends that it should be stopped three to four cycles after acne or hirsutism has completely resolved. Most conventional combined oral contraceptives have been shown to improve acne and a switch to a 'second' or 'third generation' combined pill is acceptable after symptoms have resolved with Dianette.

QUESTION

For women with a past history of ectopic pregnancy, does use of Dianette increase the risk of subsequent ectopic pregnancy?

POPULATION: Women with a past history of ectopic pregnancy.
INTERVENTION: Dianette.
OUTCOMES: Risk of future ectopic pregnancy.

ANSWER

There is no contraindication to the use of Dianette by women with a past history of ectopic pregnancy. The *WHO Medical Eligibility Criteria for Contraceptive Use* considers past history of ectopic pregnancy as 'category 1' for combined contraceptive use (no restriction upon use). The MHRA recommends that Dianette is not used solely for contraception – it can be used for women with moderate to severe acne or hirsutism which has failed to respond to other treatments.[1]

The *Medical Eligibility Criteria for Contraceptive Use* does not contraindicate any contraceptive method for women with a history of ectopic pregnancy – including an IUD or progestogen-only pill. A method of contraception that suppresses ovulation (such as combined contraception, progestogen-only implant or injectable) would be the preferred option, since this will reduce the likelihood of any pregnancy (intrauterine and extrauterine).

Dianette suppresses ovulation, like conventional combined oral contraceptives, and would therefore represent an appropriate treatment for a woman with a past history of ectopic pregnancy who also has an androgen-related condition such as acne or hirsutism.

QUESTION

For women with cerebral palsy and acne, is the cyproterone acetate-containing pill, Dianette, a safe method of contraception?

POPULATION: Women with cerebral palsy and acne.
INTERVENTION: Dianette.
OUTCOMES: Safety.

ANSWER

Cerebral palsy comprises a group of motor or postural abnormalities observed during early development that may be caused by prenatal, perinatal or postnatal events. The *WHO Medical Eligibility Criteria for Contraceptive Use* does not specifically address contraceptive choices for women with cerebral palsy.

The CEU could find no evidence in the literature that a combined oral contraceptive would not be a safe option for a woman with cerebral palsy, provided that she is not severely immobilised, which might increase her risk of VTE. Dianette should only be used in the management of women with moderate to severe acne. If used in such women, it would also provide effective contraception but it should not be used solely as a contraceptive.

QUESTION

For women with primary sclerosing cholangitis, is the cyproterone acetate-containing pill, Dianette, a safe method of contraception?

POPULATION: Women with primary sclerosing cholangitis.
INTERVENTION: Dianette.
OUTCOME: Safety.

ANSWER

Primary sclerosing cholangitis is a chronic cholestatic liver disease of unknown aetiology and is the most common hepatobiliary disorder associated with inflammatory bowel disease. The CEU has produced guidance on contraceptive choices for women with inflammatory bowel disease,[8] which refers to the *WHO Medical Eligibility Criteria for Contraceptive Use*.

The health risks for women with primary sclerosing cholangitis using combined oral contraceptives are **unacceptable** (WHO category 4). For women with primary sclerosing cholangitis, the risks of using DMPA, the progestogen-only pill, progestogen-only implant (Implanon) or the LNG-IUS, generally outweigh the benefits (WHO category 3). The copper IUD is a suitable long-term method of contraception.

The MHRA advises that Dianette (ethinylestradiol and cyproterone acetate) is licensed as a treatment for moderate to severe acne. Although it also acts as a contraceptive, it is not licensed to be used solely as a contraceptive.

The CEU does not recommend Dianette (or conventional combined oral contraceptives) for women with primary sclerosing cholangitis.

QUESTION

For women with familial cardiomyopathy, is the cyproterone acetate-containing pill, Dianette, a safe method of contraception?

POPULATION: Women with familial cardiomyopathy.
INTERVENTION: Dianette.
OUTCOME: Safety.

ANSWER

Familial cardiomyopathy of various kinds occurs with autosomal dominant inheritance. The *WHO Medical Eligibility Criteria for Contraceptive Use* does not specifically address contraceptive choice for women with familial cardiomyopathy. However, for women with multiple risk factors for arterial cardiovascular disease (such as older age, smoking, diabetes and hypertension) the *Medical Eligibility Criteria* advises that combined oral contraception should **not** be used (WHO category 3/4). For women with uncomplicated valvular heart disease, the benefits of using combined oral contraception generally outweigh the risks (WHO category 2), while women with complicated valvular heart disease (pulmonary hypertension, atrial fibrillation, history of subacute bacterial endocarditis) are advised **not** to use combined oral contraception (WHO category 4).

The MHRA has reviewed epidemiological evidence that showed that the risk of VTE in Dianette users may be four times higher than in users of low-dose 'second generation' combined oral contraceptives. Although it seems likely that this higher risk occurs during the first year of use, and is not related to duration of use, the MHRA has advised that Dianette is indicated for severe acne that has not responded to oral antibiotics or for moderately severe hirsutism but not for use solely as a contraceptive. Treatment with Dianette should be stopped three to four cycles after the acne or hirsutism has resolved.

As a woman with familial cardiomyopathy requires continuing evaluation, it seems reasonable to equate this condition to that of a woman with complicated valvular heart disease, which implies that combined oral contraception, including Dianette, should not be used.

QUESTION

For women with PCOS using a LNG-IUS, can Dianette be used concurrently?

POPULATION: Women with PCOS and using a LNG-IUS.
INTERVENTION: Dianette.
OUTCOME: Safety.

ANSWER

The Summary of Product Characteristics for Dianette states that clinical trials on animals reveal that feminisation of male fetuses may occur if it is taken during embryogenesis. Women using this medication must thus ensure that they take it reliably if they are also relying on it as a contraceptive method.

The MHRA advises that Dianette is not indicated solely as a contraceptive and is a treatment option for women with severe acne not responding to oral antibiotics or for severe hirsutism. The incidence of VTE may be higher in Dianette users than for women using low-dose combined oral contraceptives.

A guideline from the RCOG[9] advises that women with PCOS who are oligomenorrhoeic or amenorrhoeic can be managed with any combined oral contraceptive to regulate menstruation, provide contraception and reduce the risk of endometrial malignancy.

CEU guidance on first prescription of combined oral contraception[10] supports the MHRA recommendations. There is no indication for Dianette use for women with PCOS, unless they have symptoms of androgen excess. Any combined oral contraceptive will increase sex hormone-binding globulin and decrease free testosterone and can be useful for women with PCOS.

CEU guidance on the LNG-IUS in contraception and reproductive health[11] advises that women be informed that, although hormonal symptoms such as acne are reported by LNG-IUS users, these are not significantly different from copper IUD users. However, wide inter-individual variation in serum levonorgestrel occurs and some women may experience worse symptoms than others. Discontinuation of the LNG-IUS may itself cause improvement in symptoms.

There is no evidence on concurrent use of the LNG-IUS and a combined oral contraceptive. Rather than using two hormonal methods of contraception simultaneously, a woman may choose to have a copper IUD inserted for contraception. Clinicians may then use their judgement to decide which combined pill, if any, is needed to manage specific symptoms of PCOS.

QUESTION

For a woman using Dianette as combined oral contraception, how can she delay her menstrual bleed?

POPULATION: Women taking Dianette.
INTERVENTION: Adjustment of regimen.
OUTCOME: Safety and efficacy at delaying menstrual bleeding.

ANSWER

Despite extensive searching, the CEU could find no evidence in the literature specifically regarding delaying a bleed for women using Dianette. However, advice for women using combined oral contraception in general is that avoiding a pill-free week can delay the onset of a withdrawal bleed.[10] Women may **avoid** the withdrawal bleed by completely omitting the pill-free interval or they can continue to take pills only for as long as a **delay** in the withdrawal bleed is required. The CEU suggests that this advice would be the same for Dianette users.

QUESTION

For women who have responded to Dianette as treatment for acne, which combined oral contraceptive is best to avoid recurrence? (Two similar enquiries.)

POPULATION: Women who have responded to Dianette as treatment for acne.
INTERVENTIONS: Different brands of combined oral contraception.
OUTCOME: Risk of recurrence of acne.

ANSWER

Evidence from a Cochrane Review[12] suggests that combined oral contraceptives containing either levonorgestrel or desogestrel improve acne lesions to a similar extent. When changing a woman from Dianette to a standard combined oral contraceptive, a conventional pill containing levonorgestrel, such as Eugynon 30® (Schering Health), Logynon® (Schering Health), Microgynon 30® (Schering Health) or Ovranette® (Wyeth), represents an appropriate first-line choice. As for any woman, choice of pill will be governed by many factors, including the woman's own preferences. However, there is no trial evidence to suggest that any specific pill is any better than any other in respect of risk of acne recurrence.

References

1. Committee on Safety of Medicines. Cyproterone acetate (Dianette): risk of venous thromboembolism (VTE). *Curr Probl Pharmacovigilance* 2002;28:9–10 [www.mhra.gov.uk/home/idcplg?IdcService=SS_GET_PAGE&useSecondary=true&ssDocName=CON007451&ssTargetNodeId=368].
2. Lidegaard O, Edstrom B, Kreiner S. Oral contraceptives and venous thromboembolism: a five year national case–control study. *Contraception* 2002;65:187–96.
3. Spitzer WO. Cyproterone acetate with ethinylestradiol as a risk factor for venous thromboembolism: an epidemiological evaluation. *J Obstet Gynaecol Can* 2003;25:1011–18.
4. Seaman HE, de Vries CS, Farmer RD. Venous thromboembolism associated with cyproterone acetate in combination with ethinyloestradiol (Dianette): observational studies using the UK General Practice Research Database. *Pharmacoepidemiol Drug Saf* 2004:13:427–36.
5. Regidor PA, Speer K, Regidor M, Schindler EM. Long-term adverse effects following cyproterone acetate containing therapy in gynecology. *Zentralbl Gynakol* 2000;122:268–73.
6. Vasilakis-Scaramozza C, Jick H. Risk of venous thromboembolism with cyproterone or levonorgestrel contraceptives. *Lancet* 2001;358:1427–9.
7. Lidegaard O. Absolute and attributable risk of venous thromboembolism in women on combined cyproterone acetate and ethinylestradiol. *J Obstet Gynaecol Can* 2003;25:575–7.
8. Faculty of Family Planning and Reproductive Health Care Clinical Effectiveness Unit. Contraceptive choices for women with inflammatory bowel disease. *J Fam Plann Reprod Health Care* 2003;29:127–34.
9. Royal College of Obstetricians and Gynaecologists. *Long-Term Consequences of Polycystic Ovary Syndrome*. Guideline No. 33. London: RCOG; 2003.
10. Faculty of Family Planning and Reproductive Health Care Clinical Effectiveness Unit. First prescription of combined oral contraception. *J Fam Plann Reprod Health Care* 2003;29:209–22.
11. Faculty of Family Planning and Reproductive Health Care Clinical Effectiveness Unit. The levonorgestrel-releasing intrauterine system (LNG-IUS) in contraception and reproductive health. *J Fam Plann Reprod Health Care* 2004;30:99–109.
12. Arowojolu AO, Gallo MF, Grimes DA, Garner SE. Combined oral contraceptive pills for treatment of acne. *Cochrane Database Syst Rev* 2004.

2 PROGESTOGEN-ONLY CONTRACEPTION

Progestogen-only pills

Patient selection

QUESTION

For women intending to use progestogen-only pills, is blood pressure monitoring required?

POPULATION: Women intending to use progestogen-only pills.
INTERVENTION: Blood pressure monitoring.
OUTCOME: Safety.

ANSWER

The WHO *Selected Practice Recommendations* recommends that blood pressure should be measured and recorded before initiating a progestogen-only pill. This was supported in the UK version of the recommendations (FFPRHC *UK Selected Practice Recommendations for Contraceptive Use*) which states the following: A 12-month supply of progestogen-only pills can be given at a first and subsequent visits. Annual follow up is not required for progestogen-only pill users. Nevertheless, a review of medical, drug and family history as well as BMI and blood pressure might be appropriate once a year.

The WHO Collaborative Study did not identify an increased risk of cardio-vascular disease (venous thrombosis, myocardial infarction or stroke) for women using progestogen-only pill or injectables.[1] A literature review, which included non-randomised trials of normotensive progestogen-only pill users and followed up for 2 years, found no association between progestogen-only pills and hypertension.[2] The CEU provides recommendations on use of progestogen-only pills by specific patient groups: young people[3] and women over 40 years of age.[4]

The CEU recommends that blood pressure should be measured and recorded prior to initiating progestogen-only pills and may be repeated yearly (with review of medical history) but this review can be tailored to individual women.

QUESTION

Should women weighing over 70 kg who use progestogen-only pills containing norethisterone, levonorgestrel or etynodiol diacetate take two pills a day to improve contraceptive efficacy? (Nine similar enquiries.)

POPULATION: Women over 70 kg in weight who use progestogen-only pills.
INTERVENTION: Two pills/day.
OUTCOME: Contraceptive efficacy.

ANSWER

Some health professionals in the UK advise women using a progestogen-only pill containing norethisterone, levonorgestrel or etynodiol diacetate who weigh more than 70 kg to take two pills together every day.[5] Direct evidence to support this practice was not identified.

A large cohort study investigated the relationship between oral contraceptive failures and body weight.[6] The Pearl Index for progestogen-only pills was 3.36/100 woman-years at age 25–29 years and 0.28/100 woman-years at ages 40–44 years. The failure rates for the progestogen-only pill and combined oral contraceptive pill were adjusted for age alone and for age and parity in relation to body weight, height and BMI. No associations were found between failure rates and body weight, height or BMI. This study may not have had sufficient power to prove or disprove the hypothesis that an increase in body weight correlates with increased contraceptive failure in women using combined oral contraceptive pills or progestogen-only pills.

Studies show that obese women using the levonorgestrel-only implant (Norplant, now discontinued) had higher failure rates than non-obese women.[7,8] Cumulative pregnancy rates with Norplant differed significantly with body weight at 5 and 7 years of use.[9] Women weighing 80 kg or more had higher failure rates. The levonorgestrel-only implant (like progestogen-only pills containing norethisterone, levonorgestrel or etynodiol diacetate) does not inhibit ovulation in all women particularly in the first year of use. A multinational study identified few pregnancies with Norplant but those recorded occurred in women weighing more than 70 kg.[10] Data were extrapolated from these studies to a potential effect of weight on efficacy of progestogen-only pills.

The CEU recommends that women who are taking progestogen-only pills (containing levonorgestrel, norethisterone or etynodiol diacetate) who weigh more than 70 kg should be advised to take two pills together every day. Women should be informed that use of two progestogen-only pills in this way is outside the terms of the product licence.[5]

QUESTION

Should women weighing more than 70 kg who use the desogestrel-only pill be advised to take two pills a day to maintain contraceptive efficacy?

POPULATION: Women over 70 kg in weight who use the desogestrel-only pill.

INTERVENTION: Two pills a day.

OUTCOME: Contraceptive efficacy.

ANSWER

The desogestrel-only pill is more effective at inhibiting ovulation than progestogen-only pills containing levonorgestrel.[11] The desogestrel-only pill inhibits ovulation in 97% of cycles (compared with 60% of cycles with the levonorgestrel-only pill).[11] If women weighing more than 70 kg are using a desogestrel-only pill, no increase in dose is required.

The CEU recommends that, because ovulation is so reliably inhibited with the desogestrel-only pill, women should be advised to take only one a day regardless of their weight.

QUESTION

For women weighing over 70 kg who are 6 weeks postpartum and breastfeeding, are progestogen-only contraceptives, particularly the progestogen-only pill, effective?

POPULATION: Women over 70 kg in weight who are 6 weeks postpartum and breastfeeding.

INTERVENTION: Progestogen-only contraceptives, particularly the progestogen-only pill.

OUTCOME: Efficacy.

ANSWER

The *WHO Medical Eligibility Criteria* recommends that progestogen-only contraception (pills, injectables or implants) can be used without restriction from 6 weeks postpartum by women who are breastfeeding (WHO category 1). Evidence to support the use of two progestogen-only pills per day by women weighing more than 70 kg is indirect and based on women using levonorgestrel-only implant and on non-breastfeeding women.

Studies have not supported a detrimental effect on breast milk or infant growth associated with progestogen-only pill use at less than 6 weeks postpartum.[12] The CEU (and the UK *Medical Eligibility Criteria*) recommends that a progestogen-only pill can be started before 6 weeks postpartum (from day 21) in breastfeeding women.

Breastfeeding itself can inhibit ovulation and reduce fertility. Lactational amenorrhoea can be relied upon as an effective contraceptive (preventing 98% of pregnancies) if women are fully, or nearly fully, breastfeeding, less than 6 months postpartum and amenorrhoeic.[12,13] If breastfeeding is reduced (particularly cessation of night feeds), if menstruation returns or the woman is more than 6 months postpartum, the contraceptive efficacy of lactational amenorrhoea is reduced and an alternative contraceptive method should be used.

The CEU recommends that breastfeeding women weighing more than 70 kg can use a progestogen-only pill. As breastfeeding itself may reduce fertility, and in order to limit the amount of hormone in breast milk, only one progestogen-only pill a day is advised even when women weigh more than 70 kg. This dose can be reviewed on an individual basis when the frequency of breastfeeding reduces, when menstruation recurs, or when the mother is 6 months postpartum.

QUESTION

For women aged 50 years, can the progestogen-only pill be continued?

POPULATION: Women aged 50 years.
INTERVENTION: Progestogen-only pills.
OUTCOME: Efficacy and safety.

ANSWER

Fertility declines with increasing age but it is generally accepted that women require contraception until: 1 year after the last menstrual period if this occurs over the age of 50 years or 2 years after the last menstrual period if this occurs under the age of 50 years.[5] Women should be given information on all contraceptive methods to allow them to make an informed decision on use.

Decisions on which contraceptive to use and when to stop for women in this age group can be difficult (Figure 1).[4] For women using a progestogen-only pill, amenorrhoea is unreliable for diagnosing the menopause.

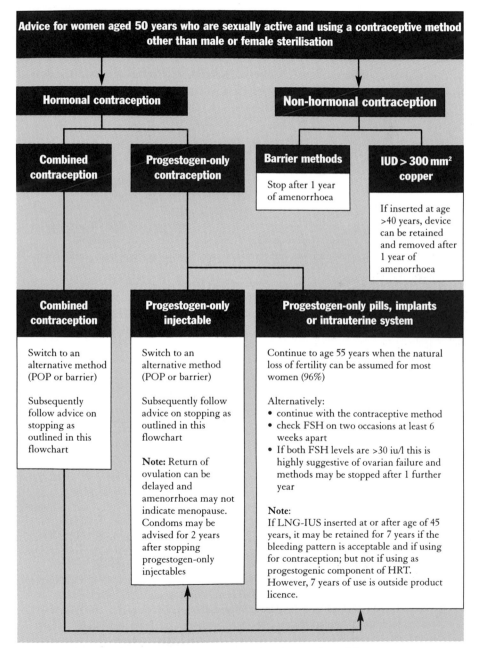

Figure 1. Advice for women aged 50 years on stopping contraception[6]

If a woman wishes, she can continue the progestogen-only pill until the age of 55 years then stop all contraception, as the vast majority of women will then be postmenopausal. Alternatively, the progestogen-only pill can be discontinued at 50 years and a barrier method used to allow the assessment of menstrual bleeding pattern. Another option is to measure serum follicle-stimulating hormone (FSH) concentration while continuing to take the progestogen-only pill. If FSH concentration is more than 30 iu/l on two or more occasions at least 6 weeks apart, the menopause is likely. Nevertheless, contraception is advised for 1 further year (or 2 years if aged less than 50 years).

The CEU advises that women using the progestogen-only pill can continue to use this method safely until the age of 55 years, when the majority of women will be postmenopausal.[5]

References

1. World Health Organization Collaborative Study of Cardiovascular Disease and Steroid Hormone Contraception. Cardiovascular disease and use of oral and injectable progestogen-only contraceptives and combined injectable contraceptives. *Contraception* 1998;57:315–24.
2. Hussain Sabina F. Progestogen-only pills and high blood pressure: is there an association? A literature review. *Contraception* 2003;69:89–97.
3. Faculty of Family Planning and Reproductive Health Care Clinical Effectiveness Unit. Contraceptive Choices for Young People. *J Fam Plann Reprod Health Care* 2004;30:237–51.
4. Faculty of Family Planning and Reproductive Healthcare Clinical Effectiveness Unit. Contraception for Women Aged over 40 Years. *J Fam Plann Reprod Health Care* 2005;31:51–64.
5. Faculty of Family Planning and Reproductive Health Care Clinical Effectiveness Unit. The use of contraception outside the terms of the product licence. *J Fam Plann Reprod Health Care* 2005;31:225–41.
6. Vessey M, Painter R. Oral contraception and ear disease: findings in a large cohort study. *Contraception* 2001;63:61–3.
7. Sivin I. International experience with Norplant and Norplant-2 contraception. *Stud Fam Plann* 1988;19:81–94.
8. Koetsawang S, Ji G, Krishna U, Cuadros A, Dhall GI, Wyss R, *et al*. Microdose intravaginal levonorgestrel contraception: a multicentre clinical trial. III. The relationship between pregnancy rate and body weight. World Health Organization. Task Force on Long-Acting Systemic Agents for Fertility Regulation. *Contraception* 1990;41:143–50.
9. Sivin I, Mishell DRJ, Diaz S, Biswas A, Alvarez F, Darney P, *et al*. Prolonged effectiveness of Norplant capsule implants: a 7-year study. *Contraception* 2000;61:187–94.
10. Sivin I, Campodonico I, Kiriway O. The performance of levonorgestrel rod and Norplant contraceptive implant: a 5-year randomised study. *Hum Reprod* 1998;13:3371–8.
11. Collaborative Study Group on the Desogestrel-containing Progestogen-only Pill. A double-blind study comparing the contraceptive efficacy, acceptability and safety of two progestogen-only pills containing desogestrel 75 μg/day or levonorgestrel 30 μg/day. *Eur J Contracept Reprod Health Care* 1998;3:169–78.

12. Faculty of Family Planning and Reproductive Health Care Clinical Effectiveness Unit. Contraceptive choices for breastfeeding women. *J Fam Plann Reprod Health Care* 2004;30:181–9.
13. Knight J, Pyper C. Postnatal contraception: what are the choices? *Nurs Pract* 2002;(May):23–5.

Elective surgery

QUESTION

Should women using progestogen-only contraception undergoing elective surgery be advised to stop these methods preoperatively to reduce the risk of VTE?

POPULATION: Women using progestogen-only contraception.
INTERVENTION: Elective surgery.
OUTCOME: Risk of VTE.

ANSWER

The Scottish Intercollegiate Guidelines Network developed recommendations on the prophylaxis of VTE,[1] based on a systematic review of the literature. They recommend that women using combined oral contraception, higher-dose progestogens, HRT or raloxifene, who are undergoing surgery, should be counselled regarding hormone use preoperatively. Oral norethisterone (used in the management of menorrhagia) was shown to increase risk of VTE. The WHO Collaborative Study found that progestogen-only pills and injectables are not associated with an increased risk of VTE.[2]

The *WHO Medical Eligibility Criteria* recommends that there is no need to discontinue progestogen-only contraception for women undergoing major surgery with **or** without immobilisation. The benefits of using progestogen-only contraception (pills, injectables, implants or the levonorgestrel-releasing intrauterine system) by women undergoing major surgery with immobilisation generally outweigh any risks (WHO category 2). For major surgery without immobilisation, use is unrestricted (WHO category 1).

The CEU recommends that women undergoing major surgery, even with immobilisation, may continue using progestogen-only contraception (pills, injectables, implants or LNG-IUS).

QUESTION

Should women using the desogestrel-only pill be advised to discontinue this prior to elective orthopaedic surgery to reduce the risk of thromboembolism?

POPULATION:	**Women using the desogestrel-only pill.**
INTERVENTION:	**Discontinuation of the desogestrel-only pill prior to elective orthopaedic surgery.**
OUTCOME:	**Reduction in the risk of thromboembolism.**

ANSWER

The WHO Collaborative Study found that progestogen-only pills and injectables are not associated with an increased risk of VTE.[2] The desogestrel-only pill was not included in this study. Other studies showed no alteration in thrombogenic factors associated with desogestrel-only pill use.[3]

The *WHO Medical Eligibility Criteria* recommends that there is no need for women undergoing major surgery with immobilisation to discontinue progestogen-only pills; the benefits of using progestogen-only pills by women undergoing major surgery with immobilisation generally outweigh any risks (WHO category 2).

The CEU supports the WHO recommendations that there is no need to stop the desogestrel-only pill prior to orthopaedic surgery.

References

1. Scottish Intercollegiate Guidelines Network. *Prophylaxis of Venous Thromboembolism*. SIGN Publication No. 62. Edinburgh: SIGN; 2003.
2. Hussain Sabina F. Progestogen only pills and high blood pressure: is there an association? A literature review. *Contraception* 2003;69:89–97.
3. Winkler UH, Howie H, Buhler K, Korver T, Geurts TBP, Coelingh Bennink H. A randomized controlled double-blind study of the effects on haemostasis of two progestogen-only pills containing 75 microgram desogestrel or 30 micrograms levonorgestrel. *Contraception* 1998;57:385–92.

Bone mineral density

QUESTION

In women with osteoporosis requesting contraception, does the desogestrel-only pill affect bone mineral density?

POPULATION: Women with osteoporosis.

INTERVENTION: Desogestrel-only pill.

OUTCOME: Effect on bone mass density.

ANSWER

The desogestrel-only pill inhibits ovulation in 97% of cycles.[1] Nevertheless, serum concentrations of estrogen are not reduced. Currently, there is no evidence to suggest that the desogestrel-only pill has any effect on bone mineral density.

The CEU recommends that women with reduced bone mineral density or osteoporosis can safely use the desogestrel-only pill.

Reference

1.   Rice CF, Killick SR, Dieben T, Coelingh Bennink H. A comparison of the inhibition of ovulation achieved by desogestrel 75 µg and levonorgestrel 30 µg daily. *Hum Reprod* 1999;14:982–5.

Family history of breast cancer

QUESTION

Do women who have a family history of breast cancer and use the progestogen-only pill have an increased risk of breast cancer?

POPULATION: Women with a family history of breast cancer.

INTERVENTION: The progestogen-only pill.

OUTCOME: Risk of breast cancer.

ANSWER

A genetic contribution to breast cancer risk is suggested by the finding of an increased incidence of disease in women with a family history of breast cancer and by the observation of rare families in which multiple family members are affected with breast cancer. Nevertheless, most cases of breast cancer are sporadic.[1]

Studies investigating the effects of progestogen-only pills on risk of breast cancer do not include women using the newest desogestrel-only pill. A national, population-based, case–control study investigated the influence of the progestogen-only pill on women's risk of breast cancer. The relative risk of breast cancer in women who had ever used the progestogen-only pill did not appear to be increased and was estimated to be 1.1 (95% CI 0.73–1.5).[2] The UK National Case–Control Study found that use of a progestogen-only pill did not appear to be associated with an increased risk of breast cancer.[3]

The *WHO Medical Eligibility Criteria* recommends that women with a family history of breast cancer may have unrestricted use of the progestogen-only pill (WHO category 1).

The CEU advises that women with a family history of breast cancer are not at any further increased risk with progestogen-only pill use.

References

1. National Cancer Institute. *Genetics of Breast and Ovarian Cancer* (Physician Data Query). 2006 [www.cancer.gov/cancertopics/pdq/genetics/breast-and-ovarian/healthprofessional].
2. Skegg DCG, Paul C, Spears GF, Wiliams SM. Progestogen-only oral contraceptives and risk of breast cancer in New Zealand. *Cancer Causes Control* 1996;7:513–19.
3. UK National Case–Control Study Group. Oral contraceptive use and breast cancer risk in young women. *Lancet* 1989;i:973–82.

Risks and sequelae

QUESTION

Are women using progestogen-only contraception at increased risk of breast cancer?

POPULATION:	Women of reproductive age.
INTERVENTION:	Progestogen-only contraception.
OUTCOME:	Risk of breast cancer.

ANSWER

Many factors influence the risk of developing breast cancer:

● increasing age

● family history (especially a first-degree relative under the age of 50 years)

● specific genetic tendency (*BRCA1* gene mutations)

- reproductive factors (such as early menarche, late menopause, late age at first childbirth)

- long-term postmenopausal estrogen and progestogen replacement therapy

- lifestyle factors (such as obesity, weight gain after the menopause, alcohol consumption, and physical inactivity)

- radiation therapy to the chest (especially in childhood)

- a personal history of breast cancer

- specific breast changes (on biopsy).[1]

Worldwide, the use of progestogen-only contraception is low and therefore data on breast cancer risk associated with progestogen-only contraception are limited but nevertheless reassuring. A national, population-based, case–control study investigated the influence of the progestogen-only pill on a woman's risk of breast cancer. The relative risk of breast cancer in women who had ever used the progestogen-only pill did not appear to be increased and was estimated to be 1.1 (95% CI 0.73–1.5).[2] The UK National Case–Control Study found that use of the progestogen-only pill did not appear to be associated with an increased risk of breast cancer.[3]

The CEU suggests that, in view of the small number of subjects studied worldwide, it is not possible, with confidence, to exclude a small association between breast cancer risk and use of progestogen-only contraception. However, the available data do not support an increased risk of breast cancer associated with use of progestogen-only contraception.

QUESTION

For women with a history of functional ovarian cysts while using the progestogen-only pill, what is the risk of developing further ovarian cysts with other progestogen-only methods of contraception?

POPULATION: Women with a past history of functional ovarian cysts while using the progestogen-only pill.

INTERVENTION: Progestogen-only methods of contraception.

OUTCOME: Risk of ovarian cysts; complications of ovarian cysts.

ANSWER

Functional ovarian cysts are common in women of reproductive age. Evidence on the incidence of ovarian cysts with progestogen-only contraception is limited. One study suggested an increased risk of functional ovarian cysts in women using progestogen-only pills.[4] Other studies found no difference in the incidence of ovarian cysts in women using the LNG-IUS when compared with women using a copper IUD.[5] Contraceptive methods which inhibit ovulation (such as the combined oral contraceptive pill) may reduce the incidence of ovarian cyst formation.[6,7]

The *WHO Medical Eligibility Criteria* recommends that women with current or past history of benign ovarian tumours can use progestogen-only methods of contraception without restriction (WHO category 1).

The CEU suggests that women with a history of ovarian cysts might particularly consider contraceptive methods that inhibit ovulation, such as combined oral contraception. However, any method of contraception (hormonal or non-hormonal) can be used.

QUESTION

For women using the desogestrel-only pill, what is the incidence of ovarian cysts compared with other progestogen-only pills?

POPULATION: Women using the desogestrel-only pill.
INTERVENTION: Other progestogen-only pills.
OUTCOME: Incidence of ovarian cysts.

ANSWER

Women using progestogen-only pills are at increased risk of developing functional ovarian cysts.[4] Ovarian cysts may present with symptoms such as pain, but are often asymptomatic.

The *WHO Medical Eligibility Criteria* recommends that women with benign ovarian cysts or tumours have no restriction on the use of progestogen-only pills (WHO category 1).

The desogestrel-only pill is more effective at inhibiting ovulation than a levonorgestrel-only pill (97% of cycles anovulatory compared with 60%).[8] The Summary of Product Characteristics for the desogestrel-only pill states that ovarian cysts are uncommon in desogestrel-only pill users (less than 1/1000). The Summaries of Product Characteristics for other progestogen-only pills (containing norethisterone, levonorgestrel or etynodiol diacetate) do not give any indication of the incidence of ovarian cysts while using any of these methods.

Since ovulation is more consistently inhibited with the desogestrel-only pill compared with the levonorgestrel-only pill, the incidence of functional ovarian cysts is likely to be reduced. Nevertheless, the CEU was unable to find any data to support this.

References

1. National Cancer Institute. *Genetics of Breast and Ovarian Cancer* (Physician Data Query). 2006 [www.cancer.gov/cancertopics/pdq/genetics/breast-and-ovarian/healthprofessional].
2. Skegg DCG, Paul C, Spears GF, Wiliams SM. Progestogen-only oral contraceptives and risk of breast cancer in New Zealand. *Cancer Causes Control* 1996;7:513–19.
3. UK National Case–Control Study Group. Oral Contraceptive use and Breast Cancer risk in Young Women. *Lancet* 1989;i:973–82.
4. Tayob Y, Adams J, Jacobs HS, Guillebaud J. Ultrasound demonstration of increased frequency of functional ovarian cysts in women using progestogen-only contraception. *Br J Obstet Gynaecol* 1985;92:1003–9.
5. Robinson GE, Bounds W, Kubba AA, Adams J, Guillebaud J. Functional ovarian cysts associated with the levonorgestrel releasing intrauterine device. *Br J Fam Plann* 1989;14:131–2.
6. Faculty of Family Planning and Reproductive Health Care Clinical Effectiveness Unit. First prescription of combined oral contraception. *J Fam Plann Reprod Health Care* 2003;29:209–22.
7. Holt VL, Daling JR, McKnight B, Moore D, Stergachis A, Weiss NS. Functional ovarian cysts in relation to the use of monophasic and triphasic oral contraceptives. *Obstet Gynecol* 1992;79:529–33.
8. Rice CF, Killick S.R., Dieben T, Coelingh Bennink H. A comparison of the inhibition of ovulation achieved by desogestrel 75 μg and levonorgestrel 30 μg daily. *Hum Reprod* 1999;14:982–5.

Management of adverse effects

QUESTION

Can women with intermenstrual bleeding which has been controlled by using two progestogen-only pills a day continue to use this regimen indefinitely?

POPULATION: Women with intermenstrual bleeding.

INTERVENTION: Continued use of two progestogen-only pills daily.

OUTCOME: Safety of this regimen.

ANSWER

Evidence for increasing the daily pill-taking regimen of progestogen-only pills relates to the use of two pills daily by women weighing more than 70 kg to maintain efficacy. No evidence was identified on the efficacy of two progestogen-only pills daily to control intermenstrual bleeding. Few studies have compared bleeding patterns associated with different progestogen-only pills. Nevertheless, progestogen-only pill users with unscheduled bleeding may choose to try a pill with a different progestogen to see if this improves the bleeding pattern.

Unscheduled bleeding is common in women using progestogen-only pills generally:

● 20% of women are anovulatory and amenorrhoeic

● 40% ovulate regularly and have a regular bleed

● 40% fluctuate between anovulatory and ovulatory cycles with erratic bleeding.

A randomised trial found that bleeding associated with desogestrel-only pill use was comparable to bleeding with the levonorgestrel-only pill despite more consistent anovulation.[1]

The WHO *Selected Practice Recommendations* and the UK version provide guidance on the management of women with abnormal bleeding while using a progestogen-only pill. Specific causes of abnormal bleeding should be considered and investigated when appropriate (such as poor pill taking, pregnancy, infection, particularly STIs or gynaecological malignancy).

The CEU does not support the routine use of two progestogen-only pills a day to improve bleeding patterns. Nevertheless, if a woman has already been given this increased dose and her bleeding has improved, this regimen may be continued. She should be counselled about the lack of evidence and that this use is outside the terms of the product licence.

QUESTION

Can women with breakthrough bleeding controlled by use of two desogestrel-only pills per day, safely continue this regimen?

POPULATION: Women with breakthrough bleeding.
INTERVENTION: Two desogestrel-only pills daily.
OUTCOME: Safety.

ANSWER

Unscheduled bleeding is common in progestogen-only pill users. A randomised controlled trial showed that abnormal bleeding was more common with a desogestrel-only pill than with a levonorgestrel-only pill.[1] After 11–13 months of pill use, almost 50% of women using a desogestrel-only pill had infrequent bleeding or amenorrhoea compared with 10% of the levonorgestrel group. It is unlikely, therefore, that women who experience unacceptable bleeding patterns with progestogen-only pills containing norethisterone, levonorgestrel or etynodiol diacetate would have better bleeding patterns with a desogestrel-only pill.

The WHO *Selected Practice Recommendations* and the UK version provide guidance on the management of women with abnormal bleeding while using progestogen-only pills. Specific causes of abnormal bleeding should be considered and investigated when appropriate (such as poor pill taking, pregnancy, infection, particularly STIs or gynaecological malignancy).

The CEU does not support the use of two desogestrel-only pills daily to improve bleeding patterns. Nevertheless, if a woman has already been given this increased regimen and her bleeding has improved, this may be continued after counselling about the lack of evidence and that this use is outside the terms of the product licence.

QUESTION

For women using progestogen-only pills who wish to avoid bleeding for one cycle, is giving norethisterone 5 mg/day effective at stopping the menstrual bleed?

POPULATION: Women using the progestogen-only pill who wish to avoid their menstrual bleed for one menstrual cycle.

INTERVENTION: Norethisterone 5 mg/day.

OUTCOME: Efficacy.

ANSWER

A randomised, double-blind trial showed that norethisterone (10 mg/day or 5 mg/day) started 3 days before the expected menstrual date and continued for 10 days is 90% or 43.3% effective respectively in delaying menstruation.[2]

The Summary of Product Characteristics for oral norethisterone supports its use to postpone menstruation. Starting 3 days before the expected onset of menstruation, 5 mg should be taken three times a day. A normal period should occur 2–3 days after stopping the norethisterone.

No data were identified on the use of norethisterone to postpone bleeding associated with progestogen-only pills. Bleeding associated with progestogen-only pills is caused by different mechanisms. Irregular bleeding can result from anovulatory and ovulatory cycles and regular bleeding can be due to the woman having regular ovulatory cycles.

No studies were identified which investigated if the use of norethisterone in women using a progestogen–only pill would have any effect on contraceptive efficacy.

The CEU recommends that, for women using a progestogen-only pill who wish to delay a bleed, oral norethisterone can be considered. The prevention or delay in bleeding cannot be guaranteed and this use is outside the terms of the product licence for norethisterone.

References
1. Collaborative Study Group on the Desogestrel-containing Progestogen-only Pill. A double-blind study comparing the contraceptive efficacy, acceptability and safety of two progestogen-only pills containing desogestrel 75 μg/day or levonorgestrel 30 μg/day. *Eur J Contracept Reprod Health Care* 1998;3:169–78.
2. Kiriwat O, Treetampinich C, Ruangvutilert P. Efficacy of norethisterone starting 3 days before expected menstrual date for postponement of menstruation. *Acta Obstet Gynecol Scand* 1997;76 Suppl 167(5):55.

Efficacy

QUESTION

For women attending for contraception who wish to use the progestogen-only pill, what evidence is available on its contraceptive efficacy?

POPULATION: Women requiring contraception.
INTERVENTION: Progestogen-only pill.
OUTCOME: Efficacy.

ANSWER

Even in controlled clinical trials, it is difficult to measure the true efficacy of hormonal contraception.[1] A true value is only possible if a study is well designed, the data are collected accurately, the study population will closely resemble women in the general population, pregnancies are determined and recorded accurately, and all participants use the method correctly and consistently during the trial. Trials assess 'method failure' but 'user failure' is also important in determining contraceptive efficacy. Factors such as age, weight and interacting medication can all influence contraceptive efficacy.

A critical review of the literature found a range of Pearl Indices for progestogen-only pills (1.3/100 to 2.7/100 woman years).[2] Clinical experience with progestogen-only pills has been investigated in a retrospective case note review of 358 women (18 125 woman-months of use).[3] The Pearl Index was 0.2/1000 woman years (three pregnancies occurred). A randomised, double-blind study compared the contraceptive efficacy, acceptability and safety of two progestogen-only pills (75 micrograms desogestrel-only pill and 30 micrograms levonorgestrel-only pill).[4] The Pearl Indices were 0.41/100 women-years for desogestrel-only pill users (95% CI 0.085–1.204) and 1.55/100 woman years for levonorgestrel-only pill users (95% CI 0.422–3.96). However, this study was under-powered to compare efficacy reliably.

Progestogen-only pills appear to have lower failure rates in older women. A large cohort study found that the Pearl Index for progestogen-only pills was 3.36/100 woman-years at age 25–29 years and 0.28/100 women-years at age 40–44 years.[5]

Evidence that body weight more than 70 kg is associated with reduced efficacy of progestogen-only pills is indirect. A cohort study investigated the relationship between oral contraceptive failures and body weight.[5] When failure rates of progestogen-only pills were adjusted for age alone and for age and parity in relation to body weight, height and BMI, no associations were found. This study may not have had sufficient power to prove or disprove the hypothesis that an increase in body weight correlates with increased contraceptive failure in women using a progestogen-only pill.[5] It has been generally accepted in the UK that efficacy is decreased in women weighing more than 70 kg and that such women should be advised to take two progestogen-only pills per day.[6]

The concurrent use of liver enzyme-inducing drugs can reduce the efficacy of progestogen-only pills.[7] Use of broad-spectrum, non-liver-enzyme-inducing antibiotics does not affect contraceptive efficacy of progestogen-only pills.[7]

The CEU suggests that, in general, if used consistently and correctly, progestogen-only pills can prevent more than 99% of pregnancies. This is supported by patient information from the fpa (Family Planning Association).

QUESTION

For women who use the desogestrel-only pill and who report physical symptoms coinciding with day 14, is inhibition of ovulation guaranteed?

POPULATION:	Women who use the desogestrel-only pill and who report physical symptoms coinciding with day 14.
INTERVENTION:	Continuation of the desogestrel-only pill.
OUTCOME:	Inhibition of ovulation.

ANSWER

The desogestrel-only pill works primarily by inhibition of ovulation. However, not all cycles are anovulatory and cervical mucus provides a barrier to prevent sperm penetrating the upper reproductive tract. The effects of desogestrel and levonorgestrel on the inhibition of ovulation after 7 and 12 months of use were observed over a total of 59 cycles (desogestrel-only pill) and 57 cycles (levonorgestrel-only pill).[8] Ovulation was inhibited with desogestrel in 58 of the 59 cycles studied (98.3%). In the levonorgestrel group, ovulation was inhibited in 41 cycles of the 57 cycles studied (71.9%). In this study, inhibition of ovulation was better than expected for progestogen-only pills containing levonorgestrel.

The CEU concludes that, on theoretical grounds, the desogestrel-only pill is expected to be more effective at inhibition of ovulation than other progestogen-only pills. Clinicians cannot guarantee women that ovulation will always be prevented with the desogestrel-only pill.

QUESTION

For a woman using a progestogen-only pill who wishes to discontinue contraception but does not wish to be pregnant, is additional contraceptive protection advised in the week before stopping?

POPULATION:	Women stopping the progestogen-only pill.
INTERVENTION:	Additional contraceptive protection in the week before stopping.
OUTCOME:	Pregnancy risk.

ANSWER

All progestogen-only pills work by thickening cervical mucus so that it becomes more difficult for sperm to penetrate into the upper reproductive tract. Sperm can survive for up to 6 hours in the acidic environment of the vagina if they are unable to gain access to the upper reproductive tract. The contraceptive effect on cervical mucus is lost 27 hours after taking the last progestogen-only pill. For desogestrel-only pill users, ovulation is inhibited in 97% of cycles and contraceptive protection may be reduced if more than 36 hours have elapsed since taking the last pill.

The CEU advises that if a woman wants to stop her progestogen-only pill but does not wish to be pregnant, contraceptive protection would continue until the last pill has been taken. She should be informed that contraceptive protection will be lost 3 hours after her next pill would have been due (norethisterone, levonorgestrel or etynodiol diacetate containing progestogen-only pills) or 12 hours after her next pill would have been due (desogestrel-only pill). Sex after this time will be 'unprotected' and may result in pregnancy. There is no evidence to support using barrier contraception or abstinence in the week prior to stopping a progestogen-only pill.

References

1. Burkman RT. Clinical Pearls: factors affecting reported contraceptive efficacy rates in clinical studies. *Int J Fertil Womens Med* 2002;47:153–61.
2. Trussell J, Kost K. Contraceptive failure in the United States: a critical review of the literature. *Stud Fam Plann* 1987;18:237–83.
3. Broome M, Fotherby K. Clinical experience with the progestogen-only pill. *Contraception* 1990;42:489–95.
4. Collaborative Study Group on the Desogestrel-containing Progestogen-only Pill. A double-blind study comparing the contraceptive efficacy, acceptability and safety of two progestogen-only pills containing desogestrel 75 μg/day or levonorgestrel 30 μg/day. *Eur J Contracept Reprod Health Care* 1998;3:169–78.
5. Vessey M, Painter R. Oral contraception and ear disease: findings in a large cohort study. *Contraception* 2001;63:61–3.
6. Faculty of Family Planning and Reproductive Health Care Clinical Effectiveness Unit. The use of contraception outside the terms of the product licence. *J Fam Plann Reprod Health Care* 2005;31:225–41.
7. Faculty of Family Planning and Reproductive Health Care Clinical Effectiveness Unit. Drug Interactions with Hormonal Contraception. *J Fam Plann Reprod Health Care* 2005;31:139–50.
8. Rice CF, Killick S.R., Dieben T, Coelingh Bennink H. A comparison of the inhibition of ovulation achieved by desogestrel 75 μg and levonorgestrel 30 μg daily. *Hum Reprod* 1999;14:982–5.

Missed pills and potential failures

QUESTION

For women using a progestogen-only pill containing norethisterone, levonorgestrel or etynodiol diacetate who miss a pill by more than 3 hours, for how long should they be advised to use additional contraceptive protection?

POPULATION: Women who are using a progestogen-only pill containing norethisterone, levonorgestrel or etynodiol diacetate who miss a pill by more than 3 hours.

INTERVENTION: Additional contraceptive protection.

OUTCOME: Contraceptive efficacy restored.

ANSWER

Progestogen-only pills that containing norethisterone, levonorgestrel and etynodiol diacetate work by thickening cervical mucus to inhibit sperm penetration into the upper reproductive tract (and for some women they also work by inhibiting ovulation). Within 4 hours of taking a progestogen-only pill there is evidence of thickening of cervical mucus. This effect on cervical mucus wears off 27 hours after taking the last progestogen-only pill.

Women using progestogen-only pills are advised to take their pill at the same time every day. If a pill is taken more than 27 hours since the last pill (i.e. more than 3 hours late) contraceptive protection is potentially lost. In this situation, women are advised to use additional contraceptive protection (such as condoms) or abstain from sex for 48 hours or until two consecutive pills have been correctly taken. This advice is outside the terms of the product licence for most progestogen-only pills as the Summaries of Product Characteristics advise that additional contraception should be used for 7–14 days.

The WHO *Selected Practice Recommendations* and the UK version recommend that if a women has missed one or more progestogen-only pills by more than 3 hours she should:

- take a pill as soon as possible
- continue taking the pills as usual (one each day)
- abstain from sex or use additional contraceptive protection (such as condoms) for the next 2 days.

QUESTION

For women taking the progestogen-only pill who have sexual intercourse but miss the next day's pill, is emergency contraception indicated to reduce the risk of pregnancy?

POPULATION: Women taking the progestogen-only pill who have sexual intercourse but miss the next day's pill.

INTERVENTION: Emergency contraception.

OUTCOME: Risk of pregnancy.

ANSWER

CEU guidance on emergency contraception[1] advises that emergency contraception is indicated if one or more progestogen-only pills have been missed (or been taken more than 3 hours late) and unprotected sex has occurred in the following 2 days. The progestogen-only pill should be continued with additional barrier methods (such as condoms) or abstinence until pills have been taken correctly on 2 consecutive days. After this, thickened cervical mucus can reliably prevent sperm penetration.

The desogestrel-only pill has been shown in a randomised controlled trial to inhibit ovulation in 97% of cycles.[2] The Summary of Product Characteristics for the desogestrel-only pill allows women to be up to 12 hours late taking their next pill before contraceptive protection may be reduced.

The CEU advises that, theoretically, the risk of pregnancy is low for a woman who takes her usual progestogen-only pill on time, has sexual intercourse that day then on the next day omits her pill (or is late taking it). This is because cervical mucus hostility was not reduced until **after** she had sex. Sperm should not have been able to gain access to the upper reproductive tract. She should be advised to use condoms or abstain for the next 2 days. If she has unprotected sex or condom failure in these next 2 days, however, emergency contraception is indicated. This is because sperm may have been able to gain access to the upper reproductive tract because the contraceptive thickening of cervical mucus had not yet been restored.

QUESTION

For women using the desogestrel-only pill, when is emergency contraception indicated for missed pills? (Five similar enquiries.)

POPULATION:	**Women taking the desogestrel-only pill.**
INTERVENTION:	**Emergency contraception if pills are missed.**
OUTCOME:	**Efficacy.**

ANSWER

A randomised, double-blind trial showed that a 75-microgram desogestrel-only pill was sufficient to inhibit ovulation in 97% of cycles.[2] Inhibition of ovulation is the primary mode of action of the desogestrel-only pill. Nevertheless, in 3% of cycles women rely on thickened cervical mucus to prevent sperm penetration into the upper reproductive tract.

The Summary of Product Characteristics suggests that if a desogestrel-only pill is taken more than 36 hours since the last pill (that is, more than 12 hours late) condoms are required for 7 days, as contraceptive efficacy may have been reduced. The CEU however, upholds recommendations from the WHO *Selected Practice Recommendations* and the UK version that additional contraceptive protection (such as condoms) or abstinence is required for only 2 days (or until two consecutive pills have been taken correctly). Advice on progestogen-only pills from the fpa supports these recommendations. After taking two consecutive desogestrel-only pills, thickened cervical mucus is restored. If unprotected sex (or failed barrier method) occurs **before** two consecutive pills have been taken, emergency contraception is indicated.[1]

In summary, the CEU recommends that the desogestrel-only pill should be taken at the same time every day. If a pill is taken more than 12 hours late, additional contraceptive protection (such as condoms) or abstinence is advised for the next 2 days. If unprotected sex occurs in the 2 days before consecutive pills have been taken, emergency contraception may be indicated.

References

1. Rice CF, Killick S.R., Dieben T, Coelingh Bennink H. A comparison of the inhibition of ovulation achieved by desogestrel 75ug and levonorgestrel 30 μg daily. *Hum Reprod* 1999;14:982–5.
2. Faculty of Family Planning and Reproductive Health Care Clinical Effectiveness Unit. Emergency contraception. *J Fam Plann Reprod Health Care* 2003;29:9–16.

Concurrent use of topical vaginal estrogens or HRT

QUESTION

In women aged 50 years who are using the progestogen-only pill, will the use of estrogen-containing vaginal cream to treat vaginal dryness reduce contraceptive efficacy? (Two similar enquiries.)

POPULATION: Women 50 years old using a progestogen-only pill.

INTERVENTION: Use of an estrogen-containing vaginal cream.

OUTCOME: Reduced contraceptive efficacy.

ANSWER

Vaginal estrogens can improve the symptoms of vaginal atrophy and dryness. Systemic absorption of vaginal estrogen is low.[1] Changes in 'ferning' (crystallisation) and *spinnbarkeit* (stretchiness) of cervical mucus have been noted but their clinical significance has not been determined. No studies were identified which investigated if the contraceptive efficacy of progestogen-only pills is reduced by concurrent use of a vaginal estrogen.

Women using a progestogen-only pill who are amenorrhoeic are likely to be anovulatory. It is unlikely that systemic absorption of estrogen from vaginal estrogen would induce ovulation. Progestogen-only pills have been found to inhibit ovulation in 50–60% of women.[2,3] If women using a progestogen-only pill continue to bleed, then ovulation and/or anovulation may be occurring. Contraceptive protection in these women is due to cervical mucus thickening. No direct evidence was identified to suggest that vaginal estrogen could counteract this contraceptive effect of progestogen on cervical mucus. Non-hormonal treatments for vaginal dryness (such as the bioadhesive Replens) may be considered as an alternative to vaginal estrogens in women using a pro-gestogen-only pill.[4]

The CEU could find no evidence to suggest that vaginal estrogen might reduce the contraceptive efficacy of progestogen-only pills. If concerned, an alternative (such as Replens) could be considered, particularly if the bleeding pattern suggests that thickened cervical mucus alone is providing contraceptive protection.

QUESTION

For women using the desogestrel-only pill, will the use of a vaginal estrogen (Vagifem®, Novo Nordisk) for vaginal dryness necessitate the addition of another progestogen to protect the endometrium from hyperplasia?

POPULATION: Women using a desogestrel-only pill.

INTERVENTION: Use of vaginal estrogen (Vagifem®).

OUTCOME: Endometrial hyperplasia or malignancy.

ANSWER

Vaginal estrogens improve the symptoms of vaginal atrophy and dryness. The Summary of Product Characteristics for Vagifem suggests that it can be used to treat vaginitis due to estrogen deficiency. Vagifem can be used for 3 months without the need for endometrial protection. It should be discontinued and symptoms reassessed after 3 months use.

Women using progestogen-only pills are not hypoestrogenic as such. The CEU was unable to find any direct evidence on the efficacy of vaginal estrogens in women using hormonal contraception. There is some systemic absorption of estrogen with vaginal preparations (Vagifem). For women using the desogestrel-only pill, 97% of cycles are anovulatory and it is unlikely that systemic absorption of estrogen would induce ovulation. No evidence was identified on the use of the desogestrel-only pill to provide protection against endometrial hyperplasia with Vagifem use. However, such protection does not appear to be required for short-term use. If treatment of vaginal dryness is required for longer, other treatments, such as Replens, may be considered.

QUESTION

For women using a progestogen-only pill, will the use of HRT for vasomotor symptoms reduce contraceptive efficacy?

POPULATION: Women using a progestogen-only pill.

INTERVENTION: Use of HRT.

OUTCOME: Reduction in contraceptive efficacy.

ANSWER

No studies were identified which investigated if the efficacy of a progestogen-only pill is reduced by the use of oral HRT. Progestogen-only pills containing levonorgestrel inhibit ovulation in up to 60% of women.[3] Women who are anovulatory are usually amenorrhoeic; therefore, bleeding patterns do not indicate the natural menopause in women using progestogen-only pills. Women using progestogen-only pills can present with vasomotor symptoms as a result of a natural decline in endogenous estrogen as they approach the menopause. HRT can be given to relieve vasomotor symptoms. The addition of a sequential HRT is likely to lead to the recurrence of a withdrawal bleed, which may be unacceptable to some women. Continuous combined HRT is traditionally used only in women over the age of 54 years, as abnormal bleeding can be a problem if used during the perimenopause. However, women who are amenorrhoeic while using a progestogen-only pill can use continuous combined HRT.[5]

If women continue to bleed while using a progestogen-only pill, they are likely to be ovulating. Thickened cervical mucus provides contraceptive efficacy. No studies were identified which have investigated whether vaginal estrogens or oral HRT counteract this contraceptive effect on cervical mucus.

References

1. Gabrielsson J, Wallenbeck I, Birgerson L. Pharmacokinetic data on estradiol in light of the estring concept. *Acta Obstet Gynecol Scand* 1996;163:26–31.
2. McCann MF, Potter LS. Progestin-only oral contraception: a comprehensive review. *Contraception* 1994;50:S159–88.
3. Rice CF, Killick SR, Dieben TOM, Coelingh Bennink H. A comparison of the inhibition of ovulation achieved by desogestrel 75 microgrammes and levonorgestrel 30 microgrammes daily. *Hum Reprod* 1999;14:982–5.
4. Nachtigall LE. Comparative study: Replens versus local estrogen in menopausal women. *Fertil Steril* 1994;61:178–80.
5. Faculty of Family Planning and Reproductive Healthcare Clinical Effectiveness Unit. Contraception for women aged over 40 Years. *J Fam Plann Reprod Health Care* 2005;31:51–64.

Progestogen-only injectable contraceptives

Most evidence on progestogen-only injectable contraceptives identified by the CEU relates to use of DMPA. Evidence regarding the less commonly used norethisterone enanthate is limited.

Patient selection

QUESTION

For women with a high BMI, is DMPA an effective method of contraception? (Two similar enquiries.)

POPULATION: Women with a high BMI.
INTERVENTION: DMPA.
OUTCOME: Efficacy and safety.

ANSWER

A person with a BMI greater than 30 kg/m² is classified as clinically obese.[1] The risk of VTE in women of reproductive age is very low but is almost doubled when BMI is greater than 30 kg/m².[2] Use of a combined oral contraceptive pill increases this risk further.[3,4] Evidence regarding use of progestogen-only contraception and risk of VTE is limited. However, the WHO Collaborative Study found no increase in the risk of VTE for women using progestogen-only pills or injectables.[5] The *WHO Medical Eligibility Criteria* recommends that for women with a BMI of 30 kg/m² or more the benefits of using DMPA generally outweigh the risks (WHO category 2).

Weight gain may be a problem for women using DMPA. A study with up to 5 years follow up found that women using DMPA gained more weight than women using a copper IUD.[6] Adolescent DMPA users gained significantly more weight than combined oral contraceptive pill users.[7] Moreover, a high baseline BMI was associated with more weight gain when using DMPA.[7]

A retrospective study found that excess weight or obesity is associated with a decreased risk of excessive bleeding with DMPA use.[8] This may potentially improve compliance and satisfaction.

The CEU found no evidence to contraindicate the use of DMPA in women with a body mass index over 30. The usual dosage regimen and injection interval should be followed.

QUESTION

For women who are 8 weeks postpartum, when is it safe to start DMPA and when is additional contraceptive protection needed?

POPULATION: **Women who are 8 weeks postpartum.**
INTERVENTION: **DMPA.**
OUTCOME: **Efficacy and safety.**

ANSWER

Recommendations for the use of DMPA postpartum depend on whether or not the woman is breastfeeding or bottle feeding.

For women who are not breastfeeding, the Summary of Product Characteristics suggests that DMPA may be commenced within 5 days postpartum. Heavy and prolonged bleeding can be a problem. The WHO *Medical Eligibility Criteria* recommend that DMPA can be used without restriction by women who are not breastfeeding and less than 21 days postpartum (WHO category 1).

The WHO *Selected Practice Recommendations* recommends that, for women who are not breastfeeding and 6 weeks or more postpartum, the first injection of DMPA can be given up to and including day 5 after the start of menstrual bleeding. No additional contraceptive protection is needed. If it is reasonably certain she is not pregnant, a woman can have the first injection at any other time but she will need to abstain from sexual intercourse or use additional contraceptive protection, such as condoms, for the next 7 days.

For women who are breastfeeding, the Summary of Product Characteristics suggests that DMPA should not be given until at least 6 weeks postpartum. The WHO *Medical Eligibility Criteria* recommends that, for women who are breastfeeding and less than 6 weeks postpartum, the risks associated with DMPA generally outweigh the benefits (WHO category 3). When the mother is more than 6 weeks postpartum, the use of DMPA is unrestricted (WHO category 1). The WHO and UK *Selected Practice Recommendations* recommend that if a woman is between 6 weeks and 6 months postpartum and amenorrhoeic, she can have her first injection of DMPA at any time. If fully (or nearly fully) breastfeeding then no additional contraceptive protection is needed. Full breastfeeding is defined as 'exclusive' when no other liquids or solids are given or 'almost exclusive' when vitamins, water or juice are given infrequently in addition to breast feeds.[9]

The use of DMPA by women who are breastfeeding and less than 6 weeks postpartum is not advised. Nevertheless, the majority of studies show that DMPA has no adverse effects on breastfeeding, breast milk volume and infant growth or development, even if used in the first 6 weeks postpartum.[10] On this basis, the UK *Medical Eligibility Criteria* recommends that the use of progestogen-only injectables by women who are breastfeeding and are less than 6 weeks postpartum outweigh the risks (UK Category 2). If DMPA is to be used, ideally it should not be given until day 21 postpartum. Women should be informed that use of DMPA in this situation is outside the terms of the product licence.[11]

The CEU advises that DMPA can be used by women who are 8 weeks postpartum (breastfeeding or not breastfeeding). It can be started in the first 5 days after the start of menstruation without the need for additional contraceptive protection. Moreover, if it is reasonably certain she is not pregnant, the first injection can be given at any time but she will need to abstain from sexual intercourse or use additional contraceptive protection for the next 7 days.

QUESTION

For women aged under 18 years, does DMPA cause a decrease in bone mineral density?

POPULATION: Women under the age of 18 years.
INTERVENTION: DMPA.
OUTCOME: Decrease in bone mineral density.

ANSWER

The early reproductive years are an important time for the attainment of peak bone mineral density. Longitudinal prospective studies show that the maximum increase in bone density occurs between the ages of 11 and 14 years.[12-14] Many factors (nutrition, exercise, smoking, calcium intake) are likely to have more effect on bone mineral density than contraceptive hormones.[15] Pregnancy itself can have a detrimental effect on bone mineral density and risks and benefits of contraceptive use, compliance, patient choice, and risk of pregnancy all need to be considered. Studies in young women using DMPA are limited by small sample sizes, high rates of attrition, limited follow up and failure to adjust for potential confounding factors. In addition, because long-term use in this age group is rare, concerns about the effects of injectable progestogen-only contraception on bone mineral density in young women are probably over emphasised. Indeed, a retrospective case note review found that less than one-third of young women who start DMPA at the age of 16 years continued it for more than 1 year.[16]

Studies have suggested a reduction in bone mineral density in young women with DMPA use. A prospective study of young women (aged 12–21 years) using DMPA found that bone mineral density decreased by 1.5% after 1 year of use and by 3.1% after 2 years of use.[17] Another cross-sectional study found that bone mineral density with DMPA use was significantly lower in young women (aged 18–21 years) compared with women aged over 21 years.[18] Bone mineral density decreased further with increasing duration of contraceptive use. Small prospective studies in young women (aged less than 18 years) using DMPA have confirmed a decrease in bone mineral density in the spine and femoral neck.[19] When young women using DMPA were followed up 15 months after stopping contraception, bone mineral density remained lower than in young women who had never used DMPA.[20] Current evidence indicates a reduction in bone mineral density associated with use of DMPA and although recovery is expected after cessation this may take longer in women aged less than 18 years than in older women. The clinical significance of reduced bone mineral density is unknown.

The *WHO Medical Eligibility Criteria* recommend that DMPA can be used without restriction by women from the age of 18 years (WHO category 1). For women aged less than 18 years, the benefits of using DMPA generally outweigh the risks (WHO category 2).

The CEU advises that all women should be counselled about the effects of DMPA on bone mineral density. This information must be balanced against the need for a contraceptive method that will provide effective pregnancy prevention. After counselling, women aged less than 18 years may choose DMPA over other contraceptive methods.[21] Re-evaluation every 2 years is appropriate for women who wish to continue with this method of contraception.

Update to Answer

In October 2005, the National Institute for Health and Clinical Excellence published a clinical guideline on long-acting reversible contraception.[22] The recommendations relating to DMPA for young women are entirely compatible with the advice given above: 'Because of the possible effect on bone mineral density, care should be taken in recommending DMPA to adolescents, but it may be given if other methods are not suitable or acceptable' and 'Women who wish to continue DMPA use beyond 2 years should have their individual clinical situations reviewed, the balance between the benefits and potential risks discussed, and be supported in their choice of whether or not to continue'.

QUESTION

For women aged over 40 years who are amenorrhoeic using DMPA, can this method be used until the menopause and how can the menopause be confirmed?

POPULATION: Women aged over 40 years.
INTERVENTION: DMPA.
OUTCOME: Diagnosing the menopause and osteoporosis risk.

ANSWER

The *WHO Medical Eligibility Criteria* recommends that that benefits of using injectable progestogen-only methods over the age of 45 years generally outweigh the risks (WHO category 2). Previous opinion was to discontinue at the age of 45 years when any loss of bone density could recover before the natural decline with the menopause.[23] No evidence was identified to support this practice and the CEU supports the use of DMPA up to the age of 50 years, at which time an alternative contraceptive method should be used.[24]

Diagnosing the menopause can be difficult when a woman is using DMPA. Age alone cannot be used as the average age of the menopause is 50.7 years and most women are menopausal by age 55 years.[25,26] Menstrual bleeding patterns and amenorrhoea are unhelpful clinically, as these may be influenced by the medroxyprogesterone acetate and need not reflect ovarian failure. Moreover, the return of ovulation and menstruation following the cessation of DMPA can be delayed. Amenorrhoea may not be indicative of the menopause and condoms may be advised for 2 years after stopping progestogen-only contraception.[24] Serum FSH can be measured when women are using DMPA. Ovarian failure is highly likely if two measurements of FSH of more than 30 iu/l are obtained at least 1 month apart.

The CEU supports the use of DMPA up to the age of 50 years.[24] At age 50 years, women should be counselled about the risks and benefits of progestogen-only injectable and advised to switch to a suitable alternative contraceptive (such as progestogen-only pills, implant, intrauterine system or non-hormonal methods) until the menopause can be confirmed.

Update to Answer

In October 2005, the National Institute for Health and Clinical Excellence published a clinical guideline on long-acting reversible contraception.[22] The recommendation relating to DMPA for older women is entirely compatible with the advice given above: 'Because of the possible effect on bone mineral density, care should be taken in recommending DMPA to women older than 40 years, but in general the benefits outweigh the risks, and it may be given if other methods are not suitable or acceptable'.

QUESTION

For African Caribbean women who are perimenopausal, can DMPA be used safely until the menopause?

POPULATION: African Caribbean women who are perimenopausal.
INTERVENTION: DMPA.
OUTCOME: Safety of use until the menopause.

ANSWER

A SIGN guideline on the management of osteoporosis[27] states that African Caribbean women have a higher bone mineral density than white women at all ages due to a higher peak bone mass and slower rate of loss.[28,29] White women have a 2.5-fold greater risk of osteoporosis.[28] Despite extensive searching, however, the CEU could find no specific information in the literature on any difference in the risk of osteoporosis in African Caribbean women compared with white women when using DMPA. We summarise the available evidence on women using DMPA here.

The *WHO Medical Eligibility Criteria* recommends that the benefits of DMPA outweigh the risks in women aged over 45 years. Conflicting evidence exists around the degree of bone loss around the menopause.[30] Women over the age of 40 years who are continuing or initiating DMPA should be advised that studies have found an association between long-term use and loss of bone mineral density. Women with additional risk factors for low bone mineral density (smokers, those on long-term high-dose corticosteroid therapy, women with thyroid disease or with a family history) should be discouraged from using DMPA. After counselling about the unknown effects on bone density and recovery of any bone loss, women may choose to continue the use of DMPA over the age of 45 years. Advice is to discontinue the method at the age of 50 years and switch to an alternative contraceptive (progestogen-only pills, implant or non-hormonal methods), which can be continued to the age of 55 years when natural loss of fertility is assumed.[24]

The MHRA advises that for women of all ages who are using DMPA, re-evaluation of the risks and benefits of treatment should be carried out in those who wish to continue use for more than 2 years. In women with significant lifestyle and/or medical risk factors for osteoporosis, other methods of contraception should be considered. There is no suggestion that this re-evaluation need include bone density measurement by dual energy X-ray absorptiometry (DEXA) scanning but should involve clinical history-taking and lifestyle assessment.

The CEU recommends that African Caribbean women aged over 40 years should be advised that their risk of osteoporosis is lower than for white women. However, there is no specific evidence available on any difference in risk of osteoporosis in African Caribbean women compared with white women using DMPA. After counselling about the unknown effects on bone density and recovery of any bone loss, women may choose to continue the use of DMPA to age 50 years, at which time an alternative method of contraception is advised.

References

1. Department of Health. *Obesity Prodigy Guidance*. London: DH. [www.prodigy.nhs.uk/guidance.asp?gt=Obesity].
2. Farmer RDT, Lawrenson RA, Todd JC, Williams TJ, MacRae KD, Tyrer F, *et al.* A comparison of the risks of venous thromboembolic disease in association with different combined oral contraceptives. *Br J Pharmacol* 2000;49:580–90.
3. Nightingale AL, Lawrenson RA, Simpson EL, Williams TJ, MacRae KD, Farmer RDT. The effects of age, body mass index, smoking and general health on the risk of venous thromboembolism in users of combined oral contraceptives. *Eur J Contracept Reprod Health Care* 2000;5:265–74.
4. Lidegaard O, Edstrom B, Kreiner S. Oral contraceptives and venous thromboembolism. A case–control study. *Contraception* 1998;57:291–301.
5. World Health Organization Collaborative Study of Cardiovascular Disease and Steroid Hormone Contraception. Cardiovascular disease and use of oral and injectable progestogen-only contraceptives and combined injectable contraceptives. *Contraception* 1998;57:315–24.
6. Bahamondes L, Del Castillo S, Tabares G, Arce XE, Perrotti M, Petta C. Comparison of weight increase in users of depot medroxyprogesterone acetate and copper IUD up to 5 years. *Contraception* 2001;64:223–5.
7. Mangan SA, Larsen PG, Hudson S. Overweight teens at increased risk for weight gain while using depot medroxyprogesterone acetate. *J Pediatr Adolesc Gynecol* 2002;15:79–82.
8. Connor PD, Tavernier LA, Thomas SM, Gates D, Lytton SM. Determining risk between Depo-Provera use and increased uterine bleeding in obese and overweight women. *J Am Board Fam Pract* 2002;15:7–10.
9. Pyper CMM. Fertility awareness and natural family planning. *Eur J Contracept Reprod Health Care* 1997;2:131–46.
10. Faculty of Family Planning and Reproductive Health Care Clinical Effectiveness Unit. Contraceptive choices for breastfeeding women. *J Fam Plann Reprod Health Care* 2004;30:181-9.

11. Faculty of Family Planning and Reproductive Health Care Clinical Effectiveness Unit. The use of contraception outside the terms of the product licence. *J Fam Plann Reprod Health Care* 2005;31:225–41.

12. Theinz G, Buchs B, Nizzolo R. Longitudinal monitoring of bone mass accumulation in healthy adolescents: evidence for a marked reduction after 16 years of age at the levels of lumbar spine and femoral neck in female subjects. *J Clin Endocrinol Metab* 1992;75:1060–5.

13. Matkovic V, Jelic T, Wardlaw GM. Timing of peak bone mass in Caucasian females and its implication for the prevention of osteoporosis: inference from a cross-sectional model. *J Clin Invest* 1994;93:799–808.

14. Teegarden D, Proulx WR, Martin BR. Peak bone mass in young women. *J Bone Miner Res* 1995;10:711–15.

15. Cromer B, Harel Z. Adolescents: At increased risk for osteoporosis? *Clin Pediatr* 2000;39:565–74.

16. Lim SW, Rieder J, Coupey SM, Bijur PE. Depot medroxyprogesterone acetate use in inner-city, minority adolescents: continuation rates and characteristics of long-term users. *Arch Pediatr Adolesc Med* 1999;153:1068–72.

17. Cromer BA, McArdle Blair J, Mahan JD, Zibners L, Naumovski Z. A prospective comparison of bone density in adolescent girls receiving depot medroxyprogesterone acetate (Depo-Provera), levonorgestrel (Norplant), or oral contraceptives. *J Pediatr* 1996;129:671–6.

18. Scholes D, Lacroix AZ, Ott SM, Ichikawa LE, Barlow WE. Bone mineral density in women using depot medroxyprogesterone acetate for contraception. *Obstet Gynecol* 1999;93:233–8.

19. Busen NH, Britt RB, Rianon N. Bone mineral density in a cohort of adolescent women using depot medroxyprogesterone acetate for one to two years. *J Adolesc Health* 2003;32:257–9.

20. Scholes D, LaCroix AZ, Ichikawa LE, Barlow WE, Ott SM. Injectable hormone contraception and bone density: results from a prospective study. *Epidemiology* 2002;13:581–7.

21. Faculty of Family Planning and Reproductive Health Care Clinical Effectiveness Unit. Contraceptive choices for young people. *J Fam Plann Reprod Health Care* 2004;30:237–51.

22. National Collaborating Centre for Women's and Children's Health. *Long-acting Reversible Contraception: the effective and appropriate use of long acting reversible contraception.* London: RCOG Press; 2005.

23. Brechin S, Gebbie A. Perimenopausal contraception a Faculty aid to continued professional development topic. *J Fam Plann Reprod Health Care* 2000;26 Millennium Edition (insert).

24. Faculty of Family Planning and Reproductive Healthcare Clinical Effectiveness Unit. Contraception for women aged over 40 years. *J Fam Plann Reprod Health Care* 2005;31:51–64.

25. Treloar AE. Menarche, menopause and intervening fecundability. *Hum Biol* 1974;46:89.

26. van Noord PAH, Dubas JS, Dorland M, Boersma H, te Velde E. Age at natural menopause in a population-based screening cohort: the role of menarche, fecundity, and lifestyle factors. *Fertil Steril* 1997;68:95–102.

27. Scottish Intercollegiate Guidelines Network. *Management of Osteoporosis.* Guideline No. 71. Edinburgh: SIGN; 2003 [www.sign.ac.uk/guidelines/fulltext/71/index.html].

28. Snelling A, Crespo C, Schaeffer M, Smith S, Walbourn L. Modifiable and nonmodifiable

factors associated with osteoporosis in postmenopausal women: results from the Third National Health and Nutrition Examination Survey, 1988–1994. *J Womens Health Gend Based Med* 2001;10:57–65.

Aloia J, Vaswan IA, Yeh J, Flaster E. Risk for osteoporosis in black women. *Calcif Tissue Int* 1996;59:415–23.

50. Prior JC. Perimenopause: the complex endocrinology of the menopuase transition. *Endocr Rev* 1998;19:397–428.

Bone mineral density

QUESTION

For women using DMPA, what evidence is there for it reducing bone mineral density and are there age limits to its use? (Five similar enquiries.)

POPULATION:	**Healthy women.**
INTERVENTION:	**DMPA.**
OUTCOME:	**Evidence for low bone mineral density or age restriction for use.**

ANSWER

Women considering the use of DMPA should be advised that studies have suggested an association between its use and loss of bone mass. Direct causation is difficult to determine as many other variables affect bone mineral density (diet, exercise, underlying medical conditions, smoking). The risk of fracture is not increased in women using DMPA and the clinical significance of reduced bone density is unknown. Bone loss recovers after cessation.[1]

Guidance from the Department of Health on amenorrhoea states that there is no consensus on the need for bone mineral density measurements, assessment of estrogen status, or the use of 'add-back' estrogen therapy and other measures for long-term DMPA users.[2] The *WHO Medical Eligibility Criteria* supports the unrestricted use of DMPA by women aged 18–45 years (WHO category 1) and for women aged under 18 years or over 45 years the benefits of use generally outweigh the risks (WHO category 2). The MHRA advises that, for women who wish to continue DMPA for more than 2 years, a re-evaluation of the risks and benefits of treatment should be performed. There is no suggestion that this re-evaluation need include bone density measurement by DEXA scanning but it should involve clinical history taking and lifestyle assessment.

The CEU recommends that women should be advised that DMPA is assoc-iated with loss of bone mass. The CEU supports the use of DMPA up to the age of 50 years.[3] At age 50 years, women should be counselled about the risk and benefits of progestogen-only injectable and be advised to switch to a suitable alternative (such as progestogen-only pills, implant, intrauterine system or non-hormonal methods).

QUESTION

For women using DMPA who are amenorrhoeic, how long can the method be continued without adverse effects on bone mineral density? (Two similar enquiries.)

POPULATION: Women using DMPA who are amenorrhoeic.

INTERVENTION: Continued use of DMPA.

OUTCOME: Effects on bone mineral density.

ANSWER

Almost two-thirds of women using DMPA will be amenorrhoeic after 12 months of use.[4] Amenorrhoea reflects the effect of DMPA on the endometrium and does not identify women with low estradiol concentrations or those at risk of low bone density. Moreover, most women using DMPA have estradiol concentrations similar to those seen in the early follicular phase of the menstrual cycle.

The Summary of Product Characteristics for DMPA does not suggest a maximum duration of use. The *WHO Medical Eligibility Criteria* support the use of DMPA from age 18–45 years (WHO category 2). The CEU supports the use of DMPA up to the age of 50 years.[3]

Women considering the use of DMPA should be advised that studies have suggested an association between its use and loss of bone mass. Direct causation is difficult to determine as many other variables affect bone mineral density (diet, exercise, underlying medical conditions, smoking). Bone loss appears maximal in the first 5 years of use; thereafter, continued loss of bone mineral density is less. Use of DMPA for more than 5 years does not result in a continued rate of bone loss.[5] Moreover, any reduction in bone mineral density recovers after cessation.[1]

The MHRA advises, that for women who wish to continue DMPA for more than 2 years, a re-evaluation of the risks and benefits of treatment is undert-aken. There is no suggestion that this re-evaluation need include bone density measurement by DEXA scanning but should involve clinical history taking and lifestyle assessment.

The CEU supports the use of DMPA for any duration and up to the age of 50 years with re-evaluation every 2 years.

QUESTION

For women using DMPA who have osteopenia, can this contraceptive method be continued?

POPULATION: Women using DMPA who have osteopenia.
INTERVENTION: Continued use of DMPA.
OUTCOME: Risk of osteoporosis.

ANSWER

DMPA use is associated with a reduction in bone mineral density at specific sites (spine, femur and radius). Direct causation is difficult to determine as many other factors influence bone mineral density. A bone mineral density of more than 2.5 standard deviations below the mean for a young adult is indicative of osteoporosis. Osteopenia is diagnosed when bone mineral density is 1.0–2.5 standard deviations below the mean. Concerns regarding the use of DMPA and reduction in bone mineral density are related to its potential to lower serum estradiol, which may affect bone density. Nevertheless, most DMPA users are not estrogen-deficient.

The effect, if any, of DMPA on bone density in women with osteopenia is unknown. No evidence was identified which investigated bone density with continued DMPA use in women with proven osteopenia or osteoporosis. If a woman does not wish to consider alternative contraceptives, DMPA can be continued after counselling. If continued, a further DEXA scan may be advised approximately 2 years later to ensure no further deterioration in bone mineral density. If bone loss had not worsened, the continuation of DMPA could be considered but no evidence was identified to support this.

QUESTION

For women who are smokers, what are the relative and absolute risks of a reduction in bone mineral density or an osteoporotic fracture and how does this relate to advice for women using progestogen-only injectable contraception?

POPULATION:	Women of reproductive age using DMPA.
INTERVENTION:	Smoking.
OUTCOME:	Bone mineral density or risk of osteoporotic fracture.

ANSWER

The strongest risk factors associated with the development of osteoporosis are age and gender. Smoking and low BMI are also important modifiable risk factors. The OFELY study,[6] however, did not find that smoking was linked to risk of osteoporosis. The most important predictors of incident osteoporotic fractures were (in descending order):

- age

- past falls

- total hip bone mineral density

- grip strength

- maternal history of fracture

- low physical activity

- previous history of fracture.

Other studies have indicated that smoking is related to risk of osteoporosis. A meta-analysis of studies looking at the effect of smoking showed that bone mineral density in smokers was 2% lower with each increasing decade after the menopause than in non-smokers, with a 6% difference at 80 years.[7] Female smokers have been shown to be at greater risk of hip fracture than non-smokers, with the risk increasing with an increased number of cigarettes smoked. The level of risk declines after giving up smoking but is not significantly reduced until 10 years after cessation.[8] A large cohort study found that smoking was associated with an increase in all types of fracture.[9]

A cohort study observed two groups of American women using DMPA or a non-hormonal contraceptive over 24 months.[10] In women using DMPA, the mean hip bone mineral density declined by 5.8% at 24 months, whereas the non-DMPA users remained within 1% of the baseline at 24 months. Calcium intake, physical activity and smoking did not influence bone mineral density in either group.

The CEU recommends that all women who smoke should be advised of the potential effects of smoking on bones. It is not possible to identify relative or absolute risks of reduction in bone mineral density or of osteoporosis resulting from smoking itself, or in combination with use of DMPA. All women who wish to continue to use DMPA should be counselled and reviewed every 2 years.

QUESTION

For women using DMPA long-term who have low serum estradiol concentrations, what management is necessary to prevent adverse effects on bone mineral density? (Four similar enquiries.)

POPULATION: Women with long-term DMPA use and low estradiol concentrations.
INTERVENTION: Treatment with estradiol.
OUTCOME: Effects on bone mineral density.

ANSWER

There is no consensus as to whether or not there is a relationship between serum estradiol concentration and bone mineral density and if so, what threshold of serum estradiol would indicate referral for bone densitometry. Many concerns about the long-term use of DMPA relate to its hypoestrogenic effects and possible consequences for bone mineral density. Nevertheless, serum estradiol concentrations in women using DMPA are usually within the early follicular phase range (15–318 picomoles/litre) and thus most women are not estrogen-deficient. The routine measurement of serum estradiol in women using DMPA is not justified. There is no evidence to support the use of estrogen replacement in women using DMPA to prevent a reduction in bone density.

The CEU does not recommend assessment of serum estradiol concentrations or estrogen replacement in the management of women on long-term DMPA.

QUESTION

For women with a low bone mineral density who are using DMPA, does estrogen replacement reduce the risk of further bone loss?

POPULATION: Women with low bone density using DMPA.
INTERVENTION: Estrogen replacement therapy.
OUTCOME: Reduced risk of further bone loss.

ANSWER

Concerns about long-term use of DMPA relate to its hypoestrogenic effects and possible consequences on bone mineral density. Most women using DMPA will have normal follicular phase concentrations of estradiol. Some women will have lower serum concentrations of estradiol but this does not appear to correlate with the risk of osteopenia or osteoporosis.

There is no evidence to support the use of estrogen replacement in women using DMPA to prevent a reduction in bone density. There appears to be rapid reduction in bone loss in the first 5 years of use, no further loss thereafter, and recovery of bone mineral density after discontinuation. Care should be taken when using DMPA in women with risk factors for low bone density, when bone densitometry may be considered to help in the decision-making and counselling processes. Otherwise, re-evaluation every 2 years for women who wish to continue with this method of contraception is appropriate.

References

1. Cundy T, Cornish J, Evans MC, Roberts H, Reid IR. Recovery of bone density in women who stop using medroxyprogesterone acetate. *BMJ* 1994;308:247–8.
2. Department of Health. Amenorrhoea. PRODIGY Guidance. London: DH [www.prodigy.nhs.uk/ProdigyKnowledge/Guidance/Amenorrhoea].
3. Faculty of Family Planning and Reproductive Health Care Clinical Effectiveness Unit. Contraceptive choices for young people. *J Fam Plann Reprod Health Care* 2004;30:237–51.
4. Sangi-Haghpeykar H, Poindexter AN, Bateman L, Ditmore JR. Experiences of injectable contraceptive users in an urban setting. *Obstet Gynecol* 1996;88:227–33.
5. Tang OS, Tang G, Yip PS, Li B. Further evaluation on long-term depot-medroxyprogesterone acetate use and bone mineral density: a longitudinal cohort study. *Contraception* 2000;62:161–4.
6. Albrand G, Munoz F, Sornay-Rendu E, DuBoeuf F, Delmas PD. Independent predictors of all osteoporosis-related fractures in healthy postmenopausal women: the OFELY study. *Bone* 2003;32:78–85.
7. Hannan MT, Felson DT, Dawson-Hughes B, Tucker KL, Cupples LA, Wilson PW, *et al.* Risk factors for longitudinal bone loss in elderly men and women: the Framingham osteoporosis study. *J Bone Miner Res* 2000;15:710–20.
8. Cornuz J, Feskanich D, Willett WC, Colditz GA. Smoking, smoking cessation, and risk of hip fracture in women. *Am J Med* 1999;106:311–14.
9. Porthouse J, Birks YF, Torgerson DJ, Cockaynes S, Puffer S, Watt I. Risk factors for fracture in a UK population a prospective cohort study. *QJM* 2004;97:569–74.
10. Clark MK, Sowers MR, Nichols S, Levy B. Bone mineral density changes over two years in first-time users of depot medroxyprogesterone acetate. *Fertil Steril* 2004;82:1580–6.

Abnormal bleeding

QUESTION

For women considering use of a progestogen-only injectable contraceptive, what advice is there regarding DMPA and its effect on bleeding?

POPULATION: Healthy women.
INTERVENTION: DMPA.
OUTCOME: Bleeding patterns.

ANSWER

Women considering DMPA should be informed that abnormal bleeding is common, particularly in the first 3 months of use. A retrospective study investigated bleeding patterns in 536 women using DMPA.[1] Frequent bleeding was reported by 15.3% of women in the first 3 months of use; this fell to 6.2% after 12 months. Amenorrhoea was reported by 46% of the women after 3 months of DMPA use; this increased to 53.3% after 6 months and to 58.5% after 12 months. Bleeding episodes were reported to be longer than usual by 18.5% of women after 12 months use. However, lighter bleeding was described by 16.4% of women after 12 months. Research from the WHO showed that women using DMPA tolerate far greater menstrual disturbances that women using other methods (combined pills, progestogen-only pills and vaginal rings).[2] Women using DMPA were more likely to have been counselled regarding bleeding disturbances than women using other methods.

Women considering the use of DMPA should be counselled about the potential bleeding patterns associated with its use and reassured that bleeding disturbances appear to decrease with increasing duration of use.

QUESTION

For women using DMPA, how should abnormal bleeding be managed? (Three similar enquiries.)

POPULATION: Women using DMPA.
INTERVENTION: Management of abnormal bleeding.
OUTCOME: Improvement in bleeding patterns.

ANSWER

Women considering the use of DMPA should be informed of the common bleeding patterns that can occur with its use. Abnormal bleeding is common in women using DMPA and even after 12 months of use, 6% of women have frequent bleeding.[1]

The WHO *Selected Practice Recommendations* provides evidence-based recommendations on the management of menstrual abnormalities in women using progestogen-only injectable contraceptives. Spotting or light bleeding and heavy or prolonged bleeding (more than 8 days or twice as much as a usual period) are common in the first injection cycle. If problematic bleeding persists, gynaecological conditions and infections (chlamydia and other STIs) should be investigated and treated. If problematic bleeding continues or becomes a threat to the woman's health, the progestogen-only injectable should be discontinued and another method chosen. The UK version of the WHO *Selected Practice Recommendations* supports the short-term use of a low-dose combined oral contraceptive pill to manage unacceptable bleeding. There is no evidence to support an increased dose of DMPA or a reduction in the injection interval to improve bleeding patterns.

QUESTION

For a woman with a BMI of 43 kg/m² who is using DMPA, how should abnormal bleeding be managed?

POPULATION: Women with high BMI using DMPA.
INTERVENTION: Management of abnormal bleeding.
OUTCOME: Improvement in bleeding patterns.

ANSWER

Abnormal bleeding patterns are common in women using DMPA particularly in the first 3 months of use.[1] A retrospective study found that excess weight or obesity is associated with a decreased risk of excessive bleeding with DMPA use[3] and compliance and satisfaction may be improved.

The WHO *Selected Practice Recommendations* provides evidence-based recommendations on the management of menstrual abnormalities in women using progestogen-only injectable contraceptives. No recommendation was given regarding use of combined oral contraception in the management of abnormal bleeding due to progestogen-only injectables. However, the UK version of

Selected Practice Recommendations supports the use of a low-dose combined oral contraceptive pill in the short-term to manage abnormal bleeding.

The *WHO Medical Eligibility Criteria* suggests that the benefits of using combined hormonal contraception by women with a BMI over 30kg/m^2 generally outweigh the risks (WHO category 2). However, the UK version of this document suggests that, as the risk of VTE increases two- to four-fold with increasing BMI, progestogen-only methods may be more appropriate if BMI is over 35kg/m^2. Nevertheless, the short-term use of combined oral contraception to control unacceptable bleeding with DMPA may be considered as the *WHO Medical Eligibility Criteria* provide eligibility criteria for contraceptives used solely for fertility control and not for use in the management of other medical conditions. Use of the method should be considered on an individual basis.

The WHO *Selected Practice Recommendations* and the UK version state that DMPA should be given every 12 weeks. There is no evidence to suggest that shortening the injection interval improves bleeding and indeed it may exacerbate the bleeding.

The CEU advises that women should be informed of the bleeding patterns that can occur with DMPA. The use of a combined oral contraceptive pill in the short term can be useful for women without contraindications but use should be considered on an individual basis. If abnormal bleeding persists, consideration should be given to other causes (sexually transmitted diseases and gynaecological pathology).

References

1. Sangi-Haghpeykar H, Poindexter AN, Bateman L, Ditmore JR. Experiences of injectable contraceptive users in an urban setting. *Obstet Gynecol* 1996;88:227–33.
2. Belsey EM. The association between vaginal bleeding patterns and reasons for discontinuation of contraceptive use. *Contraception* 1988;38:207–25.
3. Pyper CMM. Fertility awareness and natural family planning. *Eur J Contracept Reprod Health Care* 1997;2:131–46.

Administration

QUESTION

For women choosing DMPA, where should the injection be given?

POPULATION: Women choosing DMPA.

INTERVENTION: Choosing correct injection site.

OUTCOME: Contraceptive efficacy.

ANSWER

The Summary of Product Characteristics for DMPA recommends a dose of 150 mg every 3 months by deep intramuscular injection either in the gluteal or deltoid muscle. Women should be advised to avoiding rubbing the injection site as this may reduce the duration of contraceptive efficacy by hastening absorption.[1]

QUESTION

For women using DMPA, should the injection be given in the deltoid if BMI is over 35 kg/m² and what advice should be given if the injection is spilled? (Two similar enquiries.)

POPULATION: Women with BMI over 35 kg/m² using DMPA.

INTERVENTION: Choosing the appropriate injection site.

OUTCOME: Contraceptive efficacy.

ANSWER

The Summary of Product Characteristics for DMPA recommends a dose of 150 mg every 3 months by deep intramuscular injection either in the gluteal or deltoid muscle. It may be appropriate when women are overweight to administer the injection into the deltoid muscle to ensure it is given intramuscularly. This will need to be decided on an individual basis.

The *WHO Medical Eligibility Criteria* suggests that the benefits of using progestogen-only injectable contraception by women with a BMI over 30 kg/m² generally outweigh the risks (WHO category 2).

The CEU was unable to identify any evidence on what to do if a small amount of the injection is spilled during administration. If spillage occurs prior to administration, it may be appropriate to discard that syringe and use another. If spillage occurs from the injection site after the injection has been given, there is no evidence to guide clinicians on any potential reduction in contraceptive efficacy or if the injection interval should be shortened. The 150-mg dose of DMPA provides serum concentrations of medroxyprogesterone acetate sufficient to inhibit ovulation for as long as 6 months.[2] It would be unlikely that a small spillage would reduce contraceptive efficacy. Nevertheless, it may be appropriate to consider giving the next injection up to 2 weeks early.

References

1. Pharmacy Access Partnership. *IC Guidelines and Procedures*. Oakland, CA: Pharmacy Access Partnership; 2003 [www.pharmacyaccess.org/BecomingICProvider.htm#IC_Guidelines_and_Procedures].
2. Oritz A, Hirol M, Stanczyk FZ, Goebelsmann U, Mishell DR. Serum medroxyprogesterone acetate (MPA) concentrations and ovarian function following intramuscular injection of depo-MPA. *J Clin Endocrinol Metab* 1977;44:32–8.

Anaphylaxis

QUESTION

For women who choose to use DMPA, is there a risk of anaphylaxis? (Two similar enquiries.)

POPULATION:	Healthy women.
INTERVENTION:	DMPA.
OUTCOME:	Risk of anaphylaxis.

ANSWER

The Summary of Product Characteristics reports very few cases of anaphylaxis with DMPA. Nevertheless, anaphylaxis is potentially the most serious complication that could arise from a DMPA injection. Anaphylaxis could be attributable to the medicine itself or to the latex rubber in the syringe plunger. An anaphylactic reaction may occur immediately after the injection is given or may be delayed by a few hours. Anaphylaxis may also occur from the use of other injectable methods, such as norethisterone enanthate. Protocols on the management of anaphylaxis and an emergency pack should be readily available in clinics where progestogen-only injectable contraceptives are given.

QUESTION

If women are receiving a first or second DMPA injection, should they be asked to wait in the clinic for 20 minutes following the injection, in case of allergic or anaphylactic reaction? (Two similar enquiries.)

POPULATION: Women receiving the first or second DMPA injection.

INTERVENTION: Waiting for 20 minutes following the injection.

OUTCOME: Monitoring of allergy or possible anaphylactic reaction.

ANSWER

Anaphylaxis could be caused by the medicine itself or by the latex rubber in the syringe plunger. An anaphylactic reaction may occur immediately after the injection is given or may be delayed by a few hours.

No recommendation is given in the product licence to ask women to wait in the clinic for 20 minutes after the first or second injection. Nevertheless, this is policy in some family planning clinics in the UK. All clinics should develop their own policies and staff should be trained in basic resuscitation. An emergency pack should be readily available in clinics where progestogen-only injectable contraceptives are given.[1]

QUESTION

What resuscitation equipment or measures should be available in a family planning clinic where DMPA injections are given, in order to minimise the risk of serious complications?

POPULATION: Women having DMPA injections.

INTERVENTION: Resuscitation equipment or measures available in the clinic.

OUTCOME: The risk of serious complications following the injection.

ANSWER

The Summary of Product Characteristics reports very few cases of anaphylaxis with DMPA. Nevertheless, anaphylaxis is potentially the most serious complication that could arise from a DMPA injection.

Resuscitation in the family planning setting was the topic of a Faculty Aid to Continuing Professional Development Topic (FACT),[2] in which the contents of an emergency shock pack, which should be available in all clinics, are detailed. Protocols on the management of anaphylactic shock based on guidance from the Resuscitation Council UK should be available. A suitable protocol is summarised in Figure 2.

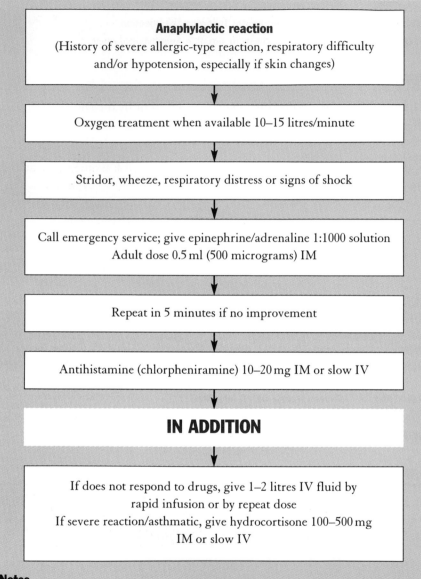

Anaphylactic reaction
(History of severe allergic-type reaction, respiratory difficulty
and/or hypotension, especially if skin changes)

Oxygen treatment when available 10–15 litres/minute

Stridor, wheeze, respiratory distress or signs of shock

Call emergency service; give epinephrine/adrenaline 1:1000 solution
Adult dose 0.5 ml (500 micrograms) IM

Repeat in 5 minutes if no improvement

Antihistamine (chlorpheniramine) 10–20 mg IM or slow IV

IN ADDITION

If does not respond to drugs, give 1–2 litres IV fluid by
rapid infusion or by repeat dose
If severe reaction/asthmatic, give hydrocortisone 100–500 mg
IM or slow IV

Notes
If bronchospasm is severe, an inhaled beta 2-agonist such as salbutamol may be used.
For life-threatening shock give CPR/ALS. Consider slow IV adrenaline (epinephrine) 1:10000
solution. This is only for experienced practitioners. Never give 1:1000 adrenaline (epinephrine) IV.
Home-use devices, such as Epipen, deliver 300 micrograms of adrenaline. Half-doses may be safer if
the patient takes amitryptaline, imipramine or beta-blockers.
A crystalloid may be safer than a colloid.

Figure 2. Resuscitation Council guidance for adults with anaphylactic reactions
treated by first medical responders[1]

QUESTION

In women with a previous anaphylactic response to DMPA, what is the risk of exposure to other progestogen-containing contraceptives?

POPULATION: Women with a previous anaphylactic reaction to DMPA.

INTERVENTION: Other progestogen-containing contraceptives.

OUTCOME: Risk of anaphylaxis.

ANSWER

The Summary of Product Characteristics for DMPA reports few cases of anaphylaxis. No case reports were identified for anaphylaxis induced by the LNG-IUS, the progestogen implant or the progestogen-only pill.

It is unclear which component of the DMPA is responsible for the hypersensitivity. Anaphylaxis could be due to the medicine itself or to the latex rubber in the syringe plunger. It is difficult to predict whether there is likely to be any crossover hypersensitivity to other progestogen-containing contraceptives.

The clinician posing the question was specifically interested in the risks of inserting the LNG-IUS. The woman concerned had also had an apparent anaphylactic reaction following the use of a combined oral contraceptive pill containing levonorgestrel. If the LNG-IUS is to be used, it should be inserted in a setting where resuscitation facilities are readily available. Consideration should be given to referral for allergy testing.

QUESTION

For women who developed an urticarial rash after the first injection of DMPA, do subsequent injections carry an increased risk of adverse effects?

POPULATION: Women who developed a urticarial rash after the first injection of DMPA.

INTERVENTION: Subsequent injections.

OUTCOME: Risk of adverse effects or anaphylaxis.

ANSWER

The Summary of Product Characteristics for DMPA states that 1–5% of women in a large clinical trial conducted over 7 years developed a rash following injection. Adverse effects of the injection may occasionally include sensitivity reactions such as urticaria. Use of DMPA is contraindicated in women with sensitivity to medroxyprogesterone acetate or any other ingredient.

It would seem prudent for a clinician to discuss the fact that anaphylactic reactions may occur with DMPA with the woman and every clinic where progestogen-only injections are administered should have an emergency pack ready for such an event. The development of the urticarial rash may just be a coincidence but there is no way of knowing if this was a hypersensitivity reaction and predicting what would happen after a repeat a DMPA injection. A repeat injection would have to be given on a clinician's own judgement, after evaluating the individual woman and taking her needs into account.

QUESTION

For a woman who develops a lump around the site of a DMPA injection (on the buttock), can use be continued safely?

POPULATION: Women who develop lumps around sites of DMPA injections.
INTERVENTION: Continued use of DMPA.
OUTCOME: Safety.

ANSWER

Despite extensive searching, the CEU could find no information in the literature on the occurrence of lumps at the DMPA injection site. No evidence was identified to support or refute a reduction in contraceptive efficacy if a haematoma or other lump is apparent. If the woman wishes a further injection, it may be advisable to give this into the other buttock. The CEU is unable to provide an evidence-based response to this enquiry.

References

1. Project Team of the Resuscitation Council. *The Emergency Medical Treatment of Anaphylactic Reactions for First Medical Responders and for Community Nurses.* Revised January 2002, May 2005. Originally published July 1999. London: Resuscitation Council (UK) [www.resus.org.uk/pages/reaction.htm].
2. Bennett A. Resuscitation in the family planning and reproductive health care setting. *J Fam Plann Reprod Health Care* 2001;27:165–9.

Dose and regimens

QUESTION

For a woman who has had DMPA at 12-week intervals in the past and now presents 14 weeks after her last injection, would the contraceptive still be effective? (Three similar enquiries.)

POPULATION: Women using DMPA.

INTERVENTION: Late injection at 14 weeks.

OUTCOME: Contraceptive efficacy.

ANSWER

The WHO *Selected Practice Recommendations* and the UK version of this document recommend that repeat DMPA injections should be given every 3 months or 12 weeks.

The risk of ovulation is thought to be negligible within 2 weeks of the time for a repeat injection. A repeat DMPA injection can therefore be given up to 2 weeks late (up to 14 weeks after the last injection) without the need for additional contraceptive protection. This use is outside the terms of the product licence.[1] If a woman presents more than two weeks late (more than 14 weeks after the last injection), the repeat injection may be given if it is reasonably certain that the woman is not pregnant and she is willing to abstain from sex or use additional contraception such as condoms for the next 7 days.

The CEU recommends that DMPA should be given every 12 weeks but contraceptive protection is provided for up to 14 weeks from the last injection.

QUESTION

For women who are late for a repeat injection of DMPA, when is the earliest ovulation likely to occur?

POPULATION: Women using DMPA.

INTERVENTION: Late injection.

OUTCOME: Risk of ovulation and reduced efficacy.

ANSWER

DMPA injections should be administered every 12 weeks. The risk of ovulation is felt to be negligible within 2 weeks of the time a repeat injection is due. Therefore, a repeat injection can be given up to 2 weeks late (up to week 14) without additional contraceptive protection being required.

This practice is supported by evidence from a small study in women given a single 150-mg dose of intramuscular medroxyprogesterone acetate.[2] Serum medroxyprogesterone concentrations and ovarian activity (assessed by serum progesterone and luteinising hormone) were observed. Concentrations of medroxyprogesterone gradually declined and remained relatively constant at 1 ng/ml for 2–3 months. Thereafter, serum concentrations declined to 0.2 ng/ml by 6 months. Concentrations were undetectable at 7–9 months. Serum estradiol concentrations remained in the early to midfollicular range for 4–6 months after the injection. Estradiol was raised to ovulatory concentrations only when serum medroxyprogesterone concentrations were less than 0.5 ng/ml. In some women, medroxyprogesterone acetate can be identified in serum for as long as 9 months after injection.[3]

Further evidence to suggest a negligible risk of ovulation when an injection of DMPA is late was obtained from a study of Thai women. A delay in return to fertility was noted after discontinuation of DMPA.[4] Women who stopped using DMPA (796) or who had a copper IUD removed (125) were followed up for 2 years. Women discontinuing the IUD had a median delay to conception of 4.5 months. Women discontinuing DMPA had a median delay to conception of 5.5 months (in addition to the estimated duration of the effect of the last injection). A delay to conception of approximately 9 months occurs in women who discontinue DMPA.

There is little direct evidence for the CEU to be certain of the earliest ovulation likely to occur in a woman following a late injection of DMPA. Nevertheless, the available evidence (that serum concentrations of medroxyprogesterone are sufficient to inhibit ovulation for 4–6 months after a single injection and that clinically there is a delay in return to fertility) supports giving DMPA injections every 12 weeks and if necessary up to 2 weeks late without a risk ovulation.

QUESTION

For women who are late for repeat injection of DMPA, when is emergency contraception required? (Thirty-two similar enquiries.)

POPULATION: Women who attend late for repeat injection of DMPA.
INTERVENTION: Need for emergency contraception and continuation of DMPA.
OUTCOME: Contraceptive efficacy.

ANSWER

The UK *Selected Practice Recommendations* support the WHO *Selected Practice Recommendations* that DMPA should be given every 12 weeks. If necessary repeat injections can be given 2 weeks early (10 weeks after last injection) or 2 weeks late (14 weeks after last injection). Based on the available evidence, the risk of ovulation within 2 weeks of when DMPA is due is thought to be negligible.

If a woman presents up to 14 weeks after her last injection, contraceptive protection is still provided and emergency contraception is not required.

If a woman presents more than 14 weeks after her last injection, contraceptive protection should be assumed to have been lost. If it is reasonably certain that she is not pregnant, the repeat injection can be given. She should be advised to abstain from sex or use additional contraceptive protection, such as condoms, for the next 7 days.

The use of emergency contraception and advice regarding repeat injections will need to be considered on an individual basis. Clinicians should consider if unprotected intercourse has occurred since the contraceptive effect has been lost and how long ago this was. Emergency contraception can be considered if unprotected sex has only occurred in the 3–5 days before she presents to the clinic. Progestogen-only emergency contraception or a copper IUD can be considered. If emergency contraception is given, the repeat injection of DMPA may be provided but condoms or abstinence is advised for the next 7 days. Follow-up for a pregnancy test 3 weeks later is appropriate.

References

1. Faculty of Family Planning and Reproductive Health Care Clinical Effectiveness Unit. The use of contraception outside the terms of the product licence. *J Fam Plann Reprod Health Care* 2005;31:225–41.
2. Oritz A, Hirol M, Stanczyk FZ, Goebelsmann U, Mishell DR. Serum medroxyprogesterone acetate (MPA) concentrations and ovarian function following intramuscular injection of depo-MPA. *J Clin Endocrinol Metab* 1977;44:32–8.
3. Mishell DRJ, Kharma KM, Thorneycroft IH, Nakamura RM. Estrogenic activity in women receiving and injectable progestogen for contraception. *Am J Obstet Gynecol* 1972;113:372–6.
4. Pardthaisong T. Return of fertility after use of the injectable contraceptive Depo-Provera: an updated data analysis. *J Biosoc Sci* 1984;16:23–4.

Adverse effects

QUESTION

Do women with a family history of breast cancer who use DMPA long-term have an increased risk of breast cancer?

POPULATION: Women with a family history of breast cancer.
INTERVENTION: Long-term use of DMPA.
OUTCOME: Risk of breast cancer.

ANSWER

Several factors influence the risk of developing breast cancer, including: increasing age, family or personal history of breast cancer, a genetic tendency, reproductive and menstrual history, long-term postmenopausal estrogen and progestogen replacement therapy, lifestyle factors and radiation therapy.[1]

The *WHO Medical Eligibility Criteria* advises that women with a family history of breast cancer may have unrestricted use of DMPA (WHO category 1).

Data on the risk of breast, endometrial, ovarian and cervical cancer in women using DMPA were summarised in a review which included major case–control studies.[2] A pooled analysis of two studies found that women using DMPA had no increased overall risk of breast cancer.[3] The relative risk of breast cancer for women who had ever used DMPA was 1.1 (95% CI 0.97–1.4) and no increase in risk was observed with increasing duration of use. Women who were current or recent DMPA users had a higher relative risk of 2.0 (95% CI 1.5–2.8). This may be due to the availability of better detection methods or acceleration of growth of pre-existing tumours. Those who had used DMPA more than 5 years previously had no increase in risk and this was not affected by duration of use. Women under the age of 35 years at the time of diagnosis and those who began DMPA use before age 25 years had a marginally statistically significant increase in risk of breast cancer but these differences are difficult to interpret and may reflect bias in patient selection.

A case–control study of 484 women with breast cancer and 1625 controls in South Africa investigated the risk of breast cancer in relation to use of injectable progestogen contraceptives and combined oral contraceptives.[4] The relative risk of breast cancer for women who had used injectable progestogen contraceptives (mostly DMPA) was 0.9 (95% CI 0.7–1.2). There were no consistent associations with age, when the contraceptive was used or length of use. The results suggest that injectable progestogens do not increase the risk of breast cancer.

The CEU advises that current evidence suggests no increased risk of breast cancer with DMPA, even with increasing duration of use. Variations in relative risk between current and previous users as well as younger and older users and those who begin the contraceptive at an earlier age have been reported. Nevertheless, these differences are difficult to interpret and may reflect selection bias.

QUESTION

For healthy women using DMPA, is there a risk of cardiovascular disease?

POPULATION: Healthy women.
INTERVENTION: DMPA.
OUTCOME: Risk of cardiovascular disease.

ANSWER

Few studies have been large enough to evaluate the risk of cardiovascular disease associated with use of progestogen-only contraception. In part, this is due to a low incidence of cardiovascular morbidity in women of childbearing age and in part because of the relatively limited use of progestogen-only contraception worldwide. A WHO Collaborative Study evaluated the risks of cardiovascular disease with oral and injectable progestogen-only contraceptives.[5] Although limited by the small numbers of women using these methods, the data suggest that there is little or no increase in risk of VTE, stroke or acute myocardial infarction associated with use of progestogen-only pills and injectables.

The *WHO Medical Eligibility Criteria* recommends that for women with multiple risk factors for arterial cardiovascular disease (such as older age, smoking, diabetes and hypertension), the risks of using DMPA generally outweigh the benefits (WHO category 3). For women with current, or a history of, ischaemic heart disease the benefits of **initiating** DMPA generally outweigh the risks (WHO category 2) but for **continuing**, the risks generally outweigh the benefits (WHO category 3).

A small non-randomised study compared arterial function in 13 women using DMPA and ten non-users.[6] The findings suggested that a magnetic resonance marker of arterial function was impaired in women who were long-term users of DMPA. Although further research may be indicated, clinicians would not be justified in altering long-standing practice on the basis of this small study.

QUESTION

For women who use DMPA, does long-term use increase the risk of cardiovascular disease?

POPULATION: Healthy women.
INTERVENTION: Long-term use of DMPA.
OUTCOME: Risk of cardiovascular disease.

ANSWER

The CEU supports the WHO advice that risks of DMPA generally outweigh benefits in women with cardiovascular disease. No evidence was identified to suggest that DMPA increases the risk of cardiovascular events. If other contraceptive methods such as progestogen-only pills, implant, intrauterine system or copper IUD are unacceptable, progestogen-only injectables can be considered on an individual basis and with specialist advice.

QUESTION

For women using DMPA, is there an increased risk of developing scleroderma?

POPULATION: Healthy women.
INTERVENTION: DMPA.
OUTCOME: Risk of scleroderma.

ANSWER

The Summary of Product Characteristics cites scleroderma among the infrequent undesirable effects that have been reported with use of DMPA (in less than 1% of users). No other publications were identified to provide additional information on the frequency of this association or to support causation. Those few (non-English language) publications that were identified suggested that progestogens have been used in the treatment of scleroderma.

QUESTION

For women with mood disturbance or depression while using DMPA, what is the evidence for an increased dose of 300 mg?

POPULATION: Women using DMPA.

INTERVENTION: 300 mg DMPA.

OUTCOME: Prevention of mood swings or depression.

ANSWER

The Summary of Product Characteristics lists depression as a possible adverse effect associated with use of DMPA. The evidence to support this is conflicting. The *WHO Medical Eligibility Criteria* considers that DMPA can be used without restriction (WHO category 1) by women with depression.

Some observational studies of variable quality suggest an association between DMPA and depressive symptoms.[7] Women using DMPA and non-users were followed up for 3 years and depressive symptoms were monitored using a questionnaire every 6 months. On multivariate analysis, women who were continuous users of DMPA were more likely to report depressive symptoms (OR 1.44; 95% CI 1.00–2.07). No studies were identified which recommend the use of 300 mg medroxyprogesterone acetate as an effective treatment for depression.

The CEU supports the use of progestogen-only methods of contraception in women with depression with appropriate follow up and liaison with any other healthcare professional supporting the woman.

QUESTION

For women who discontinue DMPA and then conceive, is there an increased risk of ectopic pregnancy?

POPULATION: Women of reproductive age.

INTERVENTION: Discontinuation of DMPA.

OUTCOME: Risk of ectopic pregnancy.

ANSWER

The Summary of Product Characteristics for DMPA suggests that of women who wish to conceive, 83% can expect to do so within 15 months of administration of the last injection. There is no mention of ectopic pregnancy.[8]

The CEU found one study that found no increase in ectopic pregnancy rate or fetal anomalies in women who conceived while using DMPA.[9] No studies were identified which investigate the contribution of DMPA to ectopic pregnancy rates after discontinuation.

The *WHO Medical Eligibility Criteria* advises that women with a past ectopic pregnancy may have unrestricted use of DMPA (WHO category 1).

The CEU could find no evidence that women using DMPA have an increased risk of ectopic pregnancy during use or after discontinuation.

QUESTION

For women who conceive during DMPA use, are there any adverse effects on the fetus?

POPULATION: Pregnant women.
INTERVENTION: DMPA during pregnancy.
OUTCOME: Risk of adverse effects.

ANSWER

DMPA acts as a contraceptive primarily by suppression of ovulation but also has secondary effects on cervical mucus, ovum transport and the endometrium. Pregnancy during use of DMPA is rare and thus only one study that reported on pregnancies during DMPA use was identified.[9] The crude rate of pregnancy for women using DMPA was 0.42 pregnancies/1000 woman years. Pregnancy was diagnosed after the first trimester in 46% of the women. There was no increase in ectopic pregnancy rate and no fetal anomalies were reported.

QUESTION

For women using DMPA who develop transient facial numbness, can this method of contraception be continued safely?

POPULATION: Women who develop transient facial numbness when using DMPA.
INTERVENTION: Continuation of DMPA.
OUTCOME: Safety.

ANSWER

The Summary of Product Characteristics for DMPA states that less than 1% of 3900 women in a clinical trial conducted over 7 years reported paralysis or facial palsy. Development of transient facial numbness appears to be a rare event and there is no way of predicting what would happen after a repeat injection. There is no way of reversing the effects of DMPA once given and a repeat injection would have to be given on a clinician's own judgement after evaluating the individual woman and taking her needs into account.

References

1. National Cancer Institute. *Genetics of Breast and Ovarian Cancer* (Physician Data Query). 2006 [www.cancer.gov/cancertopics/pdq/genetics/breast-and-ovarian/healthprofessional].
2. Kaunitz AM. Depot medroxyprogesterone acetate contraception and the risk of breast and gynecologic cancer. *J Reprod Med* 1996;41 (5 Suppl):419–27.
3. Skegg DC, Noonan EA, Paul C, Spears GF, Meirik O, Thomas DB. Depot medroxyprogesterone acetate and breast cancer. A pooled analysis of the World Health Organization and New Zealand studies. *JAMA* 1995;273:799–804.
4. Shapiro S, Rosenberg L, Hoffman M, Truter H, Cooper D, Rao S, *et al*. Risk of breast cancer in relation to the use of injectable progestogen contraceptives and combined estrogen/progestogen contraceptives. *Am J Epidemiol* 2000;151:396–403.
5. World Health Organization Collaborative Study of Cardiovascular Disease and Steroid Hormone Contraception. Cardiovascular disease and use of oral and injectable progestogen-only contraceptives and combined injectable contraceptives. *Contraception* 1998;57:315–24.
6. Sorensen MB, Collins P, Ong PJ, Webb CM, Hayward CS, Asbury EA, *et al*. Long-term use of contraceptive depot medroxyprogesterone acetate in young women impairs arterial endothelial function assessed by cardiovascular magnetic resonance. *Circulation* 2002;106:1646–51.
7. Civic D, Scholes D, Ichikawa L, Lacroix AZ, Yoshida CK, Ott SM, *et al*. Depressive symptoms in users and non-users of depot medroxyprogesterone acetate. *Contraception* 2000;61:385–90.
8. Pardthaisong T. Return of fertility after use of the injectable contraceptive Depo-Provera: an updated data analysis. *J Biosoc Sci* 1984;16:23–4.
9. Borgatta L, Murthy A, Chuang C, Beardsley L, Burnhill MS. Pregnancies diagnosed during Depo-Provera use. *Contraception* 2002;66:169–72.

Norethisterone enanthate

QUESTION

For women who are using DMPA, can norethisterone enanthate be used as an alternative and are there any long-term sequelae associated with its use?

POPULATION:	Women using DMPA.
INTERVENTION:	Alternative use of norethisterone enanthate.
OUTCOME:	Long-term sequelae.

ANSWER

DMPA and norethisterone enanthate have similar modes of action and contra-ceptive efficacy. While norethisterone enanthate is presently licensed only for short-term use in the UK, it is registered for use in over 60 other countries. No evidence was found that explained why norethisterone enanthate is not licensed as a long-term contraceptive besides the fact that it is a more expensive and painful injection and has to be administered more frequently.

The CEU suggests that in the event that norethisterone enanthate has to be given instead of DMPA (for example depleted stocks), contraceptive protection is likely to be maintained. Women should be informed that the mechanism of action and adverse effects are similar to those for DMPA. Women should be informed that the next injection should be given 8 weeks later.

QUESTION

For women using norethisterone enanthate, what evidence is there for low bone mineral density and are there age limits to its use?

POPULATION: Healthy women.

INTERVENTION: Norethisterone enanthate.

OUTCOME: Bone mineral density.

ANSWER

Despite an extensive literature search, the CEU could find no direct evidence on the risk of reduced bone mineral density in women using norethisterone enanthate. Norethisterone enanthate is licensed to be used only as a short-term contraceptive method and therefore effects on bone density are likely to be small. The evidence in this response relates to the use of DMPA in the long term. Direct causation has not been shown.

The *WHO Medical Eligibility Criteria* suggests that the benefits of progestogen-only injectable use generally outweigh the risks for women aged between 18 years and 45 years (WHO category 2). Studies are limited by study design, measuring techniques, short follow-up and failure to correct for confounding and bias. There is rapid bone loss in women aged 37–49 years during the first 5 years of DMPA use; this loss levels off after 5 years use.[1] One study found that recovery of bone loss occurs following the discontinuation of therapy.[2] For women of all ages, careful re-evaluation of the risks and benefits of DMPA use should be carried out in those who wish to continue use for more than 2 years.

No direct evidence was identified on the effects, if any, of norethisterone enanthate on bone mineral density. This is likely to be due to the fact that norethisterone enanthate is licensed only as a short-term contraceptive method and therefore effect on bone density are likely to be small.

QUESTION

Can women using DMPA receive norethisterone enanthate in addition, to delay a bleed, and would this practice affect contraceptive efficacy?

POPULATION: Women using DMPA.

INTERVENTION: Norethisterone enanthate.

OUTCOME: Delay of bleeding and efficacy.

ANSWER

DMPA is licensed as a first-line contraceptive while norethisterone enanthate is licensed in the UK only for short-term use (two consecutive injections). Abnormal bleeding patterns are common in the first few months of using progestogen-only injectable contraception and women should be counselled about this.

The WHO *Selected Practice Recommendations* does not provide guidance on how to delay a bleed. WHO advises that DMPA injections should be given every 3 months while norethisterone enanthate injections should be given every 2 months. Repeat injections for either progestogen-only injectable can be given up to 2 weeks early but no evidence suggests that shortening the injection interval improves irregular bleeding. There is no evidence that using both injectables together would delay a bleed or improve bleeding patterns. The UK *Selected Practice Recommendations* supports the short-term use of a combined oral contraceptive pill for women with problematic bleeding when using progestogen-only injectables.

If bleeding persists with progestogen-only injectable use, gynaecological conditions and infections (such as chlamydia and other STIs) should be investigated and treated. If bleeding continues or becomes a threat to the woman's health, the progestogen-only injectable contraceptive should be discontinued and another method chosen.

The CEU found no evidence to support the use of norethisterone enanthate in addition to DMPA to improve or delay bleeding.

QUESTION

For women using norethisterone enanthate who are late for a repeat injection, when is emergency contraception required?

POPULATION: Women using norethisterone enanthate who are late for repeat injection.

INTERVENTION: Emergency contraception.

OUTCOME: Pregnancy prevention.

ANSWER

The *UK Selected Practice Recommendations* recommends that women should have repeat injections of norethisterone enanthate every 8 weeks. A repeat injection of norethisterone enanthate can be given up to 2 weeks late (10 weeks after the last injection). Contraceptive protection is maintained until 10 weeks after the last injection. If a woman is more than 2 weeks late for a repeat injection (more than 10 weeks after the last injection) she should be advised to abstain from sex or use additional contraceptive protection, such as condoms, for the next 7 days. The use of emergency contraception should be considered if unprotected sex has occurred.

References

1. Tang OS, Tang G, Yip P, Li B, Fan S. Long-term depot-medroxyprogesterone acetate and bone mineral density. *Contraception* 1999;59:25–9.
2. Cundy T, Cornish J, Evans MC, Roberts H, Reid IR. Recovery of bone density in women who stop using medroxyprogesterone acetate. *BMJ* 1994;308:247–8.

Progestogen-only implants

Patient selection

QUESTION

In women weighing over 70 kg, do progestogen-only implants provide effective contraception? (Five similar enquiries.)

POPULATION: Women weighing over 70 kg.
INTERVENTION: Progestogen-only implant.
OUTCOME: Efficacy.

ANSWER

Until 2005, no pregnancies had been reported in the literature in women using the subdermal progestogen-only implant (Implanon®, Organon). However, in a post-marketing survey from Australia, 13 true failures were identified.[1] A sufficient dose of etonogestrel is released during the 3 year licensed duration of use to inhibit ovulation in 100% of women.[2] At present, there is no direct evidence to show that progestogen-only implants are less effective in women weighing more than 70 kg or that the implant should be replaced earlier. The Summary of Product Characteristics for Implanon does not recommend changing the implant before the 3-year duration in women weighing more than 70 kg.

The previously available levonorgestrel-releasing implant (Norplant®) did not inhibit ovulation in all women. The 5-year cumulative pregnancy rates for Norplant and Norplant II were less than 1.5/100 women years. Weight over 70 kg and age at insertion less than 25 years both increased the failure rates for Norplant and Norplant II.

A multinational, randomised trial, which recruited 1198 women using Norplant and 600 women using Norplant II, identified no pregnancies in the first 4 years of use.[3] In the 5th year of use, the annual pregnancy rate was 1/100 woman years. Three pregnancies occurred in Norplant users: two in year 5 and one after 35 months of use in a woman using concurrent rifampicin. All women in whom pregnancy occurred weighed more than 70 kg.[4] Higher failure rates have been shown in women weighing more than 70 kg using Norplant or the levonorgestrel-releasing intravaginal ring.[5]

The CEU advises that, for women weighing more than 70 kg, the etonogestrel-only implant (Implanon) provides effective contraception for the 3 years licensed duration of use.

QUESTION

For women using the etonogestrel-only implant who weigh more than 70 kg, when should the implant be replaced? (Two similar enquiries.)

POPULATION: Women using the progestogen-only implant Implanon, who weigh more than 70 kg.

INTERVENTION: Replacement.

OUTCOME: Contraceptive efficacy.

ANSWER

The efficacy of the etonogestrel-only implant (Implanon) is related to plasma concentration of etonogestrel, which is inversely related to body weight and decreases with time after insertion. Pharmacokinetic studies on Implanon have found that the highest etonogestrel concentrations are found in women weighing less than 50 kg and the lowest levels are in women who weigh more than 70 kg.[6,7] The release rate of etonogestrel from the implant decreases over the 3 years of use from 60–70 micrograms/day in year 1 to 25–30 micrograms per day at the end of year 3. Concentrations of etonogestrel are sufficient to inhibit ovulation in 100% of women throughout the 3 years licensed duration of use.

A review of studies highlighted that most obese women are purposely excluded from studies on Implanon.[8] However, in studies that did include a small number of women (175 in total) weighing more than 70 kg, no pregnancies occurred during Implanon use.

The Summary of Product Characteristics for Implanon states that, as clinical experience with Implanon in heavier women in the third year of use is limited, it cannot be excluded that the contraceptive effect at this time for these women may be lower than for women of normal weight. Clinicians may consider earlier replacement of Implanon in heavier women.

The CEU advises that women weighing more than 70 kg can rely on the etonogestrel-only implant (Implanon) for the usual 3 years licensed duration of use and early removal and/or replacement of the implant is not required.

QUESTION

For women weighing 140 kg, do progestogen-only implants provide effective contraception?

POPULATION: Women weighing 140 kg.

INTERVENTION: Use of progestogen-only implant (Implanon).

OUTCOME: Contraceptive efficacy.

ANSWER

A postmarketing survey has identified 13 true failures with Implanon.[1] A sufficient dose of etonogestrel is released during the 3-year licensed duration of use to inhibit ovulation in 100% of women using this method.[2] At present, there is no direct evidence to show that Implanon is less effective in women weighing 140 kg or that the implant should be replaced earlier. The Summary of Product Characteristics for Implanon does not recommend changing the implant before the 3-year duration in women weighing more than 70 kg.

The CEU advises that for women weighing 140 kg, the etonogestrel-only implant (Implanon) provides effective contraception for its 3 years licensed duration of use.

QUESTION

For women aged 43 years, is it safe to use the progestogen-only implant, Implanon?

POPULATION:	**Women aged 43 years.**
INTERVENTION:	**Progestogen-only implant (Implanon).**
OUTCOME:	**Safety.**

ANSWER

The *WHO Medical Eligibility Criteria for Contraceptive Use* recommends that for women aged 18–45 years the progestogen-only implant can be used without restriction (WHO category 1).

The Summary of Product Characteristics for the etonogestrel-only implant (Implanon) states that safety and efficacy have been established in women aged 18–40 years. The information in the Summary of Product Characteristics comes from clinical trials that only included women aged 18–40 years.

The CEU recommends that the etonogestrel-only implant can be used by women up to the age of 54 years, if wished. After this time, most women can be assumed to be postmenopausal.[9]

References
1. Harrison-Woolrych M, Hill R. Unintended pregnancies with the etonogestrel implant (Implanon): a case series from postmarketing experience in Australia. *Contraception* 2005;71:306–8.

2. Croxatto HB. Mechanisms that explain the contraceptive action of progestin implants for women. *Contraception* 2002;65:21–7.
3. Sivin I, Campodonico I, Kiriway O. The performance of levonorgestrel rod and Norplant contraceptive implant: a 5-year randomised study. *Hum Reprod* 1998;13:3371–8.
4. Sivin I, Mishell DR, Darney P, Wan L, Christ M. Levonorgestrel capsule implant in the United States: a 5 year study. *Obstet Gynecol* 1998;92:337–44.
5. World Health Organization Special Programme of Research. Microdose intrauterine levonorgestrel for contraception. *Contraception* 1987;35:363–79.
6. Huber J, Wenzl R. Pharmakokinetics of Implanon. An integrated analysis. *Contraception* 1998;58:85–90S.
7. Bennink HJ. The pharmacokinetics and pharmacodynamics of Implanon, a single-rod etonogestrel contraceptive implant. *Eur J Contracept Reprod Health Care* 2000;5:12–20.
8. Glasier A. Implantable contraceptives for women; effectiveness, discontinuation rates, return to fertility, and outcomes of pregnancy. *Contraception* 2002;65:29–37.
9. Faculty of Family Planning and Reproductive Healthcare Clinical Effectiveness Unit. Contraception for Women Aged over 40 Years. *J Fam Plann Reprod Health Care* 2005;31:51–64.

Efficacy

QUESTION

For women who have had an etonogestrel-only implant in place for more than 3 years, is the method still effective?

POPULATION: **Women who have had an etonogestrel implant, Implanon, in place for more than 3 years.**

INTERVENTION: **Additional contraceptive methods.**

OUTCOME: **Efficacy.**

ANSWER

The etonogestrel-only implant (Implanon) is licensed to provide contraception for 3 years. The Summary of Product Characteristics recommends that it should not be left in place for more than 3 years.

A cohort study investigated women using an etonogestrel-only implant for up to 4 years.[1] Although 200 women were recruited to the trial, only 96 continued with the implant for 4 years. There were no pregnancies reported during 658 woman-years of exposure to the implant (Pearl Index of 0.0; 95% CI 0.0–0.6). Other cohort studies looked at the continuous use of an etonogestrel-only implant for 4 years and reported no pregnancies with 296 woman-years[2] and 645 woman-years[3] of use.

A post-marketing surveillance study found 13 true failures.[4] In general, however, from the available evidence, no pregnancies have been reported in studies of women using an etonogestrel-only implant for up to 4 years. The CEU recommends that women who have had an Implanon in place for more than 3 years should be advised that this is outwith the product licence and that they should use barrier methods of contraception or abstain until the implant has been replaced or they have started another method of contraception.

QUESTION

For women with body mass index of 36 kg/m² who are using a progestogen-only implant which is due to be removed at 3 years, which contraceptive methods are suitable while awaiting sterilisation?

POPULATION: Women with a BMI more than 30 kg/m² who are due to have Implanon removed at 3 years.

INTERVENTION: Alternative contraception while awaiting sterilisation.

OUTCOME: Safety.

ANSWER

Laparoscopic sterilisation has a 1/200 failure rate (up to 1/500 at 10 years follow up).[5] There is a 1/1000 risk of laparotomy due to damage to blood vessel, bowel or bladder. This risk of laparotomy is increased for women with increased BMI. An effective method of contraception should be used until sterilisation is performed. Alternative contraceptive options, including vasectomy, should be considered by all women requesting sterilisation.

The etonogestrel-only implant (Implanon) can be used for 3 years even if women have a raised BMI or weigh more than 70 kg. There are some data indicating that failure rates of Implanon are low even beyond 3 years use.[1–3] Efficacy of the etonogestrel implant is unaffected by BMI or weight but it should not be used beyond the licensed duration of 3 years. If used after this time, an additional method (such as condoms or a progestogen-only pill) may be advised while awaiting sterilisation.

A progestogen-only pill can be used by women weighing more than 70 kg but current opinion is that two pills should be taken at the same time every day to provide effective contraception. The new desogestrel-only pill has been shown to inhibit ovulation in 97% of cycles and can be taken as one tablet per day for women weighing more than 70 kg. Progestogen-only pills could be used along with the etonogestrel-only implant while awaiting sterilisation.

Women with BMI over 30 kg/m² are at an inherent increased risk of VTE. The *WHO Medical Eligibility Criteria* recommends that for women with a BMI over 30 kg/m² the benefits of using combined hormonal contraception generally outweigh the risks (WHO category 2). The CEU suggests that that non-estrogen containing methods (progestogen-only pills, injectables, intrauterine system or copper IUD) might be more appropriate as they are not associated with an increased risk of VTE.[6,7] Women awaiting laparoscopic sterilisation who are using combined hormonal contraception should be advised to continue with the method until the procedure is complete and stop combined hormonal methods at the end of the packet following sterilisation.

The CEU advises that for women with BMI over 30 kg/m², laparoscopic sterilisation may be associated with an increased risk of laparotomy and women should be informed about this.[2] Alternative contraceptive methods should be considered. If women are using an etonogestrel-only implant (which was inserted 3 years ago), an additional method of contraception (such as condoms or a progestogen-only pill) should be used as an alternative, or in addition, to the implant while awaiting sterilisation. The etonogestrel-only implant can then be removed at the time of sterilisation.

QUESTION

For women aged 47 years with menopausal symptoms who have been using the levonorgestrel-only implant (Norplant) for 5 years, can the device be retained beyond this time to provide continuing contraception.

POPULATION: Women who are 47 years old who have menopausal symptoms.
INTERVENTION: Subdermal progestogen-only contraception (Norplant) use beyond 5 years.
OUTCOME: Continued contraceptive efficacy.

ANSWER

The levonorgestrel-only implant will not prevent or mask vasomotor symptoms associated with the menopause. Amenorrhoea in women using the levonorgestrel-only implant cannot be used to diagnose the menopause. It is accepted practice in the UK to continue an effective method of contraception until 1 year after the last menstrual period if aged over 50 years (or for 2 years if aged less than 50 years).[8]

One study was identified which investigated the use of the levonorgestrel-only implant (Norplant) beyond the recommended 5 years use.[9] Data were derived from 1210 women who took part in two independent studies. A noncomparative trial enrolled women in the USA and the Dominican Republic. The second study was a randomised, controlled trial which aimed to compare Norplant with another implant (Jadelle®, Population Council). The long-term pregnancy rates were low. The 5-year cumulative efficacy of the implant in these combined studies was 1.1/100 woman years. This low failure rate at 5 years meant that efficacy could be investigated into the 7th year of use. For all women, the cumulative pregnancy rate was 1.1/100 woman years at 5 years and 1.9/100 woman years at 7 years.

For women who used Norplant after the age of 30 years, this study suggested a near-zero pregnancy risk at anytime in the 7 years after insertion if body weight was less than 100 kg. For women aged 18–27 years at the time of Norplant insertion, use at 7 years was associated with a cumulative pregnancy rate of 22.5/1000 per year (95% CI 1.7–43.4). For women aged 28–33 years at the time of Norplant insertion, the cumulative pregnancy rate after 7 years use was 17.7 (95% CI 0.0–38.5) and for women aged 34–44 years at the time of Norplant insertion, the cumulative pregnancy rate was 0 (95% CI 0–0).

The CEU does not generally recommend the use of Norplant beyond the 5 years licensed duration. There are some data to suggest contraception continues beyond the 5 years licensed duration. After counselling, women aged 47 years may wish to continue to rely on this as their only method of contraception.

Update to Answer

The levonorgestrel-releasing implant system (Norplant®, Hoechst Marion Roussel) was discontinued in October 1999; any system still in place should have been removed by the end of 2004.

References

1. Affandi B, Korver T, Geurts TB, Coelingh Bennink HJ. A pilot efficacy study with a single-rod contraceptive implant (Implanon) in 200 Indonesian women treated for < or = 4 years. *Contraception* 1999;59:167–74.
2. Kiriwat O, Patanayindee A, Koetsawang S, Korver T, Bennink HJ. A 4-year pilot study on the efficacy and safety of Implanon, a single rod hormonal contraceptive implant, in healthy women in Thailand. *Eur J Contracept Reprod Health Care* 1998;3:85–91.
3. Zheng SR, Zheng HM, Qian SZ, Sang GW, Kaper RF. A long-term study of the efficacy and acceptability of a single-rod hormonal contraceptive implant (Implanon) in healthy women in China. *Eur J Contracept Reprod Health Care* 1999;4:85–93.
4. Harrison-Woolrych M, Hill R. Unintended pregnancies with the etonogestrel implant (Implanon): a case series from postmarketing experience in Australia. *Contraception* 2005;71:306–8.

5. Royal College of Obstetricians and Gynaecologists. *Male and Female Sterilisation.* Evidence-based Clinical Guideline Number 4. London: RCOG Press; 2004.

6. Faculty of Family Planning and Reproductive Health Care Clinical Effectiveness Unit. First prescription of combined oral contraception. *J Fam Plann Reprod Health Care* 2003;29:209–22.

7. World Health Organization Collaborative Study of Cardiovascular Disease and Steroid Hormone Contraception. Cardiovascular disease and use of oral and injectable progestogen-only contraceptives and combined injectable contraceptives. *Contraception* 1998;57:315-24.

8. Faculty of Family Planning and Reproductive Healthcare Clinical Effectiveness Unit. Contraception for women aged over 40 years. *J Fam Plann Reprod Health Care* 2005;31:51–64.

9. Sivin I, Mishell DRJ, Diaz S, Biswas A, Alvarez F, Darney P, *et al.* Prolonged effectiveness of Norplant capsule implants: a 7-year study. *Contraception* 2000;61:187–94.

Insertion and removal

QUESTION

For women who are using combined oral contraception but wish to change methods, when can progestogen-only implants be inserted?

POPULATION: Women using combined oral contraception.
INTERVENTION: Switching to progestogen-only implants.
OUTCOME: Efficacy.

ANSWER

The WHO *Selected Practice Recommendations* recommends that, if a woman has being using her combined oral contraception consistently and correctly and it is reasonably certain that she is not pregnant, a progestogen-only implant can be inserted immediately. There is no need to wait until her next menstrual period, and no additional contraceptive protection is needed. Advice on when to stop her combined oral contraceptive pill safely will vary depending on her individual circumstances.

The CEU suggests that a woman can be advised to continue her combined oral contraceptive pill until the end of the packet then stop or she may be advised to stop her combined oral contraceptive pill as soon as the implant is inserted. If she chooses to stop her combined oral contraceptive pill immediately after insertion of the implant, advice on need for contraceptive protection will depend on how many combined oral contraceptive pills she has taken from the pack. If seven or more pills from the pack have been taken when the implant is inserted, additional contraceptive protection (such as condoms) is not required. If less than seven pills have been taken from the pack, women should be advised to use additional contraception for a further 7 days (either condoms or continue the combined pill for 7 days).

QUESTION

For women using the etonogestrel-only implant, what is the effect of timing of insertion on efficacy in terms of pregnancies and ectopic pregnancies?

POPULATION: Women using the etonogestrel implant.
INTERVENTION: Time of implant insertion.
OUTCOME: Efficacy in terms of pregnancies and ectopic pregnancies.

ANSWER

The WHO *Selected Practice Recommendations* recommends that the etonogestrel-only implant can be inserted up to and including day 5 of the menstrual cycle without the need for additional contraceptive protection. Implants can be inserted after this time if there has been no risk of pregnancy. Additional contraceptive protection (such as condoms) is advised for the next 7 days.

The Summary of Product Characteristics for the etonogestrel-only implant (Implanon) states that no pregnancies have occurred in clinical trials of women aged 18–40 years with a total exposure of 59 800 cycles. The Pearl Index in these trials was 0.0 (95% CI 0.00–0.08). More recent data report 13 true, 'method' failures and five ectopic pregnancies among all failures.[1]

During the development of Implanon, 13 studies were undertaken that met the requirements for good clinical practice. These core data studies, involving 1716 women from ten countries, assessed 4103 woman-years of use of Implanon in which no pregnancies occurred. The Pearl Index in these trials was 0.0 (95% CI 0.00–0.09). Another four studies were not compliant with good clinical practice, but brought the total exposure to 5629 women-years with no pregnancies.[2]

The CEU advises that Implanon can be inserted up to and including day 5 of the menstrual cycle to provide immediate contraceptive protection from pregnancy (intrauterine and extrauterine). If inserted after this time, additional contraceptive protection (such as condoms) will be required for 7 days.

QUESTION

For women awaiting removal of an etonogestrel-only implant, is abstinence before removal advised? (One similar enquiry.)

POPULATION: Women awaiting removal of an etonogestrel-only implant.

INTERVENTION: Abstinence prior to removal.

OUTCOME: Risk of pregnancy.

ANSWER

The etonogestrel-only implant (Implanon) works by inhibition of ovulation and also thickens cervical mucus thus preventing sperm penetration into the upper reproductive tract. On removal, contraceptive protection is lost. If pregnancy is not desired, another method of contraception should be commenced before, or at the time of, removal. The progestogenic effects of etonogestrel on cervical mucus inhibit sperm penetration into the upper reproductive tract. This effect is lost only after removal and therefore women do not need to abstain 7 days prior to removal.

QUESTION

For women who have a progestogen-only implant, what is the best method of removal to avoid fractured rods or failed removals? (Two similar enquiries.)

POPULATION: Women who have a progestogen-only contraceptive implant.

INTERVENTION: Removal.

OUTCOME: Avoidance of complications.

ANSWER

Removal of the six-rod levonorgestrel implant (Norplant) is more likely to be associated with complications than removal of the single-rod etonogestrel implant (Implanon). Norplant consists of six rods and their structure is far more flexible than the single rod of Implanon. It is recommended that a 'U' technique for removal of Norplant is employed. Clinicians who will be inserting and removing Implanon should undergo an appropriate training programme and have a certificate of competence. Details can be obtained on the FFPRHC website.

Update to Answer

The levonorgestrel-releasing implant system (Norplant®, Hoechst Marion Roussel) was discontinued in October 1999; any system still in place should have been removed by the end of 2004.

QUESTION

For women who have a complete rod, or a fragment of a rod, of a progestogen-only implant remaining in place, what is the most effective imaging modality, what are the likely systemic effects after the expiry of the contraceptive device and what is the evidence that it should be removed?

POPULATION: Women who have a progestogen-only contraceptive implant or a fragment of one.

INTERVENTION: Imaging.

OUTCOME: Menstrual pattern, fertility, local reactions, systemic effects.

ANSWER

There is evidence that the levonorgestrel-only implant (Norplant) can be visualised using both X-ray and ultrasound. The etonogestrel-only implant (Implanon) is not radio-opaque and cannot be seen with X-ray or computed tomography (CT) scan, but can be seen with high frequency ultrasound probes or magnetic resonance imaging (MRI).

Clinical estimation of any remaining contraceptive or systemic progestogenic effects of the implant can be supported by serum concentrations of the respective progestogen. When appropriate, serum concentrations of levonorgestrel or etonogestrel may need to be estimated after discussion with the medical advisor of the relevant pharmaceutical company.

There was no evidence found of any adverse effects of leaving a recalcitrant fragment in place. However, this would need to be balanced with the intentions of the woman regarding her fertility and the clinical picture.

Update to Answer

The levonorgestrel-releasing implant system (Norplant®, Hoechst Marion Roussel) was discontinued in October 1999; any system still in place should have been removed by the end of 2004.

QUESTION

For women who have just had the etonogestrel-only implant removed, when does ovulation occur and when is there a need for emergency contraception? (Two similar enquiries.)

POPULATION: Women who use the etonogestrel-only implant.

INTERVENTION: Removal of the implant.

OUTCOME: Risk of ovulation and subsequent need for emergency contraception.

ANSWER

The etonogestrel-only implant (Implanon) provides a dose of etonogestrel sufficient to prevent ovulation throughout 3 years of use.[3] The low systemic dose of etonogestrel decreases rapidly following removal of the implant. When the implant is removed, serum concentrations of etonogestrel decrease to below 20 pg/ml within 1 week.[4] Ovulation returns within 3 months of implant removal.[5] A pilot study showed that 6 of 29 women who stopped using the etonogestrel-only implant and did not use any other contraception conceived within 3 months of removal.[6]

The progestogenic effects of etonogestrel on cervical mucus inhibit sperm penetration into the upper reproductive tract. This effect is lost only after removal and therefore women do not need to abstain 7 days prior to removal. As soon as the etonogestrel-only implant is removed, however, contraceptive protection is lost. Another method of contraception will be required if pregnancy is not desired. If unprotected sex or potential contraceptive failure occurs following removal of the implant, emergency contraception should be considered.

References

1. Harrison-Woolrych M, Hill R. Unintended pregnancies with the etonogestrel implant (Implanon): a case series from postmarketing experience in Australia. *Contraception* 2005;71:306–8.
2. Croxatto HB, Urbancsek J, Massai R, Coelingh Bennik H, van Beek A. A multicentre efficacy and safety study of a single contraceptive implant, Implanon Study Group. *Hum Reprod* 1999;14:976-81.
3. Croxatto HB. Mechanisms that explain the contraceptive action of progestin implants for women. *Contraception* 2002;65:21–7.
4. Huber J, Wenzl R. Pharmakokinetics of Implanon. An integrated analysis. *Contraception* 1998;58:85–90S.
5. Davies GC, Feng LX, Newton JR, Van Beek A, Coelingh-Bennink HJ. Release characteristics ovarian activity and menstrual bleeding with a single contraceptive implant releasing 3-ketodesogestrel. *Contraception* 1993;47:251–61.

6. Kiriwat O, Patanayindee A, Koetsawang S, Korver T, Bennink HJ. A 4-year pilot study on the efficacy and safety of Implanon, a single rod hormonal contraceptive implant, in healthy women in Thailand. *Eur J Contracept Reprod Health Care* 1998;3:85–91.

Adverse effects

QUESTION

For women using an etonogestrel-only implant, is there any evidence of an association with decreased libido and how could this be managed?

POPULATION: Women using the etonogestrel-only implant.

INTERVENTION: Decreased libido.

OUTCOME: Evidence of an association and management.

ANSWER

Many premenopausal and postmenopausal women suffer from low libido, for which there is a variety causes. The Summary of Product Characteristics for the etonogestrel-only implant (Implanon) reports that libido changes are common ($\geq 1/100$ women). In a review of clinical trials of implantable contraceptives, loss of libido was reported in 2.0–5.4% of women.[1-4] In one comparative trial, 5.4% of Norplant (now discontinued) users and 3.3% of Implanon users experienced loss of libido.[2] In various Norplant and Jadelle clinical trials, the reported annual rate of loss of libido was 0.4–3.8/100 woman years, which was similar to the rate of 0.0–1.4/100 woman years reported among IUD users.[3,5,6] Overall, in the trials identified, loss of libido was a cause for discontinuation in 0–8% of women.[4]

Androgen therapy has been used to treat premenopausal women, significantly improving psychological wellbeing as well as mood, sexual thoughts, interest, satisfaction and sexual function. However, evidence is limited.

Despite extensive searching, the CEU could find no information on whether women who are experiencing loss of libido with the etonogestrel-only implant regain their libido over time while they are still using it. Furthermore, the CEU could find no information on treating loss of libido in women who are using contraceptive implants. The management of female sexual dysfunction requires thorough evaluation and consideration of all possible causes. If physical or emotional causes are likely, refer for psychosexual or other counselling is appropriate.

QUESTION

For women using an etonogestrel-only implant who develop pruritus but have normal liver function tests, should the implant be removed?

POPULATION: Women who are using an etonogestrel-only implant with pruritus and normal liver function tests.

INTERVENTION: Removal of the etonogestrel-only implant.

OUTCOME: Resolution of symptoms.

ANSWER

The Summary of Product Characteristics for the etonogestrel-only implant (Implanon) states that insertion or removal may cause bruising, slight local irritation, pain or itching. Pain and skin reaction at the insertion site are common adverse reactions with implant insertion and were found to occur in more than 1/100 women during clinical trials. Uncommon adverse skin reactions, such as general pruritus or skin rash, occurred in less than 1/100 women but more than 1/1000 women . If a condition occurs for the first time after insertion of an etonogestrel-only implant, clinical judgement should be used to decide whether removal of the implant is justified.

The *WHO Medical Eligibility Criteria* recommends that for women with compensated liver disease, the benefits of using a progestogen-only implant generally outweigh the risks (WHO category 2).

For women using an etonogestrel-only implant who develop pruritus, the CEU suggests that the implant can be retained and symptoms observed. If symptoms fail to resolve, liver function tests should be re-evaluated and consideration given to removal of the implant.

QUESTION

For women using the etonogestrel-only implant, is there a reported association with osteoporosis?

POPULATION: Women of reproductive age.

INTERVENTION: The etonogestrel implant.

OUTCOME: Risk of osteoporosis.

ANSWER

The Summary of Product Characteristics for the etonogestrel-only implant (Implanon) states that contraceptive effect is mainly achieved by inhibition of ovulation. However, ovarian activity is not completely suppressed. The mean serum estradiol concentration remains above that seen in the early-follicular phase of the menstrual cycle.

A small comparative study of women using a copper IUD or the etonogestrel-only implant investigated effects on bone mineral density over 2 years use.[7] Bone mineral density was measured in the lumbar spine, the proximal femur and the distal radius. There were no significant differences between the two groups in bone mineral density at any site. Similar results have been found in trials of the levonorgestrel-only implant (Norplant, now discontinued).[8–12]

The CEU advises that there is no evidence of an association between the etonogestrel-only implant and reduced bone mineral density or osteoporosis.

QUESTION

For women with premenstrual syndrome or endometriosis, is there any evidence that an etonogestrel-only implant is helpful in management?

POPULATION: Women with endometriosis or premenstrual syndrome.
INTERVENTION: Etonogestrel-only implant.
OUTCOME: Improvement in endometriosis or premenstrual syndrome.

ANSWER

The etonogestrel-only implant (Implanon) inhibits ovulation by prevention of the luteinising hormone surge. The *WHO Medical Eligibility Criteria* recommends that women with endometriosis can have unrestricted use of a progestogen-only implant (WHO category 1).

Medical treatment of endometriosis aims to induce atrophy of ectopic endometrial tissue with the use of hormones that suppress ovarian function. The relatively low concentrations of circulating hormone in etonogestrel-only implant users is not sufficient to completely suppress FSH and luteinising hormone secretion. Follicular activity and proliferative/secretory activity within the endometrium persist.

No studies were identified which considered the use of the etonogestrel-only implant in the management of endometriosis or premenstrual syndrome.

References

1. Croxatto HB, Urbancsek J, Massai R, Coelingh Bennik H, van Beek A. A multicentre efficacy and safety study of a single contraceptive implant, Implanon Study Group. *Hum Reprod* 1999;14:976–81.
2. Urbancsek J. An integrated analysis of nonmenstrual adverse events with Implanon. *Contraception* 1998;58:109S-15S.
3. Sivin I, Viegas O, Campodonico I, Diaz S, Pavez M, Wan L, *et al*. Clinical performance of a new two-rod levonorgestrel contraceptive implant: a three-year randomised study with Norplant implants as controls. *Contraception* 1997;55:73–80.
4. Brache V, Faundes A, Alvarez F, Cochon L. Nonmenstrual adverse events during use of implantable contraceptives for women: data from clinical trials. *Contraception* 2002;65:63–74.
5. Harrison-Woolrych M, Hill R. Unintended pregnancies with the etonogestrel implant (Implanon): a case series from postmarketing experience in Australia. *Contraception* 2005;71:306–8.
6. Sivin I. Clinical effects of Norplant subdermal implants for contraception. In: Mishell DR, editor. *Long-acting Steroid Contraception. Advances in Human Fertility and Reproductive Endocrinology*. New York: Raven Press; 1983.
7. Beerthuizen R, van Beek A, Massai R, Makararinen L, Hout J, Bennick HC. Bone mineral density during long-term use of the progestagen contraceptive implant Implanon compared to a non-hormonal method of contraception. *Hum Reprod* 2000;15:118–22.
8. Intaraprasert S, Taneepanichskul S, Theppisai U, Chaturachinda K. Bone density in women receiving Norplant implants for contraception. *J Med Assoc Thai* 1997;80:738–41.
9. Diaz S, Reyes MV, Zepeda A, Gonzalez GB, Lopez JM, Campino C, *et al*. Norplant implants and progesterone vaginal rings do not affect maternal bone turnover and density during lactation and after weaning. *Hum Reprod* 1999;14:2499–505.
10. Di X, Li Y, Zhang C, Jiang J, Gu S. Effects of levonorgestrel-releasing subdermal contraceptive implants on bone density and bone metabolism. *Contraception* 1999;60:161–6.
11. Cromer BA, McArdle Blair J, Mahan JD, Zibners L, Naumovski Z. A prospective comparison of bone density in adolescent girls receiving depot medroxyprogesterone acetate (Depo-Provera), levonorgestrel (Norplant), or oral contraceptives. *J Pediatr* 1996;129:671–6.
12. Naessen T, Olsson SE, Gudmundon J. Differential effects on bone density of progestogen-only methods for contraception in premenopausal women. *Contraception* 1995;52:35–9.

Unscheduled bleeding

QUESTION

In women using a progestogen-only implant who present with bleeding after 12 months of use, is the insertion of a second implant a recommended treatment option?

POPULATION: Women using a progestogen-only implant who present with bleeding after 12 months of use.

INTERVENTION: Insertion of a second implant.

OUTCOME: Improvement in bleeding pattern.

ANSWER

Unscheduled bleeding is the most common reason for discontinuation of progestogen-only implants.[1] A review of progestogen-only implants highlights high discontinuation rates; the discontinuation rate for the etonogestrel-only implant (Implanon) varied in different parts of the world.[2] Among 1716 women using an etonogestrel-only implant, discontinuation rates were 30% over 3 years in Europe and Canada, compared with only 1% in South East Asia. Bleeding irregularity was cited as the most common reason for discontinuation. Discontinuation rates were highest in the initial months of use and fell over the 24 months following insertion.[3] In the first 6 months after insertion, the discontinuation rate was 5.3%. The discontinuation rate for the second 6 months was 6.4% and fell to 4.1% during months 13–18 and to 2.4% during months 19–24.

Serum concentrations of etonogestrel fall with each year of use but are always sufficient to inhibit ovulation. The absorption rate of etonogestrel is 60 micrograms/day after 3 months of use.[4] This slowly decreases to 30 micrograms/day after 24 months of use. For this reason, some women may present with bleeding in the second or third year of use.

The CEU supports the WHO *Selected Practice Recommendations*, which recommends that women using an etonogestrel-only implant who present with any type of bleeding should be investigated if clinically indicated. If a gynaecological problem is identified, appropriate treatment and referral is indicated. If no gynaecological problems are found and she desires treatment, non-hormonal options are available.

Spotting or light bleeding are common during the first year of use and are not harmful. In women with persistent bleeding, or women with bleeding after a period of amenorrhoea, gynaecological problems should be excluded.

Heavy or more prolonged bleeding (more than 8 days or twice as much as her usual menstrual period) should be investigated. If a woman does not wish treatment or if treatment fails, then the implant should be removed and another contraceptive method discussed.

Treatment of light or heavy bleeding with NSAIDs or combined oral contraceptives is modestly effective (Table 2). There is no suggestion that insertion of a second implant is appropriate treatment.

Table 2. Medical treatment for abnormal bleeding in women using an etonogestrel-only implant

Treatment	Dose and duration
Non-steroidal anti-inflammatory drugs	Ibuprofen 800 mg three times daily for 5 days
	or
	Mefenamic acid 500 mg twice daily for 5 days
Hormonal	Low-dose combined oral contraception (containing 30 micrograms ethinylestradiol and 150 micrograms levonorgestrel) for 21 days

References

1.   Glasier A. Implantable contraceptives for women; effectiveness, discontinuation rates, return to fertility, and outcomes of pregnancy. *Contraception* 2002;65:29–37.
2.   Affandi B. An integrated analysis of vaginal bleeding patterns in clinical trials of Implanon. *Contraception* 1998;58:99S–107S.
3.   Edwards JE, Moore A. Implanon. A Review of clinical studies. *Br J Fam Plann* 1999;24:3–16.
4.   Huber J, Wenzl R. Pharmakokinetics of Implanon. An integrated analysis. *Contraception* 1998;58:85–90S.

The perimenopause

QUESTION

For perimenopausal women requiring both contraception and control of menopausal symptoms, is the progestogen-only implant a useful intervention?

POPULATION: Perimenopausal women requiring both contraception and control of menopausal symptoms.

INTERVENTION: The etonogestrel-only implant.

OUTCOME: Contraceptive efficacy and role in managing menopausal symptoms.

ANSWER

Like other progestogen-only methods, the etonogestrel-only implant (Implanon) is an effective and suitable method of contraception for perimenopausal women.[1] There are no studies to demonstrate that etonogestrel-only implants can serve as the progestogen component of HRT. Thus, women using etonogestrel-only implants for contraception who also desire control of menopausal symptoms should use a conventional, combined HRT.

Concurrent use of an etonogestrel-only implant and combined HRT makes diagnosis of the menopause problematic. The estrogen component suppresses FSH production. To determine when contraception can safely be discontinued in a perimenopausal woman, HRT should ideally be discontinued to allow meaningful measurement of plasma FSH. Contraception should then be continued for 12 months after two measurements of FSH within the menopausal range (greater than 30 iu/l). If a woman is reluctant to stop HRT for this purpose, then some form of contraception should be continued until the age of 55 years, at which time loss of natural fertility can be assumed.

References
1.   Faculty of Family Planning and Reproductive Healthcare Clinical Effectiveness Unit. Contraception for women aged over 40 years. *J Fam Plann Reprod Health Care* 2005;31:51–64.

3 INTRAUTERINE CONTRACEPTION

Copper intrauterine devices

Who can use the intrauterine device?

QUESTION

For women with a history of previous ectopic pregnancy, can a copper IUD or LNG-IUS be safely used?

POPULATION:	Women with a history of previous ectopic pregnancy.
INTERVENTION:	Insertion of a IUD or LNG-IUS.
OUTCOME:	Safety.

ANSWER

The *WHO Medical Eligibility Criteria for Contraceptive Use* advises that women with a past history of ectopic pregnancy may have unrestricted use of the IUD or the LNG-IUS (WHO category 1). WHO acknowledges that the absolute risk of ectopic pregnancy is low, as IUDs have a high efficacy. However, women who do become pregnant while using an IUD have a higher relative risk of ectopic pregnancy than women in the general population.

One case–control study assessed the risk of ectopic pregnancy in IUD users compared with women who did not use contraception or who chose female sterilisation.[1] Current IUD users had 91% (95% CI 87–94%) protection against ectopic pregnancy compared with women using no contraception. The study suggested that although IUD users appeared to have a 60% increased risk of ectopic pregnancy compared with women who chose female sterilisation, the difference was not statistically significant.

In a 5-year study of the clinical performance of the Nova T® 380 IUD (Schering Health) in 400 women, no ectopic pregnancies or cases of pelvic inflammatory disease (PID) were reported.[2]

Future fertility was studied among 23 women using an IUD at the time an ectopic pregnancy was diagnosed and 305 women with ectopic pregnancy but without an IUD. This study reported no recurrence of ectopic pregnancy among the IUD users while the 2-year cumulative rate of recurrence of ectopic pregnancy among women who did not use an IUD was 28% (95% CI 17–39%).[3]

QUESTION

Is there any evidence that a history of cervical weakness increases the risk of expulsion of IUDs?

POPULATION: Women with a history of cervical weakness.
INTERVENTION: IUD.
OUTCOME: Expulsion of the device.

ANSWER

The risk of expulsion of IUDs is around 5% and is most common during the first year of use, and particularly within 3 months of insertion.

One study considered whether the use of cervical dilatation at the time of insertion caused any increase in the rate of expulsion but found that expulsion rates were no higher in women who had cervical dilatation.[4] Several studies have indicated that expulsion rates of IUDs are higher in women who have heavy menstrual flow.[5–7]

No studies considering the rate of expulsion of IUDs in women with a history of cervical weakness in pregnancy were identified.

QUESTION

For women with complex medical problems who have had an IUD (Novagard®, Schering Health) in place for 6 years, does the device need to be removed or replaced, and what other contraceptive options can be used safely?

POPULATION: Women with complex medical problems, who have had an IUD
                 (Novagard) in place for 6 years.
INTERVENTION: Removal of IUD and consideration of other contraceptive methods.
OUTCOME: Safety.

ANSWER

The Nova T 380 IUD (previously known as Novagard) is licensed for 5 years use. It should then be removed or replaced.

The *WHO Medical Eligibility Criteria for Contraceptive Use* makes recommendations relating to the use of all currently available contraceptive methods by women with complex medical problems.

References

1. Skjeldestad FE. How effectively do copper intrauterine devices prevent ectopic pregnancy? *Acta Obstet Gynecol Scand* 1997;76:684–90.
2. Batar I, Kuukankorpi A, Siljander M, Elomaa K, Rauramo I. Five-year clinical experiences with NOVA T 380 copper IUD. *Contraception* 2002;66:309–14.
3. Bernoux A, Job-Spira N, Germain E, Coste J, Bouyer J. Fertility outcome after ectopic pregnancy and use of an intrauterine device at the time of index ectopic pregnancy. *Hum Reprod* 2000;15:1173–7.
4. Chi IC, Champion CB, Wilkens LR. Cervical dilatation in interval insertion of an IUD. Who requires it and does it lead to a high expulsion rate? *Contraception* 1987;36:403–15.
5. Ikomi A, Pepra EF. Efficacy of the levonorgestrel intrauterine system in treating menorrhagia: Actualities and ambiguities. *J Fam Plann Reprod Health Care* 2002;28:99–100.
6. Diaz J, Bahamondes L, Monteiro I, Petta C, Hildalgo MM, Arce XE. Acceptability and performance of the levonorgestrel-releasing intrauterine system (Mirena) in Campinas, Brazil. *Contraception* 2000;62:59–61.
7. Hildago M, Bahamondes L, Perrotti M, Diaz J, Dantas-Monteiro C, Petta C. Bleeding patterns and clinical performance of the levonorgestrel–releasing intrauterine system (Mirena) up to two years. *Contraception* 2002;65:129–32.

Which device?

QUESTION

For women having an IUD inserted, what device offers the best efficacy?

POPULATION: Women having an IUD inserted.
INTERVENTION: Choice of device.
OUTCOME: Efficacy.

ANSWER

After several randomised controlled trials with the T Safe® CU 380A (FP) IUD,[1,2] the WHO concluded that the high contraceptive efficacy provided by the device meant that it could be considered as a non-surgical, potentially reversible alternative to tubal ligation for women who wanted long-term contraception. The T Safe 380A therefore became the 'gold standard' against which all other IUDs could be compared.

However, the T Safe 380A, with a width of 32 mm, may cause difficulties in insertion. There is a slimline model (TT380S) presently available in the UK (Durbin: www.durbin.co.uk/clinic_sales.htm) but one randomised controlled trial has found that this device may have a higher expulsion rate than the standard model during the first year of use. Despite this, users of the slimline device had lower pregnancy rates than users of the T Safe 380A at 3 and 4 years.[3] The authors acknowledge that more comparative trials with the TT380S are needed to confirm this finding. A review from the FFPRHC acknowledges that providers may have difficulties in inserting the T Safe 380A and has suggested an order of preference for the use of different IUDs based on efficacy and diameter; this is reproduced in Table 3.[4]

Table 3. Suggested preference order for the use of IUDs

Situation	IUD preference
Parous women with normal periods	T Safe 380A
	Nova T380
	GyneFix
	ML 375
	Flexi-T300
Nulliparous women with normal periods	Gyne Fix
	T Safe 380A
	Nova T380
	Flexi-T300
Women with heavy periods/heavy periods with Copper IUD	LNG-IUS
Insertion difficulties encountered	Nova T380
	Flexi-T300
	GyneFix
Emergency IUD/short-term use in young women	Nova T380
	Flexi-T300
	Nova T200 (while in-date stocks remain)

Ultimately, the choice of device will depend on several factors including benefits and risks, the familiarity and experience of the clinician and the cost of the device for the service provider.

QUESTION

For women having an IUD inserted, what device (other than the T Safe 380A) can be chosen for ease of insertion?

POPULATION:	Women having an IUD inserted.
INTERVENTION:	Choice of device (other than the T Safe 380A).
OUTCOME:	Ease of insertion.

ANSWER

The T Safe 380A IUD, with a width of 32 mm, may cause difficulties in insertion. There is a Slimline model (TT380S) presently available in the UK (Durbin: www.durbin.co.uk/clinic_sales.htm) but one randomised controlled trial has found that this device may have a higher expulsion rate than the standard model during the first year of use. Despite this, users of the slimline device had lower pregnancy rates than users of the T Safe 380A at 3 and 4 years.[3]. A review from the FFPRHC acknowledges that providers may have difficulties in inserting the T Safe 380A and has suggested an order of preference for the use of different IUDs based on efficacy and diameter (Table 3).[4]

QUESTION

For women using a GyneFix® (FP) IUD, does copper corrosion affect the efficacy of the device?

POPULATION:	Women using GyneFix.
INTERVENTION:	Copper corrosion.
OUTCOME:	Contraceptive efficacy.

ANSWER

The main factor influencing IUD performance is the number of copper ions present within the uterine cavity. This is governed by positioning, solvent saturation with copper, a surface area of copper of at least 200 mm^2 and the performance of the plastic carrier.[5] The GyneFix is anchored at the fundus of the uterus, 100% of the copper surface area is available for copper release, the surface area is 330 mm² and there is no plastic component. This compares with conventional 'framed' IUDs, where an estimated 30–40% of the copper surface is ineffective as no copper release occurs from the wire in contact with the plastic frame. Intrauterine copper corrosion is a normal process affected by individual variations. *In vitro*[5,6] and *in vivo* experiments[7–11] demonstrate that tarnish, fragmentation and deposits do not modify the rate of copper release or increase pregnancy rates. The manufacturers of GyneFix are currently applying for an extended license to 8, 10 or 12 years (the current license is for a 5-year duration of use). The available evidence found by the CEU therefore suggests that contraceptive efficacy of GyneFix would be maintained despite a corroded appearance.

References

1. United Nations Development Programme, United Nations Population Fund, World Health Organization, World Bank Special Programme of Research, Development and Research Training in Hum Reprod. Long-term reversible contraception. Twelve years of experience with the TCu380A and TCu220C. *Contraception* 1997;56:341–52.
2. World Health Organization, Special Programme of Research, Development and Research Training in Hum Reprod Task Force on the Safety and Efficacy of Fertility Regulating Methods. The TCu380A, TCu220C, Multiload 250 and Nova T IUDs at 3, 5 and 7 years of use: results from three randomized multicentre trials. *Contraception* 1990;42:141–58.
3. Sivin I, Diaz J, Alvarez F, Brache V, Diaz S, Pavez M, *et al*. Four-year experience in a randomized study of the Gyne T 380 Slimline and the Standard T 380 intrauterine copper devices. *Contraception* 1993;47:37–42.
4. Dennis J, Hampton N. IUDs: Which device? *Fam Plann Reprod Health Care* 2002;28:61–8.
5. Kosonen A. Factors influencing the dissolution of copper in utero. *Contracept Deliv Syst* 1981;2:77–85.
6. Tsong YY, Nash HA. Effect of tarnish on copper release. *Contraception* 1991;44:385–92.
7. Bastidas JM, Mora N, Cano E, Polo JL. Characterization of copper corrosion products originated in simulated uterine fluids and on packaged intrauterine devices. *J Mater Sci Mater Med* 2001;12:391–7.
8. Kosonen A. Corrosion of copper in utero. *Fertil Steril* 1978;30:59–65.
9. Chantler EN, Scott K, Filho C, I, Elstein M, Faragher EB, Lorimer GW. Degradation of the copper-releasing intrauterine contraceptive device and its significance. *Br J Obstet Gynaecol* 1984;91:172–81.
10. Chantler E, Kenway P, Larouk Z, Faragher FB, Morris J, Kosonen, *et al*. An analysis of the corrosion process of the Nova-T IUD. *Adv Contracept* 1994;10:287–301.
11. Berthou J, Chretien FC, Driguez PA. Degradation of Copper IUDs in utero. The process of metallic corrosion. A scanning electron microscope study. *Gynecol Obstet Fertil* 2003;31:29–42.

When should an IUD be inserted?

QUESTION

For women wishing to use an IUD or LNG-IUS, when should the device be inserted for safe and effective contraception?

POPULATION: Women wishing to use an IUD or the LNG-IUS.

INTERVENTION: Timing of insertion.

OUTCOME: Safety and efficacy.

ANSWER

The *WHO Medical Eligibility Criteria for Contraceptive Use* advises that:

● Women who are more than 4 weeks postpartum and who are, or are not, breastfeeding (including following a caesarean birth) have no restrictions on insertion of either the copper-bearing IUD or the LNG-IUS (WHO category 1).

● For women within the first 48 hours postpartum, the contraceptive benefits of having an IUD inserted generally outweigh the risks (WHO category 2). There is an increased risk of expulsion if the LNG-IUS is inserted within this period (WHO category 3).

● There is an increased risk of perforation, which generally outweighs the contraceptive benefits, if an IUD or LNG-IUS is inserted between 48 hours and 4 weeks postpartum (WHO category 3).

● Women who have had a first-trimester termination of pregnancy have no restrictions on insertion of either the IUD or the LNG-IUS. (WHO category 1).

● The contraceptive benefits of either the IUD or the LNG-IUS generally outweigh the risk of expulsion following second-trimester abortion (WHO category 2).

● Women with puerperal sepsis, or women immediately following septic abortion, should not have an IUD inserted (WHO category 4).

The WHO *Selected Practice Recommendations for Contraceptive Use* advises, for women having menstrual cycles:

● A woman can have an IUD inserted any time within the first 12 days after the start of menstrual bleeding, at her convenience, not just during menstruation. No additional contraceptive protection is needed.

● An IUD can also be inserted at any other time during the menstrual cycle, at the woman's convenience, if it is reasonably certain that she is not pregnant. No additional contraceptive protection is needed.

For a woman who is switching from another method of contraception to the copper IUD, the WHO *Selected Practice Recommendations for Contraceptive Use* advises that the IUD can be inserted immediately if it is reasonably certain that she is not pregnant. There is no need to wait for the next menstrual period. No additional contraceptive protection is needed.

Traditionally, clinicians believed that it was better to insert an IUD during or just after menstruation when, hypothetically, the cervical canal was dilated.[1] Insertion at this time was also a way of ensuring that the woman was not pregnant. However, today it is known that the cervix does not dilate during menstruation and highly sensitive urine tests that can detect early pregnancy are widely available.

QUESTION

For women who have undergone a termination of pregnancy, when should an IUD be inserted?

POPULATION: Women who have undergone a termination of pregnancy.
INTERVENTION: IUD insertion.
OUTCOME: Safety.

ANSWER

CEU guidance provides recommendations regarding IUD insertion following termination of pregnancy.[1] These recommendations are based on the *WHO Medical Eligibility Criteria for Contraceptive Use*. WHO advises that, for women who are postpartum, the risks of inserting an IUD between 48 hours and 4 weeks postpartum generally outweigh the benefits (Category 3). WHO adds that there is an increased risk of perforation for IUD insertions performed during this period but does not cite any references to support this statement.

The CEU guidance recommends that an IUD can be inserted safely immediately following a first- or second-trimester termination of pregnancy. Evidence used in the guidance supports the view that insertion immediately following surgical termination is safe and practical and the risk of perforation if insertion is within 30 days of the procedure is low.[2,3] Readmission rates for pelvic infection are not increased by IUD insertion immediately following a first-trimester termination.[4]

As data are lacking on IUD insertion following medical abortion, the CEU suggests that an IUD is inserted immediately (within 48 hours) following first- or second-trimester medical termination or delayed until 4 weeks after termination (as WHO advises for postpartum women).

QUESTION

For women with a previous treated pelvic infection attending for IUD insertion, what timescale is recommended following treatment to avoid infective complications?

POPULATION: Women with a previous treated pelvic infection.

INTERVENTION: Insertion of an IUD.

OUTCOME: Infective complications arising after insertion of IUD.

ANSWER

The *WHO Medical Eligibility Criteria for Contraceptive Use* has classified the insertion of an IUD as WHO category 4 (an unacceptable health risk) in women with a current STI or history of infection within the last 3 months. This is because insertion of the device may increase the risk of developing PID. The CEU has found no evidence to contradict these recommendations.[3] Therefore it is recommended that women should wait 3 months after completion of treatment of an STI to have an IUD inserted.

QUESTION

For women having colposcopy with or without treatment, what is the evidence that insertion of an IUD should be delayed for 6 weeks?

POPULATION: Women having colposcopy with or without treatment.

INTERVENTION: Insertion of an IUD.

OUTCOME: Infection, pelvic inflammatory disease, expulsion, failed insertion.

ANSWER

The CEU was unable to identify any published information on the risks or benefits of IUD insertion at the time of colposcopy or within 6 weeks of treatment such as large loop excision of the transformation zone (LLETZ).

The risk of introducing ascending infection with an IUD following colposcopy might be greater if there had been treatment, rather than only examination, but no evidence was identified to support this. The clinical picture should guide whether an IUD may be inserted. If the cervix has a healthy appearance, an infection screen for *C. trachomatis* (when appropriate) is negative and the method has been discussed with the woman, then insertion might be reasonable at the time of colposcopy or within 6 weeks of colposcopy or treatment. The decision will depend on reasons for insertion (for instance, emergency contraception) and other available contraceptive methods.

References

1. Faculty of Family Planning and Reproductive Health Care. The copper intrauterine device as long-term contraception. *J Fam Plann Reprod Health Care* 2004;30:29–42.
2. Tuveng JM, Skjeldestad FE, Iversen T. Postabortal insertion of IUD. *Adv Contracept* 1986;2:387–92.
3. Heartwell S, Schlesselman S. Risk of uterine perforation among users of intrauterine devices. *Obstet Gynecol* 1993;61:31–5.
4. World Health Organization Task Force on IUDs in Fertility Regulation. IUD insertion following termination of pregnancy: a clinical trial of Cu220C, Lippes Loop D, and Copper 7. *Stud Fam Plann* 1983;14:99–108.

Investigations before IUD insertion

QUESTION

Which women having an IUD inserted should be tested for STIs?

POPULATION: Women having an IUD inserted.

INTERVENTION: Testing for STIs.

OUTCOME: Reduction in infective morbidity.

ANSWER

FFPRHC CEU guidance[1] has the following recommendations for testing for STIs prior to IUD insertion:

● STI risk should be assessed (history and examination) for all women considering an IUD.

● Women assessed to have a higher risk of STI should be offered testing for *C. trachomatis* (as a minimum) prior to IUD insertion.

● Women assessed to have a higher risk of STI may also be offered testing for *Neisseria gonorrhoea* prior to IUD insertion, depending upon local prevalence.

- There is no indication to test for other lower genital tract organisms in asymptomatic women attending for IUD insertion.

- Ideally, for women assessed as at higher risk of STI, the results of tests should be available and appropriate treatment provided prior to IUD insertion.

- For women assessed as at higher risk of STI, if results are not available and IUD insertion cannot be delayed, the use of prophylactic antibiotics may be considered.

The guidance states that STI risk may be assessed individually, taking into consideration local prevalence of infections, the woman's age, and her sexual activity.

QUESTION

For women having IUD insertion, does swabbing and testing for micro-organisms or the use of antimicrobial prophylaxis reduce the risk of infective complications?

POPULATION: Women having IUD insertion.

INTERVENTION: Cervical swabbing for microbiological testing or antimicrobial prophylaxis.

OUTCOME: Infective complications arising after insertion of IUD.

ANSWER

An RCOG Study Group[2] has recommended that testing for *C. trachomatis* and other micro-organisms should be considered for women undergoing uterine instrumentation, such as the fitting of an IUD, in the light of other risk factors such as age (as mentioned in the Chief Medical Officer's Expert Advisory Group Report in 1998).[3] However, a SIGN guideline has stated that there are no randomised controlled trials that show that routine testing prior to IUD insertion reduces the risk of ascending infections.[4] There is thus insufficient evidence to support the routine testing of women in the primary care setting prior to IUD fitting.

A Cochrane review of several randomised controlled trials has concluded that there is no justification for antimicrobial prophylaxis prior to the insertion of an IUD as there is no evidence that antimicrobial prophylaxis reduces the risk of infective complications.[5] The most recent study cited in the review was a randomised controlled trial conducted by Walsh *et al.* in 1998.[6] In this study, a group of 1985 American women were randomised to receive either 500 mg azithromycin or a placebo 1 hour before a copper IUD was inserted. They were followed up for 3 months. All the women were screened prior to IUD insertion for *C. trachomatis* and *N. gonorrhoea*. Of the women who took azithromycin, 3.8% had their IUD removed within the 3 months versus 3.4% of those who took placebo (relative risk 1.1; 95% CI 0.7–1.8). Only one individual from each arm of the study developed salpingitis. Walsh *et al.* concluded that antimicrobial prophylaxis is not justified in women who have been tested prior to insertion. Therefore, routine IUD insertion is safe with or without antimicrobial prophylaxis.

QUESTION

For women having an IUD inserted, what infections detected by pre-insertion swabs should be treated?

POPULATION: Women having an IUD inserted.
INTERVENTION: Treatment for infections identified by swabs.
OUTCOME: Effect of treatment.

ANSWER

Clinicians must establish if women have abnormal discharge or clinical signs such as uterine, adnexal or cervical motion tenderness, which might indicate that treatment for PID is required. Alternatively, women may be asymptomatic carriers who present with normal vaginal secretions, which upon testing is positive for an organism.

Asymptomatic carriers of group B streptococcus do not require treatment, even prior to IUD insertion. Symptomatic women with group B streptococcus should be treated.[7] Symptomatic women with additional organisms should be treated as for PID.

Asymptomatic genital carriage of group A streptococcus is rare. Genital infection with group A streptococcus has been reported in women using an IUD. However, serious infections rarely originate in the genitourinary tract.[8] The CEU considers that, if detected, group A streptococcus should be treated, especially prior to IUD insertion, owing to its rarity and uncertain significance.

WHO recommends that the benefits of inserting an IUD in women with bacterial vaginosis generally outweigh the risks (WHO category 2). No evidence was identified which investigated treating bacterial vaginosis before IUD insertion. Treatment is indicated in symptomatic women, women undergoing some surgical procedures and pregnant women.

The British Association for Sexual Health and HIV states that between 10% and 20% of women of reproductive age may harbour candida species in the absence of symptoms.[9] The Association suggests that these women do not require treatment.

The CEU recommends that women and their partner(s) should be treated for *Trichomonas vaginalis*.[1] WHO recommends that the benefits of inserting an IUD in women with *T. vaginalis* generally outweigh the risks (WHO category 2).

No information could be found on the detection of actinomyces-like organisms pre-IUD insertion. Asymptomatic women with actinomyces-like organisms can continue to use an IUD if they wish. Antibiotic treatment is not indicated.

For symptomatic women (that is, women who complain of abnormal discharge or have tenderness), clinicians should test for organisms implicated in PID so that treatment can be initiated. The *WHO Medical Eligibility Criteria for Contraceptive Use* recommends that an IUD should not be inserted in a woman with current PID, or who has had it within the last 3 months (WHO category 4).[9] However, FFPRHC guidance advises that, after considering other contraceptive methods, a woman may use an IUD within three months of treated pelvic infection, provided she has no signs or symptoms.[1] Treatment of PID should provide broad-spectrum coverage and should cover *N. gonorrhoea*, *C. trachomatis* and anaerobic infection.

References

1. Faculty of Family Planning and Reproductive Health Care Clinical Effectiveness Unit. The copper intrauterine device as long-term contraception. *J Fam Plann Reprod Health Care* 2004;30:29–42.
2. Recommendations from the 31st RCOG Study Group: The Prevention of Pelvic Infection. The Prevention of Pelvic Infection. In: Templeton A, editor. *The Prevention of Pelvic Infection*. London: RCOG Press; 1996. p. 267–70.
3. Chief Medical Officer's Expert Advisory Group. *Main Report of the CMO's Expert Advisory Group on Chlamydia Trachomatis*. London: Department of Health; 1998.
4. Scottish Intercollegiate Guidelines Network. *Management of Genital Chlamydia trachomatis Infection*. SIGN Guideline No.42. Edinburgh: SIGN; 2002.
5. Grimes DA, Schulz KF. Antibiotic prophylaxis for intrauterine contraceptive device insertion. *Cochrane Database Syst Rev* 2002;3.
6. Walsh T, Grimes D, Frezieres R, Nelson A, Bernstein L, Coulson A, *et al*. Randomised controlled trial of prophylactic antibiotics before insertion of intrauterine devices. *Lancet* 1998;351:1005–8.
7. Bernaldo de Quiros JC, Moreno S, Cercenado E, Diaz D, Berenguer J, Miralles P, *et al*. Group A streptococcal bacteremia: a 10-year prospective study. *Medicine* 1997;76:238–48.
8. Centers for Disease Control and Prevention Division of Bacterial and Mycotic Diseases. Prevention of perinatal group B streptococcal disease. *MMWR Morbid Mortal Wkly Rep* 2002;51(RR-11):1–28.

9. Association for Genitourinary Medicine, Medical Society for the Study of Venereal Diseases. *National Guideline on the Management of Vulvovaginal Candidiasis*. London: AGUM & MSSVD; 2002.

Procedures for routine IUD insertion

QUESTION

For women requesting contraception, what protocol should be followed for IUD insertion and what should be done at the follow-up appointment to assess that the device has been fitted correctly?

POPULATION: **Women requesting contraception.**

INTERVENTION: **IUD insertion.**

OUTCOME: **Assessing correct placement at follow-up.**

ANSWER

There is no single protocol that the CEU recommends for IUD insertion. Clinicians should be guided by the technical information provided by the manufacturer of each device. One study has attempted to define standards for the insertion of IUDs.[1] A minimum standard for documentation in the case notes is shown in Table 4.

An insertion protocol from the American Academy of Family Physicians is summarised below:[2]

1. Give nonsteroidal anti-inflammatory drug.

2. Obtain informed consent.

3. Set up instruments on a sterile field.

4. Perform pelvic examination to check for vaginitis and uterine position.

5. Insert speculum to localise the cervix.

6. Clean cervix with antiseptic.

7. Apply tenaculum to anterior lip of cervix.

8. Use sound to measure uterus and note cavity depth.

9. Give paracervical block for patients with cervical stenosis (if used).

10. Load device through sterile packaging.

Table 4. A minimum standard for documentation in case notes

Area for documentation	To be documented
History	Previous contraception used
	Parity, mode of delivery, ectopic pregnancy, usual cycle
	Stability or length of relationship
	Pelvic inflammatory disease with details of diagnosis and treatment
	Smear status and cervical surgery
	Cardiac lesions
	Allergy to local anaesthesia
	Discussion of all contraceptive options
Counselling	Efficacy and duration
	Effects on the menstrual cycle
	Insertion procedure
	Thread check: expulsion, thread moving up and perforation
	Testing for *Chlamydia trachomatis* in high-risk groups
Procedure	Bimanual examination
	Local anaesthesia (if used)
	Chlamydia/smear (if done)
	Uterocervical length
Technique	Terms include: 'no touch', 'easily with no problems', 'routine'
Comments	If any problems, document together with any actions taken
	Type of IUD, batch number and expiry date
Post-insertion	Special instruction, e.g. for Gynefix
	Patient information leaflet (fpa leaflet)
	Follow-up: 'see if any problems' is acceptable
	Letter to GP sent/not sent, depending on client's consent

11. Set stop or flange to depth indicated by sound.

12. Insert IUD until stop or flange is against cervix.

13. Release IUD (method varies with type and design of IUD).

14. Remove insertion device.

15. Cut strings to 1–2 cm from the cervical os and note length in chart.

16. Remove tenaculum.

17. Observe for bleeding.

18. Remove speculum.

19. Discharge patient with appointment for position check and review of adverse effects after post-insertion menses.

The UK *Selected Practice Recommendations for Contraceptive Use* advises a follow-up visit after the first menses or 3–6 weeks following insertion. Women are encouraged to return at any time to discuss adverse effects and other problems or if they wish to change their method of contraception. At follow-up after IUD insertion, the provider should ask about any menstrual problems, pain or expulsion. A pelvic examination can be performed to check for the IUD strings and look for signs of pelvic infection, which is most likely to occur within the first weeks after insertion. The clinician may use this opportunity to answer questions about any adverse effects, remind the woman of the warning signs of IUD complications and address any other concerns or questions she might have.

We found no evidence to suggest that sounding the cervix at the follow-up visit is standard practice.

QUESTION

For women having an IUD inserted, is povidone iodine (Betadine®, Medlock) suitable for vaginal antisepsis and does it carry any adverse effects if the solution reaches the uterus or fallopian tubes?

POPULATION: Women having an IUD inserted.
INTERVENTION: Povidone iodine (Betadine) for vaginal antisepsis.
OUTCOME: Adverse effects.

ANSWER

There are three forms of Betadine for intravaginal use: Betadine vaginal cleansing kit, Betadine vaginal gel and Betadine vaginal pessaries. Betadine vaginal cleansing kit includes a concentrate containing 250 ml of povidone iodine USP 10% w/v. Betadine vaginal gel contains povidone iodine USP 10% w/v. Betadine vaginal pessaries each contain povidone iodine USP 200 mg in a water-soluble base. All three forms are used to treat vaginitis and for preoperative preparation of the vagina and are contraindicated in prepubertal children and individuals with known or suspected iodine hypersensitivity. Regular use is contraindicated in women with thyroid disorders (particularly nodular colloid goitre, endemic goitre and Hashimoto's thyroiditis) and should be avoided by pregnant or lactating women. For all forms, compatibility with barrier contraceptives has not been established and it is not recommended that women using barrier methods use these products.

A randomised controlled trial was performed in 1981 to assess the effect of the Betadine Vaginal Cleansing Kit on cervical flora after insertion of an IUD.[3] About 4–6 weeks after insertion of an IUD, only one woman of 12 who used the solution had bacterial growth, whereas in the control group there was bacterial growth in 10 of 12 women. The bacteria that grew were of doubtful clinical significance but under the right conditions could take on a pathogenic role. The author concluded that more studies were needed to determine if the cleansing kit would significantly effect a long-term reduction of pelvic infection.

The CEU concludes that povidone iodine may be used for vaginal antisepsis prior to IUD insertion and does not carry any adverse effects for the uterus or fallopian tubes.

QUESTION

For women having an IUD inserted, does cleansing the cervix reduce the rate of subsequent pelvic infection?

POPULATION:	**Women having an IUD inserted.**
INTERVENTION:	**Cleansing the cervix.**
OUTCOME:	**Reduction in the rate of subsequent pelvic infection.**

ANSWER

There is an increased risk of pelvic infection in the 21 days following IUD insertion, which is likely to be due to the background risk of infection and uterine instrumentation leading to ascending infection.[4] A Cochrane review concluded that routine use of oral antibiotics (doxycyline or azithromycin) as prophylaxis prior to insertion did not confer any benefit, with no difference in infection or discontinuation rates compared with placebo or no treatment.[5]

Limited information was identified from the CEU literature search to determine whether cleansing of the cervix prior to IUD insertion would have any positive or negative effect. A randomised controlled trial looked at the effect of the Betadine Vaginal Cleansing Kit on cervical flora if used prior to IUD insertion.[3] This trial supported use of Betadine in that only one woman who used the kit developed bacterial growth a few weeks after the insertion but the effect on incidence of clinical infection is unknown.

QUESTION

For women having an IUD inserted, would not sounding the uterus at the time of insertion decrease the uterine perforation rate?

POPULATION:	Women having an IUD inserted.
INTERVENTION:	Uterine sounding.
OUTCOME:	Uterine perforation rate.

ANSWER

Most uterine perforations are thought to occur when the IUD or the sound or inserter tube is pushed through the myometrium. Uterine perforation is rare. The CEU has produced guidance on the copper IUD as long-term contraception, which identified evidence that uterine perforation occurs in fewer than 1/1000 insertions.[6] Limited retrospective data suggest that sounding may be protective, since it allows measurement of the length of the cavity. A retrospective review of 50 consecutive perforations reported to the National Patient Insurance Scheme Register between 1990 and 1993 was undertaken in Sweden.[7] The authors did not report whether any perforations were associated with sounding at IUD insertion. However, they did report that sounding had not been performed on 26 of the women. They concluded that uterine sounding would cause less uterine perforation by providing important information about the size of the uterus. Some authors have also discussed the hypothesis that the use of long-term progestogens, which cause uterine hypoplasia, may make users more susceptible to uterine perforation thereafter.[8,9]

In terms of reducing perforation rate, the skill of the inserter and possibly the effects of hypoplasia may be more important factors. On this basis, the CEU continues to recommend uterine sounding to assess uterine cavity length prior to IUD insertion.

QUESTION

For women having an IUD inserted, is there any evidence that traction should be applied to the cervix?

POPULATION:	Women having an IUD inserted.
INTERVENTION:	Traction of the cervix.
OUTCOME:	Ease of insertion.

ANSWER

When inserting or removing an IUD, traction can be applied to straighten the cervical and uterine canal to facilitate fundal placement of the IUD. CEU guidance recommends that a pair of forceps (such as Allis or tenaculum) should be used and an assessment of the length of the uterine cavity made, to reduce the risk of perforation and facilitate fundal placement of the IUD.[6]

Despite extensive searching, the CEU could find no information in the literature on benefits of traction of the cervix when inserting IUDs.

QUESTION

Does increasing clinician experience in fitting intrauterine contraceptive methods reduce risk of insertion problems or failure rates?

POPULATION:	Clinicians fitting intrauterine contraceptives.
INTERVENTION:	Training and increasing experience of IUD insertion.
OUTCOME:	Complications with insertion, and failure rates.

ANSWER

Evidence on associations between complications and failure rates for intrauterine contraception and clinician experience is scarce. A large prospective study, which included 17 469 insertions of the Multiload® Cu 375 (Organon) IUD by 1699 doctors, showed that doctors inserting fewer than ten IUDs in a 6-year period had significantly more perforations than those inserting 10–100 IUDs.[10]

The FFPRHC has specific training requirements for doctors wishing to obtain a letter of competence in intrauterine techniques (LoC IUT).[6] Competence in gynaecological examination and in the assessment, management and investigation of women with IUD problems are required for all clinicians inserting IUDs. Re-certification should ensure continuing competence. The LoC IUT should be updated every 5 years, with at least 2 hours of relevant continuing medical education and a log of at least twelve insertions in 12 months (or six in 6 months) using at least two different types of device in non-anaesthetised women.

References

1.   Kasliwal AP, Webb AMC. Intrauterine device insertions: setting our standards. *J Fam Plann Reprod Health Care* 2002;28:157–8.

2. Johnson BA. Insertion and removal of intrauterine devices. *Am Fam Physician* 2005;71:95–102.
3. Obaidullah M. A study to determine the effect of Betadine Vaginal Cleansing Kit on cervical flora after insertion of an intra-uterine contraceptive device. *J Int Med Res* 1981;9:161–4.
4. Farley TM, Rosenberg MJ, Rowe PJ, Chen JH, Meirik O. Intrauterine contraceptive devices and pelvic inflammatory disease: an international perspective. *Lancet* 1992;339:78–8.
5. Grimes DA, Schulz KF. Antibiotic prophylaxis for intrauterine contraceptive device insertion. *Cochrane Database Syst Rev* 2002;3.
6. Faculty of Family Planning and Reproductive Health Care Clinical Effectiveness Unit. The copper intrauterine device as long-term contraception. *J Fam Plann Reprod Health Care* 2004;30:29–42.
7. Andersson K, Ryde-Blomqvist E, Lindell K, Odlind V, Milsom I. Perforations with intrauterine devices. *Contraception* 1998;57:251–5.
8. Aust TR, Kirwan JN, Herod JJO, McVicker JT. Perforation with the GyneFix intrauterine implant: is there a common factor? *J Fam Plann Reprod Health Care* 2003;29:155–6.
9. Gandhi JD, Whitmore J, Iskander MN. Uterine perforation by GyneFix frameless IUD: two case reports. *J Fam Plann Reprod Health Care* 2001;27:153–4.
10. Harrison-Woolrych M, Ashton J, Coulter D. Uterine perforation on intrauterine device insertion: is the incidence higher than previously reported. *Contraception* 2003;67:53–6.

Complicated IUD insertion

QUESTION

For women who are 4 weeks post-caesarean section and breastfeeding, does insertion of an IUD carry an increased risk of perforation or expulsion compared with women who have had a vaginal delivery?

POPULATION: Women who are 4 weeks post-caesarean and breastfeeding.

INTERVENTION: Insertion of an IUD.

OUTCOME: Risk of perforation and expulsion compared with women who have had a vaginal delivery.

ANSWER

The *WHO Medical Eligibility Criteria* advises that women who are 4 or more weeks postpartum and are, or are not, breastfeeding (including after caesarean section), have no restrictions on insertion of either an IUD or the LNG-IUS (WHO category 1).

CEU guidance on the copper IUD as long-term contraception[1] and contraceptive choices for breastfeeding women[2] both support the advice from the WHO. The CEU states that the risk of IUD expulsion is around 1/20, but expulsion rates are lower for women who are breastfeeding compared with those who are not. Women who have IUDs inserted between 4 and 9 weeks postpartum show low rates of discontinuation of the method.

One review cited by the CEU looked at postpartum IUD insertion. It provided data on 6816 women-months of experience of insertions between 4 and 8 weeks postpartum compared with 19 733 women-months of experience of insertion after 8 weeks postpartum.[3] No perforations were reported and discontinuation rates were similar in the two groups.

In a literature review of contraceptive choices for breastfeeding women,[3] the CEU found no evidence to suggest that lactating women post-caesarean section have a higher risk of uterine perforation or expulsion from 4 weeks postpartum than women who have had vaginal deliveries.

QUESTION

For women with valvular heart disease, which regimen of antibiotic prophylaxis is recommended for insertion of an IUD?

POPULATION: Women with valvular heart disease.
INTERVENTION: Antibiotic prophylaxis for insertion of the IUD.
OUTCOME: Risk of bacterial endocarditis.

ANSWER

The BNF provides advice on antibiotic prophylaxis for the prevention of endocarditis in patients with heart valve lesions, septal defects, patent ductus or prosthetic valves. There is, however, no specific recommendation on prophylaxis for IUD or LNG-IUS insertion. For gynaecological procedures, the BNF suggests that 'prophylaxis is required only for women with prosthetic valves or those who have had endocarditis'. Such women should be managed with amoxicillin 1 g intravenously plus gentamicin 120 mg intravenously, followed by oral amoxicillin 500 mg 6 hours later. The FFPRHC CEU guidance on the IUD as long-term contraception upholds this BNF guidance.

QUESTION

For women with splenectomy, should antibiotic prophylaxis be provided for IUD insertion to prevent infection?

POPULATION: Women post-splenectomy.
INTERVENTION: Antimicrobial prophylaxis for insertion of the copper IUD.
OUTCOME: Risk of infection.

ANSWER

Fulminating infection in post-splenectomy patients is a life-long risk. A working group of the British Committee for Standards in Haematology has produced recommendations for clinical practice.[4] Lifelong prophylactic antibiotics should be offered in all cases, especially in the first 2 years following splenectomy, for children up to the age of 16 years or if there is underlying immunosuppression. In addition, patients should be offered amoxicillin to keep at home, starting use if they develop symptoms of fever, malaise and shivering. Antibiotic prophylaxis may not prevent sepsis. No recommendations were provided regarding dental procedures or IUD insertion.

The CEU, in its guidance on the IUD as long-term contraception, recommended that women with previous endocarditis or with a prosthetic heart valve require intravenous antibiotic prophylaxis to protect against bacterial endocarditis during IUD insertion or removal.[1] However, no information was identified regarding antibiotic prophylaxis to prevent fulminating sepsis for patients post-splenectomy.

As the risk of serious sepsis in post-splenectomy patients is lifelong, the CEU recommends that, for IUD or LNG-IUS insertion or removal, antibiotic prophylaxis is advised as for women at risk of bacterial endocarditis: amoxicillin 1 g intravenously plus gentamicin 120 mg intravenously, followed by oral amoxicillin 500 mg 6 hours later (BNF). In addition, obtaining the advice of a haematologist and microbiologist may be appropriate.

QUESTION

For women who have had previous expulsions of an IUD or LNG-IUS, are there any investigations for uterine abnormality that should be undertaken before insertion of a new device?

POPULATION: Women who have had previous expulsions of an IUD or LNG-IUS.
INTERVENTION: Investigations for uterine abnormality.
OUTCOME: Appropriateness of insertion of a new device.

ANSWER

The risk of expulsion of an IUD is around 5% and is most common in the first year of use, particularly within 3 months of insertion. Expulsion usually occurs during menstruation.[1] The LNG-IUS has an expulsion rate that is comparable to other IUDs.[5] The cumulative expulsion rate for the LNG-IUS increases from 4.5/100 users at 12 months to 5.9/100 users at 60 months.[6] Most contraceptive failures of the LNG-IUS are due to expulsion.

The *WHO Medical Eligibility Criteria for Contraceptive Use* recommends that for women with anatomical abnormalities or uterine fibroids that distort the uterine cavity, the IUD or the LNG-IUS should not be used (WHO category 4).

Neither the *UK Selected Practice Recommendations for Contraceptive Use* nor the Summary of Product Characteristics for the LNG-IUS, Mirena® (Schering Health Care), discuss the use of investigations for uterine abnormality in women who have had previous IUD expulsions.

Despite extensive searching, the CEU could find no information to guide clinicians on the use of investigations to identify uterine abnormality in women who have had previous IUD or LNG-IUS expulsions and who wish to have another device inserted.

QUESTION

> **When an IUD is confirmed as being intrauterine but the threads have retracted, what strategy for replacement or follow-up is appropriate?**

POPULATION: Women with an IUD in place where the threads have retracted.
INTERVENTION: Replacement or retention.
OUTCOME: Risks and benefits.

ANSWER

No research studies specifically addressing this issue were found. Guidance from the FFPRHC suggests that 'lost threads' should be managed by firstly confirming that the device is intrauterine (by retrieval of threads using a suitable instrument or by ultrasound).[1] If placement is intrauterine and the threads can be retrieved and brought down into the cervical canal, no further action is required. If the threads cannot be retrieved, it is appropriate to leave the device in place until the end of its licensed lifespan. In such a situation, no special follow-up investigations or visits are required provided that the woman is happy to retain the device. Should she prefer to have it replaced, she should be advised of the increased risk of infection associated with the procedure.

References

1. Faculty of Family Planning and Reproductive Health Care Guidance. The copper intrauterine device as long-term contraception. *J Fam Plann Reprod Health Care* 2004;30:29–42.
2. Faculty of Family Planning and Reproductive Health Care Clinical Effectiveness Unit. Contraceptive choices for breastfeeding women. *J Fam Plann Reprod Health Care* 2004;30:181–9.
3. Mishell DRJ, Roy S. Copper intrauterine contraceptive device event rates following insertion 4 to 8 weeks post partum. *Am J Obstet Gynecol* 1982;143:29–35.
4. Working Party of the British Committee for Standards in Haematology. Clinical Haematology Task Force. Guidelines for the prevention and treatment of infection in patients with an absent or dysfunctional spleen. *BMJ* 1996;312:430–4.
5. Faculty of Family Planning and Reproductive Health Care Clinical Effectiveness Unit. The levonorgestrel-releasing intrauterine system (LNG-IUS) in contraception and reproductive health. *J Fam Plann Reprod Health Care* 2004;30:99–109.
6. Cox M, Tripp J, Blacksell S. Clinical performance of the levonorgestrel intrauterine system in routine use by the UK Family Planning and Reproductive Health Research Network: 5-year report. *J Fam Plann Reprod Health Care* 2002;28:73–7.

Problems at insertion

QUESTION

For women attending for insertion of a frameless copper-bearing IUD (GyneFix), what evidence is there on risk of uterine perforation?

POPULATION: Women attending for intrauterine contraception.

INTERVENTION: Insertion of a frameless copper-bearing IUD, GyneFix.

OUTCOME: Risk of perforation.

ANSWER

No cases of perforations occurring with GyneFix were reported in the literature before 1999. From 1999 onwards, six case reports were published and the majority of women presented with pain or lost threads.[1] The Summary of Product Characteristics does not recommend an ultrasound scan to assess fundal myometrial thickness routinely prior to insertion. When a perforation is suspected, a scan should be performed to locate the device and if perforation is confirmed, the woman referred appropriately for removal.

One article has discussed the possibility that use of long-term progestogens, which may cause uterine hypoplasia, may make women more susceptible to perforation.[2] Many of the case reports of perforation with GyneFix occurred in women previously using progestogen-only implants, injectables or pill. It is unclear if this has any role to play in increasing the risk of perforation.

A Cochrane review investigated the performance of any frameless device compared with a traditional IUD.[3] Three trials were included.[4-6] The largest included data up to 8 years and involved over 5800 parous women who were randomised to receive either the frameless device or the TCu380A IUD. The three trials represent a total experience of over 23000 woman-years. No perforations were reported in two of the trials (which represent around 2450 insertions with each type of device). The Rosenberg trial did not report this outcome.[5] Cao *et al.* compared the clinical performance of GyneFix with the copper T380A device in a 9-year randomised comparative study.[7] No perforations were encountered with either device.

CEU guidance on the copper IUD as long-term contraception recommends that women be advised that uterine perforation occurs in less than 1/1000 insertions.

QUESTION

In cases where there is suspected uterine perforation by the uterine sound at IUD insertion, what follow-up action is needed to minimise adverse sequelae?

POPULATION:	Women with suspected uterine perforation by the uterine sound at IUD insertion.
INTERVENTION:	Clinical follow-up actions.
OUTCOME:	Adverse sequelae.

ANSWER

The CEU found little evidence to guide the management of women where there is suspected perforation by the uterine sound prior to IUD insertion. The reported incidence of all forms of perforation is around 2/1000 insertions.[8] Of the 28 perforation events reported among almost 17 500 insertions in this study, only one appeared to relate to perforation by the uterine sound prior to insertion of the device.[8] However, the total number of perforations reported in this and other studies is likely to be an under estimate; in the context of first-trimester abortion, six times the number of perforations were identified at laparoscopy, compared with those recognised clinically.[9]

The little evidence that is available suggests that the risk of serious sequelae from uterine perforation in non-pregnant women is low, that surgical intervention is seldom needed and that conservative management is appropriate. There is no evidence to provide guidance on the time interval after which it would be appropriate to repeat an attempt at IUD insertion following an insertion abandoned due to suspected perforation. WHO simply advises that IUD insertion should be delayed 'until any uterine perforation has healed'. On a pragmatic basis, a 6-week interval after an asymptomatic, suspected perforation would seem reasonable.

Although the literature is reassuring, it must be remembered that serious sequelae, including death, have been reported following uterine perforation, especially in the context of induced abortion. Close monitoring for at least 2 hours plus follow-up over the succeeding days would be wise precautions in any case of suspected perforation.

QUESTION

If women are attending for IUD insertion and an expired device is inserted in error, is the device still effective?

POPULATION: Women attending for IUD insertion.
INTERVENTION: Expired IUDs.
OUTCOME: Efficacy.

ANSWER

Family Planning Sales Ltd maintains that the expiry date is the date to which the sterility of the device is preserved in the packaging and that devices whose expiry date has passed should be discarded and not inserted.[10] No information was found in the literature as to whether use of an expired device increases a woman's risk of subsequent pelvic infection following insertion or whether the effectiveness of these devices is decreased.

The CEU can only advise that a clinician should inform a woman if an expired IUD has been inserted in error and allow her the option of deciding if a new device is to be fitted instead, while acknowledging that there is no evidence regarding efficacy. It is likely that most women would feel anxious to learn that an expired device had been inserted and would choose to have a new IUD fitted, even though they have to go through removal of the expired IUD followed by the insertion procedure again.

QUESTION

For women who have a vasovagal episode during or following IUD insertion, does oxygen therapy improve the outcome?

POPULATION: **Women suffering vasovagal attack during IUD insertion.**
INTERVENTION: **Oxygen administration.**
OUTCOME: **Improved recovery.**

ANSWER

The incidence of vasovagal syncope at IUD insertion ranges from 0.2% to 2.1%.[11,12] A MEDLINE and EMBASE search confirmed that cerebral oxygenation reduces during syncope.[13-15] As the CEU was unable to find specific guidance on resuscitation after vasovagal syncope, general resuscitation was reviewed. The Resuscitation Council (UK) states that 'current resuscitation guidelines emphasise the use of oxygen, and this should be available whenever possible'. The Resuscitation Council includes in 'minimum recommended equipment', oxygen and an oxygen mask with reservoir bag.[16]

The CEU could find no published research that compared oxygen versus no oxygen in terms of outcome of vasovagal episodes. The FFPRHC recommendation that oxygen is an essential requirement for clinics inserting IUDs was published in guidance on the IUD as long-term contraception.[17] A portable cylinder and oxygen mask with reservoir bag would suffice.

References

1. Wildemeersch D. Further information and recommendations to prevent perforation with the frameless GyneFix IUD. *J Fam Plann Reprod Health Care* 2001;27:241.
2. Aust TR, Kirwan JN, Herod JJO, McVicker JT. Perforation with the GyneFix intrauterine implant: is there a common factor? *J Fam Plann Reprod Health Care* 2003;29:155–6.

3. O'Brien PA, Marfleet C. Frameless versus classical intrauterine device for contraception. *Cochrane Database Syst Rev* 2003;(1).

4. Rowe PJ, Reinprayoon D, Koetswang S, Shu-rong Z, Shang-chun W, Hui-min F, *et al.* The TCu 380A IUD and the frameless IUD 'the Flexigard': interim three–year data from an International Multicenter Trial. *Contraception* 1995;52:77–83.

5. Rosenberg MJ, Foldesy R, Mishell DR Jr, Speroff L, Waugh MS, Burkman R. Performance of the TCu380A and Cu–Fix IUDs in an international randomized trial. *Contraception* 1996;53:197–203.

6. Wu S, Hu J, Wildemeersch D. Performance of the frameless GyneFix and the TCu380A IUDs in a 3–year multicenter, randomized, comparative trial in parous women. *Contraception* 2000;61:91–8.

7. Cao X, Zhang W, Gao G, Van Kets H, Wildemeersch D. Randomized comparative trial in parous women of the frameless GyneFix and the TCu380A intrauterine devices: long-term experience in a Chinese family planning clinic. *Eur J Contracept Reprod Health Care* 2000;5:135–40.

8. Harrison-Woolrych M, Ashton J, Coulter D. Uterine perforation on intrauterine device insertion: is the incidence higher than previously reported. *Contraception* 2003;67:53–6.

9. Kaali SG, Szigetvari IA, Bartfai GS. The frequency and management of uterine perforations during first-trimester abortions. *Am J Obstet Gynecol* 1989;161:406–8.

10. Family Planning Sales Ltd (personal communication).

11. Harrison-Woolrych M, Ashton J, Coulter D. Insertion of the Multiload Cu375 intrauterine device; experience in over 16,000 New Zealand Women. *Contraception* 2002;66:387–91.

12. Farmer M, Webb A. Intrauterine device insertion-related complications: can they be predicted? *J Fam Plann Reprod Health Care* 2003;29:227–31.

13. Van Lieshout JJ, Wieling W, Karemaker JM, Secher NH. Syncope, cerebral perfusion, and oxygenation. *J Appl Physiol* 2003;94:833–48.

14. Colier WN, Binkhorst RA, Hopman MT, Oeseburg B. Cerebral and circulatory haemodynamics before vasovagal syncope induced by orthostatic stress. *Clin Physiol* 1997;17:83–94.

15. Madsen P, Pott F, Olsen SB, Nielsen HB, Burcev I, Secher NH. Near-infrared spectrophotometry determined brain oxygenation during fainting. *Acta Physiol Scand* 1998;162:501–7.

16. Resuscitation Council (UK). Cardiopulmonary Resuscitation. Guidance for clinical practice and training in Primary Care. July 2001 [www.resus.org.uk/pages/cpatpc.htm].

17. Faculty of Family Planning and Reproductive Health Care Clinical Effectiveness Unit. The copper intrauterine device as long-term contraception. *J Fam Plann Reprod Health Care* 2004;30:29–42.

Follow-up

QUESTION

For women who have had an IUD inserted, are annual follow-up visits recommended to ensure correct positioning of the device?

POPULATION:	Women who have had an IUD inserted.
INTERVENTION:	Annual follow-up visits.
OUTCOME:	Improved efficacy.

ANSWER

The Clinical Effectiveness Unit[1] supports the WHO *Selected Practice Recommendations for Contraceptive Use* regarding appropriate follow-up:

- A follow-up visit should occur after the first menses or 3–6 weeks following insertion.

- Women may be advised to return at any time to discuss adverse effects or other problems, or if they want to change the method.

- For devices that have a high rate of expulsion, more frequent follow-up than above may be indicated.

- Women may be advised to return when it is time to have the IUD removed.

At the follow-up visit 3–6 weeks after IUD insertion, the provider should ask about any menstrual problems, pain or expulsion. A pelvic examination can be performed to check for the IUD strings and look for signs of pelvic infection, which is most likely to occur within the first weeks after insertion. There is therefore no reason that women should be recalled exclusively for an annual check after insertion.

Reference

1. Faculty of Family Planning and Reproductive Health Care Clinical Effectiveness Unit. The copper intrauterine device as long-term contraception. *J Fam Plann Reprod Health Care* 2004;30:29–42.

Problems during use of the IUD

QUESTION

For women using an IUD who are diagnosed with or are suspected of having pelvic inflammatory disease due to *C. trachomatis*, should the device be removed or retained?

| POPULATION: | Women using IUD with PID due to *C. trachomatis*. |

INTERVENTION: Removal versus retention of the device.

OUTCOME: Resolution of signs and symptoms and prevention of long-term sequelae.

ANSWER

Evidence on the clinical course of *C. trachomatis* infection with an IUD in place is scant. Nevertheless, a prospective cohort study showed that only 10% of women (95% CI 1–33%) with unsuspected *C. trachomatis* at the time of IUD insertion developed pelvic infection post-insertion.[1] A cohort study suggested that when women had *C. trachomatis* identified at the time of IUD insertion, risk of PID in the following month was not increased significantly compared to women without *C. trachomatis*, RR 1.7 (95% CI 0.4–7.5).[2] For women assessed as being 'at higher risk of STI', if results of microbiological testing are not available prior to insertion, the use of prophylactic antibiotics may be considered if IUD insertion cannot be delayed.

A hospital based case–control study of women with PID included 236 women with an IUD left in place, 60 women with IUD removed and 632 women without an IUD.[3] A significantly higher proportion of women who had their IUD removed remained in hospital for 3 weeks or longer compared with controls or women who had an IUD retained.

In a retrospective cohort study of 186 IUD users hospitalised for acute PID, the IUD was removed in 81 women and retained in 105 women.[4] No difference was identified in the clinical course of the infection. However, those who had the IUD removed were more likely to have a prolonged hospital stay.

FFPRHC guidance recommends that women using intrauterine contraception who are diagnosed with PID should be started on appropriate antibiotics.[5] There is no need to remove the IUD unless symptoms fail to resolve. This recommendation was supported by evidence from the WHO *Selected Practice Recommendations for Contraceptive Use* and the FFPRHC version of this document. One of the most common causes of PID in the UK is *C. trachomatis*.

A UK national guideline on the management of PID from the British Association of Sexual Health and HIV recommends that women with an IUD in place who have clinically severe PID should have the IUD removed since removal is associated with better short-term improvement in symptoms and signs.[6] However, an appraisal of the randomised controlled trial on which this recommendation is based highlights a potential for bias. The CEU concluded that this randomised controlled trial does not provide evidence of sufficient quality to recommend this change in clinical practice.

The CEU recommends that in women using an IUD who are diagnosed with PID (including that due to *C. trachomatis*) there is no need to remove the IUD. Women should be given appropriate antibiotics. Women should be reviewed within 48–72 hours to ensure resolution of symptoms.

QUESTION

For women with recurrent genital herpes, if intrauterine contraception is used, is there an increased risk of recurrences?

POPULATION:	Women with recurrent genital herpes.
INTERVENTION:	Intrauterine contraception.
OUTCOME:	Risk of recurrence.

ANSWER

Subclinical viral shedding occurs in women with genital herpes and is more common in women with frequently recurring herpes. There is lack of evidence to reassure patients taking continuous antiviral treatment that they will not shed the virus. One study has shown that condoms may reduce the risk of transmission from men to women. However, condoms cannot reduce transmission from vulval lesions and may not effectively prevent transmission from women to men.[7]

The *WHO Medical Eligibility Criteria for Contraceptive Use* advises that women with a current STI or a history of STI within the past 3 months should not have the copper IUD or the LNG-IUS inserted (WHO category 4).

The CEU was unable to find any specific evidence on the risk of recurrence of local herpes with IUD insertion.

QUESTION

For women diagnosed with methicillin-resistant *Staphylococcus aureus* (MRSA) from a wound in the genital area and who have an LNG-IUS or an IUD in place, should the device be removed to treat the infection and, if so, when can a new device be safely inserted?

POPULATION:	Women diagnosed with MRSA in a wound in the genital area who have an LNG-IUS or an IUD in place.
INTERVENTION:	Device removal and insertion of a new device after treatment.
OUTCOME:	Safety.

ANSWER

MRSA is a type of bacterium that occurs harmlessly on the skin or in the nose of healthy people. If it enters the body through breaks in the skin, it may cause mild infections such as acne or serious infections of the bloodstream, bones or joints. An endogenous infection can occur if MRSA spreads from the initial site of colonisation to a new site. A retrospective case study and two case–control studies of women with PID identified *S. aureus* as one of the most predominant aerobic isolates identified on cultures.[8–10] One UK study has found a small percentage (4%) of IUD users with *S. aureus* colonisation on their IUD.[11]

American guidelines for preventing opportunistic infections among haematopoietic stem cell transplant recipients state that any implantable devices that are infected or colonised with MRSA should be removed.[12] Despite extensive searching, the CEU could find no information on whether or not an LNG-IUS or IUD should be removed if MRSA is present in the genital area but not actually on the device. The *UK Selected Practice Recommendations for Contraceptive Use* recommends that PID should be treated with appropriate antibiotics and that there is no need for removal of the IUD if the woman wishes to continue its use.

The US guideline advises that patients with MRSA should be placed under contact precautions until all antibiotics are discontinued and three consecutive cultures, taken more than a week apart, are negative. Cultures should be taken from the anterior nares, any body site previously positive for MRSA and any wounds or surgical sites. The FFPRHC guidance on the IUD and on the LNG-IUS advises that a woman may have an IUD or LNG-IUS inserted within 3 months of treated pelvic infection, provided that she has no signs or symptoms.

Despite extensive searching, the CEU could find no information specifically addressing the removal and reinsertion of LNG-IUS or IUD in women who have MRSA in a wound in the genital area. The CEU advises that the decision to remove an IUD or LNG-IUS in women with MRSA will depend on factors such as signs or symptoms of pelvic infection. The risk of PID is increased sixfold in the 21 days following IUD or LNG-IUS insertion but thereafter women are at the same risk of infection as non-IUD users. Therefore, ascending infection from the lower genital tract is not increased in established IUD/LNG-IUS users. It is unclear if MRSA in a genital wound would be complicated by the presence of an IUD/LNG-IUS already in place but a device perhaps should not be inserted while infection is present.

QUESTION

For women using IUDs, do high-dose oral steroids affect the efficacy of the device or mask the symptoms and signs of pelvic inflammatory disease?

POPULATION: Women using IUDs.

INTERVENTION: High-dose steroid therapy.

OUTCOME: Efficacy and risk of PID.

ANSWER

There is no good evidence in the literature that the anti-inflammatory effect of steroids reduces the efficacy of a copper IUD. One review article refers to case reports and case–control studies that suggest a possible relationship between corticosteroids, anti-inflammatory drugs and reduced IUD efficacy.[13] However, the reviewers criticised the methodology of the study. They recommended larger studies to test the hypothesis.

There is no good evidence to determine whether high-dose steroids will mask the signs or symptoms of PID. Although the risk of infection following IUD insertion increases in the 20 days following insertion, the risk is low thereafter.[5] There is no evidence to inform us whether high doses of steroids will increase this risk of PID.

QUESTION

For women with an IUD or IUS, does device misplacement within the uterine cavity affect adverse effects or contraceptive efficacy?

POPULATION: Women with IUD or IUS in place.

INTERVENTION: Device misplacement.

OUTCOME: Adverse effects and contraceptive efficacy.

ANSWER

Once inserted, an IUD or IUS provides effective long-term reversible contraception. The expulsion rate is estimated at 1% and perforation rate at 0.1%. The WHO *Selected Practice Recommendations for Contraceptive Use* suggests that a follow-up visit 3–6 weeks following insertion or menstruation is advised. If threads are present and there is a pattern of regular bleeding, the IUD is assumed to be normally placed. If threads are not present, the endocervical canal can be sounded to identify if the stem of the IUD is present within the canal, which would suggest downward expulsion. If threads are not present, an ultrasound scan can be performed to assess the position of the IUD. However, evidence does not exist to guide the clinician in the interpretation of scan findings. Traditional two-dimensional scanning can assess IUD position in relation to markers within the uterus. The distance from the upper end of the vertical arm of a T-shaped IUD can be measured in relation to the fundus (IUD–fundal distance), myometrium (IUD–myometrial distance), and endometrium (IUD–endometrium distance). The standard IUD–fundus distance is 27 mm; the IUD–myometrium distance is 11 mm and the IUD–endometrium distance is 7 mm. These measurements vary with the timing of the scan in relation to the menstrual cycle, since the endometrium has a wide range of thickness throughout the normal menstrual cycle. Based on these data, a T-shaped IUD whose upper end is within 7 mm of the endometrium or 11 mm of the myometrium in the uterine fundus can be considered to be within normal limits.[14]

Evidence suggests that, when a T-shaped IUD is inserted by appropriately trained personnel it is usually placed very near to the fundus.[15] IUDs, however, tend to move within the first 3 months following insertion. This study suggested that an IUD could move upwards towards the fundus or downwards towards to cervix. In this study, 17 IUDs (7.0%) could have been classified as misplaced at insertion compared with 'standard' measurements. One-third of these remained displaced at the 3-month follow up but a clinical expulsion was identified in only one woman. Two displaced IUDs were removed because the lower part of the vertical arm was lying within the endocervix. At 3 months post-insertion, 21 IUDs (8.6%) could be classified as misplaced but only one expelled clinically. No data were available to assess the failure rates of IUDs which were not fundally placed and a larger study would be required to assess this.

The relationship between the extreme of the horizontal arm of the T and the lateral wall of the uterus cannot be studied with two-dimensional scanning. Three-dimensional scanning has been investigated to locate IUD position. The entire IUD can be identified including vertical and horizontal arms. Incomplete opening of the horizontal arms is uncommon. This method of scanning is not widely available.

A Brazilian study investigated bleeding patterns and IUD position on scanning.[14] Abnormal bleeding was described as a subjective complaint of increased volume of blood loss and increased duration of bleeding compared with volume and duration prior to IUD insertion. Results suggested that women with complaints of bleeding did not necessarily have a misplaced IUD. Long-term IUD users who have no bleeding problems have a wide range of IUD positions within the uterine cavity.

The IUS may be more difficult to identify on ultrasound scan due to the lack of a hyperechoic copper stem. No evidence was found which could identify if an IUS that was not fundally placed would alter the effects on the endometrium and potentially reduce efficacy or alter bleeding patterns.

It is unclear if a woman with no threads palpable and an IUD lying 'low in the cavity' on scan is at increased risk of device expulsion, device failure or bleeding. However, the CEU advises that an IUD works primarily by inhibiting fertilisation due to copper toxicity against sperm and ovum and this effect may not rely on fundal placement of the device. A secondary effect is to prevent implantation. A fundally placed device may therefore be more effective, as many implantations occur in the fundal area. Replacing an IUD is associated with an increased risk of infection in the 21 days following insertion. The CEU advises discussion with the woman on evidence (or its lack) and potential risks associated with device replacement so an informed choice can be made.

QUESTION

For women who use an IUD, can this be associated with postcoital bleeding?

POPULATION: Women who use an IUD.
INTERVENTION: Continued use of the IUD.
OUTCOME: Postcoital bleeding.

ANSWER

After a detailed search of the literature, the CEU was unable to find any evidence on postcoital bleeding in IUD users.

The WHO *Selected Practice Recommendations* does not refer specifically to postcoital bleeding in IUD users. However, the guidance does provide advice on two categories of bleeding:

- spotting and light bleeding occurring between menstrual bleeds

- heavier or longer bleeding than normal.

This advice is summarised in this response. Both spotting/light bleeding and heavier/longer bleeding are common during the first 3–6 months of IUD use.

Such bleeding patterns are usually not harmful and decrease over time. Persistent abnormal bleeding however, should be investigated to exclude gynaecological causes and STIs.

QUESTION

For women with IUDs in place, is use of home electrolysis kits safe?

POPULATION: Women with an IUDs in place.
INTERVENTION: Use of home electrolysis kits.
OUTCOME: Safety.

ANSWER

A detailed search of the CEU routine literature sources identified no guidelines, systematic reviews or individual papers relating to IUDs and use of home electrolysis kits. The CEU was therefore unable to provide an evidence-based response to the enquiry and recommends that women abide by the manufacturer's product safety advice.

QUESTION

For women with IUDs in place who undergo magnetic resonance imaging, is there a risk of displacement of the device?

POPULATION: Women with IUDs in place.
INTERVENTION: Magnetic resonance imaging.
OUTCOME: Risk of displacement.

ANSWER

MRI creates images through a combination of magnetic fields and radio wave pulses. Only ferromagnetic or magnetisable material should experience a static force within the MRI.[16] Most IUDs are composed of plastic with copper wire or copper bands, while some also have a central core of silver.[17] None of these materials should experience a magnetic force within the magnetic field.

In vitro studies on a Copper T380A IUD placed within the magnetic field found no significant temperature changes, no static deflection and no turning motion of the device with different gradient pulses of MRI. The authors concluded that the IUD has no magnetic or magnetisable components and that screening women for the presence of an IUD or removal of the device prior to an MRI scan is unjustified.[18]

Other *in vitro* and *in vivo* studies found that neither the Copper-7 nor Lippes Loop IUD moved under MRI or heated up during spin-echo sequences typically used in imaging the pelvis. Additionally, neither IUD produced artefacts *in vitro* or *in vivo*. The authors concluded that patients with either type of IUD may safely undergo MRI and that magnetic resonance images of the pelvis are not degraded by the presence of an IUD.

Most diagnostic centres require women to inform them of the presence of any metallic object within the body and some have policies that require an IUD to be removed before the MRI scan. The CEU however, found no evidence that there is a higher risk of displacement with a MRI scan, even if an IUD was inserted less than 6 weeks previously.

QUESTION

For a woman aged 49 years with an IUD in an extrauterine position, can it be safely left in place?

POPULATION: Women aged 49 years with an IUD in an extrauterine position.
INTERVENTION: Leaving the device in place.
OUTCOME: Safety.

ANSWER

FFPRHC CEU guidance advises that a plain abdominal X-ray should be used to determine whether an IUD is extrauterine.[5] If an IUD is in an extrauterine position, surgical retrieval is advised. The International Planned Parenthood Federation (IPPF) and WHO give similar advice.[18,19]

A case review determined that removal of extrauterine IUDs was not always necessary, as complications with IUDs and intestinal complications are very rare.[20] Indeed, intraperitoneal adhesion formation usually takes place after uterine perforation. Adhesions tend to be localised in the area of the IUD, thus preventing further displacement of the IUD. Surgical removal of the IUD may result in more peritoneal adhesions than were originally formed in the process of perforation, and may cause other intra- and postoperative complications.[21]

The CEU recommends that perimenopausal women who are found to have a previously unrecognised extrauterine IUD should be counselled about the risks of removal at laparoscopy or laparotomy. Intraperitoneal adhesions appear to be confined to areas around the IUD rather than causing generalised adhesion formation. These localised adhesions appear to prevent further migration of the device. It may be appropriate to leave the IUD in its extrauterine location if the risks of surgery outweigh the benefits of removal.

References

1. Faúndes A, Telles E, de Lourdes Cristofoletti M, Faúndes D, Castro S, Hardy E. The risk of inadvertent intrauterine device insertion in women carriers of endocervical Chlamydia trachomatis. *Contraception* 1998;58:105–9.

2. Sinei SKA, Schulz KF, Lamptey PR, Grimes DA, Mati JKG, Rosenthal SM *et al.* Preventing IUCD-related pelvic infection: the efficacy of prophylactic doxycycline at insertion. *Br J Obstet Gynaecol* 1990;97:412–9.

3. Larsson B, Wennergren M. Investigation of a Copper Intrauterine device (Cu-IUD) for possible effect on frequency and healing of Pelvic Inflammatory Disease. *Contraception* 1977;15:143–9.

4. Grimes D. Intrauterine device and upper-genital-tract infection. *Lancet* 2000;356:1013–9.

5. Faculty of Family Planning and Reproductive Health Care Clinical Effectiveness Unit. The copper intrauterine device as long-term contraception. *J Fam Plann Reprod Health Care* 2004;30:29–42.

6. British Association for Sexual Health and HIV. *Revised PID guidelines*. [www.bashh.org/guidelines/ceguidelines.htm].

7. Wald A, Zeh J, Selke S, Ashley RL, Corey L. Virological characteristics of subclinical and symptomatic genital herpes infections. *N Engl J Med* 1995; 333:770–5.

8. Audu BM, Kudi AA. Microbial isolates and antibiogram from endocervical swabs of patients with pelvic inflammatory disease. *J Obstet Gynecol* 2004;24:161–4.

9. Baveja G, Saini S, Sangwan K, Arora DR. A study of bacterial pathogens in acute pelvic inflammatory disease. *J Communic Dis* 2001;33:121–5.

10. Saini S, Gupta N, Aparna A, Batra G, Arora DR. Role of anaerobes in acute pelvic inflammatory disease. *Indian J Med Microbiol* 2003;21:189–92.

11. Lewis R. A review of bacteriological culture of removed intrauterine contraceptive devices. *Br J Fam Plann* 1998;24:95–7.

12. Centers for Disease Control and Prevention. *Guidelines for Preventing Opportunistic Infections Among Hematopoietic Stem Cell Transplant Recipients. Infectious Disease Society of America, and American Society of Blood and Marrow Transplantation.* 2001. Vol. 49 [www.cdc.gov/mmwr/PDF/rr/rr4910.pdf].

13. Thonneau P, Goulard H, Goyaux N. Risk factors for intrauterine device failure: a review. *Contraception* 2001;64:33–37.

14. Faundes D, Bahamondes L, Faundes A, Petta C, Diaz J, Marchi N. No relationship between the IUD position evaluated by ultrasound and complaints of bleeding and pain. *Contraception* 1997;56:43–7.

15. Faundes D, Perdigao A, Faundes A, Bahamondes L, Petta CA. T-shaped IUDS accommodate in their position during the first 3 months after insertion. *Contraception* 2000;62:165–8.

16. Pasquale SA, Russer TJ, Foldesy R, Mezrich RS. Lack of interaction between magnetic resonance imaging and the copper-T380A IUD. *Contraception* 1997;55:169–73.

17. Mark AS, Hricak H. Intrauterine contraceptive devices: MR imaging. *Radiology* 1987;162:311–4.
18. World Health Organization. Mechanism of action, safety and efficacy of intrauterine devices. Report of a WHO Scientific Group. *World Health Organ Tech Rep Ser* 1987;753:1–91.
19. International Planned Parenthood Federation. *IMAP Statement on Intrauterine Devices.* New York: International Planned Parenthood Federation; 2003.
20. Adoni A, Ben Chetrit A. The management of intrauterine devices following uterine perforation. *Contraception* 1991;43:77–81.
21. Markovitch O, Klein Z, Gidoni Y, Holzinger M, Beyth Y. Extrauterine mislocated IUD: Is surgical removal mandatory? *Contraception* 2002;66:105–8.

Discontinuation or removal

QUESTION

For women aged 39 years with flushing who are using a copper IUD, is contraception still required?

POPULATION: Women with menopausal symptoms.
INTERVENTION: Copper IUD.
OUTCOME: Assessment of contraceptive requirements.

ANSWER

The menopause can only be diagnosed in retrospect and is identified when a woman has been period-free for 12 months. The average age of the menopause is 50.8 years, although women may have menopausal symptoms at a much younger age. The majority of women will be anovulatory by the age of 54 years. It is accepted practice to advise women that contraception is required for 2 years after the last menstrual period if this occurs under 50 years. If the last period occurs over the age of 50 years, contraception is required for only one further year.[1] Advising women regarding their contraceptive requirements if they are amenorrhoeic with vasomotor symptoms can be fairly straight-forward. Difficulties arise when women have been using hormonal contraception or are currently using HRT. If a woman is having flushes but is still menstruating, she still requires contraception.

In women not using hormones, FSH levels can be helpful and if levels are greater than 30 iu/l on two or more occasions at least 6 weeks apart, this is suggestive of ovarian failure. The risk of further ovulation following raised FSH levels in women in their early forties is unknown. If a woman is having flushes but still having menstrual cycles, she is likely to be ovulating and will still require contraception.

If a copper IUD is inserted after the age of 40 years, it can remain in place without being replaced until 2 years after the menopause (if aged over 50 years) or 1 year after the menopause (if aged under 50 years). For women under the age of 40 years, an IUD should be removed at its expiry date and replaced or alternative contraception used.

QUESTION

For a woman who continues a pregnancy with an IUD or LNG-IUS in place, may the device be retained for contraception after the pregnancy?

POPULATION:　　Women who continue a pregnancy with an IUD or LNG-IUS in place.
INTERVENTION:　Retention of the device for future contraception.
OUTCOME:　　　Safety and efficacy.

ANSWER

The CEU searches identified no literature directly related to this clinical question. Advice from both the FFPRHC[2,3] and from the WHO *Selected Practice Recommendations for Contraceptive Use* is that, in general, an IUD or LNG-IUS is best removed if a coexisting pregnancy is to continue. Nevertheless, in some instances, a woman may choose to continue a pregnancy with an IUD/LNG-IUS in place or it may prove impossible to remove the device during the pregnancy. In these circumstances, the IUD would usually be expelled at the time of delivery, miscarriage, or abortion. It is conceivable that an IUD/LNG-IUS might remain, correctly located, following a delivery, miscarriage or abortion. In such a circumstance, a decision would be required on removal or retention of the device. Our searches found no evidence to guide this decision.

It seems unlikely that a woman would wish to rely for future contraception on a device which had already failed. It is theoretically possible that pregnancy may have resulted from a manufacturing fault (for example, omission of levonorgestrel from the device). Thus, on theoretical grounds, the CEU advises that an IUD/LNG-IUS should be removed in such circumstances and a new device, or alternative method of contraception, chosen. Nevertheless, if a woman chose to retain her existing device, there would appear to be no absolute contraindication to this.

QUESTION

For women over the age of 40 years who present for fitting of an IUD, does the IUD have to be changed or removed before the menopause for effective contraception?

POPULATION: Women over the age of 40 years who present for fitting of an IUD.

INTERVENTION: Change or removal of the IUD before the menopause.

OUTCOME: Efficacy.

ANSWER

A Review from the FFPRHC suggests that it is acceptable for any copper-containing IUD which is inserted in a woman over the age of 40 years to be left in place until after the menopause. The device is likely to afford contraceptive cover until she reaches the menopause.[1] Menopause is often confirmed by measurements of FSH greater than 30 iu/l indicating ovarian failure. Women over the age of 40 years have very low risks of pelvic infection, expulsion and ectopic pregnancy associated with IUD use.[4] The FFPRHC review states that it is accepted practice that contraception is required for a further year when the menopause occurs in a woman over the age of 50 years and for 2 years when it occurs in a woman under the age of 50 years.

The WHO conducted research on the menopause throughout the 1990s and acknowledges that men and women continue to be fertile and sexually active after the age of 40 years.[5] Up to 50% of women are able to become pregnant until well into their fifth decade.[5] However, pregnancy-related risks rise as much as 50-fold for this age group compared with women in their twenties.[4] Providers are therefore encouraged to assist perimenopausal women in choosing an appropriate method according to their circumstances and needs.

QUESTION

For a woman who had an IUD inserted in the 1960s, who is requesting removal of the device, but in whom the device cannot be identified by scanning or X-ray, what action should be taken?

POPULATION: Women who had an IUD inserted in the 1960s, who are requesting removal of the device, but the device cannot be identified by scanning or X-ray.

INTERVENTION: Action to be taken.

OUTCOME: Safety.

ANSWER

During the 1960s and 1970s, all IUDs were made of plastic (polyethylene), with some barium sulfate added so that they would show up on X-rays. The Lippes Loop, first used in 1964, and the Saf-T-Coil, introduced in 1967, were still prevalent in the UK until the end of the 1980s. So some women may still be using them.[6]

If the threads of an IUD are not visible, the device may have been expelled, it may still be in the uterus or it may have perforated the myometrium and be extrauterine.

The FFPRHC CEU's guidance on IUDs recommends that IUD retrievers can be effective in locating lost threads.[2] If no threads are seen and uterine placement of the IUD cannot be confirmed clinically, an ultrasound scan should be arranged. If the IUD is confirmed as intrauterine and contraception is required it can be retained. Despite lack of evidence linking IUDs in postmenopausal women with diseases such as endometrial cancer, the presence of these devices may be a hindrance to investigations if the patient presents later. Some conditions such as postmenopausal bleeding, which may necessitate an endometrial biopsy or ultrasound, may be difficult to diagnose. If the IUD is no longer needed for contraception, it should be removed.

The risk of infection must be discussed when removing a device only because threads are not palpable.

If an ultrasound scan cannot locate the IUD and there is no definite evidence of expulsion, a plain abdominal X-ray should be arranged to identify an extrauterine device. Hysteroscopy is not readily available in all settings, but can be useful if the ultrasound scan is equivocal. Surgical retrieval of an extrauterine IUD is advised. The CEU recommends that women who are found to have a previously unrecognised extrauterine IUD should be counselled about the risks of removal at laparoscopy or laparotomy. Intraperitoneal adhesions appear to be confined to areas around the IUD rather than causing generalised adhesion formation. These localised adhesions appear to prevent further migration of the device. It may be appropriate to leave the IUD in its extrauterine location if the risks of surgery outweigh the benefits of removal.

If an IUD cannot be seen on X-ray, ultrasound or hysteroscopy, it can be presumed to have been expelled.

QUESTION

For a postmenopausal woman with an IUD in place, is it necessary to remove the device surgically if there are difficulties with standard removal; and is there any merit in replacement with a LNG-IUS?

POPULATION: Postmenopausal women with IUD in place.

INTERVENTIONS: Surgical removal following problems with standard removal; replacement of IUD with LNG-IUS.

OUTCOME: Safety, risks, benefits.

ANSWER

In general, the CEU advises that an IUD should be removed at the menopause.[2] However, if standard removal proves impossible, then the risks of surgical removal and the risks of retention (isolated case reports of actinomyces-like organisms, uterine carcinoma and pyometra) should be weighed up individually, taking into account the preferences of the woman. If an individual woman is averse to the prospect of surgical removal, then there is no absolute requirement that this be performed. If she opts to retain a problem-free IUD, then she should be counselled that there have been isolated case reports of complications and advised to reattend if she experiences symptoms such as postmenopausal bleeding or vaginal discharge.

There is no merit in inserting an LNG-IUS in a postmenopausal woman, except as the progestogen component of a combined HRT regimen.[3]

QUESTION

For women who are using an Orthogyn T, how long does it last and should the device be removed?

POPULATION: Women using an Orthogyn T.

INTERVENTION: Removal or retention of the device.

OUTCOME: Efficacy.

ANSWER

The Orthogyn T (Gyne T380S) is no longer available in the UK. This device had a licensed duration of use of 10 years. If a woman presents with this device in place, she can continue with the device for 10 years. Long-term randomised clinical trials of copper IUDs report low cumulative pregnancy rates for the second-generation copper IUDs after use for a 10-year period: pregnancy rates were 2.1/100 women with the T380A and 5.7 with the T220C.[7,8] If her device was fitted at, or after, the age of 40 years, a woman can be advised to continue with this IUD (as for other IUDs) until the menopause. The device can be removed after 1 year of amenorrhoea if the last menstrual period occurred over the age of 50 years or removed after 2 years of amenorrhoea if the last period occurred under the age of 50 years.

QUESTION

For postmenopausal women with a Lippes Loop in place for many years, is leaving the device in place after unsuccessful attempted removal associated with any adverse consequences?

POPULATION: Postmenopausal women with Lippes Loop *in utero* for many years.
INTERVENTION: Unsuccessful attempted removal of the IUD.
OUTCOME: Consequences if the IUD is left in place.

ANSWER

Although the evidence linking IUDs in postmenopausal women with diseases such as endometrial cancer is lacking, the presence of these devices in the uterine cavity may later make it difficult for a clinician to diagnose conditions such as postmenopausal bleeding or perform procedures such as endometrial biopsy if required. There have been case reports of postmenopausal women with a Lippes loop IUD developing actinomycotic infection and endometrial carcinoma.

The CEU recommends that in postmenopausal women, the Lippes loop IUD should be removed even if the woman does not present with any symptoms. If there has been difficulty in the clinic setting, this will require referral to a gynaecologist for removal in theatre.

References

1. Brechin S, Gebbie AE. *Perimenopausal Contraception. FACT Topic for the FFPRHC.* Supplement Review 2000/01. London: FFPRHC; 2000.
2. Faculty of Family Planning and Reproductive Health Care Clinical Effectiveness Unit. The copper intrauterine device as long-term contraception. *J Fam Plann Reprod Health Care* 2004;30:29–42.
3. Faculty of Family Planning and Reproductive Health Care. The levonorgestrel-releasing intrauterine system (LNG-IUS) in contraception and reproductive health. *J Fam Plann Reprod Health Care* 2004;30:99–108.

4. Riphagen FE, Fortney JA, Koelb S. Contraception in women over forty. *J Biosoc Sci* 1988;20:127–42.
5. World Health Organization. *Research on the Menopause in the 1990s*. WHO Technical Report Series. No. 866. Geneva: WHO; 1996.
6. Thomsen RJ, Rayl DL. Dr Lippes and his loop: Four decades in perspective. *J Reprod Med* 1999;44:833–6.
7. Task Force on the Safety and Efficacy of Fertility Regulating Methods. WHO Special Programme of Research, Development and Research Training in Hum Reprod. The Cu380A, Tcu220C, Multiload 250 and Nova T IUD at 3,5 and 7 years of use: results from three randomised multi-centre trials. *Contraception* 1990;42:141–58.
8. World Health Organization. WHO randomized multicenter comparative trials of copper IUDs. Personal communication.

The levonorgestrel-releasing intrauterine system

Effectiveness

QUESTION

For women attending for contraception, how does the efficacy of female sterilisation compare to the efficacy of the LNG-IUS?

POPULATION: Women requesting contraception.
INTERVENTION: Female sterilisation compared with the LNG-IUS.
OUTCOME: Efficacy.

ANSWER

Contraceptive failure rates are usually calculated using two different methods: Pearl Index or Life Table Analysis. Pearl Indices calculate failure rates based on a defined endpoint such as study completion, pregnancy, or discontinuation of the contraceptive method. Life Table Analysis is a cumulative method that combines separate failure rates for each month of contraceptive use and is considered superior to the Pearl Index.[1]

The Pearl Index for the LNG-IUS is usually quoted as 0.1%, which means that of 1000 women who use the LNG-IUS, one may become pregnant within the first year of use.

A RCOG guideline on male and female sterilisation advises clinicians to counsel women that pregnancies can still occur following tubal occlusion and to quote a lifetime failure rate of 1/200 for women of all ages.[2] This value, calculated by Life Table Analysis, equates to a 5/1000 lifetime risk of failure.

From data from the CREST study, the lifetime failure rate decreases with increasing age.[3] The younger a women is at the time of sterilisation, the longer she has for sterilisation to fail and a pregnancy to occur.

Carignan and Pati discussed the implications of the CREST data and advised that, for women younger than 30 years, the IUD should be discussed and seriously considered as an alternative to sterilisation, since sterilisation may be less effective than this method when used consistently over 10 years.[4] They acknowledge that some women may not tolerate the adverse effects associated with the IUD and decide to have it removed. This would reduce the long-term efficacy of the IUD and make it comparable to sterilisation.

References

1. Hatcher RA, Trussell J, Stewart F, Cates W Jr, Stewart GK, Guest F *et al. Contraceptive Technology.* New York: Ardent Media; 1998.
2. Royal College of Obstetricians and Gynaecologists. *Male and Female Sterilisation.* Evidence Based Clinical Guidelines No. 4. London: RCOG Press; 2004.
3. Peterson HB, Xia Z, Hughes JM, Wilcox LS, Taylor LR, Trussel J. The risk of pregnancy after tubal sterilization: Findings from the US Collaborative Review of Sterilization. *Am J Obstet Gynecol* 1996;174:1161–70.
4. Carignan CS, Pati S. Tubal occlusion failures: implications of the CREST study on reducing the risk. *Medscape Women's Health eJournal* 1997;2 [www.medscape.com/viewarticle/408874].

Who can use the LNG-IUS?

QUESTION

For women with a history of genital tract infection and menorrhagia who require contraception, would an LNG-IUS have efficacy, acceptability and low risk of infective complications?

POPULATION:	Women with a history of genital tract infection and menorrhagia who require contraception.
INTERVENTION:	Use of the LNG-IUS.
OUTCOME:	Efficacy, acceptability and risk of infective complications.

ANSWER

One in 20 women aged 30–49 years consults her GP with menorrhagia and 60% of these women will have a hysterectomy within 5 years.[1] It is estimated that only 58% of women receive medical therapy for their menorrhagia before referral to a specialist and about £7 million is spent annually on primary care prescriptions for menorrhagia.

The RCOG has published guidance for the initial management of menorrhagia, which states that both the combined oral contraceptive pill and the LNG-IUS are effective.[1]

The *WHO Medical Eligibility Criteria for Contraceptive Use* has classified the insertion of the LNG-IUS as category 4 (an unacceptable health risk) in women with a current STI or history of STI in the past 3 months, including purulent cervicitis. Given this advice from WHO, the CEU recommends that the combined oral contraceptive pill is prescribed for 3 months, after which the LNG-IUS may be inserted for contraception and the treatment of menorrhagia.

QUESTION

For women with menorrhagia using the LNG-IUS, what level of bleeding is acceptable during its 5 years of use?

POPULATION: Women with menorrhagia.
INTERVENTION: LNG-IUS.
OUTCOME: Bleeding patterns.

ANSWER

The LNG-IUS is licensed for the treatment of idiopathic menorrhagia and randomised trials have shown a 94% reduction in menstrual blood loss by 3 months of use.[2] A strong progestational effect provides a thin inactive endometrium. This mode of action is the mechanism by which the IUS reduces menstrual blood loss. Large epidemiological studies performed in the early 1990s have shown that continuation rates at 5 years are good; but continued bleeding increases the likelihood of premature removal three-fold.[3] The continuation rates overall for the IUS are good: 93% at 1 year, 87% at 2 years, 81% at 3 years, 75% at 4 years and 65% at 5 years. Amenorrhoea can be expected in up to 25% of women after 6 months use. A non-randomised prospective study however, reported that up to 44% of women are amenorrhoeic at 6 months.[4] Spotting (occasional unpredictable bleeding) was evident in

25% of women at 6 months and had decreased to 8% and 11% at 18 and 24 months, respectively.

Counselling regarding bleeding patterns is crucial when women are considering using an IUS. Although bleeding can be unpredictable, discontinuation rates over 5 years are generally low. There are safety data to suggest contraceptive efficacy of the IUS persists for 18 months beyond the 5-year lifespan and therefore it is unlikely that insufficient hormone release causes onset of bleeding in women who have been amenorrhoeic with the IUS.[5] If other causes of bleeding such as infection and gynaecological pathology are excluded, women may wish to continue with this method despite unpredictable bleeding.

QUESTION

For women with antiphospholipid syndrome and menorrhagia who use an LNG-IUS what bleeding patterns are expected in the initial months of use?

POPULATION: Women with antiphospholipid syndrome and menorrhagia.
INTERVENTION: The LNG-IUS.
OUTCOME: Bleeding patterns.

ANSWER

The *WHO Medical Eligibility Criteria for Contraceptive Use* does not mention the hereditary thrombophilias. The benefits of the progestogen-only pill, DMPA, the implant (Norplant, now discontinued) and the LNG-IUS generally outweigh the risks (WHO category 2) for women with a history of deep vein thrombosis or pulmonary embolism.

Guidance from the FFPRHC CEU on the LNG-IUS in contraception and reproductive health advises that women should be informed that the LNG-IUS may reduce menstrual blood loss by over 90% and that altered patterns of menstrual bleeding (prolonged bleeding or amenorrhoea) are common.[6] Abnormal bleeding is most common in the first few months following LNG-IUS insertion but bleeding patterns should improve with time. This should be discussed when counselling prior to insertion.

RCOG guidance on the initial management of menorrhagia states that the LNG-IUS is an effective treatment for menorrhagia, particularly when contraception is required.[1] If after 6 months of using a LNG-IUS the woman is still unhappy about the amount of menstrual blood loss, the RCOG recommends referral. RCOG guidance on managing menorrhagia in secondary care has been published.[7]

The CEU recommends that women are counselled regarding potential abnormal bleeding which can occur with the LNG-IUS. If problematic bleeding persists after 6 months, referral for further investigation may be required.

QUESTION

For women with a bicornuate uterus, can the LNG-IUS be effectively used?

POPULATION: Women with a bicornuate uterus.
INTERVENTION: The LNG-IUS.
OUTCOME: Efficacy.

ANSWER

A bicornuate uterus is a uterus that has two horns and a heart shape; it has a wall inside and a partial split outside. Bicornuate uterus has a mean incidence of approximately 1% in the general population and is the second most common uterine anomaly.[8]

The CEU was unable to find any evidence on the use of the LNG-IUS by women with a bicornuate uterus. Previous case studies have focused on women with a bicornuate uterus using unmedicated IUDs which, in these instances, have led to perforation and unplanned pregnancy.[9,10] It is not known whether the effects of the levonorgestrel released by the LNG-IUS would extend to the entire uterus, even if placed in only one of the bicornuate cavities, and thus provide effective contraception.

The *WHO Medical Eligibility Criteria for Contraceptive Use* advises that women with a distorted uterine cavity (any congenital or acquired uterine abnormality distorting the uterine cavity in a manner that is incompatible with IUD insertion) should not use this method of contraception (WHO category 4). Additionally, the Summary of Product Characteristics for the LNG-IUS lists uterine abnormality as a contraindication.

The CEU does not recommend the use of the LNG-IUS by women with a bicornuate uterus.

QUESTION

For women with bacterial vaginosis, can the LNG-IUS be used to reduce recurrent attacks?

POPULATION: **Women with bacterial vaginosis.**
INTERVENTION: **LNG-IUS.**
OUTCOME: **Reduction of recurrent attacks.**

ANSWER

The *WHO Medical Eligibility Criteria for Contraceptive Use* recommends that the benefits of initiating or continuing use of the LNG-IUS generally outweigh the risks in women with bacterial vaginosis (WHO category 2). Bacterial vaginosis has been identified in women using an IUD; however despite extensive searching, the CEU could find no evidence relating to bacterial vaginosis in women using the LNG-IUS.

The CEU could find no information on whether or not the LNG-IUS reduces the incidence of bacterial vaginosis.

References

1.   Royal College of Obstetricians and Gynaecologists. *The Initial Management of Menorrhagia.* National Evidence-Based Clinical Guidelines No. 28. London: RCOG Press; 2002.
2   Irvine G, Campbell-Brown M, Lumsden MA. Randomised comparative trial of levonorgestrel intrauterine system and norethisterone for the treatment of idiopathic menorrhagia. *Br J Obstet Gynaecol* 1998;105:592–8.
3.   Backmann T, Huhtala S, Blom T, Luoto R, Rauramo l, Kuskenvuo M. Length of use and symptoms associated with premature removal of the levonorgestrel intrauterine system: a nation-wide study of 17,360 users. *BJOG* 2000;107:335–9.
4.   Hidalgo M, Bahamondes L, Perrotti M, Diaz J, Dantas-Monteiro C, Petta CA. Bleeding patterns and clinical performance of the levonorgestrel-releasing intrauterine system (Mirena) up to two years. *Contraception* 2002;65:129–32.
5.   Ronnerdag M, Odlind V. Health effects of long-term use of the intrauterine levonorgestrel-releasing system. A follow-up study over 12 years of continuous use. *Acta Obstet Gynecol Scand* 1999;78:716–21.
6.   Faculty of Family Planning and Reproductive Health Care. The levonorgestrel-releasing intrauterine system (LNG-IUS) in contraception and reproductive health. *J Fam Plann Reprod Health Care* 2004;30:99–109.
7.   Royal College of Obstetricians and Gynaecologists. *The Management of Menorrhagia in Secondary Care.* National Evidence-Based Clinical Guidelines. London: RCOG; 1999.
8.   Grimbizis GF, Camus M, Tarlatzis BC, Devroey P. Clinical implications of uterine malformations and hysteroscopic treatment results. *Hum Reprod Update* 2001;7:161–74.
9.   Das Gupta, S. Perforation of bicornuate uterus by intrauterine contraceptive device. *J Obstet Gynaecol Br Commonw* 1970;77:1140–1.
10. Chaturachinda K, Ajjimakorn S. Perforation of bicornuate uterus by Lippes loop. *J Med Assoc Thai* 1971;54:656–9.

Investigations before insertion

QUESTION

For women having an LNG-IUS fitted, is screening for chlamydia necessary to prevent infective complications?

POPULATION: Women having an LNG-IUS fitted.
INTERVENTION: Testing for chlamydia.
OUTCOME: Infective complications.

ANSWER

The evidence found related to chlamydia screening in the context of IUDs as a whole and it is assumed that similar recommendations will apply to the LNG-IUS.

The RCOG has recommended[1] that screening for *C. trachomatis* and other microorganisms should be considered for women undergoing uterine instrumentation (such as the fitting of an IUD) in the light of other risk factors such as age (as mentioned in the Chief Medical Officer's Expert Advisory Group Report in 1998).[2] However, a SIGN guideline has stated that there are no randomised controlled trials that show that routine screening prior to IUD insertion reduces the risk of ascending infections.[3] There is thus insufficient evidence to support the routine screening of women in the primary care setting prior to IUD fitting.

A Cochrane review of several randomised controlled trials has concluded that there is no justification for antimicrobial prophylaxis prior to the insertion of an IUD, as there is no evidence that antimicrobial prophylaxis reduces the risk of infective complications.[4] The most recent study cited in the review was a randomised controlled trial conducted by Walsh *et al.* in 1998.[5] In this study, a group of 1985 American women were randomised to receive either 500 mg azithromycin or a placebo 1 hour before a copper IUD was inserted. They were followed up for 3 months. All the women were screened prior to IUD insertion for *C. trachomatis* and *N. gonorrhoeae*; 3.8% of the women who took azithromycin had their IUD removed within the time period as against 3.4% of those who took a placebo (relative risk 1.1; 95% CI 0.7–1.8). Only one individual from each arm of the study developed salpingitis. Walsh *et al.* concluded that antimicrobial prophylaxis is not justified in women who have been screened prior to insertion.

Routine IUD insertion is therefore safe with or without antimicrobial prophylaxis.

References

1. Templeton A, editor. *The Prevention of Pelvic Infection*. London: RCOG Press; 1996.
2. Chief Medical Officer. *Expert Advisory Group Report on Chlamydia trachomatis*. London: Department of Health; 1998.
3. Scottish Intercollegiate Guidelines Network. *Management of Genital Chlamydia trachomatis Infection*. Guideline 42. Edinburgh: SIGN; 2002.
4. Screening for chlamydial infection: recommendations and rationale. *Am J Prev Med* 2001;20:90–4.
5. Walsh T, Grimes D, Frezieres R, Nelson A, Bernstein L, Coulson A, *et al*. Randomised controlled trial of prophylactic antibiotics before insertion of intrauterine devices. *Lancet* 1998;351:1005–8.

Insertion and removal

QUESTION

For a woman with an LNG-IUS in place, what resuscitation equipment or emergency measures should be available to remove the device at home and minimise the risk of serious complications?

POPULATION: Women with an LNG-IUS in place.

INTERVENTION: Resuscitation equipment or emergency measures for removal of the device at home.

OUTCOME: Risk of serious complications.

ANSWER

The FFPRHC published a Faculty Aid to CPD Topic (FACT) in 2001 entitled *Resuscitation in the family planning and reproductive health care setting*,[1] which listed the contents of an emergency shock pack that each family planning clinic should have. Guidance on the correct response to anaphylactic shock from Resuscitation Council UK is presented in this response. In the event that a vasovagal faint occurs, the patient's legs should be raised and her head lowered until she recovers. An ambulance should be called if there is persistent bradycardia with pulse under 60 beats/minute or systolic blood pressure under 90 mmHg, ventricular arrhythmia or signs of heart failure. If the heart rate drops below 40 beats/minute or the systolic blood pressure below 90 mmHg, then 500 micrograms of atropine can be administered by slow intravenous injection.[1]

The two emergency situations that are most likely to occur in the family planning clinic are anaphylactic reaction and vasovagal attack. These emergencies may be encountered following an injection of DMPA, after insertion or removal of an IUD or following vasectomy.

No evidence was identified specifically relating to LNG-IUS removal in the home situation. Vasovagal episodes may occur with LNG-IUS removal and if clinicians choose to perform these interventions in a nonclinical setting, an emergency pack and appropriate assistance should be available.

QUESTION

For women having an IUD or LNG-IUS inserted, does treatment of asymptomatic bacterial vaginosis avoid risk of infective morbidity?

POPULATION: Women having an IUD or LNG-IUS inserted.

INTERVENTION: Treatment for bacterial vaginosis.

OUTCOME: Reduction in infective morbidity.

ANSWER

Bacterial vaginosis involves an imbalance of the normal vaginal flora. Hydrogen-producing lactobacilli are diminished and *Gardnerella vaginalis*, anaerobes and mycoplasmas are increased. Many women with bacterial vaginosis are asymptomatic. Amsel's criteria are used to diagnose bacterial vaginosis and include: presence of a discharge, a vaginal pH greater than 4.5, positive amine test and 'clue cells' on microscopy.

A cohort study suggested that bacterial vaginosis is a strong predictor of STI risk in women aged 15–40 years.[2] Compared with women with normal vaginal flora, women with bacterial vaginosis were more likely to test positive for *N. gonorrhoea* (odds ratio 4.1; 95% CI 1.7–9.7) or *C. trachomatis* (odds ratio 3.4; 95% CI 1.5–7.8). However, no evidence was identified in which asymptomatic bacterial vaginosis was treated before IUD or LNG-IUS insertion.

Bacterial vaginosis has been identified in women using an IUD; however, despite extensive searching, the CEU could find no evidence specifically relating to bacterial vaginosis in women using a LNG-IUS. A number of studies have identified a positive association between bacterial vaginosis and IUD use.[3-5] A cohort study in Indonesia identified bacterial vaginosis in 47.2% of IUD users compared with 29.9% of hormonal contraceptive users.[6] Women in this study were married with only one sexual partner, a low-risk group. However, two cohort studies from Sweden[7] and Chile[8] investigated the association between bacterial vaginosis and different contraceptive methods and found no association between bacterial vaginosis and IUD use.

No evidence was identified which investigated treating bacterial vaginosis before IUD or LNG-IUS insertion. The clinical relevance of bacterial vaginosis in women having IUD insertion who have a negative STI screen is unclear. National guidelines for treatment of bacterial vaginosis make no reference to treatment of bacterial vaginosis in women currently using an IUD or LNG-IUS or in women who are considering IUD or LNG-IUS insertion.

QUESTION

For women with cardiomyopathy stable on warfarin, which regimen of antimicrobial prophylaxis is recommended for insertion of the LNG-IUS to reduce the risk of bacterial endocarditis?

POPULATION: Women with cardiomyopathy, stable on warfarin.

INTERVENTION: Antimicrobial prophylaxis for insertion of the LNG-IUS.

OUTCOME: Risk of bacterial endocarditis.

ANSWER

Cardiomyopathies are diseases of the myocardium associated with ventricular dysfunction.[9] Oral anticoagulants such as warfarin may be used by women with cardiomyopathy. However, these oral anticoagulants are teratogenic and carry a risk of placental and fetal haemorrhage thus necessitating the need for reliable contraception.

The *WHO Medical Eligibility Criteria for Contraceptive Use* does not address contraceptive choice for women with cardiomyopathy. However, for women with multiple risk factors for arterial cardiovascular disease such as older age, smoking, diabetes and hypertension or with uncomplicated or complicated valvular heart disease (pulmonary hypertension, atrial fibrillation, history of subacute bacterial endocarditis), the benefits of using the LNG-IUS generally outweigh the risks (WHO category 2). Prophylactic antibiotics are advised for insertion for women with the two latter conditions.

BNF focuses on antibiotic prophylaxis for the prevention of endocarditis in patients with heart-valve lesion, septal defect, patent ductus or prosthetic valve and there is no specific recommendation for prophylaxis with IUD or LNG-IUS insertion. For gynaecological procedures, BNF suggests that prophylaxis is required only for women with prosthetic valves or those who have had endocarditis. In this case they should be managed with amoxicillin 1 g intravenously plus gentamicin 120 mg intravenously, followed by oral amoxicillin

500 mg 6 hours later. The expert group for the FFPRHC CEU guidance on the IUS as long-term contraception upheld BNF guidance.

In the absence of evidence, women will need to be managed individually, perhaps with input from their cardiologist. Local protocols should be developed based on the evidence which does exist from the American Heart Association[10] and the BNF.

QUESTION

For women who are using an LNG-IUS, have there been case reports of anaphylaxis?

POPULATION:	**Women requiring contraception.**
INTERVENTION:	**LNG-IUS.**
OUTCOME:	**Anaphylaxis.**

ANSWER

No case reports of anaphylaxis with the LNG-IUS have been reported in the literature. Anaphylaxis following levonorgestrel implants has been reported but related to use of local anaesthetic rather than the progestogen.[11]

References

1. Bennett A. Resuscitation in the family planning and reproductive health care setting. *J Fam Plann Reprod Health Care* 2001;27:165–9.
2. Wiesenfeld HC, Hillier SL, Krohn MA, Landers DV, Sweet RL. Bacterial vaginosis is a strong predictor of *Neisseria gonorrhoea* and *Chlamydia trachomatis* infection. *Clin Infect Dis* 2003;36:663–8.
3. Sanchez J, Campos PE, Courtois B, Gutierrez L, Carrillo C, Alarcon J, *et al*. Prevention of sexually transmitted diseases (STDs) in female sex workers: prospective evaluation of condom promotion and strengthened STD services. *Sex Transm Dis* 2003;30:273–9.
4. Guerreiro D, Gigante MA, Teles LC. Sexually transmitted diseases and reproductive tract infections among contraceptive users. *Int J Gynecol Obstet* 1998; 63:S167–S17.
5. Calzolari E, Masciangelo R, Milite V, Verteramo R. Bacterial vaginosis and contraceptive methods. *Int J Gynecol Obstet* 2000;70:341–6.
6. Joesoef MR, Karundeng A, Runtupalit C, Moran JS, Lewis JS, Ryan CA. High rate of bacterial vaginosis among women with intrauterine devices in Mando, Indonesia. *Contraception* 2001;64:169–72.
7. Shoubnikova M, Hellberg D, Nilsson S, Mardh P. Contraceptive use in women with bacterial vaginosis. *Contraception* 1997;55:355–8.
8. Castro E, Dominguez M, Navarrete P, Boggiano G, Zemelman R. Prevalence of bacterial vaginosis in women attending family planning clinics. *Anaerobe* 1999;5:399–401.

9. Kasper EK. Cardiomyopathy and Heart Failure Practice – Definitions 2003 [www.hopkinsmedicine.org/cardio/heart/definitions.html].

10. American College of Obstetrics and Gynecology Practice Bulletin. Antibiotic prophylaxis for gynecologic procedures. *Obstet Gynecol* 2001;23:1–9.

11. Gbolade BA. Post-Norplant implants insertion anaphylactoid reaction: a case report. *Contraception* 1997;55:319–320.

Extrauterine location

QUESTION

For women with an LNG-IUS which is lying in the peritoneal cavity will progestogen release from IUS have an effect on injectable progestogen-only contraception?

POPULATION: Women with an LNG-IUS which is lying in the peritoneal cavity.

INTERVENTION: Starting DMPA.

OUTCOME: Additional effects of progestogen from extrauterine IUS affecting DMPA.

ANSWER

The LNG-IUS releases 20 micrograms of levonorgestrel into the uterine cavity every 24 hours. Levonorgestrel is absorbed from capillaries in the endometrium and levels are detectable in serum within 15 minutes of insertion, maximum concentrations seen within a few hours and plasma levels stabilise after the first few weeks.[1] There are data to suggest that the LNG-IUS will remain effective for up to 7 years after insertion but it should be replaced after 5 years. Evidence from a case report suggests that absorption from the LNG-IUS in an abdominal position may occur.[2] It is unlikely that any levonorgestrel being absorbed from the LNG-IUS in the peritoneal cavity will affect the efficacy or adverse effects of injectable progestogen-only contraception. The dose of medroxyprogesterone acetate in Depo-Provera is 150 mg. Adding a small amount of levonorgestrel to that large dose should make no difference to the safety or efficacy of the method. No evidence was identified as to whether leaving the LNG-IUS in the abdominal cavity would lead to complications or infertility.

References

1. Faculty of Family Planning and Reproductive Health Care Clinical Effectiveness Unit. The levonorgestrel-releasing intrauterine system (LNG-IUS) in contraception and reproductive health. *J Fam Plann Reprod Health Care* 2004;30:99–109.

2.   Bobrow C, Cooling H, Bisson D. Amenorrhoea despite displaced levonorgestrel intra-uterine system. *Br J Fam Plann* 2000;26:105–6.

Problems during use of the LNG-IUS

QUESTION

For women with menorrhagia using the LNG-IUS, what level of bleeding is acceptable after 18 months of use?

POPULATION:	**Women with menorrhagia.**
INTERVENTION:	**LNG-IUS.**
OUTCOME:	**Bleeding patterns.**

ANSWER

The LNG-IUS is licensed for the treatment of idiopathic menorrhagia and randomised trials have shown a 94% reduction in menstrual blood loss by 3 months of use. A strong progestational effect provides a thin inactive endometrium. This is the main mechanism by which the LNG-IUS reduces menstrual blood loss.

A large epidemiological study has shown that continuation rates at 5 years are good but continued bleeding increases the likelihood of premature removal three-fold.[1] Continuation rates overall for LNG-IUS in the study were 93% at 1 year, 87% at 2 years, 81% at 3 years, 75% at 4 years and 65% at 5 years.

Amenorrhoea can be expected in up to 25% of women after 6 months of use. A non-randomised prospective study, however, has identified that up to 44% of women are amenorrhoeic at 6 months after insertion.[2] Spotting (occasional unpredictable bleeding) was evident in 25% of women at 6 months and had decreased to 8% and 11% at 18 and 24 months, respectively.

Counselling regarding bleeding patterns is important when women are considering using an LNG-IUS. Although bleeding can be unpredictable, discontinuation rates over 5 years are generally low. If other causes of bleeding such as STI and gynaecological causes are excluded, women may wish to continue with this method despite unpredictable bleeding.

QUESTION

For women with regular prolonged bleeding a year following LNG-IUS insertion for menorrhagia, what other management options could be employed?

POPULATION:	Women with prolonged bleeding after insertion of the LNG-IUS for menorrhagia.
INTERVENTION:	Other management options.
OUTCOME:	Reduction in menstrual bleeding.

ANSWER

The RCOG has published guidance on the initial management of menorrhagia, which states that both the combined oral contraceptive pill and the LNG-IUS are effective treatments options, particularly when contraception is also required.[3] If, after 6 months of using a LNG-IUS, the woman is still unhappy about the amount of menstrual blood loss, the RCOG recommends referral to a gynaecologist.

Guidance on the management of menorrhagia in secondary care advises clinicians to confirm that there is no change to the history of menstrual cycles, perform a bimanual, abdominal and speculum examination and consider only at this stage if thyroid function and coagulation tests are indicated.[4] Further assessment includes endometrial sampling in combination with ultrasound scan and/or hysteroscopy.

A pragmatic approach is often taken to managing women with menorrhagia depending on age, risk factors for endometrial disease and availability of investigation procedures locally.

First-line medical treatments for menorrhagia include the NSAID, mefenamic acid,[5] and the antifibrinolytic agent, Cyklokapron® (Meda).[6] Both of these have been shown to reduce menstrual blood loss in women with menorrhagia. Cyklokapron has been shown to be useful in the management of menorrhagia in women using a copper-bearing IUD[7] but there is no evidence for its use in women using a LNG-IUS. There are, however, few contraindications to its use.

QUESTION

For women requiring long-term contraception, is use of LNG-IUS associated with an increase in weight?

POPULATION: **Women requiring long-term contraception.**
INTERVENTION: **The LNG-IUS.**
OUTCOME: **Increase in weight.**

ANSWER

A small follow-up study of 12 years of continuous use of the LNG-IUS found that body weight increased, with an annual increase of 0.49 kg.[8] A review of progestin-releasing intrauterine systems identified that weight increase with the LNG-IUS was similar to that associated with use of the copper IUD of 0.5 kg/year over the 5-year period of licensed use.[9] It is likely that the weight gain is a consequence of time and ageing rather than a direct effect of levonorgestrel.

Evidence therefore suggests that weight gain associated with use of the LNG-IUS is similar to that associated with IUD use of about 0.5 kg/year and is probably not due to the contraceptive method *per se*. Prolonged use may be associated with an increase in weight but the mechanism of this is unknown.

QUESTION

For women diagnosed as nasal and pharyngeal carriers of MRSA who have had a LNG-IUS fitted, is eradication of infection possible with the device in place?

POPULATION: **Women diagnosed as nasal and pharyngeal carriers of MRSA.**
INTERVENTION: **The LNG-IUS.**
OUTCOME: **Eradication of infection with the device in place**

ANSWER

Certain strains of MRSA are resistant to the antibiotics methicillin and flucloxacillin.[10] MRSA is a type of bacterium that occurs harmlessly on the skin and/or in the noses of healthy people. If it enters the body through breaks in the skin, it may cause serious infection of the bloodstream, bones or joints. Most MRSA infections occur in hospitals but an endogenous infection can occur if the MRSA spread from the initial site of colonisation to a new site. MRSA can also spread between patients and hospital staff through direct and indirect contact. Patients with simple MRSA colonisation may have mupirocin applied to their skin or the inside of their nose.

An extensive search of the literature failed to identify any specific evidence or recommendations relating to retaining or removing an IUD during treatment of MRSA. The only evidence found related to the role of the IUD in relation to pelvic infection. The WHO *Selected Practice Recommendations for Contraceptive Use* recommends that women diagnosed with PID do not have to have an IUD removed prior to antibiotic therapy. One small randomised trial has also concluded that the presence of an IUD did not influence the outcome of antibiotic therapy for acute salpingitis.[11] It is unknown whether the efficacy of the LNG-IUS would be compromised by antibiotic therapy but this is unlikely as the LNG is released in the uterus.

The CEU advises that if a woman has been diagnosed as a carrier of MRSA, the clinician should establish if she wishes to continue using the device. If she does, the device may be retained. If she does not, the device should be removed after antibiotic therapy has started.

QUESTION

For women with genital herpes, is continued use of the LNG-IUS advisable?

POPULATION: Women with genital herpes.

INTERVENTION: Continuation of the LNG-IUS.

OUTCOME: Risk of recurrence

ANSWER

The traditional view of genital herpes was that of a low prevalence STI caused by herpes simplex virus type 2 (HSV-2)[12] which often goes unrecognised. Among patients in the UK presenting with an initial genital herpes infection, herpes simplex virus type 1 (HSV-1) accounts for 20–60% of cases.[13-15]

A major concern for those infected with genital herpes is that they may infect their sexual partners.[16] It was previously believed that transmission only occurred during periods of acute genital blistering and ulceration.[17,18] Subclinical viral shedding occurs in women with genital herpes, whether the infection is caused by herpes simplex virus type 2 (HSV-2) or type 1 (HSV-1). Viral shedding occurs only on a few days overall but is more common in women with frequently recurring herpes.[19] There is lack of evidence to reassure patients taking continuous antiviral treatment that they will not shed the virus. Asymptomatic oral shedding of HSV-1 is common and adults who practice oral sex and do not have immunity to HSV-1 are at risk of genital HSV-1 infection.

The WHO *Medical Eligibility Criteria for Contraceptive Use* does not refer specifically to herpes but advises that women with a current STI or a history of such infection within the past 3 months should not continue use of the LNG-IUS (WHO category 4). Women who have not had a recurrence of herpes within the past 3 months may have a LNG-IUS inserted. The CEU was unable to find any evidence on the risk of recurrence of local herpes with a LNG-IUS in place.

As herpes is a chronic infection, there appears to be no justification for removal of the LNG-IUS if contraception is required; but women should bear in mind that this method will not prevent viral transmission. One study has shown that barrier methods, such as condoms, may reduce the risk of transmission from men to women.[20] However, they cannot cover vulval lesions totally and may not effectively prevent transmission from women to men.

This evidence has implications for the management of patients with genital herpes. Patients should still be advised to abstain from genital contact when they have early or minor genital symptoms and that viral shedding may occur without genital symptoms.

The CEU was unable to find any evidence on the risk of recurrence of local herpes with a LNG-IUS in place.

QUESTION

For women requiring contraception, is there any evidence of an association between the LNG-IUS and breast lumps?

POPULATION: Women requiring contraception.
INTERVENTION: LNG-IUS.
OUTCOME: Association with breast lumps.

ANSWER

The WHO *Medical Eligibility Criteria for Contraceptive Use* recommends that women with benign breast disease can have unrestricted use (WHO category 1) of the LNG-IUS. The benefits of the LNG-IUS generally outweigh the risks (WHO category 2) in women with an undiagnosed breast mass.

The Summary of Product Characteristics for the LNG-IUS states that benign breast conditions have been reported as an adverse event. However, the Summary does not report the actual numbers or rates of benign breast conditions that occur in LNG-IUS users.

Despite extensive searching, the CEU could find no other evidence in the literature regarding the occurrence of breast lumps in women using the LNG-IUS.

QUESTION

For women using the LNG-IUS is there evidence of low estradiol concentrations?

POPULATION: Women of reproductive age.

INTERVENTION: The LNG-IUS.

OUTCOME: Low estradiol concentrations.

ANSWER

Despite extensive searching, the CEU could find no published information to link the use of the LNG-IUS with low estradiol concentrations. The Summary of Product Characteristics for the LNG-IUS suggests that because levonorgestrel is released directly into the uterine cavity with very low plasma concentrations, only minor effects on metabolism are seen. Most women (over 75%) continue to ovulate while using the LNG-IUS and will have their own endogenous levels of estradiol.[21,22] Serum estradiol levels are greater than 100 pg/ml in most women.[23] The LNG-IUS has minimal effects on the hypo-thalamo-pituitary-ovarian axis.[23]

The CEU found no evidence to suggest the use of the LNG-IUS reduces endogenous estrogens.

QUESTION

Are thyroid function tests altered by the use of the levonorgestrel-containing intrauterine system?

POPULATION: Women of reproductive age.

INTERVENTION: LNG-IUS.

OUTCOME: Altered thyroid function tests.

ANSWER

No evidence was found to suggest that the LNG-IUS alters thyroid function tests. The WHO *Medical Eligibility Criteria for Contraceptive Use* states that the

LNG-IUS can be used in women with simple goitre, hypothyroidism or hyperthyroidism.

QUESTION

For women with hirsutism, is there any evidence of an association with the use of the LNG-IUS?

POPULATION: Healthy women.
INTERVENTION: LNG-IUS.
OUTCOME: Hirsutism.

ANSWER

Excessive hair growth in androgen-dependent areas of a woman's body (hirsutism) is caused by increased androgen action on hair follicles, either from increased circulating levels of androgens (endogenous or exogenous) or from increased sensitivity of hair follicles to normal levels of circulating androgens.

Increased androgen action can be familial, idiopathic or caused by excess androgen secretion by the ovary (tumours or PCOS). It can also be caused by excess secretion of androgens by adrenal glands (congenital adrenal hyperplasia, Cushing syndrome, tumour) or exogenous pharmacological sources of androgens. Exogenous pharmacological agents, including danazol, anabolic steroids and testosterone, may cause hirsutism.

The progestogens levonorgestrel, norethindrone and norgestrel have strong androgenic effects, while etynodiol diacetate, norgestimate and desogestrel appear *in vitro* to be less androgenic.[24,25]

Despite extensive searching, the CEU could find no evidence of an association between the LNG-IUS and hirsutism.

QUESTION

For women requiring contraception who use the LNG-IUS, is there a risk of osteoporosis?

POPULATION: Women requiring contraception.
INTERVENTION: The LNG-IUS.
OUTCOME: Risk of osteoporosis.

ANSWER

No studies were identified which examine the relationship between long-term use of the LNG-IUS and bone mineral density. However, the Summary of Product Characteristics for the LNG-IUS mentions that the low plasma concentrations of levonorgestrel with the LNG-IUS cause only minor effects on metabolism.

The CEU examined the literature on the relationship between the levonorgestrel implant (Norplant, now discontinued) and bone mineral density.[26-33] Although the available evidence is conflicting, there does not appear to be a reduction in bone mineral density associated with progestogen-only implants. The CEU has therefore found no evidence that suggests that women who use the LNG-IUS have an increased risk of osteoporosis.

References

1. Backmann T, Huhtala S, Blom T, Luoto R, Rauramo l, Kuskenvuo M. Length of use and symptoms associated with premature removal of the levonorgestrel intrauterine system: a nation-wide study of 17,360 users. *BJOG* 2000;107:335–9.
2. Hidalgo M, Bahamondes L, Perrotti M, Diaz J, Dantas-Monteiro C, Petta CA. Bleeding patterns and clinical performance of the levonorgestrel-releasing intrauterine system (Mirena) up to two years. *Contraception* 2002;65:129–32.
3. Royal College of Obstetricians and Gynaecologists. *The Initial Management of Menorrhagia*. National Evidence-Based Clinical Guidelines No. 28. London: RCOG Press; 2002.
4. Royal College of Obstetricians and Gynaecologists. *The Management of Menorrhagia in Secondary Care*. National Evidence-based Clinical Guidelines No. 29. London: RCOG Press; 2002.
5. Cameron IT, Haining R, Lumsden M-A, Thomas VR, Smith SK. The effects of mefenamic acid and norethisterone on measured menstrual blood loss. *Obstet Gynecol* 1990;76:85–8.
6. Bonnar J, Sheppard B. Treatment of menorrhagia during menstruation: randomised controlled trial of ethamsylate, mefenamic acid and tranexamic acid. *BMJ* 1996;313:579–82.
7. Ylikorkala O, Viinikka L. Comparison between antifibrinolytic and antiprostaglandin treatment in the reduction of increased menstrual blood loss in women with intrauterine contraceptive devices. *Br J Obstet Gynaecol* 1983;90:78–83.
8. Ronnerdag M, Odlind V. Health effects of long-term use of the intrauterine levonorgestrel-releasing system A follow-up study over 12 years of continuous use. *Acta Obstet Gynecol Scand* 1999;78:716–21.
9. Luukkainen T, Pakarinen P, Toivonen J. Progestin-releasing intrauterine systems. *Semin Reprod Med* 2001;19:355–63.
10. Johnson A. Methicillin-resistant *Staphylococcus aureus* (MRSA) infection. 2002 [www.netdoctor.co.uk].
11. Soderberg G, Lindgren S. Influence of an intrauterine device on the course of an acute salpingitis. *Contraception* 1981;24:137–43.

12. Dowdle WR, Nahmias AJ, Harwell RW, Pauls FP. Association of antigenic type of Herpes virus hominis with site of viral recovery. *J Immunol* 1967;99:974–80.
13. Barton IG, Kinghorn GR, Najem A, Al-Omar LS, Potter CW. Incidence of herpes simplex virus types 1 and 2 isolated in patients with herpes genitalis in Sheffield. *Br J Vener Dis* 1982;58:44–7.
14. Ross JDC, Smith IW, Elton RA. The epidemiology of herpes simplex type types 1 and 2 infection of the genital tract in Edinburgh 1978-1991. *Genitourin Med* 1993;69:381–3.
15. Scoular A, Leask BGS, Carrington D. Changing trends in genital herpes due to herpes simplex virus type 1 in Glasgow, 1985–88. *Genitourin Med* 1990;66:226–8.
16. Catotti DN, Clarke P, Catoe KE. Herpes revisited. Still a cause of concern. *Sex Transm Dis* 1993;20:77–80.
17. Robertson DHH, McMillan A, Young H. *Clinical Practice in Sexually Transmissible Diseases*. Tunbridge: Pitman Medical; 1980.
18. Hayward Medical Communications. *Genital Herpes Simplex: A Self-help Guide*. London: Hayward Medical Communications; 1993.
19. Patel R, Cown FM, Barton SE. Advising patients with genital herpes. *BMJ* 1997;314:85–6.
20 Wald A. Effect of condoms on reducing the transmission of herpes simplex virus type 2 from men to women. *JAMA* 2001;285:3100–6.
21. Nilsson CG, Lähteenmäki PLA, Luukkainen T. Ovarian function in amenorrheic and menstruating users of a levonorgestrel-releasing intrauterine device. *Fertil Steril* 1984;41:52–5.
22. Ratsula K, Toivonen J, Lähteenmäki P, Luukkainen T. Plasma levonorgestrel levels and ovarian function during the use of a levonorgestrel-releasing intracervical contraceptive device. *Contraception* 1989;39:195–204.
23. Kurunäki H, Toivonen J, Lähteenmäki PLA, Luukkainen T. Pituitary and ovarian function and clinical performance during the use of a levonorgestrel-releasing intracervical contraceptive device. *Contraception* 1984;29:31–43.
24. Hunter MH, Carek PJ. Evaluation and treatment of women with hirsutism. *Am Fam Phys* 2003;67:2565–72.
25. Griffing GT, Melby JC. Hirsutism causes and treatments. *Hosp Pract* 1991;26:43–58.
26. Naessen T, Olsson SE, Gudmundon J. Differential effects on bone density of progestogen-only methods for contraception in premenopausal women. *Contraception* 1995;52:35–39.
27. Banks E, Berrington A, Casabonne D. Overview of the relationship between use of progestogen-only contraceptives and bone mineral density. *BJOG* 2001;108:1214–21.
28. Beerthuizen R, van Beek A, Massai R, Makarainen R, Hout J, Bennink HC. Bone mineral density during long-term use of the progestagen contraceptive implant Implanon compared to a non-hormonal method of contraception. *Hum Reprod* 2000;15:118–22.
29. Petti B, Piaggio G, Mehta S, Cravioto M C, Meirik O. Steroid hormone contraception and bone mineral density: a cross sectional study in an international population. *Obstet Gynecol* 2000;95:736–44.
30. Cromer BA, Blair JM, Mahan JD, Zibner L, Naumovski Z. A prospective comparison of bone density in adolescent girls receiving depot medroxyprogesterone acetate (Depo-Provera), levonorgestrel (Norplant) or oral contraceptives. *Contraception* 1995;52:35–9.
31. Diaz S, Reyes MV, Zepeda A, Gonzalez GB, Lopez JM, Campino C, *et al*. Norplant implants and progesterone vaginal rings do not affect maternal bone turnover and density during lactation and after weaning. *Hum Reprod* 1999;14:2499–505.
32. Di X, Li Y, Zhang C, Jiang J, Gu S. Effects of levonorgestrel-releasing subdermal contraceptive implants on bone density and bone metabolism. *Contraception* 1999;60:161–6.

33. Petitti DB, Piaggio G, Mehta S, Cravioto MC, Meirik O, For the WHO Study of Hormonal Contraception and Bone Health. Steroid hormone contraception and bone mineral density: a cross-sectional study in an international population. *Obstet Gynecol* 2002;95:736–44.

Continuation and removal

QUESTION

For women using the LNG-IUS, is the device safe and effective for use longer than 5 years?

POPULATION:	Women using the LNG-IUS.
INTERVENTION:	Use beyond 5 years.
OUTCOME:	Efficacy and safety.

ANSWER

Randomised trials have shown that the LNG-IUS has contraceptive efficacy for up to 7 years of continuous use.[1,2] Forty percent of the levonorgestrel load is still present in the LNG-IUS after 5 years use and one study has shown that the LNG-IUS is safe for up to 12 years use (with device replacement every 5 years).[3]

CEU guidance on the LNG-IUS in contraception and reproductive health care recommends that women should be informed that the LNG-IUS is licensed for 5 years of use.[4] It is good practice that all women using the LNG-IUS should be advised to return for review after 5 years of use, to discuss the need for removal and replacement.

Despite evidence from the randomised trials mentioned above, the CEU and the expert group that contributed to the development of this guidance decided to endorse the Summary of Product Characteristics recommendation that women using the LNG-IUS for contraception have the device replaced after 5 years. In the absence of evidence to suggest otherwise, this recommendation also applies to women aged over 40 years at the time of insertion. However, women using the LNG-IUS for menorrhagia only and whose symptoms are well controlled, may continue with the LNG-IUS beyond its licensed duration particularly if they are amenorrhoeic.

QUESTION

> **For women aged 51 years with no menopausal symptoms who have had a LNG-IUS in place for 5 years, can the device be left or should it be replaced?**

POPULATION: Women aged 51 years with no menopausal symptoms, who have had a LNG-IUS system in place for 5 years.

INTERVENTION: Continuation of the LNG-IUS.

OUTCOME: Efficacy.

ANSWER

The Summary of Product Characteristics for the LNG-IUS states that it is effective for 5 years and should be removed or replaced after 5 years of use.

FFPRHC guidance presents evidence from randomised trials[4,5] that show that the LNG-IUS is effective for up to 7 years of continuous use. FFPRHC Guidance on the LNG-IUS for contraception and reproductive health recommends that women should be advised to have the LNG-IUS replaced or removed after 5 years, unless they are using it for the management of menorrhagia only and bleeding patterns remain acceptable.[4] No evidence was found to suggest that this should be different for women aged over 40 years at the time of insertion.

The average age of the menopause is 50.8 years and it can only be diagnosed in retrospect when a woman has been period-free for 12 months. However, for women using the LNG-IUS, amenorrhoea may occur due to the device. Approximately 20–25% women using the LNG-IUS will also be anovulatory. FSH can be helpful in diagnosing the menopause and if levels are greater than 30 iu/l on two or more occasions at least 6 weeks apart this is highly suggestive of ovarian failure. Levels of FSH can be checked when a woman is using the progestogen-only pill. However, no evidence was identified to guide clinicians on the usefulness of FSH in the diagnosis of the menopause for women using the LNG-IUS. The accuracy of FSH levels (greater than 30 iu/l) in detecting the menopause in women using the LNG-IUS is unknown. It is also unclear if assessing FSH levels in women using the LNG-IUS will assist in decision-making regarding LNG-IUS removal.

Women using the LNG-IUS may present with vasomotor symptoms, suggestive of the perimenopause. The CEU suggests that a woman aged 51 years with a LNG-IUS in place for 5 years has several options regarding future contraception:

- After counselling about the continued efficacy of the LNG-IUS beyond 5 years and the natural decrease in fertility in women in their 40s and 50s, a woman may choose to continue with the LNG-IUS for more than 5 years. However, she should be made aware that this use is outside product licence and the same dilemma will exist regarding discontinuing the LNG-IUS after this extended duration of use.

- She may choose to stop the LNG-IUS and use a barrier method. If she remains amenorrhoeic for 1 year, the barrier method can also be discontinued.

- She may choose to have the LNG-IUS replaced and continue to use it to age 55 years, at which time it can be removed as natural loss of fertility is assumed.

QUESTION

For postmenopausal women with intramural uterine fibroids who are using the LNG-IUS, is leaving the device in place after unsuccessful attempted removal associated with any adverse consequences?

POPULATION: Postmenopausal women using the LNG-IUS, who have intramural fibroids.

INTERVENTION: Unsuccessful removal.

OUTCOME: Consequences if the LNG-IUS is left in place.

ANSWER

The *WHO Medical Eligibility Criteria for Contraceptive Use* recommends that when uterine fibroids are present without distortion of the uterine cavity, the benefits of using the LNG-IUS generally outweigh the risks (WHO category 2). However, if uterine fibroids are distorting the uterine cavity, the LNG-IUS must not be used (WHO category 4).

Evidence in the literature suggests that the removal of IUDs should be mandatory in postmenopausal women. Despite lack of evidence linking IUDs in postmenopausal women with diseases such as endometrial cancer, the presence of these devices may be a hindrance to investigations if the woman presents later. Some conditions such as postmenopausal bleeding, which may necessitate an endometrial biopsy or ultrasound, may be difficult to diagnose. It is recommend that if the IUD is no longer needed for contraception, it should be removed. Cobellis *et al.*[6] suggest that the removal of an IUD should be mandatory in postmenopausal women because of the risk of pelvic actino-mycosis.

No evidence was identified on the removal of the LNG-IUS in postmeno-pausal women. However, the CEU recommends that when the 5-year licence has expired, the LNG-IUS should be removed even if the woman does not present with symptoms. If there has been difficulty in the clinic setting, she will require referral to a gynaecologist for removal.

References

1. Sivin I, Stern J, Coutinho E, Mattos CER, el Mahgoub S, Diaz S, *et al*. Prolonged intrauterine contraception: a seven-year randomized study of the levonorgestrel 20 mcg/day (LNg 20) and the copper T380 Ag IUDs. *Contraception* 1991;44:473–80.
2. Díaz J, Faúndes A, Díaz M, Marchi N. Evaluation of the clinical performance of a levonorgestrel-releasing IUD, up to seven years of use, in Campinas, Brazil. *Contraception* 1993;47:169–75.
3. Rönnerdag M, Odlind V. Health effects of long-term use of the intrauterine levonorgestrel-releasing system. A follow up study over 12 years of continuous use. *Acta Obstet Gynecol Scand* 1999;78:716–21.
4. Faculty of Family Planning and Reproductive Health Care. The levonorgestrel-releasing intrauterine system (LNG-IUS) in contraception and reproductive health. *J Fam Plann Reprod Health Care* 2004;30:99–108.
5. Faculty of Family Planning and Reproductive Healthcare Clinical Effectiveness Unit. Contraception for Women Aged over 40 Years. *J Fam Plann Reprod Health Care* 2005;31:51–64.
6. Cobellis L, Messalli EM, Pierno G. Pelvic actinomycosis in menopause: a case report. *Maturitas* 2001;39:79–81.

Condoms

QUESTION

For women requiring contraception, are condoms lubricated with nonoxynol-9 or non-spermicidally lubricated condoms more effective? (Three similar enquiries.)

POPULATION: Women requiring contraception.

INTERVENTION: Condoms lubricated with spermicidal (nonoxynol-9) or non-spermicidal lubricant.

OUTCOME: Efficacy.

ANSWER

The WHO reviewed the safety and effectiveness of nonoxynol-9 in the family planning setting (spermicide alone, spermicide with diaphragms and cap, and spermicidally lubricated condoms).[1] No evidence was identified that showed that spermicidally lubricated condoms provide additional protection against pregnancy compared with non-spermicidally lubricated condoms. Nonoxynol-9 lubricated condoms should not be promoted over non-spermicidally lubricated condoms.

The CEU recommends that based on current evidence non-spermicidally lubricated condoms are as effective in preventing pregnancy as nonoxynol-9 lubricated condoms.

QUESTION

Do women requiring contraception who use nonoxynol-9 have an increased risk of vaginal ulceration and subsequent STI? (Five similar enquiries.)

POPULATION: Women requiring contraception.

INTERVENTION: Nonoxynol-9.

OUTCOME: Increased risk of vaginal ulceration and STI.

ANSWER

The WHO identified some evidence that nonoxynol-9 can cause epithelial damage in the vagina and rectum with recurrent use. This epithelial damage may predispose to STI and HIV. A randomised controlled trial[2] compared condoms lubricated with nonoxynol-9 to condoms lubricated with silicone for use in prophylaxis against STIs in sex workers. The study concluded that non-spermicidally lubricated condoms (silicone) are as effective at preventing cervical infection and STIs as condoms lubricated with nonoxynol-9. Most evidence on the risk of HIV and nonoxynol-9 has been obtained from studies in sex workers using repeated doses of intravaginal nonoxynol-9.

The CEU recommends that women who use nonoxynol-9 lubricated condoms are not at an increased or decreased risk of STI compared to women using condoms which are not spermicidally lubricated.

References

1. World Health Organization. *WHO/CONRAD Technical Consultation on Nonoxynol-9.* Geneva: WHO; 2001.
2. Roddy RE, Cordero M, Ryan KA, Figueroa J. A randomised controlled trial comparing nonoxynol-9 lubricated condoms with silicone lubricated condoms for prophylaxis. *Sex Transm Infect* 1998;74:116–19.

Diaphragms

QUESTION

For women using a diaphragm, does use without spermicide reduce the contraceptive efficacy of the diaphragm?

POPULATION:	Women using a diaphragm.
INTERVENTION:	Use without a spermicide.
OUTCOME:	Efficacy of the diaphragm.

ANSWER

A systematic review[1] investigated the contraceptive efficacy of diaphragm use alone compared with use with spermicide. One randomised controlled trial[2] identified no significant difference in pregnancy rates between women using a diaphragm with or without spermicide. A trend towards higher pregnancy rates in women using a diaphragm without spermicide was noted but the trial was underpowered to detect differences in failure rates between the two groups and no conclusions can be drawn from these results.

The 12-month cumulative pregnancy rate per 100 women for typical use of the diaphragm without spermicide was 28.6/100 woman (95% CI 17.4–39.8). The 12-month cumulative pregnancy rate for typical use of diaphragm with spermicide was 21.2/100 woman (95% CI 11.0–31.4).[2] The 12-month cumulative pregnancy rate/100 women for consistent use (no unprotected intercourse and use of only this method) for diaphragm without spermicide was 19.3/100 women (95% CI 7.5–31.1) and diaphragm with spermicide was 12.3/100 women (95% CI 2.8–21.8).

The CEU concludes that there is insufficient evidence to justify changing standard practice in the UK, which is to recommend that a diaphragm should be used with spermicide.

QUESTION

For women using a diaphragm who are allergic to nonoxynol-9, is there a spermicide which does not contain this ingredient which could be used as an alternative?

POPULATION: Women using a diaphragm who are allergic to nonoxynol-9.
INTERVENTION: Spermicide which does not contain nonoxynol-9.
OUTCOME: Efficacy.

ANSWER

Standard clinical practice in the UK is to recommend use of spermicide with a diaphragm. There is insufficient evidence however, to support or refute this. A systematic review[1] on the contraceptive efficacy of diaphragms alone compared to diaphragms with spermicide identified one randomised controlled trial,[2] which found no significant difference in pregnancy rates (with typical or consistent use) between the two groups.

All spermicides available in the UK (foams, creams, gels, and pessaries) contain nonoxynol-9. For women (or men) who are presumed to be allergic to nonoxynol-9 there is no alternative spermicide.

The CEU suggests that if women (or their male partners) are allergic to nonoxynol-9 another method of contraception may be considered. Alternatively women can be counselled that there is no evidence that contraceptive efficacy is increased or decreased when a diaphragm is used without spermicide. After counselling and considering other contraceptive options women may choose to use the diaphragm without spermicide.

References

1. Cook L, Nanda K, Grimes D. Diaphragm versus diaphragm with spermicides for contraception. *Cochrane Database Syst Rev* 2003;(1).
2. Bounds W, Guillebaud J, Dominik R, Dalberth BT. The diaphragm with and without spermicide. A randomized, comparative efficacy trial. *J Reprod Med* 1995;40:764–74.

5 STERILISATION, FERTILITY AWARENESS-BASED METHODS AND NON-UK METHODS

Female sterilisation

QUESTION

Is anyone in the UK using Essure® (Conceptus Inc.)?

POPULATION: Clinicians within the UK.

INTERVENTION: Essure (permanent birth control).

OUTCOME: Clinical experience within the UK.

ANSWER

Essure, previously known as STOP, is a non-incisional, non-surgical form of female sterilisation launched in the UK and Ireland in 2002. It involves inserting micro-inserts made from polyester fibres and metals (nickel-titanium, and stainless steel) via hysteroscopy into the fallopian tubes.[1] The procedure is usually completed under local anaesthesia and/or intravenous sedation. The micro-inserts cause scar tissue that ultimately blocks the tubes preventing conception. The procedure takes around 30 minutes to complete and most women can return home and resume normal activities 45 minutes after completion. It is recommended that additional contraception is used for 3 months afterwards and that at 3 months an imaging procedure is performed to confirm the correct placement of the micro-inserts and tubal occlusion. Currently, this is the only hysteroscopic tubal occlusion method licensed in the UK. Conceptus conducted four separate clinical trials in the USA, Europe, Australia and Mexico: phase IA (placement feasibility of micro-inserts), phase IB (placement feasibility and comfort of micro-inserts); phase II (preliminary safety and effectiveness) and a trial of safety and effectiveness.[1] The phase II trial involved 130 women and bilateral placement of the inserts was achieved in 85%, with unilateral placement in 3%.[2] During the safety and effectiveness trial, an attempt was made to insert Essure in 507 women of whom 92% had successful bilateral placement and 98% of those attending the 3-month follow-up had complete tubal occlusion.[3] Combining the data from the phase II and safety and effectiveness studies, Conceptus concluded that Essure is 99.8% effective in preventing pregnancy at 2 years of follow-up. However, they mention that there are few data on the effectiveness of the procedure beyond this time and, as no contraceptive method is 100% effective, there is a small chance of pregnancy, even many years after the procedure.

The RCOG guidance on male and female sterilisation published in January 2004 stated that 'hysteroscopic methods for tubal occlusion are still under evaluation and should only be used within the present guidance system for new surgical interventions'.[4] The National Institute for Health and Clinical Excellence (NICE) has responsibility for assessing whether new interventions are sufficiently safe and effective for routine National Health Service use. A NICE document published in October 2003 highlighted that long-term data were limited to 2 years but that no pregnancies had been reported. One study included in the review described complications and adverse effects. Postoperative cramps, mild bleeding, pain and nausea were the most commonly noted. Uterine perforation was reported in 1.1–2.9% of women.[5]

Currently, no evidence exists from randomised control trials comparing tubal ligation by laparoscopy and tubal occlusion by hysteroscopy. Evidence from other studies conducted beyond the Conceptus clinical trials revealed that: placement of the inserts was highly successful in most women (ranging from 85%[2] to 98%[6]) at first attempt; the procedure was well tolerated and accepted;[7,8] there were limited adverse events both operatively and postoperatively[8] and no pregnancies had been reported up to 2 years.[9] The Essure system is the first hysteroscopic method to be approved by the Food and Drug Administration in the USA (in 2003). Reasons cited for approval were that hysteroscopic tubal occlusion is less invasive than laparoscopic sterilisation and benefits women with contraindications to laparoscopic sterilisation such as obesity and previous pelvic surgery.[10]

A review by Weisberg in the International Planned Parenthood Federation Medical Bulletin[11] suggested that this method was comparable to male sterilisation (vasectomy) in terms of its invasiveness, recovery time, and morbidity.

Considerations with Essure:[2]

- Essure is a new but irreversible procedure and removal of the micro-inserts would require surgery.

- No contraceptive method including Essure can be considered 100% effective.

- Some women do not achieve successful insertion of the micro-inserts.

- A reliable contraceptive method must be used for at least 3 months before the procedure.

Women who are not suitable to use Essure include:[2]

- those uncertain about their desire to end fertility

- those who are pregnant or suspect they may be pregnant

- those who have delivered a baby, had a miscarriage or an abortion within 6 weeks before the procedure

- those who have had an active or recent pelvic infection

- those who have had a uterine abnormality

- those who have an allergy to contrast media used to identify successful placement of micro-inserts

- those who have a known hypersensitivity or allergy to nickel confirmed by a skin test

- those who are not willing to use a reliable method of contraception for 3 months before the procedure

- those who are not willing to undergo a hysterosalpingogram 3 months after the procedure

- those who have had a prior tubal ligation.

The CEU contacted Conceptus to ask if Essure was being used in the UK. A telephone call with a representative revealed that Essure is being used in some centres in England, Sheffield being one.

References

1. Conceptus Inc. What is Essure? 2004.
2. University of Birmingham. *New and Emerging Technology Briefing: Selective tubal occlusion (Essure) for female sterilisation*. Birmingham: National Horizon Scanning Centre; 2002.
3. Kerin JF, Carignan CS, Cher D. The Safety and effectiveness of a new hysteroscopic method for permanent birth control; results of the first Essure pbc clinical study. *Aus N Z J Obstet Gynaecol* 2001;41:364–70.
4. Royal College of Obstetricians and Gynaecologists. *Male and Female Sterilisation*. Evidence-based Clinical Guidelines No. 4. London: RCOG Press; 2004.

5. National Institute for Clinical Excellence. *Interventional Procedure Overview of Hysteroscopic Sterilisation by Tubal Cannulation and Placement of Intrafallopian Implant.* IP Guidance Number: IPG044. London: NICE; 2003 [www.nice.org.uk/page.aspx?o=IP_218&c=dg.gynaecology].
6. Kerin JF, Munday DN, Ritossa MG, Pesce A, Rosen D. Essure hysteroscopic sterilization: results based on utilizing a new coil catheter delivery system. *J Am Assoc Gynecol Laparosc* 2004;11:388–93.
7. Menez C, Lopes P. A new hysteroscopic method for sterilization. *J Gynecol Obstet Biol Reprod (Paris)* 2004;33:221–8.
8. Ubeda A, Labastida R, Dexeus S. A new device for hysteroscopic tubal sterilization in an outpatient setting. *Fertil Steril* 2004;82:196–9.
9. Dewulf S, Decudin B, Engrand JB, Wierre L, Resibois JP, Horrent S, *et al.* Permanent female sterilization by micro-insert (Essure system) placement: A feasibility study. *J Pharm Clin* 2004;23:249–52.
10. Magos A, Chapman L. Hysteroscopic tubal sterilization. *Obstet Gynecol Clin North Am* 2004;31:705–19.
11. Weisberg E. Essure: a new contraceptive device for outpatient female sterilisation. *IPPF Med Bull* 2002;36.

Male sterilisation

QUESTION

Are healthy men having a vasectomy at an increased risk of prostatic cancer?

POPULATION: Healthy men.
INTERVENTION: Vasectomy.
OUTCOME: Risk of prostatic cancer.

ANSWER

Three case–control studies have investigated the risk of prostatic cancer following vasectomy.[1–3] A Canadian retrospective case–control study suggested an increased risk;[1] however, bias and confounding factors may explain this finding. A large population based case–control study carried out in New Zealand did not identify any association.[2] This study identified 923 new cases of prostatic cancer among men aged 40–74 years from the New Zealand Cancer Registry. Controls (1224) were randomly identified from the general electoral roll. Cases and controls were interviewed by telephone between January 1997 and November 1999. The main outcome measure was the relative risk of prostatic cancer for men who had had a vasectomy compared to those who had not. No association was identified between prostatic cancer and vasectomy (relative risk 0.92; 95% CI 0.75–1.14) or with time since vasectomy (relative risk 0.92; 95% CI 0.68–1.23) for more than 25 years following vasectomy. Another population based case–control study from the USA also reported no link between vasectomy and prostatic cancer (odds ratio 1.1; 95% CI 0.9–1.4).[3] No differences were identified according to age, race or family history.

A systematic literature review of the safety and efficacy of vasectomy identified publications from 1964 to 1998. The weight of evidence suggests that men are not at increased risk of either prostatic or testicular cancer following vasectomy.[4] Animal and human data also indicate no increase in risk of atherosclerosis following vasectomy.

Guidance from the RCOG on male and female sterilisation suggests that men can be reassured that vasectomy is not associated with any long term effects.[5] The CEU could find no further evidence to contradict this recommendation; in particular, current evidence suggests that there is no association between vasectomy and prostatic cancer.

References

1. Emard J-F, Droudin G, Thouez J-P, Ghadirian P. Vasectomy and prostate cancer in Quebec, Canada. *Health Place* 2001;7:131–9.
2. Stanford JL, Wicklund KG, McKnight B, Daling JR, Brawer MK. Vasectomy and risk of prostate cancer. *Cancer Epidemiol Biomarkers Prev* 1999;8:881–6.
3. Cox B, Sneyd MJ, Paul C, Delahunt B, Skegg DCG. Vasectomy and risk of prostate cancer. *JAMA* 2002;287:3110–15.
4. Schwingl PJ, Guess HA. Safety and effectiveness of vasectomy. *Fertil Steril* 2000;73:923–36.
5. Royal College of Obstetricians and Gynaecologists. *Male and Female Sterilisation*. National Evidence- Based Clinical Guidelines No. 4. London: RCOG Press; 2004.

Fertility awareness-based methods

QUESTION

For women who wish to use natural family planning methods, is the Calista® (Donna) saliva ovulation test an effective method of contraception?

POPULATION: **Women who wish to use natural methods of family planning.**
INTERVENTION: **Calista saliva ovulation test.**
OUTCOME: **Efficacy.**

ANSWER

Calista is a saliva ovulation test comprising a portable, pocket microscope by which saliva ferning is used to identify the fertile and infertile periods during a woman's monthly cycle.[1] Increasing levels of estrogen cause mucous membranes to produce more salt; the increased amount of salt causes saliva to crystallise and form a 'fern-like' structure which can be seen when viewing saliva on a slide through a microscope.[2] The fern-like pattern can usually be identified 3–4 days prior to ovulation. Calista was developed following studies that had examined natural methods of family planning and changes in saliva during the menstrual cycle.[3-7] Calista is manufactured by BioPhytoTech International (www.ecobrands.co.uk), whose products are available from high street outlets, as well as independent pharmacies and retailers.

After a literature search, the CEU was unable to find any studies that have evaluated the efficacy of Calista, although the manufacturers claim that the test is 98% accurate at ovulation detection and is reuseable for 24 months.[1] Advice on natural fertility awareness is that any ovulation predictor test should be considered as a 'fourth tool' in fertility indication and should be used along with charting of basal body temperature, cervical fluid and cervical position.[2]

Calista is being marketed as a product that 'tells you the best days to conceive your baby'. It is noteworthy that the manufacturer's instructions accompanying the product state that Calista is not intended for contraceptive use.[1] The manufacturers also state that Calista is unsuitable for women with poor vision, in advanced menopause, using hormonal contraception, who have been pregnant in the last 2 months or are receiving fertility drugs such as clomifene citrate.

References

1. Calista Saliva Ovulation Test [www.ecpbrands.co.uk].
2. Webwomb. Ovulation prediction [www.webwomb.com/ovutest.htm].
3. Zondek B, Rozin S. Cervical mucus arborization: its use in determining of corpus luteum function. *Obstet Gynecol* 1954;3:463–70.
4. Barbato M, Boerci M, Bozzo G, Parent IG. Natural methods for fertility control. *New Trends in Gynaecology and Obstetrics* 1986;2(3):325-332
5. Calamera JC, Vilar O, Nicholson R. Change in sialic acid concentration in human saliva during the menstrual cycle. *Int Fertil* 1986;31:s43–5.

6. Folan J, Gosling JP, Finn MF, Fottrell PF. Solid phase, enzimoimmunoassay of estrone in saliva. *Clin Chem* 1989;35:s569–71.

7. Natural fertility regulation today. *Suppl Int J Gynecol Obstet* 1989;1:1–167.

Contraceptive methods not licensed in the UK

QUESTION

Should a woman who is using a vaginal ring and has a vaginal discharge be treated if *Staphylococcus aureus* is identified?

POPULATION: Women who are using a vaginal ring who have vaginal discharge and also have *S. aureus* identified.

INTERVENTION: Treatment.

OUTCOME: Safety.

ANSWER

S. aureus is a coagulase positive, Gram positive organism that can invade traumatised tissue. It may cause necrotising fasciitis and toxic shock syndrome.[1]

The combined contraceptive vaginal ring (Nuvaring®) contains 15 micrograms ethinylestradiol and 120 micrograms etonogestrel. It is inserted into the vagina, providing effective contraception for 3 weeks. Contraceptive protection is maintained during the 'ring-free week', when withdrawal bleeding occurs. Vaginal contraceptive rings are not currently available in the UK.

Information was found on the incidence of vaginal discharge in women using vaginal rings. In a study of a non-medicated vaginal ring, several women were reported to have experienced vaginal discharge in their first cycle.[2] Over 12 months, 28% of women were reported to have had vaginal discharge in a trial studying a different version of the vaginal ring.[3] In a comparative trial of different versions of the ring spanning four cycles, 5% of all women had vaginal discharge.[4] It has been suggested that the reporting of vaginal discharge is higher in women using a vaginal ring compared with women using oral contraception.[3] Finally, in a randomised cross-over study comparing Nuvaring with an oral contraceptive containing 20 micrograms ethinylestradiol and 150 micrograms desogestrel, 63% of women reported vaginal wetness during ring-use compared with 43% during pill-use.[5] There were no differences in yeast colony counts, Nugent gram stain scores, vaginal white blood cell counts, vaginal pH or discharge weight between the methods.

Despite extensive searching, the CEU could find no specific information in the literature regarding the possibility of toxic shock in women with contraceptive vaginal rings. There was also no information on the occurrence of *S. aureus* in women using vaginal rings and whether or not it should be treated.

QUESTION

For women using monthly injectable contraception, is amenorrhoea a recognised adverse effect?

POPULATION: **Women requiring contraception.**

INTERVENTION: **Monthly injectable contraception.**

OUTCOME: **Amenorrhoea.**

ANSWER

No monthly injectable contraceptives are licensed for use in the UK. A number of monthly injectables containing combinations of estrogen and progestogen are available in other countries. Thus, UK practitioners may encounter patients using combined injectables which they have obtained elsewhere. To our knowledge, there are no monthly progestogen-only methods of contraception available anywhere.

Combined injectables may contain estradiol valerate (5 mg) plus norethisterone enantate (50 mg) (Mesigyna®, Schering) or estradiol cypionate (5 mg) plus medroxyprogesterone acetate (25 mg) (Lunelle®, Pharmacia; Cyclofem®, various companies).

The patient information for Lunelle indicates that 'most women experience alterations of menstrual bleeding. Bleeding patterns may vary from a single monthly bleed to no bleeding at all'. The incidence of amenorrhoea is cited as approximately 15%. In contrast, product information for Mesigyna indicates that amenorrhoea is rarely encountered and that bleeding episodes usually occur at 30-day intervals. The Mesigyna product information indicates that if no bleeding occurs within 30 days of an injection, pregnancy must be ruled out by means of a suitable test.

A US study comparing Lunelle with a combined oral contraceptive reported more frequent episodes of missed periods or amenorrhoea among women using the monthly injectable method. While most women experienced a monthly withdrawal bleed, 14.6% experienced no bleeding in a given cycle.[6]

QUESTION

If women have a Chinese steel ring IUD in place, should it removed under general anaesthesia and what device should be used?

POPULATION: Women with a Chinese steel ring IUD in place.
INTERVENTION: Removal under general anaesthesia.
OUTCOME: Successful removal.

ANSWER

A report compiled by the WHO states that two-thirds of the 156 million women who are estimated to use IUDs are in China.[7] IUDs are the most popular method of contraception in China and are used by 45% of married women. There are several different types of IUDs available including locally manufactured versions of devices available on the international market and some which are manufactured only within China.

The stainless steel ring was first produced in Shanghai in the 1970s and became known as the 'Shanghai ring'.[8] The ring is about one inch in diameter, springy and flexible, and does not have a thread attached to it because it was not designed to be removed easily (due to China's 'one child per family policy'). It was used for immediate post-placental insertion (that is, within 10 minutes of the delivery of the placenta). An unpublished analysis from China's State Family Planning Commission in 1992 estimated that the stainless steel ring accounted for 90% of the IUDs in use at that time.[7]

A meta-analysis by Li Yong *et al.* of 22 published and unpublished studies compared the efficacy of the steel ring IUD to copper-bearing IUDs.[9] During the first year of use, women were six times more likely to experience contraceptive failure with the steel ring than with a copper IUD. The steel ring was more prone to failure than the copper IUD (19.0% versus 5.9%) and to expulsion (16.5% versus 5.8%). Following findings which showed the cost benefit of switching from a steel ring to a modern copper-bearing IUD, the State Family Planning Commission asked Chinese factories to stop producing the steel rings in January 1993.[7]

The use of three-dimensional ultrasound imaging in detecting the type and location of IUDs is discussed in one study by Zhang *et al.* performed in China.[10] This found that satisfactory ultrasound images were obtained in 97% of cases, allowing clinicians to view the type and location of the IUD and the relationship between the IUD and the uterine cavity. The IUD was subsequently removed successfully at one attempt in 26 of 28 cases by hysteroscopy, laparoscopy or laparotomy, showing the value of three-dimensional ultrasound in selecting a therapeutic plan.[10]

A further study focused on the transcervical removal of foreign bodies and attempted to investigate the effectiveness of monitoring methods.[11] This study recruited 113 women in China with residual IUDs, residual pregnancy products or other foreign bodies, which were not removed during routine curettage or IUD removal. Foreign bodies were removed from 109 women by transcervical removal. The conclusion was that transcervical removal is safe and efficient when there is sufficient cervical dilatation. The value of ultra-sonography as a noninvasive method of monitoring transcervical removal is mentioned. Women with risk factors for uterine perforation are recommended to have laparoscopic monitoring as well.[11]

There have been documented accounts of attempts to remove steel ring IUDs. Methods include: the insertion of a hooked IUD remover into the uterine cavity following local anaesthetic intracervical block and dilatation of the cervix,[12] and the use of paracervical block and small hook curettes or 'alligator' forceps after confirmation by ultrasound that the IUD is in place.[13]

QUESTION

If a woman is referred for colposcopy with a Chinese steel ring IUD in place, how can the device be removed and can diathermy be performed if the device is not removed?

POPULATION: Women referred for colposcopy with a Chinese steel ring IUD in place.
INTERVENTION: Removal of the device.
OUTCOME: Effect of diathermy if the device is not removed.

ANSWER

No evidence was found on the risk of diathermy treatment with a steel ring IUD in place. However, copper IUDs should not be used during diathermy treatments and diathermy has been considered inappropriate for anyone with a pacemaker or another implanted device containing metal.[14] It is therefore preferable, for safety reasons, that a steel ring IUD is removed prior to com-mencing treatment with diathermy.

QUESTION

For women who prefer oral contraceptives, is centchroman an effective method of contraception?

POPULATION: Women who prefer oral contraceptives.
INTERVENTION: Centchroman, the weekly nonsteroidal oral contraceptive.
OUTCOME: Efficacy.

ANSWER

Centchroman (ormeloxifene trans-1-[2-[4-(7-methoxy-2,2-dimethyr-3-phenyl] -phenoxy)-ethyl] pynolidine) is a nonsteroidal estrogen antagonist with weak estrogenic activity which prevents pregnancy in the rat, mouse, dog and rhesus monkey when administered within 24 hours of coitus. It was developed at the Central Drug Research Institute in Lucknow and is marketed in India as a regimen comprising 30 micrograms twice weekly for 12 weeks and once weekly thereafter. It reaches peak concentrations in women within 4–6 hours of administration and has a half life of 7 days.[15]

Centchroman has no effect on the hypothalamo-pituitary-ovarian axis and doses as high as 120 mg/week fail to inhibit ovulation or disturb cyclical ovarian activity. It is thought to act by inhibiting implantation by accelerating ovum transport through the fallopian tube and preventing endometrial decidual-isation thus causing asynchrony between the arrival of the blastocyst in the uterine cavity and endometrial receptivity.[16]

Contraceptive failure rates are usually calculated using two different methods: Pearl Index or Life Table Analysis. Pearl Indices calculate failure rates based on a defined endpoint such as study completion, pregnancy or discontinuation of the contraceptive method. Life Table Analysis is a cumulative method that combines separate failure rates for each month of contraceptive use and is considered superior to the Pearl Index.[17]

Two small multicentre phase III clinical trials have been performed on long-term use of Centchroman; neither trial reported continuation rates with the drug or sufficient information on user failure.

Puri *et al*. conducted the first of these trials in ten centres in India and recruited 898 women, all of whom took one dose (30 mg) of centchroman weekly for a total exposure of 13 483 months.[18] They calculated the pregnancy rate (defined as the Pearl Index) for centchroman to be 2.84. The only adverse event reported was delayed menstruation (defined as a cycle longer than 45 days) in 8% of users.

The second clinical trial was conducted by the Central Drug Research Institute in 11 centres in India and recruited 376 women who initially took 30 mgs of centchroman twice weekly for 3 months, and then a single dose of 30 mg weekly for a total exposure of 3959 months.[19] The Pearl Index in this trial was 1.83 and the cumulative pregnancy rate, using life table analysis, was 1.63 at 12 months. The only adverse event reported was delayed menstruation in 6% of users. Of 37 women who desired a pregnancy and withdrew from this trial, 97% were able to conceive within varying intervals ranging from 6 months to 1 year after stopping the drug.

Centchroman has been reported to be effective in women as a postcoital contraceptive using a single dose of 60 mg. In a study of 103 parous women using the method for 650 months, only one pregnancy occurred.[16]

The contraceptive effect is readily reversible. Animal studies have suggested that centchroman is not teratogenic.[20] Pharmacokinetic studies have found that at therapeutic doses, centchroman does not affect cholesterol, triglycerides, high-density lipoprotein or platelet function.[21]

The review found by the CEU concluded that available evidence on centchroman suggests it is a promising new oral contraceptive which has high efficacy and appears to be free of the adverse effects associated with oral contraceptives containing steroids. However, the evidence available is based on a small number of women and larger trials of the drug are needed. No organisation in the developed world has seriously considered exploring the drug for contraceptive development.

References

1. Todar's Online Textbook of Bacteriology at UW-Madison. Staphylococcus. 2004 [www.textbookofbacteriology.net/stoph.html].
2. Roumen F, Dieben T, Assendrop R, Bouckaert P. The clinical acceptability of a non-medicated vaginal ring. *Contraception* 1990;42:201–7.
3. Weisberg E, Fraser IS, Lacarra M, Mishell DR, Alvarez F, Brache V, *et al*. Efficacy, bleeding patterns, and adverse effects of a 1-year contraceptive vaginal ring. *Contraception* 1999;59:311–18.
4. Weisberg E, Fraser IS, Mishell DR, Lacarra M, Darney P, Jackanicz TM. A comparative study of two contraceptive vaginal rings releasing norethindrone acetate and differing doses of ethinyl estradiol. *Contraception* 1999;59:305–10.
5. Verse S, Miller L, Burington B. A comparison between the vaginal ring and oral contraceptives. *Obstet Gynecol* 2004;104:555–63.
6. Kaunitz AM, Garceau RJ, Cromie MA. Comparative safety, efficacy and cycle control of Lunelle monthly contraceptive injection (medroxyprogesterone acetate and estradiol cypionate injectable suspension) and Ortho-Novum 7/7/7 oral contraception (norethindrone/ethinyl estradiol triphasic). *Contraception* 1999;60:179–81.
7. The intrauterine device (IUD): worth singing about. *Prog Reprod Health Res* 2002;(60):1–8.
8. Bradley J. OBGYN.net, Ultrasound Section: 'Chinese Ring' [www.obgyn.net].
9. Li Yong P, Bourne KL, Rowe PJ, Wei ZD, Xian WS, Yin ZH, *et al*. The demographic

impact of conversion from steel to copper IUDs in China. *Int Fam Plann Perspect* 1994;20:124–30.

10. Zhang S, Ying W, Xu J, Yang M, Xu K, Luo Q. [The use of three-dimensional ultrasound imaging in detecting the type and location of intrauterine contraceptive device]. *Chin Med J* 2002;82:459–61. [Chinese]

11. Xia E, Duan H, Huang X, Zheng J, Yu D, Cheng L. Hysteroscopic removal of foreign bodies and its method of monitoring. *Chin Med* 2003;116:125–8.

12. Stillwell. How to remove a Chinese IUD. *J Fam Plann Reprod Health Care* 2003;29:60.

13. Stewart F, Hatcher B. What IUDs are used in China and do tailless IUDs need to be removed? [www.managingcontraception.com/questions_new/iuds/q-a_iu_08-28.html].

14. Planned Parenthood Federation of America, Inc. Understanding IUDs. [www.plannedparenthood.org/BC/IUD.HTM].

15. Lal J, Asthana OT, Nityanand S, Gupta RC. Pharmacokinetics of centchroman in healthy female subjects after oral administration. *Contraception* 1995;52:297–300.

16. Kamboj VP, Ray S, Dhawan BN. New Products : Centchroman. *Drugs Today* 1992;28:227–32.

17. Trussell J, Hatcher RA, Cates W Jr, Stewart FH, Kost K. A guide to interpreting contraceptive efficacy studies. *Obstet Gynecol* 1990;76:558–67.

18. Results of multicentric trial of Centchroman. In: Puri BN, *et al.*, editor. *Pharmacology for Health in Asia*. New Delhi: Allied Publishers; 1988.

19. Central Drug Research Institute India. Centchroman (non-steroidal oral contraception) [www.cdriindia.org/centchroman.htm].

20. Reproductive Health Online (ReproLine): a family planning and reproductive health training website by JHPIEGO Corporation. Centchroman [www.reproline.jhu.edu/english/1fp/1advances/old/1centch/ceorvw.htm].

21. Vaidya R, Joshi U, Meherji P, Rage N, Betrabet, Joshi L, *et al.* Activity profile of Centchroman in healthy female volunteers. *Indian J Exp Biol* 1977;15:1173–6.

6 PROGESTOGEN-ONLY EMERGENCY CONTRACEPTION

Patient selection

QUESTION

For women who are postnatal and not breastfeeding, when, following unprotected sexual intercourse, is the earliest time that emergency contraception would be required?

POPULATION: Women who are postnatal and not breastfeeding.
INTERVENTION: Unprotected sex.
OUTCOME: Need for emergency contraception.

ANSWER

The FFPRHC *UK Selected Practice Recommendations for Contraceptive Use* states that there appears to be a very low risk of ovulation within 4 weeks of delivery. Oral hormonal methods of contraception can be commenced on day 21 following a delivery without the need for additional contraceptive protection. If commenced after day 21, barrier contraception is advised for the next 7 days. Before day 21 postpartum, a women will not require emergency contraception since her risk of ovulation is negligible. The risk of ovulation before day 28 postpartum is low but, taking into consideration sperm survival in the upper female reproductive tract for up to 7 days, emergency contraception may be considered if unprotected sex or contraceptive failure has occurred after day 21.

The *WHO Medical Eligibility Criteria* recommends that the risks of using a copper intrauterine contraceptive device before 4 weeks postpartum is greater than any potential benefit because of increased risk of expulsion and perforation. Thus, if emergency contraception is required at this time, the hormonal method would be preferable.

QUESTION

For women who are breastfeeding, can progestogen-only emergency contraception be given? (Three similar enquiries.)

POPULATION: Women who are breastfeeding and who have had unprotected sex.
INTERVENTION: Progestogen-only emergency contraception.
OUTCOME: Effect on breast milk.

ANSWER

Women who are fully or nearly fully breastfeeding can use lactational amenorrhoea as a method of contraception.[1] For women who are not fully breastfeeding, anovulation cannot be guaranteed and unprotected sex or contraceptive failure can result in pregnancy.

The Summary of Product Characteristics for levonorgestrel-only emergency contraception suggests that there may be a very small amount of active ingredient in breast milk following its use. This is not thought to be harmful to the baby. If women are concerned, they should take the progestogen-only emergency contraception following a breastfeed. Taken in this way, and well before another feed, reduces the amount of active ingredient in breast milk.

QUESTION

For women weighing around 140 kg, should an increased dose of progestogen-only emergency contraception be provided to ensure efficacy?

POPULATION: Women weighing around 140 kg.
INTERVENTION: An increased dose of progestogen-only emergency contraception.
OUTCOME: Efficacy.

ANSWER

The CEU has been unable to find any evidence relating to the dose of progestogen-only emergency contraception that should be given to women who are clinically obese.

An IUD should be offered to all women attending for emergency contraception, even those who present within 72 hours of unprotected sexual intercourse. This non-hormonal method of emergency contraception is unlikely to be affected by weight.

QUESTION

For young women under the age of 16 years, is use of levonorgestrel emergency contraception (Levonelle®, Schering Health) associated with any particular safety issues?

POPULATION: Young women aged less than 16 years.

INTERVENTION: Progestogen-only emergency contraception.

OUTCOME: Safety.

ANSWER

The Summary of Product Characteristics for progestogen-only emergency contraception indicates that the products are not recommended for young women under 16 years without medical supervision. The manufacturers acknowledge that limited data are available specifically relating to women aged under the age of 16 years. However, none of the guidance or reviews identified by the CEU have raised any concerns regarding safety in this patient group. On the basis of available evidence and on theoretical grounds, risks associated with adverse effects are considered extremely unlikely and certainly less than the risks associated with a pregnancy, whether carried to term or terminated.

QUESTION

For women aged over 40 years who have infrequent sexual intercourse, can progestogen-only emergency contraception safely be prescribed on repeat prescription or advance supply?

POPULATION: Women over 40 years who have infrequent sexual intercourse.

INTERVENTION: Progestogen-only emergency contraception on repeat prescription or advance supply.

OUTCOME: Safety and efficacy.

ANSWER

Background fertility falls in women aged over 40 years but pregnancy can result in high rates of spontaneous or induced abortion. An effective method of contraception should be encouraged for sexually active women in their 40s.

The Summary of Product Characteristics for progestogen-only emergency contraception advises that it is suitable only as an emergency measure, and that it is not as effective as a conventional regular method of contraception. The

WHO *Medical Eligibility Criteria for Contraceptive Use* recommends that woman can use levonorgestrel emergency contraception repeatedly without restriction (WHO category 1).

Guidance from the FFPRHC CEU supports the provision of an advance supply of emergency contraception: it is safe, is not associated with an increase in unprotected sex, is used correctly by most women, does not decrease the uptake and use of other contraceptive methods, and may reduce the rate of unintended pregnancies. A large epidemiological study did not show a reduction in abortion rates with advance supply but did show that women were enabled to use emergency contraception as soon as possible after unprotected sex.

High pregnancy rates (up to 20%) have been estimated when emergency contraception is used as the only method of contraception. However, efficacy can be consistently good (pregnancy rates less than 2%) when levonorgestrel emergency contraception is used as the sole method of contraception over 1 year if women are enabled to take emergency contraception within an hour of unprotected sex.

Although a more effective regular method of contraception is the preferred option for sexually active women in their 40s, after counselling about all other methods, some women having infrequent intercourse may opt to rely on using emergency contraception when required. The provision of an advance supply of emergency contraception is outside the product licence. Pharmacists cannot knowingly sell levonorgestrel over-the-counter in advance of need. Nevertheless, clinicians may consider providing an advance supply to facilitate early use for women who wish to use this following infrequent sexual intercourse. The number of packs supplied in advance will need to be considered individually.

References

1. Faculty of Family Planning and Reproductive Health Care Clinical Effectiveness Unit. Contraceptive choices for breastfeeding women. *J Fam Plann Reprod Health Care* 2004;30:181–9.

Dose, timing and efficacy

QUESTION

For women requesting progestogen-only emergency contraception, does ingestion of the second dose of levonorgestrel at time intervals other than 12 hours after the first dose compromise efficacy?

POPULATION: Women requesting emergency contraception.

INTERVENTION: Second dose of levonorgestrel at time intervals other than 12 hours after the first dose.

OUTCOME: Efficacy.

ANSWER

A randomised controlled trial found that 85% of expected pregnancies were prevented if 0.75 mg of levonorgestrel was taken within 72 hours of unprotected intercourse and a second 0.75-mg dose was taken 12 hours later.[1] The Summary of Product Characteristics suggested that the second dose of levonorgestrel could be taken within 16 hours of the first dose.

Pharmacokinetic studies showed that plasma concentrations of levonorgestrel were similar when taken either as a single dose or divided doses taken 12 or 24 hours apart.[2,3]

A randomised controlled trial by WHO which compared the efficacy of a single 1.5-mg dose compared to the usual divided regimen suggested the single dose was as effective as the divided regimen.[4] This large study prompted a change in the product licence for progestogen-only emergency contraception in the UK.

The randomised controlled trials which have measured efficacy of progestogen-only emergency contraception have involved the second dose being administered 12 hours after the first dose. However, pharmacokinetic studies do not suggest that serum concentrations of levonorgestrel are significantly affected if the 12-hour interval is increased to 24 hours. Moreover, the product licence supported a delay of up to 16 hours in taking the second dose. However, in keeping with new data, the CEU now recommends that progestogen-only emergency contraception is given as a single 1.5-mg dose within 72 hours of unprotected intercourse.

QUESTION

For women who require progestogen-only emergency contraception, is a single dose of 1.5 mg the recommended regimen? (Six similar enquiries.)

POPULATION: Women using a progestogen-only emergency contraception.

INTERVENTION: A single 1.5-mg dose of levonorgestrel.

OUTCOME: Efficacy.

ANSWER

A large randomised-controlled trial by the WHO compared the efficacy of a single 1.5-mg dose of levonorgestrel compared with the usual divided regimen (and compared with 10-mg of mifepristone) in preventing expected pregnancies.[4]

Equivalence between the single and divided regimens cannot be proved with absolute certainty. However, the single and divided regimes appeared equivalent. This large WHO study prompted a change in the product licence for progestogen-only emergency contraception in the UK.

The CEU recommends a single dose of 1.5-mg of levonorgestrel to be given as soon as possible, and within 72 hours, after unprotected intercourse. For women using liver enzyme-inducing drugs, current advice is to increase the dose by 50%. BNF states that this can be taken either as 1.5-mg of levonorgestrel followed 12 hours later by a 0.75-mg dose or as a single 2.25-mg dose. This increased dose is outside the terms of the product licence and women should be informed about this and about the use of a copper IUD which is unaffected by liver enzyme-inducing drugs.

Update to Answer

Subsequent to preparing this response, the 0.75-mg tablet of levonorgestrel has been discontinued and replaced by a 1.5-mg tablet. Thus, the option of giving a total dose of 2.25-mg is no longer available. Advice from the FFPRHC is to give 3-mg as a single dose if only 1.5-mg tablets are available.

QUESTION

For women who attend more than 72 hours after unprotected sexual intercourse, can progestogen-only emergency contraceptive be given and how effective is it? (Two similar enquiries.)

POPULATION: Women attending for emergency contraception 73–120 hours after unprotected sexual intercourse.

INTERVENTION: Progestogen-only emergency contraception.

OUTCOME: Efficacy.

ANSWER

A large randomised-controlled trial by the WHO compared 10 mg of mifepristone with single and divided regimens of levonorgestrel as emergency contraception.[4] Data from the WHO trial showed that when used between 73 and 120 hours after unprotected sex, the divided regimen prevented 60% of expected pregnancies and the single regimen prevented 63%. Very few women were recruited to the trial beyond 72 hours (11% of total) and confidence intervals were wide.

The CEU has previously not recommended the use of progestogen-only emergency contraception routinely beyond 72 hours.[5] However, more recently, the CEU has suggested that, after counselling, women may consider use of progestogen-only emergency contraception between 73 and 120 hours after unprotected sex.[6] This use is outside the terms of the product licence.

A copper IUD has a lower failure rate than progestogen-only emergency contraception regardless of the timing of intercourse. A copper IUD can be inserted up to 5 days (120 hours) after the first episode of unprotected sex or up to 5 days after the expected date of ovulation in a regular cycle.

The CEU recommends that women presenting between 73 and 120 hours after unprotected sex should be informed that a copper IUD is the most effective method of emergency contraception. However, where use of a copper IUD is unacceptable, progestogen-only emergency contraception can be considered and may continue to prevent up to 63% of expected pregnancies.

References

1. Task Force on Postovulatory Methods of Fertility Regulation. Randomised controlled trial of levonorgestrel versus the Yuzpe regimen of combined oral contraceptives for emergency contraception. *Lancet* 1998;352:428–33.
2. Tremblay D, Gainer E, Ulmann A. The pharmocokinetics of 750 μg levonorgestrel following administration of one single dose or two dose at 12- or 24-h interval. *Contraception* 2001;64:327–31.
3. Johansson E, Brache V, Alvarez F, Faundes A, Cochon L, Ranta S, *et al*. Pharmocokinetic study of different dosing regimens of levonorgestrel for emergency contraception in healthy women. *Hum Reprod* 2002;17:1472–6.
4. von Hertzen H, Piaggio G, Ding J, Chen J, Song Si, Bartfai G, *et al*. Low dose mifepristone and two regimens of levonorgestrel for emergency contraception: a WHO multicentre randomised trial. *Lancet* 2002;360:1803–10.
5. Faculty of Family Planning and Reproductive Health Care Clinical Effectiveness Unit. Emergency contraception. *J Fam Plann Reprod Health Care* 2003;29:9–16.
6. Faculty of Family Planning and Reproductive Health Care Clinical Effectiveness Unit. The use of contraception outside the terms of the product licence. *J Fam Plann Reprod Health Care* 2005;31:225–41.

Use more than once in a cycle

QUESTION

For women who receive progestogen-only emergency contraception and then have a further episode of unprotected sexual intercourse in the same cycle, can it be given again?

POPULATION: Women who receive progestogen-only emergency contraception and then have a further episode of unprotected sexual intercourse in the same cycle.

INTERVENTION: A further prescription of progestogen-only emergency contraception.

OUTCOME: Safety and efficacy.

ANSWER

A woman's risk of pregnancy varies within the menstrual cycle and can range from low (2–4%) to high (20–30%) in days 10–17.[1] When a woman has a further episode of unprotected sex after taking progestogen-only emergency contraception, the clinician needs to reassess her risk of pregnancy based on her menstrual cycle and time since the new episode of unprotected sex. This may not be applicable to women with irregular cycles or those who are uncertain about the date of their last menstrual period.

Although there is no time in the menstrual cycle when there is **no** risk of pregnancy following unprotected sex, this approach should enable clinicians to determine the need for further progestogen-only emergency contraception. There is no evidence available to indicate that a certain time interval is necessary between the first and second prescription of progestogen-only emergency contraception for women who have had another episode of unprotected sex in the same cycle.

The Summary of Product Characteristics does not recommend use more than once in a cycle, however it is not contraindicated. Patient Group Directions can be written to include use outside product licence.

The CEU recommends that progestogen-only emergency contraception can be used more than once in a cycle if clinically indicated. Efficacy in this situation is unclear. Women with repeated episodes of unprotected sex should consider the use of a copper IUD which can be inserted up to 5 days after a first episode of unprotected sex or up to 5 days after the expected date of ovulation in a regular cycle (regardless of the timing and number of episodes of unprotected sex) without loss of efficacy (which is greater than 99%).

QUESTION

For women who receive progestogen-only emergency contraception and then have a further episode of unprotected sexual intercourse in the same cycle, is a time interval necessary before emergency contraception can be prescribed again?

POPULATION: Women who receive progestogen-only emergency contraception and then have a further episode of unprotected sexual intercourse in the same cycle.

INTERVENTION: Timing of a further prescription of progestogen-only emergency contraception.

OUTCOME: Safety and efficacy.

ANSWER

CEU guidance on emergency contraception[2] advises that progestogen-only emergency contraception does not protect against pregnancy for the rest of the cycle. Progestogen-only emergency contraception can be used more than once in a cycle if clinically indicated.

There is no evidence available to indicate that a certain time interval is necessary between the first and second prescription of levonorgestrel for women who have had another episode of unprotected sex in the same cycle.

Update to Answer

Updated CEU guidance on emergency contraception was published in April 2006.[3] This guidance included consensus-based advice from the development group that if further unprotected sex occurs within 12 hours of a dose of levonorgestrel emergency contraception, no further treatment is indicated.

QUESTION

Are there any contraindications to using progestogen-only emergency contraception twice within the same cycle for women under the age of 16 years?

POPULATION: Women under the age of 16 years.

INTERVENTION: Use of levonorgestrel emergency contraception twice in same cycle.

OUTCOME: Safety.

ANSWER

No evidence could be found by the CEU regarding contraindications to using progestogen-only emergency contraception more than once in the same cycle for women aged less than 16 years.

CEU guidance on emergency contraception[2] suggests that progestogen-only emergency contraception can be used more than once in the same cycle. This good practice point applies to women of all ages. Young women should be counselled on the failure rates of hormonal emergency contraception and age should not restrict regular contraception choices, which should also be discussed at the time of initiating emergency contraception.

References

1.   Wilcox AJ, Weinberg CR, Baird DD. Timing of sexual intercourse in relation to ovulation: Effects on the probability of conception, survival of the pregnancy and sex of the baby. *N Engl J Med* 1995;333:1517–21.
2.   Faculty of Family Planning and Reproductive Health Care Clinical Effectiveness Unit. Emergency contraception. *J Fam Plann Reprod Health Care* 2003;29:9–16.
3.   Faculty of Family Planning and Reproductive Health Care Clinical Effectiveness Unit. FFPRHC guidance (April 2006). Emergency contraception. *J Fam Plann Reprod Health Care* 2006;32:121–8.

Continuing contraception after emergency contraception

QUESTION

For women given a 1.5-mg single dose of progestogen-only emergency contraception, when should their usual contraception be recommended?

POPULATION: Women using a single 1.5-microgram dose of progestogen-only emergency contraception.

INTERVENTION: Restarting their usual contraception.

OUTCOME: Continued efficacy.

ANSWER

In our guidance on emergency contraception,[1] the CEU recommended that following progestogen-only emergency contraception, the usual method of contraception is recommenced at the usual time. If this would be more than 12 hours after taking progestogen-only emergency contraception, the usual method should be restarted early so that no more than 12 hours has elapsed.

WHO has published 'updated missed pill rules' and these were endorsed by the FFPRHC.[2] Emergency contraception is indicated if combined hormonal contraceptive pills are missed in week 1 of the pill pack. Emergency contraception is not indicated if combined hormonal contraceptive pills are missed in weeks 2 or 3.

Women using a 30-microgram combined oral contraceptive pill who miss three or more pills in week 1, and had unprotected sex in the pill-free interval or in week 1, should: take the most recent missed pill as soon as possible; continue pill-taking at the usual time (this may even mean taking two pills at the same time); use condoms or abstain from sex for 7 days (or until seven consecutive pills have been taken). Progestogen-only emergency contraception can be given as soon as she presents. Similar advice is given for women using a 20-microgram combined oral contraceptive pill who miss two or more pills in week 1.

The CEU advises that a woman's usual contraceptive method be continued regardless of timing of progestogen-only emergency contraception.

References

1. Faculty of Family Planning and Reproductive Health Care Clinical Effectiveness Unit. Emergency contraception. *J Fam Plann Reprod Health Care* 2003;29:9–16.
2. FFPRHC Clinical Effectiveness Unit. Faculty Statement from the CEU on a new publication: WHO *Selected Practice Recommendations for Contraceptive Use* Update. Missed pill rules: new recommendations. *J Fam Plann Reprod Health Care* 2005;32:153–5.

QUESTION

For women undergoing induced abortion, what strategy of antibiotic prophylaxis/microbiology testing is most effective in reducing the risk of post-abortion infective morbidity?

POPULATION: Women undergoing induced abortion.
INTERVENTION: Antibiotic/microbiology testing.
OUTCOME: Risk of post-abortion infective morbidity.

ANSWER

The current RCOG guideline on the care of women requesting induced abortion (2004)[1] includes recommendations on suitable strategies for prevention of infective complications of abortion. These are as follows:

● Abortion care should encompass a strategy for minimising the risk of post-abortion infective morbidity. As a minimum, services should offer antibiotic prophylaxis.

● Ideally, services should offer testing for lower genital tract organisms with treatment of positive cases.

The first of these recommendations is based on a meta-analysis of randomised trials from Sawaya et al.[2] which demonstrated that antibiotic prophylaxis is associated with a reduction in the risk of subsequent infective morbidity of around 50%. The results of the meta-analysis are convincing: that use of some form of antibiotic prophylaxis does reduce post-abortion infection. Unfortunately, the 12 trials included in the meta-analysis employed a wide variety of prophylactic regimens. All were single-agent regimens; some effective against chlamydia/gonorrhoea and some effective against anaerobes. These problems with interpreting and applying the findings of the meta-analysis were discussed at an RCOG Study Group on the prevention of pelvic infection.[3]

The RCOG guideline refers to a range of studies that have shown that the presence of any of *C. trachomatis, N. gonorrhoeae* or bacterial vaginosis in the lower genital tract at the time of abortion is associated with an increased risk. On this basis, the prophylactic regimens advocated by the RCOG within the guideline serve to cover against both chlamydia and bacterial vaginosis. They would also cover most strains of gonorrhoea. However, to our knowledge, there are no trials which directly compare single-agent and combination prophylactic regimens for periabortion antibiotic prophylaxis. Thus, the recommended regimens are based on indirect evidence and theoretical considerations.

The second of the RCOG recommendations indicates that a strategy of offering testing for relevant lower genital tract infections (with treatment of positive cases) is preferable to the universal prophylaxis strategy. In fact, this recommendation is based on less robust evidence than the first; we do not have a meta-analysis showing that a 'screen and treat' policy reduces morbidity. The favouring of 'screen and treat' over universal prophylaxis was based on the consensus view of the RCOG guideline development group that the former strategy carried important public health benefits. Clearly, 'screen and treat' allows identification of women carrying chlamydia or gonorrhoea and allows for appropriate follow-up and notification and treatment of partners.

A randomised trial from Scotland attempted to compare the effectiveness of the universal prophylaxis and 'screen and treat' strategies.[4] It found that universal prophylaxis was, if anything, slightly more effective in reducing effective morbidity and much cheaper for a service to implement.

This Scottish study found that women testing negative for all three infections studied (gonorrhoea, chlamydia and bacterial vaginosis) still fared better if given a prophylactic regimen (metronidazole plus doxycycline). This finding may have been explained by under-diagnosis of infections by the tests used or by elimination of other organisms not detected by testing. Another theoretical advantage of universal prophylaxis is that the antibiotics can consistently be given in the peri-abortion period; with 'screen and treat', inevitable delays in receipt of results mean that treatment is delayed for some women.

In the light of the differing advantages of the universal prophylaxis and 'screen and treat' strategies, some authorities advocate a 'belt and braces' strategy, combining the two. The RCOG acknowledged that such a strategy would combine the benefits of the other two approaches but also combines the costs.

QUESTION

For women testing positive for *C. trachomatis* or bacterial vaginosis, can suction termination of pregnancy (with or without IUD insertion) safely be performed before completion of antibiotic treatment? (Two similar enquiries.)

POPULATION: Women testing positive for *C. trachomatis* or bacterial vaginosis.

INTERVENTION: Suction termination of pregnancy (with or without IUD insertion) before completion of antibiotic treatment.

OUTCOME: Risk of post-abortion infective morbidity.

ANSWER

National evidence-based guidelines recommend a strategy of either universal antibiotic prophylaxis or testing for lower genital tract infections prior to induced abortion.[1] Many different antibiotic regimens are described, both in the context of prophylaxis and of treatment of documented infections. Studies provide overwhelming evidence that antibiotics at the time of abortion reduce the risk of subsequent infective morbidity, for women overall and particularly for those testing positive for either *C. trachomatis* or bacterial vaginosis.[2] However, few studies have directly compared different antibiotic regimens in terms of the agents used or the route and timing of administration. Many studies (including one from our own group based in Aberdeen)[4] have employed regimens in which treatment was initiated only perioperatively or following recovery from anaesthetic. Meta-analyses addressing IUD insertion (both generally and in the context of abortion) have identified a very low risk of infective morbidity. Prophylactic antibiotics are not recommended to cover IUD insertion.

In terms of general good practice, identified infections should be treated as soon as possible after receipt of laboratory confirmation. However, there is no evidence to suggest that delaying initiation of treatment until after an abortion procedure increases the risk of infective sequelae. IUD insertion at the time of abortion has been shown to be both safe and practical. Again, there is no evidence of any advantage in delaying IUD insertion until treatment of any identified lower genital tract infection has been completed.

QUESTION

For women receiving mifepristone as part of a medical abortion regimen, is an observation period of 60 minutes after administration necessary for the safety and efficacy of the regimen?

POPULATION: **Women receiving mifepristone as part of a medical abortion regimen.**
INTERVENTION: **60 minutes observation after administration.**
OUTCOME: **Safety and efficacy.**

ANSWER

Mifepristone, an anti-progesterone used in abortion procedures, is marketed in the UK as Mifegyne® (Exelgyn). Until 1997, Mifegyne was marketed by Roussel. The product data sheet of that era included the instruction that 'the patient should be observed for at least 2 hours following administration'. Roussel also published *Mifegyne: a guide to its use in clinical practice,* which provided detailed instructions for use. This document indicated that the purpose of the 2-hour observation period was to ensure that the woman did not vomit during this time. If vomiting did occur, the clinician was advised to refer the woman for alternative treatment. The document stated, 'apart from nausea and occasional vomiting, there should be little effect of treatment within the first 12 hours after administration of Mifegyne'.

In 1997, ownership of Mifegyne was transferred to Exelgyn laboratories. The current Summary of Product Characteristics for Mifegyne makes no mention of any requirement for an observation period following Mifegyne administration. It does, however, indicate that women should be observed for a minimum of 3 hours following the administration of prostaglandin as part of a medical abortion regimen.

There are numerous reports of medical abortion regimens in the literature. However, for this response, the CEU has reviewed two large case series from established UK centres. The first, from Edinburgh,[5] described 3161 consecutive women managed with a regimen of mifepristone 200 mg orally followed by gemeprost 0.5 mg vaginally. Women were observed in the clinic for only 10–15 minutes after mifepristone administration. No complications following mifepristone administration were reported.

The second study, from Aberdeen, included 4132 consecutive women managed with a regimen of mifepristone 200 mg orally followed by misoprostol 0.8 mg vaginally.[6] There was no mention of any period of observation after mifepristone administration. Again, no complications following mifepristone administration were reported.

To meet the legal requirements of the Abortion Act, mifepristone, as an abortifacient, must be administered within an NHS hospital or an approved private-sector place. However, there is no requirement for a period of observation thereafter.

QUESTION

For women immediately after medical termination of pregnancy, does starting hormonal contraception or fitting an IUD prolong bleeding or affect the complete abortion rate?

POPULATION:	Women immediately after medical termination of pregnancy.
INTERVENTION:	Hormonal contraception or an IUD.
OUTCOME:	Bleeding patterns and complete abortion rate.

ANSWER

A Cochrane review highlighted that the initiation of contraception immediately following termination of pregnancy has advantages. The woman is known not to be pregnant, her motivation for effective contraception is high and she is already accessing health care.[7] In addition, it has been shown that ovulation occurs within a month of first-trimester abortion in over 90% of women.[8]

The *WHO Medical Eligibility Criteria for Contraceptive Use* recommends that combined oral contraception, progestogen-only pills, implants and injectables can be started immediately following abortion (WHO category 1). Ideally, these methods should be commenced at the time of abortion, when contraceptive protection is immediate. If started after this time, additional barrier contraception is required for 7 days (combined pills) or for 2 days (progestogen-only pills).

After first-trimester abortion, *WHO Medical Eligibility Criteria for Contraceptive Use* recommends that IUDs may be inserted immediately (WHO category 1) and recommends that the benefits of IUD insertion after second-trimester abortion generally outweigh any risks (WHO category 2).

There are few data specifically relating to IUD insertion following medical abortion. The FFPRHC guidance on the copper intrauterine device as long-term contraception recommends that an IUD may be inserted immediately (i.e. within 48 hours) after first- or second-trimester medical abortion. Otherwise, insertion should be postponed until 4 weeks following medical abortion.[9]

In terms of the use of hormonal contraception after medical abortion, two prospective, randomised, placebo controlled trials by Tang *et al.* have investigated bleeding patterns in women taking either a combined pill (containing 30 micrograms ethinylestradiol and 0.15 mg levonorgestrel) or placebo immediately after first-trimester abortion.[10,11] In both studies, the median duration of bleeding in the pill and placebo groups was similar; 53% of the women in the pill group and 59% of the women in the placebo group described their bleeding as more, or much more, than their normal menses.[10] The median measured blood loss was 69.9 ml in the pill group and 72.8 ml in the placebo group. Over 70% of all women in this study had a total blood loss of less than 100 ml.[11] These studies also observed that there was no difference in complete abortion rates between the pill and placebo groups. In the first study, 98% of the pill group had complete abortions and 99% of the placebo group had complete abortions.[10] Similarly, in the second study, 98% and 92% in the pill and placebo groups respectively had complete abortions.[11]

QUESTION

Can women attending for medical abortion receive DMPA if they have not passed products of conception, and does this affect the rate of successful abortion?

POPULATION: **Women immediately after medical abortion.**
INTERVENTION: **DMPA.**
OUTCOME: **Complete abortion rate.**

ANSWER

The CEU has been unable to find any information in the literature specifically on use of DMPA by women attending for medical abortion who have not passed products of conception. Nor could we find information on whether such use would increases the failure rate of medical abortion.

The Summary of Product Characteristics for DMPA does not mention use after medical abortion.

The *WHO Medical Eligibility Criteria for Contraceptive Use* advises that DMPA may safely be used immediately after a first- or second-trimester abortion (WHO category 1). WHO does not differentiate between surgical and medical abortion.

An article on the management of medical abortion advises that if DMPA is chosen as a method of contraception following a medical abortion, it may be given at the follow-up appointment after verification of pregnancy termination by ultrasound.[12] If DMPA is given in the first 5 days after abortion, it will be effective immediately. The WHO *Selected Practice Recommendations for Contraceptive Use* states that it may be given after this time if there has been no unprotected sex but condoms are advised for 7 days.

QUESTION

For women immediately post-abortion, is DMPA an effective method of contraception?

POPULATION: Women after induced abortion.
INTERVENTION: DMPA.
OUTCOME: Contraceptive efficacy.

ANSWER

The failure rate for DMPA is low. The Pearl Index is quoted as 0.3/100 woman years.

Studies have shown that fertility returns soon after an induced abortion and therefore it is important that women use an effective method of contraception to avoid a future unplanned pregnancy. Fertility has been shown to return within 2 weeks after first-trimester abortions and within 4 weeks after second-trimester abortions. Within 6 weeks of abortion, 75% of women will have ovulated.[13]

The *WHO Medical Eligibility Criteria for Contraceptive Use* advise that DMPA may be used safely, without restriction, immediately after a first- or second-trimester abortion (WHO category 1).

No specific evidence was identified on DMPA failure rates when administered post-abortion but DMPA should provide immediate and effective contraception if given immediately following abortion. If given more than 7 days after abortion, a barrier method is advised in addition for 7 days following the injection.

QUESTION

For women undergoing surgical abortion who have an IUD or IUS inserted at the time, are complications and adverse effects increased?

POPULATION: Women having surgical abortion.
INTERVENTION: Immediate insertion of IUD or IUS.
OUTCOME: Complications and adverse effects.

ANSWER

The insertion of intrauterine contraception immediately following induced abortion has potential advantages: it is known that the woman is not pregnant;

her motivation for effective contraception is high; she is already accessing health care and she can perhaps have the device inserted under the same general anaesthetic. Concerns have been raised regarding the potential for increased risk of perforation, expulsion, bleeding irregularity, infection and discontinuation with immediate post-abortal insertion compared to delayed insertion.

The safety and efficacy of IUD insertion immediately after spontaneous miscarriage or induced abortion has been investigated in a systematic review.[7] Eight randomised trials were included giving a total of 4476 woman-years of data. However, the multicentre trials used IUDs which are rarely used in current clinical practice – Lippes Loop, Copper 7 and TCu 200.

This Cochrane review concluded that:

- insertion of an IUD immediately post-abortion is both safe and practical (this was true for induced abortion and for spontaneous miscarriage)

- IUD expulsion rates were higher after second-trimester abortion than after earlier procedures

- delaying insertion following second-trimester abortion was advised

- there was insufficient evidence to compare safety and efficacy of IUD inserted immediately after abortion versus delayed insertion.

Follow-up of women who had an IUD inserted at the time of induced abortion identified three perforations in 2348 insertions (1/1000 insertions).[14] There were 157 expulsions (7%), 70 intrauterine or ectopic pregnancies (2/100 women years) and 12 cases of pelvic infection.

One further study was identified which investigated infection following post-abortal IUD insertion.[15] Among 823 consecutive women undergoing first-trimester abortion, 229 had an IUD inserted immediately and the other 594 women acted as controls. No prophylactic antibiotics were used. There was no difference between the groups in the readmission rate for infection following abortion.

Only one study was identified which addressed the use of LNG-IUS following abortion.[16] This study compared bleeding patterns associated with post-abortal use of both IUD and IUS with routine postmenstrual insertion. Women having IUS or IUD inserted post-abortion were significantly younger than women receiving the methods postmenstrually. Loss to follow up was high and results must be interpreted with caution. Bleeding in the IUD group settled quickly to around 5 days/month; in the IUS group, bleeding decreased continuously over 12 months.

The number of days of bleeding/month over the whole year was the same for women receiving IUD postmenstrually or post-abortion. In women receiving the IUS, the number of days of bleeding was lower from the first to the sixth month after insertion in women receiving the IUS post-abortion. Thereafter, the numbers of days of bleeding was similar in the post-abortion and post-menstrual groups. These results suggest that women receiving an IUS post-abortion have better bleeding profiles than women receiving an IUS postmenstrually.

Increasing evidence is being gathered on the use of the frameless IUD, GyneFix, post-abortion. Insertion appears to be easy by those trained in the technique. It appears to be reliable and as effective as when used postmenstrually.[17]

QUESTION

Is it safe to insert an IUD between 48 hours and 4 weeks post-abortion? (Two similar enquiries.)

POPULATION: Women after induced abortion.
INTERVENTION: Insertion of IUD between 48 hours and 4 weeks post-abortion.
OUTCOME: Safety.

ANSWER

The *WHO Medical Eligibility Criteria for Contraceptive Use* recommends that an IUD can be inserted after first-trimester abortion without restriction (WHO category 1) and that for insertion after second-trimester abortion, the risks generally outweigh the benefits (WHO category 2).

WHO recommends that, for postpartum women, the risks generally outweigh the benefits for insertions of an IUD between 48 hours and 4 weeks after delivery, owing to the increased risk of uterine perforation during this time (WHO category 3).

The RCOG guideline on the care of women requesting induced abortion[1] and FFPRHC guidance on IUDs[18] recommend that intrauterine contraception can be inserted immediately following a first- or second-trimester abortion. Otherwise, insertion should be delayed until 4 weeks following abortion (as for postpartum insertions).

One randomised[19] and another non-randomised[20] trial have found no significant differences between groups having an IUD inserted immediately or between 3 and 5 weeks (in the first trial) or immediately or at 2 weeks (in the second trial) after abortion. However, the trials were small and had big losses to follow up.

Until there is more robust evidence showing that IUD insertion between 48 hours and 4 weeks after abortion is safe, the CEU recommends that clinicians follow the recommendations made in the RCOG guideline and the FFPRHC guidance, and only insert an IUD at less than 48 hours or more than 4 weeks after abortion.

QUESTION

For women undergoing surgical abortion, when can sterilisation be performed to ensure maximum effectiveness?

POPULATION: Women after surgical abortion.
INTERVENTION: Timing of female sterilisation.
OUTCOME: Contraceptive efficacy.

ANSWER

Ensuring contraception immediately following induced abortion has advantages in that: the woman is not pregnant, her motivation is high and she is already accessing health care. Guidance on male and female sterilisation from the RCOG[21] recommends that there are no absolute contraindications to sterilisation provided the request is made by a woman of sound mind and not acting under external duress. A failure rate of 1/200 is generally quoted for female sterilisation. Specific evidence regarding failure rates of sterilisation post-abortion could not be identified. Recommendations in the RCOG guideline include:

- In order to attempt to safeguard against later regret, additional care is advised when counselling those under the age of 25 years and those without children.

- Care should also be exercised when taking decisions during pregnancy or in reaction to a failed relationship.

- Wherever possible, sterilisation should be performed after an appropriate interval following pregnancy.

- Should sterilisation be requested post-abortion, every effort should be made to make the awareness of regret and the possible increased failure rate clear.

References

1. Royal College of Obstetricians and Gynaecologists. *The Care of Women Requesting Induced Abortion*. Guideline Number 7. London: RCOG Press; 2004.
2. Sawaya GF, Grady D, Kerlikowske K, Grimes DA. Antibiotics at the time of induced abortion: the case for universal prophylaxis based on a meta-analysis. *Obstet Gynecol* 1996;87:884–90.
3. Penney GC. Prophylactic antibiotic therapy for abortion. In Templeton A, editor. *The Prevention of Pelvic Infection*. London: RCOG Press; 1996. p. 211–22.
4. Penney GC, Thomson M, Norman J, McKenzie H, Vale L, Smith R, *et al*. A randomised comparison of strategies for reducing infective complications of induced abortion. *Br J Obstet Gynaecol* 1998;105:599–604.
5. Bartley J, Tong S, Everington D, Baird DT. Parity is a major determinant of success rate in medical abortion: a retrospective analysis of 3161 consecutive cases of early medical abortion treated with reduced doses of mifepristone and vaginal gemeprost. *Contraception* 2000;62:297–303.
6. Ashok PW, Templeton AA, Wagaarachchi PT, Flett G. Factors affecting the outcome of early medical abortion: a review of 4132 consecutive cases. *BJOG* 2002;109:1281–9.
7. Grimes D, Schulz K, Stanwood N. Immediate postabortal insertion of intrauterine devices. *Cochrane Database Syst Rev* 2003;(1).
8. Cameron IT, Baird DT. The return to ovulation following early abortion: a comparison between vacuum aspiration and prostaglandin. *Acta Endocrinol* 1988;118:161–7.
9. Faculty of Family Planning and Reproductive Health Care Clinical Effectiveness Unit. The copper intrauterine device as long-term contraception. *J Fam Plann Reprod Health Care* 2004;30:29–42.
10. Tang OS, Gao PP, Cheng L, Lee SWH, Ho PC. A randomized double-blind placebo-controlled study to assess the effect of oral contraceptive pills on the outcome of medical abortion with mifepristone and misoprostol. *Hum Reprod* 1999;14:722–5.
11. Tang OS, Xu J, Cheng L, Lee SWH, Ho PC. The effect of contraceptive pills on the measured blood loss in medical termination of pregnancy by mifepristone and misoprostol: a randomized placebo controlled trial. *Hum Reprod* 2002;17:99–102.
12. Trupin RS, FACOG, Moreno C. Medical abortion: overview and management. *MedGenMed* 2002;4:1–12.
13. Lähteenmaki P, Ylöstalo P, Sipinen S, Toivonen J, Ruusuvaara L, Pikkola P, *et al*. Return of ovulation after abortion and after discontinuation of oral contraceptives. *Fertil Steril* 1980;34:246–9.
14. World Health Organization Task Force on Intrauterine Devices for Fertility Regulation. IUD insertion following termination of pregnancy: a clinical trial of TCu220C, Lippes Loop D, and Copper 7. *Stud Fam Plann* 1983;14:99–108.
15. Tuveng JM, Skjeldestad FE, Iversen T. Postabortal insertion of IUD. *Adv Contracept* 1986;2:387–92.
16. Suvisaari J, Lahteenmaki P. Detailed analysis of menstrual bleeding patterns after postmenstrual and postabortal insertion of a copper IUD or a levonorgestrel-releasing intrauterine system. *Contraception* 1996;54:201–8.
17. Batar I, Gbolade BA, Wildemeersch D. Immediate postabortal insertion of the frameless IUD: review of current experience. *Eur J Contracept Reprod Health Care* 2000;5:96–98.
18. Faculty of Family Planning and Reproductive Health Care Guidance. The copper intrauterine device as long-term contraception. *J Fam Plann Reprod Health Care* 2004;30:29–42.

19. Gillet PG, Lee NH, Yuzpe AA, Cerkus I. A comparison of the efficacy and acceptability of the Copper-7 intrauterine device following immediate or delayed insertion after first trimester therapeutic abortion. *Fertil Steril* 1980;34:121–4.

20. El-Tagy A, Sakr E, Sokal DC, Issa AH. Safety and acceptability of post-abortal IUD insertion and the importance of counseling. *Contraception* 2003;67:229–34.

21. Royal College of Obstetricians and Gynaecologists. *Male and Female Sterilisation*. Evidence-based Clinical Guidelines No. 4. London: RCOG Press; 1999.

SECTION TWO

Issues for community services

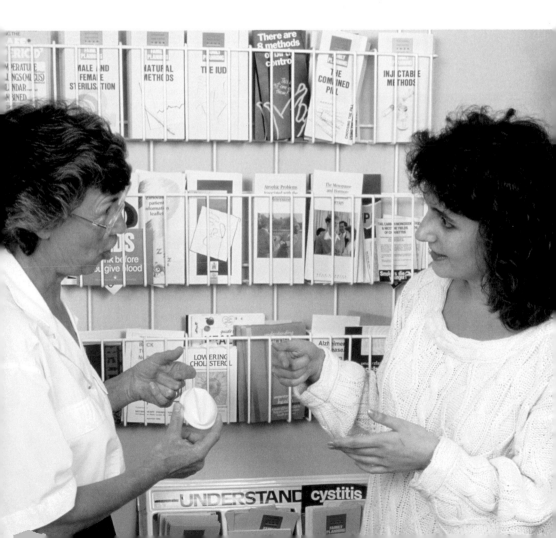

8 ORGANISATION OF FAMILY PLANNING SERVICES

Service design

QUESTION

How do 'drop-in' family planning clinics compare with 'appointment' clinics in terms of effectiveness and acceptability?

POPULATION: Family planning clinics.
INTERVENTIONS: 'Drop-in' versus 'appointment'.
OUTCOMES: Effectiveness and acceptability.

ANSWER

The CEU was unable to find any studies which compared the effectiveness and acceptability of 'drop-in' and 'appointment' family planning clinics. However, several papers examine the role and effectiveness of NHS walk-in centres. These walk-in centres were first piloted in 1999, therefore more time is needed in order to evaluate their effectiveness. However, available data suggest that use of walk-in centres is increasing and that users include a high proportion of young people (compared with general practice attendees).[1] On the negative side, walk-in consultations may be lengthy and less cost-effective than appointment consultations.[1] A study involving postal questionnaires, interviews and focus groups suggested that young people from ethnic minorities were particularly likely to access a walk-in style of service, as were people dissatisfied with previous services and those with urgent needs.[2]

This same survey provided information on the features that users want in a walk-in service. These include: a wide range of services including diagnosis, treatment, prevention and information, access to male and female doctors and nurses and availability of counsellors and interpreters. The investigators concluded that public expectations exceeded planned provision and that walk-in facilities with limited services were likely to disappoint the public.[2]

The Teenage Pregnancy Unit of the Department of Health has published *Best practice guidance on the provision of effective contraception and advice services for young people.*[3] This source identifies features of a service that will be successfully used by young people as including: age-specificity and involvement of young people, confidentiality, non-judgemental staff, accessible location and hours, a friendly atmosphere and effective publicity.

In summary, there is no direct evidence to show that 'drop-in' clinics are any more effective or acceptable than 'appointment clinics'. Indirect evidence suggests that 'hard to reach' groups such as young people from ethnic minorities do like to use 'walk-in' style services. However, these may not represent the most efficient use of scarce staff and resources and advice from the Teenage Pregnancy Unit suggests that other features of a service may be more important in assuring acceptability to young people.

QUESTION

Is it cost-effective for family planning and sexual health services to supply condoms freely on the basis of need?

POPULATION: Family planning and sexual health services.
INTERVENTION: Free provision of condoms.
OUTCOMES: Cost-effectiveness.

ANSWER

Free condom distribution appears to be effective at increasing self-reported condom use.[4] Around 20% of women of reproductive age rely on male condoms to prevent pregnancy. For condoms to be effective in preventing pregnancies and STIs, correct and consistent use is required.[5] Education on correct use and availability of supplies are prerequisites of correct and consistent use. Distribution of condoms to prevent HIV infection has been shown to be cost effective, especially for homosexual men.[6]

Condoms are relatively inexpensive and the CEU considers that free supply will contribute to consistent use. There is some evidence indicating that condom distribution represents a cost-effective health care intervention. Thus, services should seek to overcome any financial constraints that are limiting supply of condoms.

QUESTION

What attributes of a family planning clinic can improve clinical care for women with severe learning disabilities?

POPULATION: Family planning services.
INTERVENTIONS: Service modifications.
OUTCOMES: Improved care for women with learning disabilities.

ANSWER

Our CEU literature search identified only one publication, a guideline from the American Academy of Pediatrics,[7] which mentioned the special needs of children with learning disorders in relation to sexuality counselling. The guideline highlighted children with learning problems as an 'at risk' group and emphasised the importance of providing counselling about sexuality for these young people but provided no specific guidance on how services might achieve this.

QUESTION

What resuscitation equipment or emergency measures should be available in a family planning clinic to minimise the risk of serious complications?

POPULATION: Family planning services.
INTERVENTION: Provision of emergency equipment.
OUTCOMES: Risk of serious complications.

ANSWER

The two emergency situations which arise most commonly in family planning clinic settings are anaphylactic reaction and vasovagal attack. These events may occur following injection of DMPA, after insertion of an IUD or IUS, or following vasectomy. The FFPRHC has published a Faculty Aid to CPD Topics on resuscitation in the family planning clinic setting.[8] This guidance included suggestions on the contents of an 'emergency shock pack' for family planning clinics. The Resuscitation Council UK has published guidance on the correct response to anaphylactic shock.[9] Guidance from these two sources is summarised in Tables 5 and 6.

Table 5. Recommended contents of emergency shock pack for family planning clinics[8]

Essential	May be needed	Others
Atropine 0.5 mg in 1 ml 2–4 ampoules	Hydrocortisone 100 mg 2 ampoules	Needles, syringes
Adrenaline 1:1000 2 ampoules	Diazepam 2 rectal tubes	Water for injection
Chlorpheniramine 10 mg 2 ampoules	(Stored in a cool dry place)	Airway (Guedel) and Laerdel mask

Table 6. Resuscitation Council guidance for adults with anaphylactic reactions treated by first medical responders[9]

Guidance		Notes
Anaphylactic reaction (history of severe allergic-type reaction, respiratory difficulty and/or hypotension especially if skin changes)		If brochosplasm is severe an inhaled beta$_2$-agonist such as salbutamol may be used
Oxygen treatment when available 10–15 l/minute Stridor, wheeze, respiratory distress or signs of shock		For life-threatening shock give CPR/ALS. Consider slow intravenous epinephrine 1:1000 solution. This is only for experienced practitioners. Never give 1:1000 epinephrine IV
Call emergency service	Give epinephrine/adrenaline 1:1000 solution Adult dose 0.5 ml (500 micrograms) IM Repeat in 5 minutes if no improvement Antihistamine (chlorpheniramine) 10–20 mg IM or slow IV	Home-use devices such as Epipen deliver 300 micrograms adrenaline. Half-doses may be safer if the patient takes amitryptaline, imipramine or beta-blocker
In addition		A crystalloid may be safer than a colloid
If shock does not respond to drugs, give 1–2 litres IV fluid by rapid infusion or by repeat dose	If severe reaction/asthmatic, give hydrocortisone 100–500 mg IM or slow IV	

QUESTION

For women who are using contraception, what supply arrangements are recommended to ensure patient safety? (Ten similar enquiries.)

POPULATION: Women using contraception.
INTERVENTION: Supply arrangements.
OUTCOMES: Patient safety and satisfaction.

ANSWER

The WHO *Selected Practice Recommendations for Contraceptive Use* provides evidence-based recommendations for the safe use of contraceptive methods. The FFPRHC has developed a UK version which is available at www.ffprhc.org.uk. The *Selected Practice Recommendations* aims to provide flexibility of supply and ease of access should problems arise. More frequent follow up in women with medical or non-medical problems will be determined on an individual basis.

The WHO recommends that women can be offered up to 12 months' supply of combined or progestogen-only contraceptive pills at their initial visit and subsequent visits. For women using combined oral contraception, a yearly follow up visit is recommended. Advice to return at any time if there are problems is given. Follow up at 3 months is not routinely recommended. For women using the progestogen-only pill, no annual follow up is required but a follow up at 3 months after initiation is recommended. If women are breast-feeding, no follow up is necessary but they should be advised to return if problems arise or if breastfeeding ceases or reduces in frequency. For women using implants, no routine follow up is required but women should return at any time if problems arise or when it is time to have the implant removed or replaced. For women using an IUD, follow up after the first menses or 3–6 weeks after insertion is recommended and women should return if problems arise or when it is time to have the device removed.

Extending the role of nurses in family planning, general practice, accident and emergency and genitourinary medicine settings may provide improved access to contraceptive supply, and reflects the changing needs of modern clinical practice. Patient Group Directions (previously known as group protocols) can be developed for contraceptive provision in various settings.[10,11] Patient Group Directions comprise specific written instructions for the supply and administration of drugs in an identified clinical situation. Group Directions should be drawn up locally and signed by doctors, pharmacists and nurses and approved by the employer and relevant professional advisory committee. Group Directions apply to groups of patients or service users who need not be individually identified before presentation for treatment.

Guidance on Patient Group Directions has been published.[12–14] Included in a Direction should be: the time period during which the Direction has effect; the class of medicine which may be supplied on any one occasion; any restrictions to its supply and administration; the clinical situations in which the medicine may be supplied; the clinical criteria under which a person is eligible for treatment; persons excluded from treatment; circumstances under which further advice should be sought from a doctor; the dose and administration regimes of the medicine; any specific warnings such as adverse effects; any follow up arrangements which are appropriate; arrangement for referral for medical advice; and details of the record of supply and administration.

Pharmacists, registered health visitors, midwives, nurses and paramedics can supply and administer medicines under a Patient Group Direction. All health care professionals who are prescribing, supplying or administering medicines should take personal responsibility for maintaining and updating their knowledge and practice related to prescribing, including taking part in clinical audit and should never prescribe in situations beyond their professional competence.[13]

Traditionally in family planning clinics, the clinician seeing the patient would supply and administer contraception. The CEU was unable to identify any new information regarding reception staff dispensing contraceptives once they have been prescribed on a family planning prescription chart. It is the responsibility of the prescriber to ensure correct medication is supplied and administered. Reception staff are not trained to supply medication. Therefore, the CEU cannot support the dispensing of contraception by clerical or reception staff.

QUESTION

For young women aged 20–25 years, what are the current national recommendations for cervical screening?

POPULATION: Women aged 20–25 years.

INTERVENTION: Cervical screening.

OUTCOMES: National recommendations.

ANSWER

The NHS Cervical Screening Programme (NHSCSP)[15] recommends that women aged 25–65 years are eligible for free cervical smear tests. Women should receive their first invitation for screening at age 25 years and should attend every 3 years until they are aged 49 years. Women aged 50–65 years should attend every 5 years for screening. NHSCSP advises that cervical cancer is rare in women aged less than 20 years. Their bodies, in particular the cervix, are still developing and this may lead to young women getting an abnormal smear test result when there is nothing wrong. This could lead to them receiving unnecessary treatment. Lesions treated in very young women could prevent cancers from developing many years later; however, it has been suggested that screening could start at age 25 years.[16] Lesions that are destined to progress will still be screen-detectable and those that would regress will no longer be a source of anxiety. Thus, younger women do not have to undergo unnecessary investigations and treatments. NHSCSP does suggest that any woman under 25 years who is concerned about her risk of developing cervical cancer or her sexual health generally should contact her general practitioner or a genitourinary medicine clinic.[15]

The NHSCSP based its recommendation that women under 25 years do not need to be screened on evidence from a paper by Sasieni et al. (2003),[16] who analysed data from UK screening programme databases. Screening histories from 1305 women aged 20–69 years, who had been diagnosed with invasive cervical cancer, were compared with 2532 aged-matched controls. Thirty-four women aged 20–24 years had cervical cancer; 26 had had a previous negative smear and Sasieni et al. suggest that cytology is not very sensitive for these tumours in women in that age group. They recommend that women under 25 years should not be screened.

In 1999, a study looked at the number of person-years of life that are lost through deaths occurring at each year of age for six different cancers. It was found that extending cervical cancer screening to age 69 years would save more years of life than screening women aged 20–29 years.[17]

In order to predict the effect of the changes to the NHSCSP, Canfell et al. (2004) constructed a mathematical model of cervical human papillomavirus (HPV) infection, cervical intraepithelial neoplasia, and invasive cervical cancer, and of UK age-specific screening coverage rates, screening interval and treatment efficacy. From this model, the authors supported the changes to the NHSCSP, suggesting that screening women aged 20–25 years would have minimal impact, with the cumulative lifetime incidence decreasing from 0.63% to 0.61%.[18]

Peto *et al*. (2004)[19] analysed trends in mortality from cervical cancer from before 1988, when the NHSCSP was first launched, and estimated future trends in cervical cancer mortality if women are not screened. Peto *et al*. demonstrated that the death rate in women aged less than 30 years would be much higher if women were not screened before they were 30 years old.[19]

The Chairman and President of the British Society for Clinical Cytology (BSCC)[20] responded to the study by Peto *et al*.[19] which they said convincingly and comprehensively demonstrated the true effectiveness of cervical screening in the context of the underlying risk of disease for women living in the UK today. They acknowledged that many previous studies have found results similar to Peto *et al*., and hope that the study will lead the NHSCSP to revisit their decision to delay screening until age 25 years, in recognition of the death rate being substantially lower in women first screened when they were less than 30 years.[20]

In another study by Herbert (2000), UK registrations of carcinoma of the uterine cervix were compared with registrations recorded as carcinoma in situ. Herbert found that between 1971 and 1991, the peak age of registrations of carcinoma in situ moved from women aged 30–34 years to 25–29 years. Peak invasive carcinoma registrations were seen in the same age bands as the peak registrations of carcinoma in situ, and the peak age bands became progressively earlier in each birth cohort. Thus Herbert suggests that effective screening in young women is the key to preventing invasive cervical carcinoma.[21]

QUESTION

For clinicians and their patients, are there any differences in the advantages and disadvantages of metal and plastic vaginal speculums*?

POPULATION:	Clinicians and their patients.
INTERVENTION:	Use of metal or disposable plastic vaginal speculums.
OUTCOMES:	Advantages and disadvantages.

---

*Speculums or specula?

This enquirer also asked about the 'Faculty-approved' plural form of the word 'speculum'. The CEU is not aware that the Faculty has an approved form. Webster's Dictionary gives both 'speculums' and 'specula' as correct plural forms. It indicates that the word 'speculum' is middle English and derived from the Latin verb *specere*. The word 'speculum' itself is not a Latin noun and there seems no need to use a Latin form of plural. In the view of the CEU, the English form 'speculums' appears to be technically correct and compatible with the derivation of the word.

ANSWER

The RCOG has published a working party report on gynaecological examinations and guidelines for specialist practice.[22] This document describes the use of both metal and plastic speculums but does not indicate that one type is preferable to the other. It emphasises that metal speculums should be warmed before use and that a speculum of a suitable size should be chosen. Regarding plastic speculums, it is noted that the noisy ratchet may be distressing for some women and that this ratchet can be broken off and the speculum used without it. The use of a water-based lubricant when passing the speculum is advised.

Two guidelines from the USA on cervical cytology were identified. Both included guidance on the speculum examination but neither expressed any preference between metal and plastic speculums. One guideline stated that a non-lubricated speculum should be used.

Despite extending the literature search back to 1966, only two papers were identified which described comparative studies relating to vaginal speculums. The first described a comparison between a metal bivalve speculum and a 'dilating speculum', the Veda-scope.[23,24] This instrument was developed in Australia and, to our knowledge, is not available in the UK. A higher proportion of women found the examination 'comfortable' with the Veda-scope than with the conventional speculum.

The second study examined the effect of using a water-based lubricant with a plastic speculum on the quality of cervical cytology specimens.[25] The authors concluded that use of a small amount of lubricant on the inferior blade of the speculum does not change cervical cytology results. The authors comment that 'comparison of the comfort with metal and plastic speculums would be instructive'.

References

1. Salisbury C, Chalder M, Scott TM, Pope C, Moore L. What is the role of walk-in centres in the NHS? *BMJ* 2002;324:399–402.
2. Chapple A, Sibbald B, Rogers A, Roland M. Citizens' expectations and likely use of an NHS Walk-in Centre: results of a survey and qualitative methods of research. *Health Expect* 2001;4:38–47.
3. Department of Health, Teenage Pregnancy Unit. Best practice guidance on the provision of effective contraception and advice services for young people [www.info.doh.gov.uk/tpu/tpu.nsf].
4. Cohen, DA, Farley TA, Bedimo-Etame JR, Scriber R, Ward W, Kendall C, *et al.* Implementation of condom social marketing in Louisiana, 1993 to 1996. *Am J Public Health* 1999;89:204–8.

5. Weller S and Davis AR. Condom effectiveness in reducing heterosexual HIV transmission. *Cochrane Database Syst Rev* 2002;(1):CD003255.

6. Bedimo AL, Pinkerton, SD, Cohen DA, Gray B, Farley TA. Condom distribution: a cost-utility analysis. *Int J STD AIDS* 2002;13:384–92.

7. American Academy of Pediatrics. Sexuality education for children and adolescents. *Pediatrics* 2001;108:498–502.

8. Bennett A. Resuscitation in the family planning and reproductive health care setting. *J Fam Plann Reprod Health Care* 2001;27:165–9.

9. Resuscitation Council. *The Emergency Medical Treatment of Anaphylactic Reactions for First Medical Responders and for Community Nurses*. London: Resuscitation Council (UK); 2002.

10. Marshall J, Edwards C, Lambert M. Administration of medicines by emergency nurse practitioners according to protocols in an accident and emergency department. *J Accid Emerg Med* 1997;14:233–7.

11. Brittain D. Establishing an educational programme for nurses to supply emergency hormonal contraception (combined method) to protocol. *Br J Fam Plann* 1999;25:118–21.

12. The Prescription Only Medicines (Human Use) Amendment Order. Statutory Instrument No 1917. London: HMSO; 2000.

13. Department of Health. *Review of Prescribing, Supply and Administration of Medicines: A Report on the Supply and Administration of Medicines Under Group Protocols*. London: Department of Health; 1998.

14. Department of Health. The Crown Report. *Review of Prescribing, Supply and Administration of Medicines*. Statutory Instruments 1999 [www.dh.gov.uk/assetRoot/04/07/71/53/04077153.pdf].

15. National Health Service. *About the NHS Cervical Screening Programme*. 2004 [www/cancerscreening.nhs.uk/cervical/].

16. Sasieni P, Adams J, Cuzick J. Benefit of cervical screening at different ages: evidence from the UK audit of screening histories. *Br J Cancer* 2003;89:88–93.

17. Law MR, Morris JK, Wald N J. The importance of age in screening for cancer. *J Med Screen* 1999:6;16–20.

18. Canfell K, Barnabas R, Patnick J, Beral V. The predicted effect of changes in cervical screening practice in the UK: results from a modelling study. *Br J Cancer* 2004;91:530–6.

19. Peto J, Gilham C, Fletcher O, Matthews FE. The cervical cancer epidemic that screening has prevented in the UK. *Lancet* 2004;364:249–56.

20. British Society for Clinical Cytology. Chairman's Column. *Newsletter* 2004;(August).

21. Herbert A. Cervical screening in England and Wales: its effect has been underestimated. *Cytopathology* 2000;11:471–9.

22. Royal College of Obstetricians and Gynaecologists. *Gynaecological Examinations: Guidelines for Specialist Practice*. London: RCOG Press; 2002.

23. Thomas A, Weisberg E, Lieberman D, Fraser IS. A randomised-controlled trial comparing a dilating vaginal speculum with a conventional bivalve speculum. *Aust N Z J Obstet Gynaecol* 2001;41:379–86.

24. Veda-Scope making Pap smears more comfortable. [www.fpwa-health.org.au/VedaScope.htm.]

25. Amies AM, Miller L, Lee SK, Koutsky L. The effects of vaginal speculum lubrication on the rate of unsatisfactory cervical cytology diagnosis. *Obstet Gynecol* 2002;100;889–92.

Legal and ethical issues for family planning services

QUESTION

Is it necessary for a clinician to obtain written consent prior to IUD insertion? (Two similar enquiries.)

POPULATION: Women undergoing IUD insertion.
INTERVENTION: Provision of written consent.
OUTCOMES: Medico-legal concerns.

ANSWER

Published guidance from the Department of Health states that written consent is not a legal requirement for any form of medical or surgical treatment (other than for specific interventions governed by the Mental Health or Human Fertilisation and Embryology Acts).[1] Obtaining written consent *per se* confers no special medico-legal protection, as written consent does not guarantee valid consent. The Department of Health suggests that it is good practice to obtain written consent for 'any significant procedure' but the CEU is unaware of any published advice as to whether or not IUD insertion should be viewed as a 'significant procedure'. A Clinical Opinion paper in the *American Journal of Obstetrics and Gynecology* addressed consent implications related to the mode of action of the IUD (suggesting that because the mode of action of an IUD is contentious, with a significant post-fertilisation component, valid consent requires full discussion of mode of action).[2] This paper did not specifically advise that written consent was necessary.

The CEU concludes that no service or individual clinician could be criticised for failing to obtain written consent prior to IUD insertion. We have no information regarding the proportions of services or individual clinicians that have a policy of obtaining written consent for IUD insertion.

QUESTION

Should clinicians be proactive in recalling women using 'removable' methods of contraception (IUDs and implants) for removal in order to reduce adverse clinical and medico-legal sequelae?

POPULATION: Women using 'removable' methods of contraception (i.e. IUD, LNG-IUS, etonogestrel implant).

INTERVENTION: Recall by clinician at scheduled time for removal.

OUTCOMES: Clinical and medico-legal concerns.

ANSWER

Our CEU systematic literature search identified no recommendations, in any source, suggesting that the onus falls on the clinician to recall a woman at the end of the scheduled life span of a removable contraceptive method. Standard good practice requires that women are given both verbal and written information before being provided with any method of contraception. For 'removable' methods, this patient information should include advice on the life span of the device and arrangements for removal/replacement.

If resources permit, a service might choose to institute a formal recall system. However, the introduction of such a system, involving communication with patients' homes, would raise confidentiality issues. The CEU considers that a clinician could not be considered negligent for omitting to recall a woman at the end of the life span of a 'removable' contraceptive method as long as she had been given appropriate verbal and written information at the time of insertion.

QUESTION

What legal and ethical issues relating to a prescription should a clinician be aware of when caring for a young woman aged less than 16 years requesting the contraceptive pill? (Two similar enquiries.)

POPULATION: Young women aged less than 16 years.

INTERVENTION: Prescription of the contraceptive pill.

OUTCOMES: Legal and ethical concerns.

ANSWER

It is important that the clinician tailors the consultation for the adolescent age group in order to ensure optimal compliance with the oral contraceptive pill. This involves 'active listening', and addressing of issues relating to body image, such as weight gain, which adolescents may raise.

The Fraser Ruling of 1985 established that a clinician may provide contraceptive advice or treatment to a patient aged less than 16 years provided that he or she is satisfied that the patient is competent to give consent to the treatment.

The duty of confidentiality owed to a patient aged under 16 years is deemed to be as great as that owed to any other patient. All discussions and decisions, and any disclosure should be noted in the patient's records by the appropriate health professional. If in doubt about the need for disclosure, the clinician should contact the relevant local body to obtain advice by revealing only anonymous facts in the first instance.

Strategies to improve compliance with the contraceptive pill, which may be particularly relevant when caring for young patients, adapted from American guidance[3] are summarised in Box 1; the Fraser Ruling guidelines of 1985 are summarised in Box 2; key questions for clinicians to ask themselves when considering disclosure of a young person's details (adapted from Royal College of General Practitioners/British Medical Association guidance[4]) are summarised in Box 3.

(Subsequent to the preparation of this Answer, the CEU published comprehensive guidance on contraceptive choices for young people.[5] Readers requiring more detailed guidance are referred to this source.)

Box 1	Strategies to improve compliance

Show the woman the pill pack and let her repeat the instructions for its use.

The 28-day pack may be preferable to avoid confusion.

Taking the pill can be linked to a routine daily activity

Guidance should be provided about:

- potential adverse effects of the pill
- back-up methods of contraception
- how to say 'no' to sex and alternatives to intercourse
- emergency contraceptive pills
- sexually transmitted infections.

Give the patient your contact details.

Emphasise follow-up appointments and the importance of following the instructions.

Box 2	The Fraser guidelines of 1985

A young person is competent to consent to contraceptive advice or treatment if :

- the young person understands the doctor's advice
- the doctor is unable to persuade the young person to inform his or her parents or allow the doctor to inform the parents that he or she is seeking contraceptive advice
- it is likely that the young person will begin or continue sexual activity with or without the contraceptive treatment
- the young person's physical or mental health or both are likely to suffer unless he or she receives contraceptive advice or treatment
- it is in the best interests of the young person for the doctor to give contraceptive advice, treatment or both without parental consent.

Box 3	Key questions to ask before breaching confidentiality

How can the patient be best helped to protect him or herself, or others, from harm?

Would further outside advice or intervention be useful? If so, what is the best way of working with the patient towards a voluntary disclosure?

Is the situation so serious and urgent that disclosure against the patient's wishes should be considered?

What support or counselling will the patient be offered?

QUESTION

For women requiring progestogen-only emergency contraception, would the use of 'generic' levonorgestrel, rather than Levonelle be legal, safe and cost-effective?

POPULATION: Women requiring progestogen-only emergency contraception.

INTERVENTION: Use of 'generic' levonorgestrel.

OUTCOMES: Medico-legal concerns, safety, cost-effectiveness.

ANSWER

At the time of writing, the recommended regimen for progestogen-only emergency contraception was levonorgestrel 1500 micrograms as a single dose. This regimen was marketed by Schering as Levonelle (2 x 750-microgram tablets) and Levonelle One Step (1 × 1500-microgram tablet) at a price of around £5.50. Levonorgestrel was also marketed as Microval (Wyeth, now discontinued) and Norgeston® (Schering Health) as regular progestogen-only oral contraception in the form of 30-microgram tablets. Thus, to achieve a dose of 1500 micrograms would require ingestion of 50 tablets (at a price of only £1.23).

The use of Microval or Norgeston in this way is outside the manufacturer's product licence. However, a European Community Pharmaceutical Directive specifically permits doctors to use 'licensed medicines for indications or in doses or by routes of administration outside the recommendations given in the licence'.[6] Thus, the use of a 50-tablet regimen for emergency contraception is legal, low cost and probably safe. Nevertheless, the CEU considers that this would not represent a cost-effective (or humane) regimen. Reduced compliance would be likely to outweigh the financial savings.

QUESTION

In a circumstance where use of the combined pill is medically contraindicated (for instance, for a smoker aged over 35 years with hypertension) but the woman refuses to discontinue the pill, can a clinician refuse to prescribe it?

POPULATION: Women for whom the combined pill is medically contraindicated.
INTERVENTION: Refusal to prescribe.
OUTCOMES: Medico-legal concerns.

ANSWER

Combined oral contraceptive users with hypertension have an increased risk of myocardial infarction, ischaemic stroke and haemorrhagic stroke compared with normotensive users. The WHO *Medical Eligibility Criteria for Contraceptive Use* recommends that even for women with adequately controlled hypertension, the risks of using combined oral contraception outweigh the benefits. Smokers have increased risks of myocardial infarction, stroke and VTE compared with non-smokers. Use of combined oral contraception and increasing age further increase the already elevated risks associated with smoking. According to the WHO *Medical Eligibility Criteria for Contraceptive Use,* combined oral contraception poses an unacceptable health risk for women aged over 35 years who smoke more than 15 cigarettes a day. Thus, according to the WHO recommendations, the combined pill is medically contraindicated for a woman, such as the example given, with multiple risk factors.

The CEU advises against prescribing the combined pill to a woman for whom it is medically contraindicated, even though the woman may be reluctant to stop taking it (for example, because she places a high value on the beneficial 'adverse effect' of reduced menstrual bleeding.) The clinician should counsel the woman on the risks of the combined pill and provide comprehensive information on a range of contraceptive options. For example, if reduced menstrual loss is of high importance, the LNG-IUS might prove an acceptable contraceptive choice.

In a case where a woman refused to follow evidence-based medical advice, the practitioner would be best to refer her to a colleague.

QUESTION

For young women aged 14 years who have a learning disability, such as Down syndrome, can they consent to contraceptive use?

POPULATION:	Young women aged 14 years with Down syndrome.
INTERVENTION:	Contraception.
OUTCOMES:	Competency to give valid consent.

ANSWER

Regardless of age, any 'competent' young person can consent to medical treatment. An individual must have sufficient capacity to understand the procedure and its alternatives, their consent must be voluntary and their decision must be based on sufficient and accurate information. Young women with a learning disability, such as Down syndrome, may in some cases be competent to give consent. If however, the young woman is under 18 years and not believed to be competent to consent to treatment, the holder of 'parental responsibility' can give consent to treatment on her behalf. Conflict arises if the holder of parental responsibility and the clinician do not agree that treatment is in the best interests of the young person. For adults (over 18 years) with incapacity, only an appointed 'guardian' can consent to treatment on their behalf.

Importantly, the Sexual Offences Act (England and Wales) 2003 allows doctors, nurses, youth workers and others who are working with young people under the age of 16 years to provide contraceptive advice and treatment within the law. It is important however, that clinicians are alert to the possibility of sexual exploitation or coercion.

The FFPRHC CEU published comprehensive guidance on contraception for young people in the *Journal of Family Planning* in October 2004.[5]

If a young women (below the age of 16 years) with learning difficulties is likely to have unprotected sex, she could be provided with contraception either with her consent or, because she is under the age of 16 years, with parental consent, if deemed to be in her best interest.

QUESTION

For a woman who is having an IUD inserted, should her general practitioner be asked to prescribe the device?

POPULATION: Women having IUDs inserted in family planning or gynaecology services.
INTERVENTION: Prescription of the device by general practitioners.
OUTCOMES: Legal and ethical responsibilities.

ANSWER

The WHO *Medical Eligibility Criteria for Contraceptive Use* states that intrauterine contraception provides safe and effective contraception for women who fulfil medical eligibility criteria. No guidance presently exists regarding the responsibilities of health professionals involved in IUD or LNG-IUS insertion. Clinicians inserting a IUD or IUS should have the appropriate qualifications for device insertion approved by the FFPRHC. A study published in the *Journal of Family Planning and Reproductive Health Care* attempted to define standards for the insertion of IUDs.[7]

Health professionals undertaking IUD/LNG-IUS insertion are responsible for counselling regarding insertion, expulsion, perforation, infection, menstrual changes and failure rates (including ectopic pregnancy). The health professional inserting the device should ensure that appropriate resuscitation equipment is available should this be required.

The clinician who provides the prescription for a medicine or device is ultimately responsible for its use (personal communication with the Medical and Dental Defence Union Scotland advisor[8]). Medical defence advisors from the Medical and Dental Defence Union Scotland (MDDUS) provide legal advice and representation for doctors and dentists in the United Kingdom. Advice from the MDDUS is that a general practitioner should not prescribe an IUD or LNG-IUS, which they themselves are not going to insert. Such a case has never reached the law courts to test this.

The FFPRHC CEU published comprehensive guidance on the IUD as long-term contraception in January 2004.[9]

References

1. Department of Health. *Reference Guide to Consent for Examination or Treatment*. London: DH; 2001.
2. Spinnato JA. Mechanism of action of intrauterine contraceptive devices and its relation to informed consent. *Am J Obstet Gynecol* 1997;176:503–6.
3. Davis A, Wysocki S. Clinician/patient interaction: communicating the benefits and risks of oral contraceptives. *Contraception* 1999;59:S39–S42.
4. Royal College of General Practitioners; General Practitioners Committee, British Medical Association; Royal College of Nursing; Medical Defence Union. Confidentiality and young people. Improving teenagers' uptake of sexual and other health advice [www.info.doh.gov.uk/tpu/tpu.nsf].
5. Faculty of Family Planning and Reproductive Health Care Clinical Effectiveness Unit. Contraceptive choices for young people. *J Fam Plann Reprod Health Care* 2004;30:237–51.
6. European Commission. Pharmaceutical Directive. The approximation of provisions laid down by law, regulation or administrative action relating to proprietary medicinal products. *Official Journal of European Communities* 1965;22:369–75.
7. Kasliwal AP, Webb AMC. Intrauterine device insertions: Setting our standards. *J Fam Plann Reprod Health Care* 2002;28:157–8.
8. Medical and Dental Defence Union Scotland Advisor, personal communication.
9. Faculty of Family Planning and Reproductive Health Care Guidance. The copper intrauterine device as long-term contraception. *J Fam Plann Reprod Health Care* 2004;30:29–42.

GYNAECOLOGICAL PROBLEMS IN THE FAMILY PLANNING CLINIC

Pregnancy testing, cervical smears and infection

QUESTION

For women who have had a single act of unprotected sex, how soon after the incident can a pregnancy test reliably confirm or exclude pregnancy?

POPULATION: Women who have had a single act of unprotected sex.
INTERVENTION: Timing of pregnancy testing.
OUTCOME: Reliability at confirming or excluding pregnancy.

ANSWER

Implantation of the blastocyst into the endometrium occurs approximately 1 week after fertilisation, at which time the syncytiotrophoblast begins producing human chorionic gonadotrophin (hCG).[1] Serum concentrations of hCG rise in a linear fashion during the first 6 weeks of pregnancy, with a doubling time of approximately 1.3 days. The peak hCG level is reached at 9–10 weeks gestation (20 000–200 000 miu/ml). hCG is extremely stable in urine. Modern urinary pregnancy tests (including those for home use) are based on monoclonal antibodies raised against the beta subunit of hCG. These assays detect hCG concentrations in urine as low as 25 miu/ml. An assay with a sensitivity of 25 miu/ml may diagnose pregnancy as early as 3–4 days after implantation; results are positive in 98% of women by 7 days after implantation or about the time of the missed menses. Radioimmunoassay techniques for measuring beta hCG levels in serum can detect concentrations as low as 2–10 miu/ml.

Contemporary urine-based pregnancy testing kits detect levels of hCG as low as 25 miu/ml and manufacturers claim that they are reliable 'from the first day of the missed period'. However, the CEU literature search indicated that these claims should be viewed with caution: one study indicated that a limit of detection of 12.5 miu/ml would be needed to give 95% accuracy at this stage.[2] For women with erratic cycles or amenorrhoea, deciding the timing of a pregnancy test after an act of unprotected sex is even more problematic.[3] Conception can occur up to 7 days after intercourse, implantation will occur approximately 7 days after that, and that urine hCG levels will be detectable by a standard pregnancy test by 7 days after that. We would expect therefore that a standard pregnancy test could 'rule in' or 'rule out' pregnancy with reasonable reliability if undertaken more than 21 days after the act of unprotected sex.

Nevertheless, the CEU literature search indicates that clinicians should view the results of standard urine-based pregnancy tests undertaken around the time of the missed period with great caution. Even greater caution is required in women for whom it is difficult, or impossible, to estimate the time of 'missed menses'. If, in an individual case, it is considered that there is particular urgency in 'ruling in' or 'ruling out' pregnancy, then a quantitative serum hCG measurement can be requested. However, even this test cannot be positive until after implantation. In problematic cases, serial hCG testing (either urine- or serum-based) should be undertaken over a period of 7–14 days.

QUESTION

For women using hormonal contraception who have no withdrawal bleed, can over-the-counter pregnancy tests reliably confirm or exclude pregnancy?

POPULATION: Women using hormonal contraception who miss a period.
INTERVENTION: Over-the-counter pregnancy tests.
OUTCOME: Reliability at confirming or excluding pregnancy.

ANSWER

See answer above. Most published data relate to pregnancy testing in women not using hormonal contraception and no evidence was identified in women using contraception.

QUESTION

For women attending for cervical smears, are there recommended clinical guidelines for smear-taking in family planning clinics to ensure effective screening?

POPULATION: Women attending for cervical smears.

INTERVENTION: Clinical guidelines for smear taking in family planning clinics.

OUTCOME: Effective smears.

ANSWER

The importance of proper smear-taking cannot be overemphasised as studies have shown that one-half to two-thirds of false negative results are based on the condition of the patient when the smear was taken and the skill of the clinician who took the smear.[4,5,6]

The American Society of Cytopathology has released cervical cytology practice guidelines.[7] The section on the collection of specimens is summarised below (but the details on liquid-based preparations have been omitted):

Patient preparation:

● Specimens should be collected about 2 weeks (10–18 days) after the first day of the last menstrual period.

● The patient should refrain from intercourse, should not douche, use tampons, spermicides, vaginal creams or medications for 48 hours before the test.

Visualisation of the cervix:

● The patient is usually in the dorsolithotomy position.

● A sterile, or single-use, bivalve speculum of the correct size is inserted into the vagina without lubrication, although warm water may be used to assist insertion. The position of the speculum should allow the clinician to see the entire os and ectocervix.

● Most cervical changes originate in the transformation zone which may be easy to see, or too high in the endocervical canal but this should be the focus of cytology specimen collection. It may not be possible to see the transformation zone in postmenopausal women or those who have received radiation therapy and the endocervix should be sampled in these patients. In patients who have had a hysterectomy, a sample from the vaginal cuff suffices.

Collection devices:

- Plastic spatulas are preferred over wooden ones which retain cellular material. Cotton-tip swabs are not recommended. The cytobrush and spatula have been shown to provide the best specimens.

- The choice of a device depends on the size and shape of the cervix and the clinical situation, as among other factors, the transformation zone can be affected by age, parity and hormones.

Techniques for sample collection

Collection of cervical or vaginal specimens for smears using the spatula and endocervical brush:

- The vaginal fornix and ectocervix are sampled before the endocervix and transformation zone.

- A sample of the ectocervix is taken using a plastic or wooden spatula; the notched end is rotated 360 degrees around the cervical os, thus obtaining a sample on the upper surface of the spatula. The spatula is held with the specimen face up while the endocervical sample is collected.

- Visible lesions should be sampled directly and placed on another slide.

- The endocervical brush is inserted into the endocervical canal until only the bristles close to the hand are visible; it is then rotated 45–90 degrees and removed (check on the package insert if the endocervical brush being used is contraindicated in pregnant women).

- The sample on the spatula is spread evenly and thinly along the length of one half of a labelled slide using a single uniform motion. The endocervical brush is then rolled along the remaining half of the slide by turning the handle gently.

- The slide is fixed by immersion or spray and the collection devices are discarded.

Collection of cervical or vaginal specimens for smears using the 'broom-like' device:

- The ectocervix and endocervix are sampled simultaneously

- The central bristles of the broom are inserted into the endocervical canal until the lateral bristles bend against the ectocervix. It is then rotated in the same direction five times with gentle pressure.

- The broom is removed and the specimen spread with a single stroke along the slide. The broom is then turned over and the stroke repeated on the same area.

- The slide is fixed with immersion or spray and the collection device is discarded.

QUESTION

For asymptomatic women attending for routine cervical cytology, is there a need for pelvic examination to identify pelvic pathology?

POPULATION: Asymptomatic women attending for routine cervical cytology.

INTERVENTION: Routine pelvic examination.

OUTCOME: The identification of pelvic pathology.

ANSWER

The FFPRHC and RCOG have published guidance that states that routine pelvic examination is not an automatic component of every gynaecological examination. In asymptomatic women, routine screening is not justified to exclude pregnancy, ovarian conditions or fibroids and may discourage women from starting the oral contraceptive pill. The bimanual pelvic examination requires skill that takes time to develop and non-invasive imaging techniques may be more accurate. The CEU advises that pelvic examination of asymptomatic women attending for routine cervical cytology is not necessary.

Many women find vaginal speculum examination and bimanual palpation to be a very intimate and potentially embarrassing and negative procedure. For this reason the clinician should endeavour to do routine pelvic examinations only when necessary and in a skilled and sympathetic manner.

The RCOG has published guidance for specialist practice on gynaecological examinations.[8] This is summarised below:

- Pelvic examination is not an automatic part of every gynaecological examination. The clinician should consider if the examination is a 'screening' or 'diagnostic' test and whether information will be obtained later through ultrasound or examination under anaesthesia.

- The British Society for Colposcopy and Cervical Pathology considers that a bimanual examination should be done only if indicated when a woman attends for colposcopy.

● Most trainees or student doctors need practice before they can define the uterus or palpate the ovaries in overweight or postmenopausal women thus limiting the success of the technique.

● Routine pelvic examination prior to first prescription of the oral contraceptive pill has low productivity.

● Women who have difficulty with pelvic examinations should be dealt with individually depending on the complaint. Vaginal examination may be necessary for screening or chronic problems such as infertility. Sometimes examination under anaesthesia may be required or procedures such as pelvic ultrasound used instead.

● Doctors may include women with learning difficulties or mental illness in the NHSCSP if the patient can consent to speculum examination and it is in her best interests.

● No evidence supports routine vaginal examination at the first antenatal visit or later in pregnancy.

● Women with conditions such as uterovaginal prolapse or dyspareunia can benefit from digital or speculum examination and the reasons for the examination should be clearly explained. This does not have to be accompanied by bimanual palpation every time if inappropriate.

QUESTION

For women attending general practice for routine cervical smears, who should be screened for chlamydia as a priority?

POPULATION: Women attending general practice for routine cervical smears.
INTERVENTION: Endocervical swabs for *C. trachomatis.*
OUTCOME: Cost effectiveness.

ANSWER

A UK pilot study of women aged 16–24 years attending family planning, general practice, genitourinary medicine and termination services showed a prevalence of *C. trachomatis* of 9.8–11.2%.[9] Based on recommendations from the Scottish Intercollegiate Guideline Network (SIGN), opportunistic *C. trachomatis* screening should be considered in general practice.[10] Opportunity might arise during consultations relating to sexual health, such as for cervical smears, contraception and pregnancy. Opportunistic testing should be considered in sexually active women under the age of 25 years. Women aged 25 years and over with two or more partners in the last year or a change in sexual partner in the last year should also be offered testing for chlamydia.

QUESTION

For asymptomatic women having routine cervical cytology, does an incidental finding of bacteria on the report need to be treated?

POPULATION: **Asymptomatic women having routine cervical cytology with incidental detection of bacterial infection.**

INTERVENTION: **Treatment.**

OUTCOME: **Effect of treatment.**

ANSWER

Asymptomatic women who have been identified with a bacterial infection at the time of routine cervical cytology are unlikely to require treatment. In some cases however, where the bacteria are not normal commensals of the genito-urinary tract treatment may be appropriate.

Bacterial vaginosis is due to an overgrowth of *G. vaginalis*, anaerobes and myco-plasmas. Bacterial vaginosis is often asymptomatic but may cause vaginal discharge, odour and itch. Treatment is indicated only for symptomatic women.[11]

Group B streptococcus (GBS) is a vaginal commensal in 10–15% of women. There is no evidence that GBS in isolation increases the risk of PID. Asymptomatic carriers do not require treatment.

Asymptomatic genital carriage of group A streptococcus is rare and serious infections rarely originate in the genitourinary tract.[12] Because of the rarity of vaginal group A streptococcus, and the paucity of evidence about its significance, the CEU considers that this infection should be treated if detected, especially prior to IUD insertion.

Actinomycetes are normal commensals in the gastrointestinal tract. The most common is *Actinomyces israelii*. Female genital tract actinomycosis is a rare but severe disease and is associated with the use of IUDs. Evidence suggests that among IUD users, symptomatic women with actinomyces-like organisms on a cervical smear should have the device removed following the initiation of appropriate antibiotics. Asymptomatic women with actinomyces-like organisms can continue to use an IUD if they wish. Antibiotic treatment is not indicated. Women should be counselled to return if pain or symptoms of infection occur.[13]

Candida can be an incidental finding on cervical smears in asymptomatic women. The British Association for Sexual Health and HIV (BASHH) (www.mssvd.org.uk) have developed an evidence-based national guideline on the management of vulvovaginal candidiasis.[14] Between 10% and 20% of women of reproductive age may harbour candida species in the absence of symptoms. This guideline suggests that these women do not require treatment. It is unlikely that asymptomatic women with candida identified on cervical cytology require treatment.

QUESTION

For women found to have actinomyces-like organisms detected by cervical smears, what treatment is necessary?

POPULATION: Women found to have actinomyces-like organisms.

INTERVENTION: The cervical smear.

OUTCOME: Treatment of the condition.

ANSWER

Pelvic actinomycosis is an infection caused by the bacterium *A. israelii,* which uses foreign bodies such as IUDs to establish an infection.[15] Actinomycosis was first described by Israel in 1878. Women may present with abdominal pain, abnormal vaginal discharge, fever and weight loss. These women are usually diagnosed as having PID. The complications of pelvic actinomycosis involve fallopian tube damage, infertility, ectopic pregnancy and chronic pelvic pain.

A review of IUDs and PID[16] in 1996 concluded that the role of *A. israelii* related to IUD use and genital tract infection is, at best, unclear. However, available data suggest that this organism is not a major pathogen in this clinical setting. One study has suggested that the organism can be found in 7% of IUD users by cervical smear.[17] The accuracy of a cervical smear ranges between 49% and 98% and it is questionable whether detection indicates vaginal colonisation or actual infection.[18] Detection of *Actinomyces* in non-IUD users ranges between 2.9% and 27%[19,20] and it has been suggested that actinomycosis occurs on surfaces with high calcium content consistent with long-term IUD use.

A randomised controlled trial was undertaken to determine the necessity of removing the IUD, in addition to treatment with antibiotics, in women with pelvic actinomycosis.[21] The patients were divided into two groups, both of which were treated with trimethoprim and sulfamethoxazole, but women in the intervention group retained their IUD. Later, 100% of the women whose

IUD was removed had a negative cytology smear for *Actinomyces* while 66.7% of those who retained the IUD had a negative smear. The longer the woman had had an IUD, the higher the probability that *Actinomyces* infection would continue if the device was retained. The authors concluded that removal of an IUD is effective in controlling *Actinomyces* infection and offers protection in proportion to the time that the patient has used the device.[21]

All the evidence found therefore agrees that in symptomatic women with an IUD, the device should be removed followed by appropriate antibiotic treatment. Asymptomatic women with *Actinomycetes* need not have the IUD removed and do not require antibiotics.

The CEU therefore recommends that asymptomatic women with actinomyces-like organisms identified by cervical smears may continue with an IUD but should be advised of warning signs of infection and asked to report them. However, if the woman feels more comfortable having her copper device removed and replaced, this is acceptable. Users of Mirena have a very low risk of infection and there is no indication for replacing the device. Symptomatic women should have their IUD removed and should begin antibiotic therapy.

QUESTION

For women who have *S. aureus* identified on vaginal swabs, what treatment is advised for symptomatic and asymptomatic women?

POPULATION: Women who have *S. aureus* identified on vaginal swabs.
INTERVENTION: Treatment.
OUTCOME: Efficacy.

ANSWER

S. aureus transiently colonises the nares, axillae, vagina, anus, pharynx or damaged skin surface of 30–50% of healthy adults. Culture has detected vaginal *S. aureus* in 10–20 % of women. Around 10–20% of the colonising isolates produce toxic-shock-syndrome toxin. *S. aureus* biofilm can form on tampons in vivo.[22] Certain strains of *S. aureus* are resistant to the antibiotics methicillin and flucloxacillin. MRSA is a type of bacterium that occurs harmlessly on the skin and/or in the noses of healthy people. If it infects the body through breaks in the skin, it may cause mild infections such as acne or serious infection of the bloodstream, bones or joints. Most MRSA infections occur in hospitals and an endogenous infection can occur if the MRSA spread from the initial site of colonisation to a new site. MRSA can also spread between patients and hospital staff through direct and indirect contact. MRSA has been reported in women undergoing vaginal surgery.[23]

Despite extensive searching, the CEU could find no information on the treatment of symptomatic or asymptomatic women who have *S. aureus* identified on vaginal swabs. From the available evidence, the CEU would advise that women with *S. aureus* colonisation or infection in the genital area should be treated. The decision to remove an IUD or LNG-IUS in a woman with MRSA will depend on other factors such as signs or symptoms of pelvic infection. It is unclear if the presence of MRSA in the genital area would be complicated by an IUD or LNG-IUS already in place, but we suggest that a device should not be inserted when infection is identified.

QUESTION

For women being managed as outpatients for PID, which first-line oral antibiotic regimen has the greatest efficacy?

POPULATION: Women being managed as outpatients for PID.
INTERVENTION: A first-line oral antibiotic regimen.
OUTCOME: Efficacy of the antibiotic treatment.

ANSWER

The most up-to-date guidance on first-line oral antibiotic regimens for the outpatient treatment of PID comes from the US Centers for Disease Control and Prevention update on the treatment of sexually transmitted diseases.[24] All other guidance appraised was based on earlier Centers for Disease Control and Prevention recommendations for treatment of PID.

The CEU therefore advocates the use of either of the antibiotic regimens below as a first-line treatment for PID:

- ofloxacin 400 mg orally twice a day for 14 days or levofloxacin 500 mg orally once daily for 14 days with:

- metronidazole 500 mg orally twice a day for 14 days

References

1.   Paul M, Schaff E, Nichols M. The roles of clinical assessment, human chorionic gonadotropin assays, and ultrasonography in medical abortion practice. *Am J Obstet Gynecol* 2000;183:S34–S43.

2.   Cole LA, Khanlian SA, Sutton JM, Davies S, Rayburn WF. Accuracy of home pregnancy tests at the time of missed menses. *Am J Obstet Gynecol* 2004;190:100–5.
3.   Wilcox AJ, Day BD, Dunson D, McChesney R, Weinberg CR. Natural limits of pregnancy testing in relation to the expected menstrual period. *JAMA* 2001;286:1759–62.
4.   McGoogan E, Colgan TJ, Ramzy I, Cochand-Priollet B, Davey DD, Grohs HK, *et al.* Cell preparation methods and criteria for sample adequacy. International Academy of Cytology Task Force summary. Diagnostic cytology towards the 21st century: an international expert conference and tutorial. *Acta Cytol* 1998;42:25–32.
5.   Vooijs GP, Elias A, Van der Graaf Y, Poelen-van de Berg M. The influence of sample takers on the cellular composition of cervical smears. *Acta Cytol* 1986;35:251–7.
6.   Thompson DW. *Adequate Pap smears: a guide for sampling techniques in screening for abnormalities of the uterine cervix.* 2nd ed. Toronto: Ontario Medical Association, Laboratory Proficiency Testing Program; 1996.
7.   American Society of Cytopathology. *Cervical Cytology Practice Guidelines.* American Society of Cytopathology; 2000 [www.cytopathology.org:80/website/article.asp?id=382].
8.   Royal College of Obstetricians and Gynaecologists. *Gynaecological Examinations: Guidelines for Specialist Practice.* London: RCOG Press; 2002.
9.   James NJ, Wilson S, Hughes S. A pilot study to incorporate chlamydia testing in the management of women anticipating IUD insertion in community clinics. *Br J Fam Plann* 1997;23:16–9.
10.   Scottish Intercollegiate Guideline Network. *Management of Genital Chlamydia trachomatis Infection.* Guideline No. 42. Edinburgh: SIGN; 2002.
11.   Association for Genitourinary Medicine, Medical Society for the Study of Venereal Disease. *National Guideline for the Management of Bacterial Vaginosis.* London; 2002.
12.   Gisser JM, Fields MC, Pick N, Moses AE, Srugo I. Invasive group A streptococcus associated with an intrauterine device and oral sex. *Sex Transm Dis* 2002;29:483–85.
13.   Fox KL, Born MW, Cohen MA. Fulminant infection and toxic shock syndrome caused by streptococcus pyogenes. *J Emerg Med* 2002;22:357–66.
14.   Clinical Effectiveness Group, Association for Genitourinary Medicine and the Medical Society for the Study of Venereal Diseases. *National Guideline on the Management of Vulvovaginal Candidiasis.* London; 2000.
15.   Hager WD. IUD-associated infections: a diagnosis and treatment of pelvic actinomycosis. *Contemporary Obstet Gynecol* 1999;44:113–14, 117.
16.   Burkman RT. Intrauterine devices and pelvic inflammatory disease: Evolving perspectives on the data. *Obstet Gynecol Surv* 1996;51:S35–S41.
17.   Fiorino AS. Intrauterine contraceptive device-associated actinomycotic abscess and Actinomyces detection on cervical smear. *Obstet Gynecol* 1996;87:142–9.
18.   Burkman RT, Damewood MT. Actinomyces and the intrauterine contraceptive device. In: Zatuchin GL, Goldsmith A, Sciarra JJ, editors. *PARFR Series on Fertility Regulation: Intrauterine Contraception: Advances and Future Prospects.* Philadelphia: Harper and Row; 1985. p. 427–37.
19.   Persson E, Holmberg K, Dahlgren S, Nilsson L. Actinomyces israelii in the genital tract of women with and without intrauterine contraceptive devices. *Acta Obstet Gynecol Scand* 1983;62:563–8.
20.   Curtis EM, Pine L. Actinomyces in the vaginas of women with and without intrauterine contraceptive devices. *Am J Obstet Gynecol* 1981;152:287–90.
21.   Bonacho I, Pitz S, Gomez-Besteiro MI. The importance of the removal of the intrauterine device in genital colonization by actinomyces. *Gynecol Obstet Invest* 2001;52:119–23.

22. Johnson A. Methicillin-resistant *Staphylococcus aureus* (MRSA) infection. 2002 [www.netdoctor.co.uk].
23. Veeh RH, Shirtliff ME, Petik JR, Flood JA, Davis CC, Seymour JL, *et al*. Detection of *Staphylococcus aureus* biofilm on tampons and menses components. *J Infect Dis* 2003;188:519–30.
24. Centers for Disease Control and Prevention (CDC) *Pelvic inflammatory disease. Sexually transmitted diseases treatment guidelines.* Washington DC; 2002;10: 48–52.

Menarche and menopause

QUESTION

For young women after the menarche (the onset of menstruation), how long does it take to achieve regular ovulatory cycles and what is the risk of pregnancy during this time?

POPULATION: Young women after the menarche (the onset of menstruation).

INTERVENTION: Unprotected intercourse.

OUTCOME: Risk of pregnancy.

ANSWER

CEU guidance on contraceptive choices for young people includes a section on puberty and menarche.[1] This section states that young women having unprotected intercourse before the onset of menstruation (menarche) may be at risk of pregnancy. However, even after the menarche, anovulation is common. The median length of the first menstrual cycles is 34 days with 38% of cycles over 40 days.[2] Cycle regularity (three successive cycles within a range of 10 days with none of the three cycles shorter than 20 days or longer than 40 days) was apparent in only 19% of girls within three cycles of the onset of menstruation. By the 20th menstrual cycle, ovulation occurs in up to 50% of young women.[3] No evidence was identified on the use of hormonal contraception prior to menarche, or the risk of pregnancy for young women during this period. As a good practice point, the CEU recommends that young women should be advised against the use of regular hormonal contraception before menarche. If they are sexually active, condoms should be advocated.

QUESTION

For women aged over 50 years using hormonal contraception, what are the risks from pregnancy, when can contraception be safely discontinued, and how can the menopause be confirmed?

POPULATION: Women aged over 50 years.

INTERVENTION: Hormonal contraception.

OUTCOME: i) Risks of pregnancy; ii) Safety of contraception; iii) Confirmation of menopause.

ANSWER

Risks of pregnancy:

- Pregnancy in women over the age of 40 years is associated with increased maternal morbidity and mortality, increased perinatal mortality, chromosomal abnormalities (particularly Down syndrome), a miscarriage rate of up to 30% and an abortion rate of over 50%.

Continuation of contraception:

- The *WHO Medical Eligibility Criteria for Contraceptive Use* advises that, in women over 40 years old, the benefits of using combined oral contraception generally outweigh the risks (WHO category 2). WHO comments that the risk of cardiovascular disease increases with age and may increase with combined oral contraceptive use, but in the absence of other adverse clinical conditions, combined pills can be used until menopause. In women over 45 years, the progestogen-only pill can be used without restriction (WHO category 1).

- The FFPRHC has published a review on perimenopausal contraception.[4] It advises that the combined pill is suitable for women aged over 35 years, who are healthy non-smokers with no cardiovascular risk factors. Neither current nor previous pill use was found to be associated with increased risk of myocardial infarction in non-smokers.[5] Combined pill use can benefit perimenopausal women in terms of a reduction in menorrhagia, dysmenorrhoea, premenstrual syndrome, dysfunctional uterine bleeding and menopausal symptoms, and can reduce the risk of epithelial ovarian cancer and endometrial carcinoma. There is also some evidence to suggest that combined pill use in perimenopausal women will stabilise, or even increase, bone mass.[6] However, there is an increased risk of breast carcinoma diagnosis in women using combined pills compared with never-users and this risk is increased with increasing age.[7] Risk of cardiovascular disease also increases with combined pill use and age.[8] The progestogen-only pill has few contraindications in perimenopausal women and is highly effective if used correctly. However, women may experience poor cycle control with this method.

- The majority of women will be anovulatory by the age of 54 years. It is accepted practice however, to advise women that contraception is required until 1 year after the last menstrual bleed if they are over the age of 50 years, and for 2 years if under the age of 50 years.[4] Advising women regarding their contraceptive requirements if they are amenorrhoeic with vasomotor symptoms can be fairly straightforward. Difficulties arise when women have been using hormonal contraception or are using HRT. It is advisable to stop combined oral contraception at around age 50 years, and to change to another contraceptive method until menopausal status can be determined.

Confirmation of menopause:

- The menopause can only be diagnosed in retrospect and is identified when a woman has been period-free for 12 months. The average age of the menopause is 50.8 years.

- Hormonal profiles for estradiol and luteinising hormone are not helpful in diagnosing the menopause. In women not using hormones, FSH levels can be helpful and if greater than 30 iu/l on two or more occasions at least 6 weeks apart are suggestive of ovarian failure. Reference ranges for FSH can vary between laboratories and local references ranges should be identified. Levels of FSH can be checked while a woman is using the progestogen-only pill. If women are using either combined oral contraception or hormone replacement therapy, FSH measurement is inaccurate and can only be useful if the woman discontinues sex steroid hormones. There is no evidence regarding the correct timing for FSH measurement following the discontinuation of hormones. The FFPRHC review suggests testing FSH levels no earlier than 6 weeks after discontinuing hormones and repeating the level 1–2 months later.[4] Repeated FSH levels greater than 30 iu/l are suggestive of ovarian failure. If this is found to be the case, women should be advised to continue with contraception for a further year if over the age of 50 years and for a further 2 years if under the age of 50 years. If menstruation recurs after discontinuing hormones, or if FSH is less than 30 iu/l, contraception will need to be continued and reviewed at a later date.

- Women using the progestogen-only pill may present with vasomotor symptoms. A woman aged 50 years has three choices regarding use of the progestogen-only pill. Firstly, FSH levels can be checked. If FSH levels are greater than 30 iu/l and, when repeated 1 year later, again greater than 30 iu/l, the pill can be stopped. Secondly, a woman may choose to stop the pill and use a barrier method of contraception; if she remains amenorrhoeic for one year, the barrier method can be discontinued. Thirdly, she may choose to continue the progestogen-only pill to age 54 years, at which time it can be stopped as natural loss of fertility is assumed.

QUESTION

How long should women stop taking estrogen-containing preparations (combined oral contraceptives or HRT) before blood tests for the gonadotrophins (FSH and LH), thyroid function and clotting studies (activated partial thromboplastin time and prothrombin time) can usefully be performed?

POPULATION: Women using estrogen-containing preparations.

INTERVENTION: Duration of cessation.

OUTCOME: Restoration of physiological gonadotrophin, thyroid function and clotting status.

ANSWER

Gonadotrophins:

- A review of perimenopausal contraception states that there is 'no clinical evidence determining the best time to test FSH levels after stopping the combined pill to determine if the menopause has occurred'.[4] The reviewers suggest first testing 6 weeks after discontinuing combined pills and then 1–2 months later. Repeated measurements of FSH greater than 30 iu/l with amenorrhoea are suggestive of ovarian failure but alternative contraception should be continued for a further year and then discontinued only if menstruation has not resumed.

- The American Association of Clinical Endocrinologists' *Medical Guidelines for Clinical Practice for Management of Menopause* advocate FSH determination in diagnosing the menopause. They state that, in perimenopausal women who are using estrogen-containing contraceptives, measurement should be made after discontinuation for 'several weeks to months'.[9] However, a guideline from the Institute for Clinical Systems

Improvement states that measuring FSH levels on day 6 or 7 of the pill-free week of perimenopausal women taking combined pills and documenting FSH greater than 25 miu/ml suggests that contraception is no longer necessary.[10] However, this guideline does recognise that 7 days off the combined pill may not be adequate to allow the rebound of FSH in the truly menopausal woman.

Thyroid function tests:

● Low-dose combined pills have no restriction for their use in the situation of simple goitre, hyperthyroidism and hypothyroidism. Hyperestrogenic states such as pregnancy cause increased amounts of total thyroxine (T4) but no change in the amount of circulating free hormone (FT4). This effect is mediated by estrogen causing an increase in the production of thyroid-binding globulin by the liver.

● Within the restricted search undertaken, the CEU could not find any evidence to guide clinicians on when thyroid function tests should be performed after stopping estrogen-containing preparations to ensure physiological levels are measured.

Clotting studies:

● Hyperestrogenic states such as pregnancy are associated with hyper-coagulability with increased levels of factors VII, VIII, X and also a marked increase in fibrinogen levels due to increased synthesis.[11] Several studies have shown altered coagulation factors with the use of the combined pill or HRT.[12,13]

● Within the restricted search undertaken, the CEU could not find any evidence to guide clinicians on when clotting studies should be performed after stopping estrogen-containing preparations to ensure physiological levels are measured.

QUESTION

For postmenopausal women with vasomotor symptoms are progestogens effective in treating these symptoms?

POPULATION: Postmenopausal women.

INTERVENTION: Use of progestogens.

OUTCOME: Improvement in vasomotor symptoms.

ANSWER

A systematic review of menopausal symptoms concluded that progestogens reduce vasomotor symptoms.[14] No good quality evidence was identified on other outcomes, such as quality of life. Trials were limited by study size and duration. Five randomised controlled trials were identified which included 257 women recruited to trials lasting less than 12 months. Women taking progestogens noted a significant reduction in vasomotor symptoms compared to women using placebo. There are limited safety data on progestogen-only replacement therapy as it is rarely given without estrogen. One cohort study identified a five-fold increase in risk of VTE in women under the age of 50 years who were using high doses of progestogens for gynaecological problems, primarily menstrual complaints.[15]

The Canadian Breast Cancer Initiative suggests alternatives to HRT.[16] Placebo-controlled trials have shown significant improvement in vasomotor menopausal symptoms with alternative treatments such as vitamin E, clonidine and venlafaxine.

QUESTION

For a woman with a personal or family history of VTE, does prescription of HRT carry any particular risks or benefits?

POPULATION: Women with a personal or family history of VTE.
INTERVENTION: HRT.
OUTCOME: Risks and benefits.

ANSWER

A number of authoritative bodies, including the RCOG, have provided guidance on HRT and VTE.[17] This guidance has been updated in the light of the findings of the US Women's Health Initiative study, published in 2002. The CEU recommends that practitioners follow the RCOG guidance in relation to women with a personal or family history. In brief, oral HRT should be avoided in a woman with a personal history of VTE. If, after counselling, such a woman strongly wishes HRT for symptom relief, then the transdermal route is preferred. For women with a family history, thrombophilia screening is advised prior to prescription of HRT. Should a thrombophilic trait be identified, HRT is not generally recommended. However, the significance of the various thrombophilias vary and should such a woman strongly wish HRT, expert haematological advice should be sought on an individual basis.

QUESTION

For women using vaginal estrogen cream, is progestogen supplementation required to prevent endometrial stimulation?

POPULATION: Women using an estrogen-containing vaginal cream.

INTERVENTION: Addition of a progestogen.

OUTCOME: Prevention of endometrial stimulation.

ANSWER

Vaginal estrogens have been shown to improve symptoms of vaginal atrophy and dryness but they do not provide overall hormone replacement.[18] Systemic absorption of vaginally administered estrogen is low.[19] Guidance on the menopause recommends that low-dose estradiol creams, pessaries and vaginal tablets should usually only be used short-term (up to 3 months) before they are reviewed, reduced or stopped. Although only minimal systemic absorption occurs, if used long-term, consideration should be given to the addition of a progestogen to prevent endometrial stimulation. Conjugated estrogens are more likely to have an effect on circulating estrogen levels and endometrial stimulation than other estrogen preparations.[20] Vaginal rings are licensed for 2 years continuous use without the need for progestogen replacement. Alternative treatments for vaginal dryness such as the bio-adhesive Replens MD® may be alternatives to topical estrogens and have been shown to improve symptoms of vaginal atrophy.[21]

QUESTION

For women using the LNG-IUS to provide the progestogen component of combined HRT, is the risk of breast cancer different from that in women using other forms of combined HRT?

POPULATION: Women using combined HRT.

INTERVENTION: LNG-IUS for progestogen component.

OUTCOME: Risk of breast cancer.

ANSWER

The LNG-IUS effectively protects against endometrial hyperplasia and is well tolerated when used as the progestogen component of combined HRT. The association between HRT and breast cancer remains controversial.

A 5-year, follow-up study from Finland has confirmed that the LNG-IUS is well tolerated and effective as the progestogen component of HRT when combined with either oral or transdermal estradiol valerate.[22] Of 40 women enrolled to use the IUS as part of combined HRT, 32 were still using the IUS after 5 years. At removal, all endometria were suppressed with a strong progestin effect. This study provided no data on circulating levels of hormone or on breast status.

An authoritative review from Denmark has summarised currently available evidence on HRT and breast cancer, with a focus on the role of progestins.[23] This paper summarised the key findings of the most recent pooled analysis from the Collaborative Group on Hormonal Factors in Breast Cancer.[24] The summary estimate for the risk of breast cancer after five years of HRT use is 1.35 (95% CI 1.21–1.49). A summary of the latest studies indicates that the risk of breast cancer is increased for combined therapy compared with estrogen alone. In addition, the testosterone-like progestins (including levonorgestrel), particularly when administered in a continuous treatment regimen, may be more harmful with respect to the risk of breast cancer. One study found a five-fold increased breast cancer risk with continuous treatment with nor-ethisterone acetate or levonorgestrel after more than 10 years of use as compared with never-users of HRT.[25] However, the postulated increased risk of breast cancer should not be over-emphasised. A further review from Australia states that a clear consensus regarding the relationship between HRT and breast cancer risk cannot yet be drawn from the existing data.[26]

The CEU literature searches revealed no direct evidence indicating that the LNG-IUS has an impact on breast cancer risk which is any different from other forms of progestogen therapy. However, on theoretical grounds, because of the low systemic absorption, one would expect a lesser effect.

QUESTION

For women taking tamoxifen, can serum gonadotrophin levels be used to diagnose the menopause, or are results affected by tamoxifen use?

POPULATION:	**Women using tamoxifen.**
INTERVENTION:	**Gonadotrophin measurement.**
OUTCOME:	**Assessment of menopausal status.**

ANSWER

Tamoxifen is a non-selective estrogen receptor modulator, which is used in the treatment of breast cancer; it has a profound effect on the hypothalamo-pituitary-ovarian axis.[27] Premenopausal women under the age of 40 years, with breast cancer who had very short courses of chemotherapy (4 months) with tamoxifen, followed by tamoxifen alone, can resume ovulatory menstrual cycles and contraception may still be required in this young age group.

The average age of the menopause is 50.8 years. Although the menopause is usually diagnosed on a clinical basis, hormonal profiles can be used. Measurement of FSH can be helpful if women are not using hormones.[4] Advising women regarding their contraceptive requirements if they are amenorrhoeic with vasomotor symptoms can be straightforward. Difficulties arise when women have been using hormonal contraception, are currently using HRT or are using tamoxifen.

Evidence suggests that tamoxifen has an effect on the hypothalamo-pituitary axis and can reduce FSH levels thus making them less useful as an aid to the diagnosis of the menopause than in women not using hormones.

QUESTION

For women using tamoxifen who are prescribed a gonadotrophin agonist (Zoladex®, AstraZeneca) can they be assured that this combination is contraceptive?

POPULATION: Women using tamoxifen.

INTERVENTION: Concurrent use of a gonadotrophin agonist (Zoladex).

OUTCOME: Contraceptive efficacy

ANSWER

No direct evidence was identified regarding the contraceptive effect of tamoxifen and gonadotrophin releasing hormone agonist (Zoladex) in combination. Gonadotrophin-releasing hormone (GnRH) administered as monthly injection results in a transient stimulation of gonadotrophin 2 hours after the initial depot injection, followed by a sustained suppression of luteinising hormone, while FSH levels returned to the normal range.[28] Plasma estradiol concentrations fall to early follicular phase values within 14 days. Twice-weekly monitoring of urinary estrone glucuronide and pregnanediol demonstrated inhibition of ovulation and almost complete suppression of follicular activity throughout the course of treatment.

Women using tamoxifen may also have been treated with chemotherapy for breast cancer, which in itself has an affect on ovulation and fertility. The anti-estrogen tamoxifen will reduce FSH levels in women who have chemotherapy-induced amenorrhoea but will have less effect on FSH levels if ovulatory failure has not been induced by chemotherapy.

Tamoxifen and clomifene citrate and are both anti-estrogens. An observational study of women suffering infertility was performed to analyse the effects of clomifene citrate on cervical mucus.[29] Clomifene citrate significantly altered cervical mucus quality and late luteal endometrial morphology despite physiological levels of ethinylestradiol and progesterone. The effects of anti-estrogens on cervical mucus and sperm-cervical mucus interaction in patients with infertility have been investigated. The use of clomifene and tamoxifen resulted in a significant reduction in cervical mucus quality and sperm-cervical mucus interaction as judged by the distance travelled by spermatozoa.

Although a combination of tamoxifen and GnRH agonists is likely to be contraceptive, neither are licensed as contraceptives and non-hormonal contraception is advised during use of Zoladex.

References

1. Faculty of Family Planning and Reproductive Health Care. Contraceptive choices for young people. *J Fam Plann Reprod Health Care* 2004;30:237–51.
2. World Health Organization Task Force on Adolescent Reproductive Health. World Health Organization multicentre study on menstrual and ovulatory patterns in adolescent girls. II. Longitudinal study of menstrual patterns in the early postmenarcheal period, duration of bleeding episodes and menstrual cycles. *J Adolesc Health Care* 1986;7:236–44.
3. Borsos A, Lampe L, Balogh A, Csoknyay J, Ditroi F, Szekely P. Ovarian function after the menarche and hormonal contraception. *Int J Gynecol Obstet* 1988;27:249–53.
4. Brechin S, Gebbie A. *Faculty Aid to Continued Professional Development Topic; FACT, Perimenopausal Contraception*. London: FFPRHC; 2000.
5. Croft P, Hannaford P. Risk factors for adults myocardial infarction in women - evidence from RCGP Oral Contraceptive Study. *BMJ* 1989;298:165–8.
6. DeCherney A. Bone-sparing properties of oral contraceptives. *Am J Obstet Gynecol* 1996;174:15–20.
7. Collaborative Group on Hormonal Factors in Breast Cancer. Breast cancer and hormonal contraceptives: collaborative reanalysis of individual data on 53 297 women with breast cancer and 100 239 women without breast cancer form 54 epidemiological studies. *Lancet* 1996;347:1713–27.
8. Faculty of Family Planning and Reproductive Health Care Clinical Effectiveness Unit. First prescription of combined oral contraception. *J Fam Plann Reprod Health Care* 2003;29:209–22.
9. American Association of Clinical Endocrinologists. Medical guidelines for clinical practice for management of menopause. *Endocrine Practice* 1999;5:355–66.

10. Institute for Clinical Systems Improvement. *Hormone Replacement Therapy: Collaborative Decision Making and Management.* 2001 [www.icsi.org/display_file.asp?FileId=161&title=Menopause%20and%20Hormone%20Re placement%20Therapy(HT):%20Collaborative%20Decision%20Making%20and%20Mana gement].

11. Ramsay M. Appendix of Normal Values. In: James DK, Steer P, Weiner CP, Gonik B, editors. *High Risk Pregnancy: Management Options.* London: WB Saunders; 1994. p. 1259–92.

12. Demirol A, Baykal C, Kirazli S, Ayhan A. Effects of hormone replacement on hemostasis in spontaneous menopause. *Menopause* 2001;8:135–40.

13. Levine AB, Teppa J, McGough B, Cowchock FS. Evaluation of the prethrombotic state in pregnancy and in women using oral contraceptives. *Contraception* 1996;53:255–7.

14. Rymer J, Morris EP. Extracts from "Clinical Evidence": Menopausal symptoms. *BMJ* 2000;321:1516–19.

15. Vasilakis C, Jick H, Melero-Montes MD. Risk of idiopathic thromboembolism in users of progestagens alone. *Lancet* 1999;354:1610–11.

16. Pritchard KI, Khan H, Levine M. Clinical practice guidelines for the care and treatment of breast cancer: 14. The role of hormone replacement therapy in women with a previous diagnosis of breast cancer. *Can Med Assoc J* 2002;166:1017–22.

17. Royal College of Obstetricians and Gynaecologists. *Hormone Replacement Therapy and Venous Thromboembolism.* Guideline No. 19. London: RCOG; 2004.

18. Department of Health. *Menopause.* Prodigy guidance. London: DoH; 1997.

19. Notelovitz M, Funk S, Nanavati N, Mazzeo M. Estradiol absorption from vaginal tablets in postmenopausal women. *Obstet Gynecol* 2002;99:556–62.

20. Luisi M, Franchi F, Kicovic PM. A group comparative study of effects of Ovestin cream versus Premarin cream in post-menopausal women with vaginal atrophy. *Maturitas* 1980;2:311–19.

21. Nachtigall LE. Comparative study: Replens versus local estrogen in menopausal women. *Fertil Steril* 1994;61:178–80.

22. Varila E, Wahlstrom T, Rauramo l. A 5-year follow-up study on the use of a levonorgestrel intrauterine system in women receiving hormone replacement therapy. *Fertil Steril* 2001;76:969–73.

23. Stahlberg C, Pedersen AT, Lynge E, Ottesen B. Hormone replacement therapy and risk of breast cancer: the role of progestins. *Acta Obstet Gynecol Scand* 2003;82:335–44.

24. Collaborative Group on Hormonal Factors in Breast Cancer. Breast cancer and hormone replacement therapy. Collaborative reanalysis of data from 51 epidemiological studies of 52 705 women with breast cancer and 108 411 women without breast cancer. *Lancet* 1997;350:1047–59.

25. Magnusson C, Baron JA, Correia N, Bergstrom R, Adami HO, Persson I. Breast-cancer risk following long-term oestrogen and oestrogen-progestin-replacement therapy. *Int J Cancer* 1999;81:339–44.

26. Eden J. Progestins and breast cancer. *Am J Obstet Gynecol* 2003;188:1123–31.

27. Jordan VC, Fritz NF, Tormey DC. Endocrine effects of adjuvant chemotherapy and long-term tamoxifen administration on node-positive patients with breast cancer. *Cancer Res* 1987;47:624–630.

28. West CP, Baird DT. Suppression of ovarian activity by Zoladex depot (ICI 118630), a long acting luteinizing hormone releasing hormone agonist analogue. *Clin Endocrinol* 1987;26:213–20.

29. Massai MR, De Ziegler D, Lesobre V, Bergeron C, Frydman R, Bouchard P. Clomiphene citrate affects cervical mucus quality and endometrial morphology independently of the changes in plasma hormone levels induced by multiple follicular recruitment. *Fertil Steril* 1993;59:1179–88.

Miscellaneous gynaecological problems

QUESTION

Are patients with Shwachman–Diamond syndrome at increased risk of premature menopause?

POPULATION:	Women with Shwachman–Diamond syndrome.
INTERVENTION:	None.
OUTCOME:	Premature menopause.

ANSWER

Shwachman–Diamond syndrome is a rare, autosomal recessive disorder, characterised by exocrine pancreatic insufficiency, short stature and bone marrow dysfunction.[1,2] Additional clinical features include metaphyseal dysostosis, epiphyseal dysplasia, immune dysfunction, liver disease, growth failure, renal tubular defects, insulin dependent diabetes mellitus and psychomotor restriction. With regard to reproductive function it can be associated with delayed puberty.[1] The literature reports only one case of a successful term pregnancy.[3]

The natural history of the disease is not yet defined, although calculated projected median survival of patients is more than 35 years.[4]

Unfortunately the CEU was unable to identify any information concerning the risk of premature menopause in women with Shwachman–Diamond syndrome. We would advise consultation with your regional genetics department for guidance.

QUESTION

For women with premenstrual syndrome, are Vitamin B6 with evening primrose oil and spironolactone safe and effective treatments for breast tenderness or mood swings and premenstrual bloating, respectively?

POPULATION:	Women with premenstrual syndrome.
INTERVENTION:	Vitamin B6 and evening primrose oil for breast tenderness and mood swings; Spironolactone for premenstrual bloating.
OUTCOME:	Safety and efficacy.

ANSWER

Premenstrual syndrome (PMS) is a disorder characterised by the cyclical recurrence of specific symptoms during the luteal phase of the menstrual cycle. It affects millions of women typically between the ages of 25 and 35 years. Up to 85% of menstruating women report at least one premenstrual symptom, while 2–10% report debilitating symptoms. Women who are severely affected may also meet the criteria for premenstrual dysphoric disorder. The various symptoms of PMS are classified into three broad groups:

Group 1: Behavioural symptoms such as fatigue or cravings for particular foods.

Group 2: Psychological symptoms such as irritability, tearfulness or mood swings.

Group 3: Physical symptoms such as headaches, breast tenderness, abdominal pain and bloating.

Although the exact cause of PMS remains unknown, symptoms often improve when ovulation is suppressed.[5] Evidence suggests that PMS may occur in women with serotonin deficiency who are especially sensitive to progesterone.[6] Other studies suggest that symptoms may relate to prostaglandin deficiency caused by the inability of these women to convert linolenic acid to prostaglandin precursors.[7] There may also be a genetic component to the disorder.[8]

A systematic review of randomised controlled trials which looked at the effects of B6 supplementation alone or through a multivitamin on PMS, found that all trials reported improvement in symptoms.[9] Trials suggested that doses of B6 up to 100 mg/day are likely to be of benefit in treating PMS and premenstrual depression. In June 1997, the Food Advisory Committee, advised by the Department of Health's Committee on Toxicity of Chemicals in Food, Consumer Products and the Environment recommended that B6 should either be categorised as a food supplement (limited to a daily dose of 10 mg) or a medicine (available at higher doses). The Committee felt that there was a risk in taking high doses of B6 and based this on a 1987 study which showed that over half of a group of 172 women taking doses of B6 averaging 117 mg/day for periods of 3 years developed paraesthesia, hyperaesthesia, weakness or numbness which reversed when the vitamin was stopped.[10] The methodology of this study has subsequently been criticised. The Scientific Committee on Food of the European Commission concluded that a tolerable upper intake level of B6 for adults was 25 mg/day.

Evening primrose oil is made from the crushed seeds of the plant *Oenothera biennis* and is a source of gamma linolenic acid, which is needed for the production of prostaglandin PGE_1 that has anti-inflammatory and blood thinning properties. A systematic review of randomised controlled trials involving evening primrose oil demonstrated mild relief of breast tenderness but suggested lack of overall benefit in PMS.[7]

Spironolactone is a competitive aldosterone antagonist which increases sodium excretion while reducing potassium loss at the distal renal tubule. It is used for the treatment of congestive cardiac failure, hepatic cirrhosis with ascites and oedema, malignant ascites, nephrotic syndrome and the diagnosis and treatment of primary aldosteronism. Spironolactone may cross the placental barrier and feminisation has been observed in male animal fetuses exposed to the drug. It is therefore advisable that women taking the drug use a reliable form of contraception. Administered during the luteal phase of the cycle, 25–100 mg/day spironolactone has been shown to relieve symptoms due to fluid retention including breast tenderness and bloating.[11]

QUESTION

For women using norethisterone 5 mg daily to treat menorrhagia, can this also provide effective contraception?

POPULATION: Women with menorrhagia.
INTERVENTION: Norethisterone 5 mg daily.
OUTCOME: Contraceptive efficacy.

ANSWER

The Summary of Product Characteristics for norethisterone tablets (5 mg) states that they are licensed for use in women with metropathia haemorrhagica, premenstrual syndrome, dysmenorrhoea, endometriosis, menorrhagia, disseminated carcinoma of the breast and for postponement of menstruation. The Summary suggests that for the treatment of menorrhagia, norethisterone (5 mg) should be given two to three times daily from days 19–26 of the cycle. However, more effective management is achieved by higher doses: 5–10 mg three times daily from day 5–28 of the cycle.[12–14] Norethisterone tablets are not licensed for use as contraception.

The progestogen-only pills, Micronor and Noriday® (Pharmacia) each contain 0.35 mg of norethisterone. Therefore, theoretically norethisterone tablets 5 mg would work as contraception as they contain a higher dose of norethisterone. However, they are not licensed for this use. Similarly, Micronor HRT is likely to be contraceptive but is not licensed for this use.

The CEU advises that norethisterone 5 mg used to treat menorrhagia is not licensed to be used as a contraceptive. Condoms could be used in addition. Consideration should be given to alternative hormonal methods of contraception which may themselves improve bleeding. In line with RCOG guidance, if menorrhagia persists following failed medical treatment, investigation is required.[13,14]

QUESTION

For women with dysmenorrhoea, is the use of NSAIDs associated with a significant risk of gastrointestinal adverse effects?

POPULATION: Women with dysmenorrhoea.
INTERVENTION: NSAIDs.
OUTCOME: Risk of gastrointestinal adverse effects.

ANSWER

Dysmenorrhoea is cyclical lower abdominal or pelvic pain, which may also radiate to the back and thighs, occurring before and/or during menstruation. Dysmenorrhoea affects 40–70% of women of reproductive age and affects daily activities in up to 10% of women.

NSAIDs work by inhibiting prostaglandin synthesis through the inhibition of cyclo-oxygenase (COX) pathways and are thus effective in the management of dysmenorrhoea or menorrhagia. NSAIDs are contraindicated in those with a history of hypersensitivity to aspirin or any other NSAID.[15] Particular risk factors for NSAID gastrointestinal adverse effects include: a clinical history of gastroduodenal ulcer, gastrointestinal bleeding, or gastroduodenal perforation, concomitant use of medications which may increase gastrointestinal adverse effects such as corticosteroids and anticoagulants, cardiovascular disease, renal or hepatic impairment, diabetes, or hypertension or a requirement for the prolonged use of maximum recommended doses of standard NSAIDs.

The Committee on Safety of Medicines has advised that NSAIDs associated with the lowest risk should generally be preferred, to start at the lowest recommended dose, not to use more than one oral NSAID at a time and to remember that all NSAIDs are contraindicated in individuals with peptic ulceration.[15]

A Cochrane Review by Majoribanks *et al.*[16] compared all NSAIDs used in the treatment of primary dysmenorrhoea with placebo, with paracetamol, and with each other, in terms of safety and efficacy. This review included 63 randomised controlled trials, 19 of parallel design and 44 of crossover design.

Seventeen trials reported gastrointestinal adverse effects such as nausea and vomiting, and seven studies (involving a total of 432 women) were deemed suitable for meta-analysis. Four studies compared naproxen against placebo and other studies compared aspirin, fenoprofen, indomethacin and mefenamic acid against placebo. There was no statistically significant difference between the reported incidence of gastrointestinal adverse effects between any one NSAID and placebo, or between NSAIDs overall and placebo. Data on adverse effects were also extracted from ten studies comparing piroxicam, ketoprofen, indomethacin, naproxen and mefenamic acid with placebo. Six of these trials did not find any statistically significant difference for adverse events between different NSAIDs and four did not report if their results were statistically significant.

The absence of a statistically significant association when all the trials were included may be related to short-term use of NSAIDs prior to and during menstruation. The review advises that women taking NSAIDs for dysmenorrhoea should take the medication with food to minimise gastrointestinal adverse effects.

QUESTION

> **Is there any evidence that metformin has an effect on weight gain and mood swings in PCOS?**

POPULATION: Women with polycystic ovary syndrome.

INTERVENTION: Metformin.

OUTCOME: Effect on weight gain and mood swings.

ANSWER

PCOS usually presents with anovulatory infertility, oligomenorrhoea or hyperandrogenic problems such as hirsutism and acne. Although it is associated with obesity, it is also diagnosed in women with a normal BMI. Polycystic ovary syndrome is linked to a number of metabolic disturbances including type II diabetes (non-insulin-dependent) and possibly atherosclerotic conditions.

Until recently, management has largely been directed at the presenting symptom (infertility, hirsutism etc) but attention is now also being focused on the longer term implications of the metabolic disturbances.[17] Metformin is a biguanide whose primary mechanism of action is to reduce hepatic gluconeogenesis, which is pathologically increased in insulin resistance. In non-diabetic, insulin resistant patients, metformin does not produce hypoglycaemia.[18]

There have been several studies which have considered the effect on weight of treating PCOS with metformin. However, these trials involved small numbers of women with a maximum follow up of 12 months use of metformin. Several small studies into the effect of metformin on BMI or waist–hip ratio in women with PCOS have suggested that treatment may result in weight loss. In two of these studies, metformin treatment was combined with a controlled diet and it is not clear whether the weight loss resulted from the dietary restrictions or metformin.[19,20] In one study, BMI decreased at 3 months but the decrease was not significant at 6 months.[21] It has been suggested that weight loss after using metformin may be associated with a secondary effect of metformin by inhibiting intestinal glucose absorption.[22]

Other trials have suggested that metformin has no effect on weight loss in PCOS.[23–25] Five reviews of the evidence for the effectiveness of metformin on weight loss were identified. Harborne et al.[26] reviewed six studies and found that BMI decreased by an average of 4.4%. Haas et al.[27] concluded that metformin produces small, but significant, reductions in BMI. Barbieri[28] concluded that metformin plus a low calorie diet may be associated with greater weight loss than low calorie diet alone in obese women with PCOS.

However, two other reviews, including a large systematic review by the Cochrane Collaboration, concluded that although it could be predicted that metformin therapy should result in weight loss there is no evidence that metformin reduces body mass index or waist–hip ratio in women with PCOS.[29,30]

Only one paper was identified that considered the effect of metformin treatment for PCOS on depression.[31] In this case review, a woman with PCOS and major depressive disorder was reported to have remission of her depression while being treated with metformin and spironolactone. No trial data could be found to support this anecdotal report.

There are no published studies on the long-term effects or safety of using metformin in non-diabetic patients with PCOS. The RCOG has issued guidance that the 'long term use of insulin-sensitising agents for avoidance of metabolic complications of PCOS cannot as yet be recommended'.[17] The Cochrane review concludes that there are no data regarding the safety of metformin in long-term use in young women.[30]

QUESTION

For men with erectile dysfunction, is there any association with solvent abuse?

POPULATION: Sexually active men.
INTERVENTION: Solvent abuse.
OUTCOME: Erectile dysfunction.

ANSWER

Erectile dysfunction is defined as a total inability to achieve erection, an inconsistent ability to do so or a tendency to sustain only brief erections. Causes include disease, injury, adverse effects of drugs or psychological factors. Erectile dysfunction incidence increases with age, around 5% of men aged 40 years and between 15% and 25% of men aged 65 years experience it.[32]

A comparative study of 199 men with erectile dysfunction was undertaken to determine if environmental agents are risk factors. Erectile dysfunction was assessed by nocturnal tumescence and rigidity. The men were classified as having normal erections, irregular pattern of erections (short episodes) or flat erectile pattern. Exposure to solvents was determined as a risk factor for flat erectile pattern (odds ratio 12.2; 95% CI 1.2–124.8), and irregular (short episodes) erectile pattern (odds ratio 2.1; 95% CI 0.3–17.9).[33] Numbers were small and consequently the confidence intervals are wide.

Despite extensive searching, the CEU could find no other information on an association between solvent abuse and erectile dysfunction.

References

1. Rothbaum R, Perrault J, Vlachos A, Cipolli M, Alter BP, Burroughs S, *et al*. Shwachman-Diamond syndrome: report from an international conference. *J Pediatr* 2002;141:266–70.
2. Smith OP. Shwachman-Diamond syndrome. *Semin Hematol* 1903;39:95–102.
3. Alter BP, Kumar M, Lockhart LL, Sprinz PG, Rowe TF. Pregnancy in bone marrow failure syndromes: Diamond-Blackfan anaemia and Shwachman-Diamond syndrome. *Br J Haematol* 1999;107:49–54.
4. Dror Y, Freedman MH. Shwachman-diamond syndrome. *Br J Haematol* 2002;118:701–13.
5. Freeman EW, Sondheimer SJ, Rickels K. Gonadotropin-releasing hormone agonist in the treatment of premenstrual symptoms with and without ongoing dysphoria: a controlled study. *Psychopharmacol Bull* 1997;33:303–9.
6. Kessel B. Premenstrual syndrome. Advances in diagnosis and treatment. *Obstet Gynecol Clin North Am* 2000;27:625–39.
7. Budeiri D, Li Wan Po A, Dornan JC. Is evening primrose oil of value in the treatment of premenstrual syndrome? *Control Clin Trials* 1996;17:60–8.

8. Kendler KS, Karkowski LM, Corey LA, Neale MC. Longitudinal population-based twin study of retrospectively reported premenstrual symptoms and lifetime major depression. *Am J Psychiatry* 1998;155:1234–40.
9. Wyatt K, Dimmock PW, O'Brien PM. Efficacy of vitamin B-6 in the treatment of premenstrual syndrome: systematic review *BMJ* 1999; 318:1375–81.
10. Dalton K, Dalton MJT. Characteristics of pyridoxine overdose neuropathy syndrome. *Acta Neurol Scand* 1987;76:8–11.
11. Wang M, Hammarback S, Lindhe BA, Backstrom T. Treatment of premenstrual syndrome by spironolactone: a double-blind, placebo-controlled study. *Acta Obstet Gynecol Scand* 1995;74:803–8.
12. Lethaby A, Irvine G, Cameron I. Cyclical progestogens for heavy menstrual bleeding. *Cochrane Database Syst Rev* 1998;(2).
13. Royal College of Obstetricians and Gynaecologists. *The Initial Management of Menorrhagia*. National Evidence-Based Clinical Guidelines. London: RCOG Press; 1998.
14. Royal College of Obstetricians and Gynaecologists. *The Management of Menorrhagia in Secondary Care*. National Evidence-Based Clinical Guidelines. London: RCOG Press; 1999.
15. Committee on Safety of Medicines. Non-steroidal anti-inflammatory drugs (NSAIDs) and gastrointestinal (GI) safety. *Curr Probl Pharmacovigilance* 2002;28:1–2.
16. Marjoribanks J, Proctor ML, Farquhar C. Nonsteroidal anti-inflammatory drugs for primary dysmenorrhoea. *Cochrane Database Syst Rev* 2003;(1).
17. Royal College of Obstetricians and Gynaecologists. *Long-term Consequences of Polycystic Ovary Syndrome*. Guideline No. 33. London: RCOG; 2003.
18. Baillargeon JP, Iuorno MJ, Nestler JE Insulin sensitizers for polycystic ovary syndrome. *Clin Obstet Gynecol* 2003;46:325–40.
19. Glueck CJ, Papanna R, Ping W, Goldenburg N, Sieve-Smith L. Incidence and treatment of metabolic syndrome in newly referred women with confirmed polycystic ovarian syndrome. *Metabolism* 2003;52:908–15.
20. Glueck CJ, Wang P, Fontaine R, Tracy T, Sieve-Smith L. Metformin to restore normal menses in oligo-amenorrhoeic teenage girls with polycystic ovary syndrome (PCOS). *J Adolesc Health* 2001; 29:160–9.
21. Morin-Papunen L, Vauhkonen I, Koivunen R, Ruokonen A, Martikainen H, Tapanainen JS. Metformin versus ethinyl estradiol-cyproterone acetate in the treatment of nonobese women with polycystic ovary syndrome: a randomized study. *J Clin Endocrinol Metab* 2003;88:148–56.
22. Cicek NM, Bala A, Celik C, Akyurek C. The comparison of clinical and hormonal parameters in PCOS patients treated with metformin and GnRH analogue. *Arch Gynecol Obstet* 2002;268:107–12.
23. Morin-Papunen LC, Koivunen RM, Ruokonen A, Martikainen HK. Metformin therapy improves the menstrual pattern with minimal endocrine and metabolic effects in women with polycystic ovary syndrome. *Fertil Steril* 1998;69:691–6.
24. Moghetti P, Castello R, Negri C, Tosi F, Perrone F, Cputo M, *et al*. Metformin effects on clinical features, endocrine and metabolic profiles and insulin sensitivity in polycystic ovary syndrome: a randomized, double blind placebo controlled 6 month trial, followed by open long term clinical evaluation. *J Clin Endocrinol Metab* 2000;85:139–46.
25. Chou KH, von Eye CH, Capp E, Spritzer PM. Clinical, metabolic and endocrine parameters in response to metformin in obese women with polycystic ovary syndrome: a randomized, double-blind and placebo-controlled trial. *Horm Metab Res* 2003;35:86–91.

26. Harborne L, Fleming R, Lyall H, Norman J, Sattar N. Descriptive review of the evidence for the use of metformin in polycystic ovary syndrome. *Lancet* 2003;361:1894–901.

27. Haas DA, Carr BR, Attia GR. Effects of metformin on body mass index, menstrual cyclicity and ovulation induction in women with polycystic ovary syndrome. *Fertil Steril* 2003;79:469–81.

28 Barbieri RL. Metformin for the treatment of polycystic ovary syndrome. *Obstet Gynecol* 2003;101:785–93.

29. Awartani KA, Cheung AP. Metformin and polycystic ovary syndrome: a literature review. *J Obstet Gynaecol Can* 2002;24:393–401.

30. Lord JM, Flight IHK, Norman RJ. Insulin-sensitising drugs (metformin, trioglitazone, rosiglitazone, pioglitazone, D-chiro-inositol) for polycystic ovary syndrome. *Cochrane Database Syst Rev* 2004;(1).

31. Rasgon NL, Carter MS, Elman S, Bauer M, Love M, Korenman SG. Common treatment of polycystic ovarian syndrome and major depressive disorder: case report and review. *Curr Drug Targets Immune Endocr Metabol Disord* 2002;2:97–102.

32. National Kidney and Urologic Diseases Information Clearing House. *Erectile dysfunction*. Bethesda, MD: NKUDIC; 2003 [http://kidney.niddk.nih.gov/kudiseases/pubs/impotence/index.htm].

33. Oliva A, Giami A, Multigner L. Environmental agents and erectile dysfunction: a study in a consulting population. *J Androl* 2002;23:546–50.

SECTION THREE

Contraception for women with medical disorders

10 DRUG INTERACTIONS WITH CONTRACEPTION

Liver enzyme-inducers

QUESTION

For women using liver enzyme-inducers, does the injection interval for DMPA need to be reduced to maintain contraceptive efficacy? (Two similar enquiries.)

POPULATION: Women using liver enzyme-inducers.
INTERVENTION: DMPA.
OUTCOME: Efficacy.

ANSWER

The Summary of Product Characteristics for DMPA states that no dose adjustment is required for women using liver enzyme-inducing drugs. DMPA can therefore be given every 12 weeks to women using liver enzyme-inducers and does not need to be given more frequently.

Serum concentrations of medroxyprogesterone acetate following an intramuscular injection are high.[1] Concentrations of medroxyprogesterone acetate fall 2–3 months after administration but these concentrations are still higher than that required to maintain anovulation. Liver enzyme-inducers increase the rate of metabolism of medroxyprogesterone acetate, but serum concentrations are still sufficient to maintain anovulation. No reduction in contraceptive efficacy is apparent.

The CEU suggests that women using progestogen-only injectables (such as DMPA) are advised that using liver enzyme-inducers will not reduce contraceptive efficacy and the injection interval does not need to be shortened.[2]

QUESTION

For women taking liver enzyme-inducers, is the etonogestrel implant an effective method of contraception? (Three similar enquiries.)

POPULATION:	**Women taking liver enzyme-inducers.**
INTERVENTION:	**The etonogestrel implant.**
OUTCOME:	**Efficacy.**

ANSWER

Drugs which induce liver enzymes can potentially reduce the clinical effect of other medication. Women should be informed that the contraceptive efficacy of progestogen-only implants may be reduced by liver enzyme-inducers.[2] Concentrations of etonogestrel released daily via the subdermal implant are very low.[3] Liver enzyme-inducers can reduce these low serum concentrations further. Contraceptive efficacy may be reduced if serum concentrations are insufficient to inhibit ovulation. No direct evidence was identified to support this, although pregnancies have been documented in women using Norplant and phenytoin.[4]

The Summary of Product Characteristics for the etonogestrel implant (Implanon) advises that women using liver enzyme-inducers should use a barrier method of contraception in addition to the implant and continue use of the barrier method for 4 weeks after the liver enzyme-inducer is discontinued. Women using enzyme-inducers long term are advised to have the implant removed and use an alternative method of contraception. This advice is supported by the CEU.[2] The *WHO Medical Eligibility Criteria* advises that for women using liver enzyme-inducing drugs (some anti-epileptics, rifampicin, anti-retrovirals), the risks of using a progestogen-only implant generally outweigh the benefits (WHO category 3).

The CEU advises that women using a liver enzyme-inducer in the short term may choose to continue with a progestogen-only implant.[2] Additional contraceptive protection, such as condoms, is advised until 4 weeks after the enzyme inducer has been stopped. Information should be given on the use of alternative contraception if liver enzyme-inducers are to be used long term.

QUESTION

For women taking liver enzyme-inducers, do they affect the etonogestrel implant and DMPA in the same way?

POPULATION: Women using liver enzyme-inducers.

INTERVENTION: Etonogestrel implant or DMPA.

OUTCOME: Efficacy.

ANSWER

The Summary of Product Characteristics for DMPA states that the injection should be given at 12-week intervals. No dose adjustment should be made for women using liver enzyme-inducing drugs. The Summary of Product Characteristics for the etonogestrel implant (Implanon) states that a barrier method of contraception in addition to the implant is advised when liver enzyme-inducing drugs are used. Barrier contraception should be continued until 4 weeks after the enzyme-inducers are discontinued. This advice for women using liver enzyme-inducers and progestogen-only implants or injectables is supported by the CEU.[2]

Concentrations of etonogestrel released daily via the subdermal implant are very low (0.27 ng/ml).[3] The use of liver enzyme-inducers can reduce the low serum concentrations further. Contraceptive efficacy may be reduced if serum concentrations are insufficient to inhibit ovulation. No direct evidence was identified to support this although pregnancies have been documented in women using Norplant and phenytoin.[4]

The CEU suggests that liver enzyme-inducers increase the metabolism of progestogens administered via intramuscular injection or subdermal implants. The contraceptive efficacy of the injectable is not reduced, as serum concentrations are still sufficient to maintain anovulation despite an increased rate of metabolism. It is suspected that serum concentrations of etonogestrel would be reduced and ovulation a risk.

QUESTION

For women who are using liver enzyme-inducers, what dose of progestogen-only emergency contraception is advised? (Eight similar enquiries.)

POPULATION: Women who are using liver enzyme-inducers.

INTERVENTION: Progestogen-only emergency contraception.

OUTCOME: Efficacy.

ANSWER

It has been standard practice in the UK to increase the dose of levonorgestrel by 50% for women using liver enzyme-inducers. Progestogen-only emergency contraception was given as 1.5 mg levonorgestrel at first presentation followed by 0.75 mg 12 hours later.[5] There is no direct evidence to confirm if this increase in dose is required.

A large randomised controlled trial by the WHO supported the use of a single dose of levonorgestrel (1.5 mg levonorgestrel) rather than a divided regimen for women not using liver enzyme-inducers.[6] No direct evidence is available on the efficacy of a 50% increased dose taken as a single 2.25 mg of levonorgestrel for women using liver enzyme-inducers.

The BNF advises that women using liver enzyme-inducers can take 2.25 mg of levonorgestrel as a single dose. Neither of these increased regimens recommended for women using liver enzyme-inducers is licensed.[7]

The CEU recommends that women using liver enzyme-inducers who require emergency contraception should be advised: to take a total dose of 2.25 mg as soon as possible and within 72 hours of unprotected sex; that this use is outside the product licence; and about the alternative use of a copper IUD.[2] It is up to individual clinicians to decide which regimen may suit the woman better, a single or a divided regimen in terms of issues such as compliance.

Update to Answer

Subsequent to preparing this response, the 0.75-mg tablet of levonorgestrel has been discontinued and replaced by a 1.5-mg tablet. Thus, the option of giving a total dose of 2.25 mg is no longer available. Advice from the FFPRHC is to give 3 mg as a single dose if only 1.5-mg tablets are available.

QUESTION

For women taking liver enzyme-inducers who have a high BMI and a family history of DVT, which contraceptive methods are safe and effective?

POPULATION:	Women taking liver enzyme-inducers who have a high BMI and a family history of DVT.
INTERVENTION:	Contraception.
OUTCOME:	Efficacy and safety.

ANSWER

Liver enzyme-inducers increase the metabolism of estrogen and progestogen. The intended duration of use of a liver enzyme-inducer (short or long term) may influence contraceptive choice. Patient preference, medical risk factors (such as risk of VTE with increased BMI) and family history should be taken into account when helping women choose an appropriate contraceptive.

Women can be advised that the efficacy of progestogen-only injectables, the LNG-IUS and the copper IUD are unaffected by liver enzyme-inducers. These methods may be preferred if using liver enzyme-inducers long term.[2]

If combined oral contraception is used by a woman taking liver enzyme-inducers, a regimen containing at least 50 micrograms of ethinylestradiol daily is required[2] with additional contraceptive protection, such as condoms, until 4 weeks after the liver enzyme inducer is stopped. Condoms are advised with contraceptive patch use but no recommendation is made regarding an increase in dose. Progestogen-only pills are not advised for women using liver enzyme-inducers. Progestogen-only implants should be used with additional contraceptive protection, such as condoms, but an alternative method considered if the liver enzyme inducer is to be used long term.

The *WHO Medical Eligibility Criteria for Contraceptive Use* states that women with a family history of first-degree relatives with VTE (DVT or pulmonary embolism) may have unrestricted use of progestogen-only contraception (oral, injectable, implant or intrauterine) and non-hormonal methods (WHO category 1). The benefits of using combined hormonal contraception for women with a family history of VTE generally outweigh the risks (WHO category 2). The CEU recommends that women with a family history of VTE in a first-degree relative aged less than 45 years be advised that the risks of combined hormonal contraceptive use generally outweigh the benefits.

The WHO suggests that women with a high BMI may use any type of hormonal contraception. Nevertheless, because of an increased risk of VTE associated with combined hormonal contraceptive use, the CEU suggests using non-estrogen containing contraception for women with a BMI over 30.[8-10]

The CEU recommends that for a woman using a liver enzyme inducer, who has a BMI over 30 and family history of VTE in a first-degree relative aged under 45 years, the progestogen-only injectable, the LNG-IUS or a copper IUD may be suitable first-line options. Other methods may be considered after counselling.

QUESTION

For women taking bosentan for pulmonary arterial hypertension which methods of contraception are safe and effective?

POPULATION:	**Women taking bosentan for pulmonary arterial hypertension.**
INTERVENTION:	**Methods of contraception.**
OUTCOME:	**Safety and efficacy.**

ANSWER

Bosentan is an endothelin receptor antagonist for the treatment of primary pulmonary hypertension.[11] It is teratogenic and embryotoxic and women on this therapy should use an effective form of contraception. In addition, pregnancy itself may pose a health risk for women with primary pulmonary hypertension.

Bosentan is a significant inducer of liver enzymes (CYP3A4 and CYP2C9) resulting in a 50% reduction in steady-state plasma concentrations of bosentan itself and unknown reductions in the plasma concentrations of other drugs. The Summary of Product Characteristics for bosentan advises that for women of childbearing potential, it is important to exclude and avoid pregnancy during use of bosentan and hormonal contraception must not be relied upon. No published evidence was identified to support this.

In the absence of any published evidence to guide contraceptive choices for women using bosentan, the advice from the CEU is the same as that given to women using other liver enzyme-inducers.[2] Women can be advised that the efficacy of progestogen-only injectables, the LNG-IUS and the copper IUD are unaffected. These methods may be preferred if using liver enzyme-inducers long term.

If combined oral contraception is used, a regimen containing at least 50 micrograms ethinylestradiol daily is required[2] with additional contraceptive protection, such as condoms, until 4 weeks after the liver enzyme-inducer is stopped. Condoms are advised with contraceptive patch use but no recommendation is made regarding an increase in dose. Progestogen-only pills are not advised for women using liver enzyme-inducers. Progestogen-only implants should be used with additional contraceptive protection, such as condoms, but an alternative method considered if the liver enzyme inducer is to be used long term.

If intrauterine methods are used, antibiotic prophylaxis would not be indicated for insertion unless the woman had a previous history of bacterial endocarditis or a prosthetic heart valve.[12,13] The *WHO Medical Eligibility Criteria* advises that the use of combined hormonal contraception by women with pulmonary hypertension (secondary to valvular heart disease) poses an unacceptable health risk. It is likely that this advice would be similar for women with primary pulmonary hypertension.

The CEU recommends that for women using bosentan for pulmonary hypertension, the progestogen-only injectable, the LNG-IUS or a copper IUD may be suitable first-line options. Other methods may be considered after counselling but combined hormonal contraception should be avoided.

QUESTION

> **For women with pulmonary hypertension using bosentan and awaiting a lung transplant are either the progestogen-implant or the LNG-IUS effective forms of contraception?**

POPULATION: Women with pulmonary hypertension using bosentan and awaiting a lung transplant.

INTERVENTION: Progestogen-implant or the LNG-IUS.

OUTCOME: Safety and efficacy.

ANSWER

Bosentan is teratogenic and embryotoxic and is a significant inducer of liver enzymes.

The *WHO Medical Eligibility Criteria* addresses contraceptive choices for women with pulmonary hypertension secondary to valvular heart disease. It is likely that the advice would be the same for women with primary pulmonary hypertension. Women may have unrestricted use of the progestogen-only implant (WHO category 1) and the contraceptive benefits of using a copper IUD or the LNG-IUS generally outweigh the risks (WHO category 2).

In the absence of any published evidence to guide contraceptive choices for women with primary pulmonary hypertension using bosentan, the CEU advice is the same as for women using other liver enzyme-inducers. Women can be advised that the efficacy of progestogen-only injectables, the LNG-IUS, and the copper IUD are unaffected by liver enzyme-inducers. The CEU advises that these methods may be preferred and do not need to be discontinued before surgery. Combined hormonal contraception is not advised.

QUESTION

For women using oral contraception does the use of lansoprazole affect the metabolism of contraceptive steroids or reduce contraceptive efficacy?

POPULATION: Women using oral contraceptives.

INTERVENTION: Lansoprazole.

OUTCOME: Drug interaction and contraceptive efficacy.

ANSWER

The Summary of Product Characteristics for lansoprazole advises that studies have indicated that it is a weak inducer of cytochrome P450, and may interact with drugs metabolised by the liver. Caution has been advised if women take oral contraceptives concomitantly with lansoprazole.

One randomised study looked at the effects of lansoprazole on the bioavailability of a low-dose oral contraceptive containing 30 micrograms ethinylestradiol and 150 micrograms levonorgestrel.[14] All 24 women received the oral contraceptive over two cycles from days 1 to 21, with the remaining 7 days being pill-free. Lansoprazole (60 mg/day) or placebo was given for 21 days with the oral contraceptive. No significant alteration in plasma ethinylestradiol or levonorgestrel concentrations was detected. No evidence on lansoprazole and other contraceptive methods has been identified. Lack of evidence however may not exclude any adverse interaction. Nevertheless, at present the CEU advises that women should be counselled about theoretical concerns that lansoprazole may reduce the efficacy of hormonal contraception but that there is lack of evidence to support this.

QUESTION

For women using progestogen-only contraceptive implants, does use of a proton pump inhibitor, lansoprazole, reduce contraceptive efficacy?

POPULATION: Women using progestogen-only implants.

INTERVENTION: Proton pump inhibitors.

OUTCOME: Reduced contraceptive efficacy.

ANSWER

Proton pump inhibitors (omeprazole, esomeprazole, lansoprazole, pantoprazole and rabeprazole) are used to treat gastric and duodenal ulcers, gastro-oesophageal reflux disease, oesophagitis or NSAID-associated ulcers.[9]

The Summary of Product Characteristics for the proton pump inhibitor lansoprazole suggests that it is a weak liver enzyme inducer and caution is advised when used with oral contraceptives owing to its potential to reduce contraceptive efficacy. Evidence identified does not support this. The effects of lansoprazole on the bioavailability of a low-dose combined oral contraceptive were investigated in a randomised study.[14] The results showed that women did not experience any significant alteration in plasma ethinylestradiol or levonorgestrel concentrations. No evidence was identified on use of progest-ogen-only implants and proton pump inhibitors.

The CEU advises that women should be counselled that lansoprazole may potentially reduce efficacy of hormonal contraception but that there is lack of evidence to support this. There is no evidence that the proton pump inhibitor lansoprazole reduces the efficacy of progestogen-only implants; but this does not exclude an effect. After counselling, some women may choose to use condoms in addition to the implant for the duration of lansoprazole use.

QUESTION

For women using lansoprazole who need progestogen-only emergency contraception is there evidence of a drug interaction?

POPULATION: Women using lansoprazole.

INTERVENTION: Progestogen-only emergency contraception.

OUTCOME: Drug interaction and efficacy.

ANSWER

The Summary of Product Characteristics for lansoprazole advises that lanso-prazole is a weak inducer of cytochrome P450 and may interact with drugs metabolised by the liver. Caution was advised for women who take oral contraceptives and lansoprazole.

Although it has been established clinical practice in the UK to increase the dose of levonorgestrel by 50% for women using liver enzyme-inducers, there is no direct evidence to support this. For women using known potent liver enzyme-inducers (anti-epileptics, anti-retrovirals, rifampicin, griseofulvin) the CEU recommends that women who require emergency contraception should be advised: to take a total dose of 3 mg as soon as possible and within 72 hours of unprotected sex; that this use is outside the product licence; and about the alternative use of a copper IUD.[2]

The CEU found no evidence to support an increase in the dose of progestogen-only emergency contraception for women using the proton pump inhibitor lansoprazole (a weak enzyme inducer).

References

1. Oritz A, Hirol M, Stanczyk FZ, Goebelsmann U, Mishell DR. Serum medroxyprogesterone acetate (MPA) concentrations and ovarian function following intramuscular injection of depo-MPA. *J Clin Endocrinol Metab* 1977;44:32–8.
2. Faculty of Family Planning and Reproductive Health Care Clinical Effectiveness Unit. Drug interactions with hormonal contraception. *J Fam Plann Reprod Health Care* 2005;31:139–50.
3. Makarainen L, van Beek A, Tuomivaara L, Asplund B, Bennink HC. Ovarian function during the use of a single contraceptive implant: Implanon compared with Norplant. *Fertil Steril* 1998;69:714–21.
4. Haukkamaa M. Contraception by Norplant subdermal capsules is not reliable in epileptic patients on anticonvulsant treatment. *Contraception* 1986;33:559–65.
5. Faculty of Family Planning and Reproductive Health Care Clinical Effectiveness Unit. Emergency Contraception. *J Fam Plann Reprod Health Care* 2003;29:9–16.
6. von Hertzen H, Piaggio G, Ding J, Chen J, Song Si, Bartfai G *et al*. Low dose mifepristone and two regimens of levonorgestrel for emergency contraception: a WHO multicentre randomised trial. *Lancet* 2002;360:1803–10.
7. Faculty of Family Planning and Reproductive Health Care Clinical Effectiveness Unit. The use of contraception outside the terms of the product licence. *J Fam Plann Reprod Health Care* 2005;31:225–41.
8. Farmer RDT, Lawrenson RA, Todd JC, Williams TJ, MacRae KD, Tyrer F, *et al*. A comparison of the risks of venous thromboembolic disease in association with different combined oral contraceptives. *Br J Pharmacol* 2000;49:580–90.
9. Jick H, Kaye JA, Vasilakis-Scaramozza C, Jick SS. Risk of venous thromboembolism among users of third generation oral contraceptives compared with users of oral contraceptives with levonorgestrel before and after 1995: cohort and case–control analysis. *BMJ* 2000;321:1190–5.
10. Lidegaard O, Edstrom B, Kreiner S. Oral contraceptives and venous thromboembolism: a five year national case–control study. *Contraception* 2002;65:187–96.
11. Kobrin I. Bosentan therapy for pulmonary hypertension [www.fda.gov/ohrms/dockets/ac/01/slides/3775S2_01_ACTELION/sld001.htm.].
12. Faculty of Family Planning and Reproductive Health Care Clinical Effectiveness Unit. The Copper Intrauterine Device as long-term contraception. *J Fam Plann Reprod Health Care* 2004;30:29–42.
13. Faculty of Family Planning and Reproductive Health Care Clinical Effectiveness Unit. The levonorgestrel-releasing intrauterine system (LNG-IUS) in contraception and reproductive health. *J Fam Plann Reprod Health Care* 2004;30:99–109.
14. Fuchs W, Sennewald R, Klotz U. Lansoprazole does not affect the bioavailability of oral contraceptives. *Br J Clin Pharm* 1994;38:376–80.

Antibiotics

Liver enzyme-inducing antibiotics

QUESTION

For women on the progestogen-only pill who are taking rifampicin, is the efficacy of the pill compromised?

POPULATION: Women using the progestogen-only pill.
INTERVENTION: Rifampicin.
OUTCOME: Reduced efficacy.

ANSWER

Rifampicin and rifabutin are potent liver enzyme-inducers. Case series have identified pregnancies in women using combined oral contraception and rifampicin.[1,2]

A non-blind, randomised controlled trial provided evidence that rifampicin may reduce efficacy of combined hormonal contraception.[3] The pharmacokinetics of ethinylestradiol and norethisterone were altered by both rifampicin and rifabutin. Serum concentrations of ethinylestradiol and norethisterone were decreased. In addition, irregular bleeding was common; and serum concentration of FSH and luteinising hormone were increased. Nevertheless, ovulation was not identified. Other studied have shown evidence of ovulation in women using rifampicin and oral contraceptives.[4-6]

The CEU advises that rifampicin is a potent liver enzyme inducer and use of progestogen-only pills is not generally advised. If rifampicin is to be used short term (such as for prophylaxis of meningitis) women may choose to continue with the progestogen-only pill but additional contraception, such as condoms, is advised until 4 weeks after the rifampicin is stopped. If rifampicin is to be used long term, women should be advised to consider a contraceptive method which is unaffected by its use such as progestogen-only injectables, an IUS or a copper IUD.

QUESTION

For a woman who is undergoing treatment for tuberculosis with rifampicin, ethambutol and pyridoxine and takes propylthiouracil for hyperthyroidism, is the efficacy of DMPA compromised by interaction with these drugs?

POPULATION: Women undergoing treatment for tuberculosis with rifampicin, ethambutol and pyridoxine and are taking propylthiouracil for hyperthyroidism.

INTERVENTION: DMPA.

OUTCOME: Efficacy of contraception.

ANSWER

Rifampicin is a potent liver enzyme inducer, which accelerates the metabolism of some hormonal contraceptives. Nevertheless, evidence is lacking regarding any interactions between rifampicin and progestogen-only contraceptives. This lack of evidence does not necessarily imply no effect.

Serum concentrations of medroxyprogesterone acetate following an intramuscular injection are high.[7] Concentrations of medroxyprogesterone acetate fall 2–3 months after administration but these concentrations are still more than that required to maintain anovulation. Liver enzyme-inducers increase the rate of metabolism of medroxyprogesterone acetate but serum concentrations are still sufficient to maintain anovulation. No reduction in contraceptive efficacy is apparent. The Summary of Product Characteristics for DMPA recommends that no dose adjustment be made; there is no recommendation to change the usual 12-week interval between injections for women using liver enzyme-inducers. The *WHO Medical Eligibility Criteria* recommends that the use of a progestogen-only injectable by women with hyperthyroidism is unrestricted (WHO category 1).

The CEU recommends that for a women taking rifampicin, ethambutol, pyridoxine and propylthiouracil the progestogen-only injectable contraceptive is a suitable method of contraception.

References

1. Gupta KC, Ali MY. Failure of oral contraceptive with rifampicin. *Med J Zambia* 1980;15:23.
2. Skolnick JL, Stoler BS, Katz DB, Anderson WH. Rifampicin, oral contraceptives, and pregnancy. *JAMA* 1976;236:1382.

3.   LeBel M, Masson E, Guilbert E, Colborn D, Paquet F, Allard S, *et al*. Effects of rifabutin and rifampicin on pharmacokinetics of ethinylestradiol and norethindrone. *J Clin Pharmacol* 1998;38:1042–50.

4.   Meyer BH, Muller FO, Wessels P. Lack of interaction between roxithromycin and an oral contraceptive. *Eur J Pharmacol* 1990;193:1031–2.

5.   Meyer B, Müller F, Wessels P, Maree J. A model to detect interactions between roxithromycin and oral contraceptives. *Clin Pharmacol Ther* 1990;47:671–4.

6.   Joshi JV, Joshi UM, Sankolli GM, Gupta K, Rao AP, Hazari K, *et al*. A study of interaction of a low-dose contraceptive with anti-tubercular drugs. *Contraception* 1980;21:617–29.

7.   Faculty of Family Planning and Reproductive Health Care Clinical Effectiveness Unit. Drug interactions with hormonal contraception. *J Fam Plann Reprod Health Care* 2005;31:139–50.

Non-liver enzyme-inducing antibiotics

QUESTION

For women taking flucloxacillin, is efficacy of combined oral contraception reduced? (Four similar enquiries.)

POPULATION: Women taking combined oral contraception.

INTERVENTION: Flucloxacillin.

OUTCOME: Efficacy.

ANSWER

Non-liver enzyme-inducing antibiotics can reduce the efficacy of estrogen-containing contraceptives by temporarily reducing colonic bacteria, which are involved in the enterohepatic circulation of ethinylestradiol. There is no enterohepatic circulation of progestogens and therefore absorption and contraceptive efficacy of progestogen-only contraception are unaffected by antibiotic use. Women should be informed that non-liver enzyme-inducing antibiotics can reduce the contraceptive efficacy of combined hormonal contraception but there is no reduction in the efficacy of progestogen-only methods.[1] Colonic bacteria return to normal after 3 weeks of antibiotic use. Advice regarding the use of additional contraceptive protection by women using antibiotics therefore depends on the duration of antibiotic use.

Pregnancies have been documented in women using non-liver enzyme-inducing antibiotics.[2–7] Nevertheless, case series reporting pregnancies following antibiotic use do not identify causation and the potential for bias and confounding is high. All trials investigating the use of antibiotics by women using hormonal contraception are limited by small sample size, short duration, inconsistent assessment of ovulation and failure to eliminate bias.

A combined oral contraceptive pill-user taking a short course (less than 3 weeks) of non-liver enzyme-inducing antibiotics should be advised to use additional contraceptive protection, such as condoms, during treatment and for 7 days after the antibiotic has been stopped. If fewer than seven pills are left in the pack after the antibiotics have been stopped, she should omit the pill-free interval (or discard inactive pills).[1] A woman who is an established user of non-liver enzyme-inducing antibiotics (3 or more weeks) does not require additional protection when starting combined hormonal contraception unless she changes to a different antibiotic.[1]

Traditionally, the above advice was limited to women using broad-spectrum antibiotics. However, the CEU recognises that there is confusion and lack of clarity regarding what constitutes a broad-spectrum antibiotic. For simplicity and on pragmatic grounds, the CEU recommends that this advice be applied to all non-liver enzyme-inducing antibiotics.

QUESTION

For women taking penicillin long-term, is the efficacy of combined oral contraception reduced?

POPULATION: Women taking penicillin long-term.
INTERVENTION: Combined oral contraception.
OUTCOME: Reduced efficacy.

ANSWER

Non-liver enzyme-inducing antibiotics can reduce the efficacy of estrogen-containing contraceptives by temporarily reducing colonic bacteria, which are involved in the enterohepatic circulation of ethinylestradiol.

Traditionally, advice regarding additional contraceptive measures was limited to women using broad-spectrum antibiotics. However, the CEU recognises that there is confusion and lack of clarity regarding what constitutes a broad-spectrum antibiotic. For simplicity and on pragmatic grounds, the CEU recommends that this advice be applied to all non-liver enzyme-inducing antibiotics.

QUESTION

For women using metronidazole, is the efficacy of combined oral contraception reduced?

POPULATION: Women using the antibiotic metronidazole.

INTERVENTION: Combined oral contraception.

OUTCOME: Efficacy.

ANSWER

A non-systematic review of interactions between broad-spectrum (non-enzyme-inducing) antibiotics and combined oral contraception highlighted the lack of evidence.[8] Metronidazole is a narrow-spectrum antibiotic and no interaction with combined hormonal contraception is documented. Traditionally, the advice on the use of additional contraceptive protection for pill users when taking antibiotics was limited to women using broad-spectrum antibiotics. The CEU recognises that there is confusion and lack of clarity regarding what constitutes a broad-spectrum antibiotic. For simplicity and on pragmatic grounds, the CEU recommends that this advice be applied to all non-liver enzyme-inducing antibiotics. [1]

QUESTION

For women using combined oral contraception, can metronidazole and macrolide antibiotics reduce contraceptive efficacy?

POPULATION: Women using combined oral contraception.

INTERVENTION: Metronidazole and macrolide antibiotics.

OUTCOME: Efficacy.

ANSWER

A non-systematic review of interactions between broad-spectrum (non-enzyme-inducing) antibiotics and combined oral contraception highlighted the lack of evidence.[8] Metronidazole is a narrow-spectrum antibiotic and no interactions with combined hormonal contraception are documented in the Summary of Product Characteristics. Macrolides include erythromycin and azithromycin.

Traditionally, the advice on the use of additional contraceptive protection for pill users when taking antibiotics was limited to women using broad-spectrum antibiotics. The CEU recognises that there is confusion and lack of clarity regarding what constitutes a broad-spectrum antibiotic. For simplicity and on pragmatic grounds the CEU recommends that this advice be applied to all non-liver enzyme-inducing antibiotics.[1]

QUESTION

For women using penicillin V, trimethoprim and metronidazole, can combined oral contraception be used safely?

POPULATION: Women using phenoxymethylpenicillin (previously penicillin V), trimethoprim and metronidazole.

INTERVENTION: Combined oral contraception.

OUTCOME: Safety.

ANSWER

Pregnancies have been documented in women using non-liver enzyme-inducing antibiotics.[2-7] Although the evidence does not confirm direct causation, the consequences of an unplanned pregnancy are such that the CEU advocates a cautious approach when advising women.

Traditionally, the advice on the use of additional contraceptive protection for pill users when taking antibiotics was limited to women using broad-spectrum antibiotics. The CEU recognises that there is confusion and lack of clarity regarding what constitutes a broad-spectrum antibiotic. For simplicity and on pragmatic grounds the CEU recommends that this advice be applied to all non-liver enzyme-inducing antibiotics.[1]

QUESTION

For established users of combined oral contraception who take doxycycline for malaria prophylaxis, is contraceptive efficacy reduced?

POPULATION: Women taking combined oral contraception.

INTERVENTION: Doxycycline for malaria prophylaxis.

OUTCOME: Contraceptive efficacy.

Increasingly, doxycycline is used as prophylaxis against malaria and needs to be taken for many weeks. Doxycycline does not appear to affect the pharma-cokinetics of ethinylestradiol or progestogens.[9] Nevertheless, as for other non-liver enzyme-inducing antibiotics, the CEU recommends that combined oral contraceptive pill users taking doxycycline for malaria prophylaxis should be advised to use additional contraceptive protection, such as condoms, during treatment and for 7 days after the antibiotic has been stopped.[1] If fewer than seven pills are left in the pack after the antibiotics have been stopped, she should omit the pill-free interval (or discard inactive pills). After use for 3 weeks, additional contraceptive protection can be stopped.

QUESTION

For women using combined oral contraception, are there any interactions with fluconazole?

POPULATION: Women using combined oral contraception.

INTERVENTION: Fluconazole.

OUTCOME: Drug interaction and contraceptive efficacy.

ANSWER

BNF states that interactions associated with anti-fungals (triazoles) in general relate to multiple-dose treatments rather than single doses. Unintended pregnancies associated with ketoconazole and itraconazole have been reported.[10]

A small, randomised, placebo-controlled, blinded, crossover trial showed that oral fluconazole 300 mg, a dose twice as great as that used to treat vaginal candidiasis, did not reduce serum concentrations of ethinylestradiol or progestogen: Ortho-Novum® (norethindrone and ethinyl estradiol; Ortho-McNeil Pharmaceutical – not available in the UK) or Triphasil® (ethinyl estradiol and levonorgestrel; Wyeth – not available in the UK).[11] Breakthrough bleeding has been reported in combined oral contraceptive pill users taking itraconazole[12,13] and ketoconazole[14] but no pregnancies were reported. Data for other combined hormonal contraceptives and progestogen-only contraception are lacking.

The CEU does not recommend that additional barrier contraception, such as condoms, is required when women using hormonal contraception take fluconazole.

References

1.   Faculty of Family Planning and Reproductive Health Care Clinical Effectiveness Unit. Drug interactions with hormonal contraception. *J Fam Plann Reprod Health Care*

2005;31:139–50.

2. Young LK, Farquhar CM, McCowan LME, Roberts HE, Taylor J. The contraceptive practices of women seeking termination of pregnancy in an Auckland clinic. *N Z Med J* 1994;107:189–91.

3. Bollen M. Use of antibiotics when taking the oral contraceptive pill. *Aust Fam Phys* 1995;24:928–9.

4. Dossetor J. Drug interactions with oral contraceptives. *BMJ* 1984;4:467–8.

5. Bacon JF, Shenfield GM. Pregnancy attributable to interaction between tetracycline and oral contraceptives. *BMJ* 1980;280:293.

6. Silber TJ. Apparent oral contraceptive failure associated with antibiotic administration. *J Adolesc Health Care* 1983;4:287–9.

7. Bainton R. Interaction between antibiotic therapy and contraceptive medication. *Oral Surg Oral Med Oral Pathol Oral Radiol Endod* 1986;61:453–5.

8. Weaver K, Glasier A. Interaction between broad-spectrum antibiotics and the combined oral contraceptive pill. *Contraception* 1999;59:71–8.

9. Neely JL, Abate M, Swinker M, D'Angio R. The effect of doxycycline on serum levels of ethinyl estradiol, norethindrone, and endogenous progesterone. *Obstet Gynecol* 1991;77:416–20.

10. Pillans PI. Pregnancy associated with a combined oral contraceptive and itraconazole. *N Z Med J* 1993;106:436.

11. Hilbert J, Messig M, Kuye O, Friedman H. Evaluation of an interaction between fluconazole and oral contraceptives in healthy women. *Obstet Gynecol* 2001;98:218–23.

12. Meyboom RHB, van Puijenbroek EP, Vinks MHAM, Lastdrager CJ. Disturbance of withdrawal bleeding during concomitant use of itraconazole and oral contraceptives. *N Z Med J* 1997;110:300.

13. van Puijenbroek EP, Egberts ACG, Meyboom RHB, Leufkens HGM. Signalling possible drug-drug interactions in a spontaneous reporting system: delay of withdrawal bleeding during concomitant use of oral contraceptives and itraconazole. *J Clin Pharmacol* 1999;47:689–93.

14. Kovacs I, Somos P, Hamori M. Examination of the potential interaction between ketoconazole (nizoral) and oral contraceptives with special regard to products of low hormone content (rigevidon, anteovin). *Ther Hung* 1986;34:167–70.

Immunosupressants

Ciclosporin

QUESTION

For women with psoriasis taking ciclosporin, what methods of contraception can be used effectively?

POPULATION: Women with psoriasis taking ciclosporin.
INTERVENTION: Contraception.
OUTCOME: Safety and efficacy.

ANSWER

Ciclosporin is an immunosuppressant used in a variety of medical conditions. There is no increased risk of congenital abnormalities associated with ciclosporin use. There is no evidence that ciclosporin reduces the efficacy of hormonal contraception. BNF suggests that estrogens and progestogens may inhibit the metabolism of ciclosporin and therefore cause an increase in plasma ciclosporin concentration. Women choosing a hormonal contraceptive should be monitored for any increase in ciclosporin concentration, which may lead to toxicity. The LNG-IUS works by the local release of levonorgestrel into the uterine cavity. Systemic absorption of levonorgestrel is low and, theoretically, this may not affect plasma ciclosporin concentration. The CEU was unable to find any evidence in the literature to support this hypothesis.

Despite extensive searching, the CEU could find no other evidence of any drug interaction between hormonal contraception and ciclosporin. Women who choose to use hormonal contraception should be monitored for any increase in serum concentration of ciclosporin associated with contraceptive use. Effective non-hormonal methods, such as the copper IUD, may be considered.

QUESTION

For women with renal problems taking ciclosporin, would progestogen-only contraceptives or the IUD be safe and effective methods of contraception?

POPULATION: Women with renal problems.
INTERVENTION: Progestogen-only contraception or the copper IUD.
OUTCOME: Safety and efficacy.

ANSWER

There is a range of renal diseases, some of which carry a risk of progressing to end-stage renal failure and are associated with hyperlipidaemia and a risk of cardiovascular complications. This should be taken into account when considering *WHO Medical Eligibility Criteria*.

Ciclosporin is an immunosuppressant drug which acts by reducing inflammation. There is no increased risk of congenital abnormalities associated with ciclosporin use. BNF suggests that estrogens and progestogens may inhibit the metabolism of ciclosporin and therefore cause an increase in plasma ciclosporin concentration. The *WHO Medical Eligibility Criteria* does not address contraceptive choice for women with renal problems; but advises that for women with known hyperlipidaemias and ischaemic heart disease the benefits of using the progestogen-only pill, injectable and implant generally outweigh the risks (WHO category 2). Women with known hyperlipidaemia or ischaemic heart disease may have unrestricted use of the IUD (WHO category 1).

Despite extensive searching, the CEU could find no other evidence in the literature of any drug interaction between hormonal contraceptive methods and ciclosporin.

The CEU suggests that clinicians should review contraceptive options for women with renal problems using ciclosporin on an individual basis. Patient preference, concurrent medical conditions, the risk of pregnancy, and the effect of any pregnancy on disease should be taken into account when helping these women choose contraception. Women who choose to use hormonal contraception should be monitored for any increase in serum concentration of ciclosporin associated with contraceptive use. Effective non-hormonal methods such as the copper IUD may be considered.

QUESTION

For women with nephrotic syndrome taking ciclosporin, would DMPA or the LNG-IUS provide effective contraception?

POPULATION: Women with nephrotic syndrome taking ciclosporin.
INTERVENTION: DMPA or the LNG-IUS.
OUTCOME: Efficacy.

ANSWER

Nephrotic syndrome is characterised by increased permeability of the glomerular capillary wall to macromolecules and, if persistent, may carry an increased risk of cardiovascular complications and hyperlipidaemia. The *WHO Medical Eligibility Criteria* does not address contraceptive choices for women with nephrotic syndrome. For women with known hyperlipidaemias and ischaemic heart disease, the benefits of using progestogen-only injectables or the LNG-IUS generally outweigh the risks (WHO category 2).

The CEU found no evidence in the literature of drug interactions between progestogen-only injectables or the intrauterine system and ciclosporin.

BNF advises that progestogens may inhibit the metabolism of ciclosporin and therefore cause an increase in plasma ciclosporin concentration. The intrauterine system works by local release of levonorgestrel into the uterine cavity with minimal systemic absorption. Theoretically, this may not affect plasma ciclosporin concentration. The CEU was unable to find any evidence in the literature to support this hypothesis.

The CEU suggests that clinicians should review contraceptive options for women with renal problems using ciclosporin on an individual basis. Patient preference, concurrent medical conditions, the risk of pregnancy, and the effect of any pregnancy on disease should be taken into account when helping these women choose contraception. Women who choose to use hormonal contraception should be monitored for any increase in serum concentration of ciclosporin associated with contraceptive use. Effective non-hormonal methods such as the copper IUD may be considered.

Tacrolimus

QUESTION

For women taking the immunosuppressant drug tacrolimus, are there any important interactions with hormonal contraceptives?

POPULATION: Women taking the immunosuppressant tacrolimus.
INTERVENTION: Hormonal contraception.
OUTCOME: Interaction and adverse effects.

ANSWER

Transplant recipients use the immunosuppressant drug tacrolimus. Tacrolimus is metabolised by the CYP3A family of hepatic enzymes. Drugs which inhibit or induce CYP3A enzymes may alter tacrolimus concentrations. Conversely, tacrolimus has an inhibitory effect on CYP3A-dependent metabolism and this may affect the metabolism of other drugs (including estrogen and progestogens). Drug interactions between tacrolimus and contraceptive hormones could result in increased blood concentrations of tacrolimus, leading to toxicity, or a potential reduction in the efficacy of hormonal contraception.

One study was identified which investigated the effects of a combined oral contraceptive pill containing 50 micrograms ethinylestradiol and 500 micrograms norgestrel on CYP3A activity.[1] No alteration in CYP3A activity was demonstrated. These findings suggest that theoretical concerns that a combined oral contraceptive pill might inhibit metabolism of tacrolimus leading to toxicity are unfounded. No studies were identified which investigated if tacrolimus had any effect on the efficacy of hormonal contraception.

The CEU advises that, based on current limited data, the use of hormonal contraception is unlikely to exert any detrimental effect on serum concentrations of tacrolimus. The CEU found no direct evidence regarding the impact of tacrolimus on hormonal contraceptive efficacy and women who wish to use a hormonal method of contraception should be informed of this.

QUESTION

For women taking the immunosuppressant agent tacrolimus, are there interactions with hormonal contraceptives and may the progestogen-only implant (Implanon) be used safely?

POPULATION:	Women taking the immunosuppressant drug tacrolimus.
INTERVENTION:	Hormonal contraception, implant.
OUTCOME:	Interactions and efficacy.

ANSWER

Tacrolimus is metabolised by the CYP3A family of hepatic enzymes. Potential drug interactions between tacrolimus and contraceptive hormones include an increased concentration of tacrolimus leading to toxicity or a potential reduction in the efficacy of hormonal contraception.

No studies were identified which investigated if tacrolimus had any effect on the efficacy of hormonal contraception. Nevertheless, BNF advises that women taking tacrolimus should consider non-hormonal methods first.

The CEU advises that women should be informed of the lack of evidence for interaction between tacrolimus and contraceptive hormones. Non-hormonal contraception such as a copper IUD should be considered, but if hormonal contraception is preferred, women should be informed about the lack of data.

Reference

1. Belle DJ, Callaghan JTGJC, Maya JF, Mousa O, Wrighton SA, Hall SD. The Effects of an oral contraceptive containing ethinyloestradiol and norgestrel on CYP3A activity. *J Clin Pharmacol* 2001;53:67–74.

Retinoids

QUESTION

For women who need to use isotretinoin, when should contraception be started to minimise the risk of pregnancy occurring while taking the medication?

POPULATION: Women using isotretinoin.

INTERVENTION: Use of contraception.

OUTCOME: Pregnancy prevention.

ANSWER

Isotretinoin is used in the treatment of acne vulgaris. Isotretinoin is not a liver-enzyme inducer. When used during pregnancy, isotretinoin is potentially teratogenic and causes major fetal abnormalities and an increased risk of spontaneous abortion. Women of childbearing age using isotretinoin must use an effective form of contraception and should be aware of the potential teratogenic risks. When taken orally, peak blood concentrations of isotretinoin are observed after 1–4 hours. The Summary of Product Characteristics suggests that pregnancy should be ruled out 2 weeks before a woman commences isotretinoin therapy. Isotretinoin can be started on the second or third day of the next menstrual cycle.

The CEU supports the use of an effective method of contraception 1 month prior to isotretinoin treatment, during treatment, and for 1 month after treatment is discontinued. Reversible contraceptive methods which avoid daily pill taking such as combined hormonal contraceptive patches, progestogen-only implants or injectables, or intrauterine methods may be a preferred option for some women. Nevertheless, women using isotretinoin should be offered the usual range of contraceptive options.

QUESTION

For women using isotretinoin, is the combined oral contraceptive pill an effective method of contraception?

POPULATION: Women using isotretinoin.

INTERVENTION: Combined oral contraception.

OUTCOME: Efficacy.

ANSWER

Isotretinoin, used in the treatment of acne vulgaris, is potentially teratogenic and therefore sexually active women of childbearing age using this treatment must use an effective form of contraception. The Summary of Product Characteristics suggests that pregnancy should be ruled out 2 weeks before a woman commences isotretinoin therapy and the medication can then be started on the second or third day of the next menstrual cycle. An effective method of contraception should be used 1 month prior to isotretinoin treatment, during treatment and for 1 month after treatment is discontinued.

BNF advises that tretinoin reduces the contraceptive efficacy of low dose progestogens. The CEU found no evidence of any interaction between combined hormonal contraception and isotretinoin, or evidence that any increase in pill regimen is required when taking isotretinoin.

The CEU recommends that women who wish to use a combined oral contraceptive pill can be advised to start on day 1 of the menstrual cycle. This provides immediate contraceptive protection. The WHO *Selected Practice Recommendations for Contraceptive Use* and the FFPRHC *UK Selected Practice Recommendations for Contraceptive Use* both state that a combined oral contraceptive pill can be started on day 1 and up to, and including, day 5 of the cycle without the need for additional contraceptive protection. If started after day 5, additional contraceptive protection, such as condoms or abstinence, is advised for 7 days. For women who may be forgetful pill-takers reversible methods which avoid daily pill taking such as combined hormonal contraceptive patches, progestogen-only implants or injectables, or intrauterine methods may be a preferred option.

QUESTION

For women using isotretinoin, is DMPA an effective contraceptive option?

POPULATION: Women using isotretinoin.
INTERVENTION: DMPA.
OUTCOME: Efficacy.

ANSWER

Isotretinoin is used in the treatment of acne vulgaris. Isotretinoin is potentially teratogenic and therefore sexually active women of childbearing age using it must use an effective form of contraception.

There are no known interactions between the progestogen-only injectable DMPA and isotretinoin. Women who wish to use DMPA can be advised to start on day 1 of the menstrual cycle. This provides immediate contraceptive protection. In addition, the WHO *Selected Practice Recommendations for Contraceptive Use* and the FFPRHC *UK Selected Practice Recommendations for Contraceptive Use* both state that DMPA can be started up to, and including, day 5 of the cycle without the need for additional contraceptive protection. If started after day 5, additional contraceptive protection, such as condoms or abstinence, is advised for 7 days.

QUESTION

For women using an etonogestrel subdermal implant, does use of the retinoid, acitretin, reduce contraceptive efficacy? (Two similar enquiries.)

POPULATION: Women using an etonogestrel subdermal implant.
INTERVENTION: Use of the retinoid acitretin.
OUTCOME: Reduced contraceptive efficacy.

ANSWER

From a wide literature search, no evidence was identified to suggest that the efficacy of the etonogestrel subdermal implant is reduced with the use of retinoids. Concern has been raised that retinoids may interfere with the contraceptive efficacy of oral progestogen-only contraceptive pills.[1] No reduction in the efficacy of combined oral contraception has been established with retinoid use. No evidence was identified on contraceptive efficacy with use of progestogen-only implants, injectables or the intrauterine system in women using acitretin. The Summary of Product Characteristics for acitretin recommends that an effective method of contraception should be used 1 month prior to commencing therapy, during treatment, and for at least 2 years after cessation due to its teratogenic effects. The CEU supports the use of progestogen-only implants by women using retinoids.

QUESTION

For women over the age of 35 years who smoke and take acitretin, which hormonal methods of contraception are safe and effective?

POPULATION: Women over the age of 35 years who smoke and take acitretin.
INTERVENTION: Contraception.
OUTCOME: Safety and efficacy.

ANSWER

The Summary of Product Characteristics for acitretin states that it is contra-indicated in women of childbearing potential unless an effective method of contraception is used for at least 1 month before treatment, during treatment, and for at least 2 years after treatment is stopped.

The *WHO Medical Eligibility Criteria* advises that for women over the age of 35 years who smoke, the risks of using combined oral contraception generally outweigh the benefits (WHO category 3). Progestogen-only contraception and non-hormonal methods should be considered by smokers aged over 35 years.

Oral retinoids may reduce the efficacy of the progestogen-only pill.[1] There is no direct evidence on the efficacy of progestogen-only contraception (implant, injectable and intrauterine) in women using acitretin.

The CEU advises that for smokers aged over 35 years who are using acitretin, the progestogen-only injectable, implant, or intrauterine system or a copper IUD will provide effective reversible contraception.

QUESTION

For women who use acitretin and weigh over 70 kg, can the etonogestrel implant be used safely and effectively and when should it be replaced?

POPULATION: Women who use acitretin and who weigh over 70 kg.
INTERVENTION: Progestogen-only implant.
OUTCOME: Safety and replacement.

ANSWER

The retinoid acitretin is the main metabolite of etretinate. Etretinate has a long half-life of up to 120 days, owing to its deposition in adipose tissue, hence the need for effective contraception whilst using treatment and for 2 years following treatment. Despite extensive searching, the CEU could find no evidence as to whether the efficacy of the etonogestrel implant is reduced by interaction with acitretin. The Summary of Product Characteristics for Implanon does not suggest early replacement for women weighing over 70 kg.

The CEU recommends that sexually active women using acitretin should use an effective method of contraception for at least 1 month before treatment, during treatment and for at least 2 years after treatment is stopped. A progestogen-only implant would be an appropriate choice as it provides effective reversible contraception for 3 years regardless of body weight. There is no evidence to suggest efficacy will be reduced with acitretin use.

Reference

1. Berbis P, Bun H, Geiger JM, Rognin C, et al. Acitretin (RO10–1670) and oral contraceptives: interaction study. *Arch Dermatol Res* 1988;280:388–9.

Complementary medicines

QUESTION

For women using hormonal contraception, does use of St John's wort (*Hypericum perforatum*) reduce contraceptive efficacy? (Four similar enquiries.)

POPULATION:	Women using hormonal contraception.
INTERVENTION:	St John's wort.
OUTCOME:	Efficacy.

ANSWER

St John's wort is a liver-enzyme inducer. Liver-enzyme-inducers can increase the metabolism of estrogen and progestogens. Ethinylestradiol and progestogen have a narrow therapeutic range and therefore increased metabolism and reduced bioavailability may lead to a reduction in contraceptive efficacy.

Evidence that St John's wort reduces the efficacy of hormonal contraception is of poor quality.

A prospective cohort study in men provided evidence that St John's wort increases hepatic CYP34A. Evidence exists that liver enzyme-inducers such as rifampicin, which also induce these liver enzymes, are associated with contraceptive failures.[1] Evidence suggests that St John's wort increases the metabolism of other drugs.[2-6] A small, randomised double blind trial found no evidence of ovulation when St John's wort was used by women taking a 20-microgram combined oral contraceptive pill.[7,8] An increase in breakthrough bleeding was reported by women using St John's wort.[7] No data were identified on interaction between progestogen-only methods and St John's wort.

The CSM (now the Medicines and Healthcare products Regulatory Agency) advised that St John's wort should not be used by women using indinavir, warfarin, ciclosporin, oral contraceptives, digoxin and theophylline.[9]

Although there is a lack of good-quality evidence to show a reduction in efficacy of hormonal contraception when used with St John's wort, this does not imply no association. As St John's wort is a liver enzyme-inducer, the CEU upholds advice from the CSM that women using hormonal contraception should be cautious when using St John's wort and their need for St John's wort should be re-evaluated. As for women using other liver enzyme-inducers, the CEU advises that contraceptive efficacy of: progestogen-only injectables, the LNG-IUS or copper IUD is unaffected but the efficacy of combined hormonal methods, progestogen-only pills, and implants is reduced.

QUESTION

For women who start using combined oral contraception immediately after stopping St John's wort (*Hypericum perforatum*), is contraceptive efficacy reduced?

POPULATION: Women who have just stopped using St John's wort.
INTERVENTION: Combined oral contraception.
OUTCOME: Contraceptive efficacy.

ANSWER

Liver enzyme-inducers increase the metabolism of ethinylestradiol and progestogen. Ethinylestradiol and progestogen have a narrow therapeutic range and therefore increased metabolism and reduced bioavailability may lead to a reduction in contraceptive efficacy. St John's wort induces liver enzymes but is less potent than other liver enzyme-inducers such as rifampicin.[1] It can take up to 4 weeks for liver enzymes to return to normal following the discontinuation of rifampicin. It is unclear how long it takes for liver enzymes return to normal after St John's wort is stopped.

The WHO *Selected Practice Recommendations for Contraceptive Use* and the FFPRHC *UK Selected Practice Recommendations for Contraceptive Use* state that in general, the combined oral contraceptive pill can be started at any time in the menstrual cycle. If started up to, and including, day 5, additional contraceptive protection is not required. If started after day 5, additional contraceptive protection, such as condoms, is advised for 7 days.

For women using a combined oral contraceptive pill and a liver enzyme-inducer, a contraceptive pill regimen containing at least 50 micrograms ethinyl-estradiol daily is required[10] with additional contraceptive protection, such as condoms, until 4 weeks after the liver enzyme-inducer is stopped.

For women who discontinue St John's wort and start combined oral contra-ception, the CEU advises that a regimen containing at least 50 micrograms of ethinylestradiol daily is required[10] with additional contraceptive protection, such as condoms, until 4 weeks after St John's wort is stopped. After this time a standard 30-microgram ethinylestradiol regimen may be used.

QUESTION

For women requesting contraception who are using the liver enzyme-inducer St John's wort, is the efficacy of the progestogen-only pill compromised? (Two similar enquiries.)

POPULATION: Women using St John's wort.
INTERVENTION: The progestogen-only pill.
OUTCOME: Reduced efficacy due to drug interactions.

ANSWER

St John's wort is a liver enzyme-inducer. Metabolism of progestogens is increased by liver enzyme-inducers. There is a potential for reduced efficacy of progestogen-only pills.[10] Contraceptive choice will depend on patient preference and the intended duration of use of the liver enzyme-inducer.

The CEU recommends that women using the progestogen-only pill and St John's wort should be advised to consider stopping St John's wort. If St John's wort is continued, a contraceptive method which is unaffected by use of liver enzyme-inducers (for example progestogen-only injectable, the LNG-IUS or a non-hormonal method) is advised.

QUESTION

Can women using the progestogen-only implant use St John's wort and still have effective contraception?

POPULATION: Women using the progestogen-only implant.
INTERVENTION: St John's wort.
OUTCOME: Efficacy.

ANSWER

St John's wort is a liver enzyme inducer. Metabolism of progestogens is increased by liver enzyme-inducers. The efficacy of progestogen-only implants is reduced by liver enzyme-inducers.[10] Contraceptive choice will depend on patient preference and the intended duration of use of the liver enzyme-inducer. No specific drug interaction studies have been performed with the etonogestrel implant (Implanon). No case reports were identified of pregnancies in women using the etonogestrel implant when taking St John's wort.

The CEU advises that if a liver enzyme-inducer is to be taken for a short time, the progestogen-only implant may be continued or initiated with additional contraceptive protection, such as condoms, during use of the liver enzyme inducer and for 4 weeks after it has been discontinued. If, after evaluation, St John's wort is to be continued long-term then another method of contraception which is unaffected by liver enzyme-inducers (progestogen-only injectable, the LNG-IUS or a non-hormonal method) is advised.

QUESTION

For women who are using liver enzyme-inducers such as St John's wort, what dose of progestogen-only emergency contraception is advised? (Seven similar enquiries.)

POPULATION: Women who are using liver enzyme-inducers.
INTERVENTION: Progestogen-only emergency contraception.
OUTCOME: Pregnancy prevention.

ANSWER

It is standard practice in the UK to advise a 50% increase in the dose of progestogen-only emergency contraception for women using liver enzyme-inducers (such as rifampicin, some anti-epileptics and anti-retrovirals and St John's wort).[11] Evidence to support the need for this increased regimen (1.5 mg followed 12 hours later by a single 0.75-mg dose) is lacking. This increased regimen is outside the terms of the product licence.[11]

A large randomised controlled trial by the WHO found that for women not using liver enzyme-inducers, a single 1.5-mg dose of levonorgestrel is equivalent to a divided regimen. The product licence was altered to reflect this new evidence.

BNF now supports the use of 2.25 mg of levonorgestrel as a single regimen for women using liver enzyme-inducers. There is no new evidence to support this regimen.

The CEU advises that for women taking liver enzyme-inducers who require emergency contraception the total dose should be increased by 50% to a 2.25-mg total dose. Women should be informed that there is no evidence to support this increased regimen and the use of a copper IUD should also be offered, as this is not affected by liver enzyme-inducing drugs. Clinicians may decide on an individual basis if the increased regimen is taken as a single or a divided dose.

Update to Answer

Subsequent to preparing this response, the 0.75-mg tablet levonorgestrel has been discontinued and replaced by a 1.5-mg tablet. Thus, the option of giving a total dose of 2.25 mg is no longer available. Advice from the FFPRHC is to give 3 mg as a single dose if only 1.5-mg tablets are available.

QUESTION

For women using oral contraception, which herbal remedies other than St John's wort act as liver enzyme-inducers and may potentially reduce contraceptive efficacy?

POPULATION: Women using oral contraception.

INTERVENTION: Herbal remedies apart from St John's wort.

OUTCOME: Reduced efficacy.

ANSWER

Evidence on the properties and drug interactions of herbal medicine is limited. St John's wort is the only complementary medicine which is known to be a liver enzyme inducer. *Vitex agnus castus* is believed by some herbal experts to have the potential to interfere with oral contraceptives, menopausal HRT and other hormone replacement medication.[12,13] Nevertheless, evidence was not found to support this.

The CEU found no evidence of interaction between hormonal contraception and complementary medicines other than St John's wort.

QUESTION

For women using *Vitex agnus castus* (chasteberry), is there any evidence of interaction with hormonal contraception?

POPULATION: Women using *Vitex agnus castus* (chasteberry).

INTERVENTION: Hormonal contraception.

OUTCOME: Interactions.

ANSWER

Vitex agnus castus contains several active chemical constituents although it is not yet known which of the constituents are responsible for its clinical effects.[14] Some herbal experts believe that *Vitex agnus castus* could interfere with oral contraceptives, menopausal HRT and other hormone replacement medication.[12,14] The CEU conducted a detailed search of the literature but was unable to find any direct evidence on interactions between *Vitex agnus castus* and hormonal contraception. Indirect evidence from studies that have looked at the effects of *Vitex agnus castus* on the menstrual cycle in women with premenstrual syndrome, breast pain and infertility is presented here.

A randomised controlled trial on the efficacy of a *Vitex agnus castus* preparation (Strotan® capsules, Strathmann, Germany) versus placebo in the treatment of luteal phase defects due to latent hyperprolactinaemia has been reported.[15] After 3 months of treatment, prolactin concentrations were reduced in the treatment group, the length of the luteal phase was normal and luteal progesterone synthesis was normal. Two women in the treatment group conceived during the study and no adverse effects were observed. A randomised controlled trial investigated the effects of *Vitex agnus castus* in 96 women with fertility disorders such as secondary amenorrhoea, luteal phase insufficiency and idiopathic infertility.[16] Pregnancy, spontaneous menstruation in women with amenorr-hoea, and improved concentrations of luteal hormones were achieved more often by women taking the preparation than by the control group.

It is evident from these studies, that *Vitex agnus castus* has an effect on the endocrine system. No clinical trials are available to establish how the efficacy of hormonal contraception would be affected by concurrent use with *Vitex agnus castus*. The CEU can only advise that until more evidence is available, women should be informed that the efficacy of their contraceptive method may possibly be affected by drug interaction with this herbal remedy.

QUESTION

For women who take starflower oil, is efficacy of the etonogestrel-only implant reduced?

POPULATION:	**Women taking starflower oil.**
INTERVENTION:	**The etonogestrel-only implant.**
OUTCOME:	**Efficacy.**

ANSWER

Starflower (borage) oil is a rich source of gamma linolenic acid which is an important intermediary in the metabolic conversion of linolenic acid into prostaglandin E_1. The CEU was unable to find any evidence of an interaction between starflower oil and any method of hormonal contraception. The CEU can only advise that at present there is no evidence to suggest any drug interaction between starflower oil and hormonal contraception.

References

1. Skolnick JL, Stoler BS, Katz DB, Anderson WH. Rifampicin, oral contraceptives, and pregnancy. *JAMA* 1976;236:1382
2. Ruschitzka F, Meier PJ, Turina M, Lüscher TF, Noll G. Acute heart transplant rejection due to Saint John's wort. *Lancet* 2000;355:548–9.
3. Piscitelli SC, Burstein AH, Chaitt D, Alfaro RM, Falloon J. Indinavir concentrations and St John's Wort. *Lancet* 2000;355:547.
4. Mai I, Kruger H, Budde K, John A, Brockmoller J, Neumayer HH, *et al*. Hazardous pharmacokinetic interaction of Saint John's Wort (*Hypericum perforatum*) with the immunosuppressant cyclosporin. *Int J Clin Pharmacol Ther* 2000;38:500–2.
5. Bauer A, Stormer E, Johne A, Kruger H, Budde K, Neumayer HN, *et al*. Alterations in cyclosporin A pharmacokinetics and metabolism during treatment with St John's wort in renal transplant patients. *Br J Clin Pharmacol* 2003;55:203–11.

6. Breidenbach T, Hoffman MW, Becker T. Drug interaction of St John's wort with cyclosporin. *Lancet* 2000;355:1912.
7. Pfrunder A, Schiesser M, Gerber S, Haschke M, Bitzer J, Drewe J. Interaction of St John's Wort with low-dose oral contraceptive therapy: a randomized controlled trial. *Br J Clin Pharmacol* 2003;56:683–90.
8. Hall SD, Wang Z, Huang S, Hamman MA, Vasavada N, Adigun AQ, *et al*. The interaction between St John's wort and an oral contraceptive. *Clin Pharmacol Ther* 2003;74:525–35.
9. Committee on Safety of Medicines. Reminder: St John's wort (*Hypericum perforatum*) interactions. *Curr Probl Pharmacovigilance* 2000;26:1–8.
10. Faculty of Family Planning and Reproductive Health Care Clinical Effectiveness Unit. Drug interactions with hormonal contraception. *J Fam Plann Reprod Health Care* 2005;31:139–50.
11. Faculty of Family Planning and Reproductive Health Care Clinical Effectiveness Unit. The use of contraception outside the terms of the product licence. *J Fam Plann Reprod Health Care* 2005;31:225–41.
12. Newell CA, Anderson LA, Phillipson JD. *Herbal Medicines: A Guide for Health-care Professionals*. London: Pharmaceutical Press; 1996. p. 296.
13. McGuffin M, Hobbs C, Upton R, Goldberg A. *American Herbal Products Association's Botanical Safety Handbook*. Boca Raton. New York: CRC Press; 1997.
14. Gardiner P. Longwood Herbal Task Force, Centre for Holistic Pediatric Education and Research. Chasteberry (*Vitex agnus castus*) [www.longwoodherbal.org/vitex/vitex.pdf].
15. Milewicz A, Gejdel E, Sworen H, Sienkiewicz K, Jedrzejak J, Teucher T, *et al*. Vitex agnus castus extract in the treatment of luteal phase defects due to latent hyperprolactinaemia. Results of a randomized placebo-controlled double-blind study. *Arzneimittelforschung* 1993;43:752–6.
16. Gerhard II, Patek A, Monga B, Blank A, Gorkow C. Mastodynon® bei weiblicher Sterilitat. *Forsch Komplmentarmed* 1998;5:272–8.

Miscellaneous drugs

QUESTION

For women using DMPA who have breakthrough bleeding while using the antihistamine terbinafine, is there evidence that contraceptive efficacy is reduced?

POPULATION: Women using DMPA.

INTERVENTION: Antihistamine: terbinafine.

OUTCOME: Reduction of contraceptive efficacy.

ANSWER

Despite extensive searching, the CEU could find no published evidence of any interaction between progestogen-only injectable contraceptives and anti-histamines.

The WHO *Selected Practice Recommendations for Contraceptive Use* and the FFPRHC *UK Selected Practice Recommendations for Contraceptive Use* both state that breakthrough bleeding can occur with progestogen-only injectable contraceptives and should be investigated if persistent. There is no evidence that breakthrough bleeding associated with DMPA is associated with a reduction in efficacy.[1] The CEU suggests that it is unlikely that terbinafine would have any effect on efficacy of DMPA.

QUESTION

For women using the progestogen-only pill, can terbinafine reduce its contraceptive efficacy?

POPULATION: Women using the progestogen-only pill.
INTERVENTION: Terbinafine.
OUTCOME: Efficacy.

ANSWER

BNF advises that there have been occasional reports of breakthrough bleeding when terbinafine is given to women using progestogens (for contraception). It is unclear if this breakthrough bleeding is an indication of potential reduced efficacy.

The Summary of Product Characteristics for Lamisil® (Novartis) tablets (containing terbinafine) states that studies have shown terbinafine to have negligible potential to inhibit or induce the clearance of drugs that are metabolised by cytochrome P450 enzymes, such as oral contraceptives. No published case reports were identified of pregnancies following terbinafine use.

Despite extensive searching, the CEU could find no other information in the literature on interactions between terbinafine and progestogen-only pills. Women should be counselled about the potential for menstrual irregularities and the unknown effect on contraceptive efficacy. The CEU advises that in the absence of evidence, progestogen-only pill users may wish to use barrier contraception in addition for the duration of terbinafine use and for 2 days after discontinuation.

QUESTION

For women using bromocriptine, can progestogen-only emergency contraception be used safely?

POPULATION: Women using bromocriptine.
INTERVENTION: Progestogen-only emergency contraception.
OUTCOME: Safety an efficacy.

ANSWER

Bromocriptine inhibits the secretion of prolactin from the pituitary gland. It is used to treat amenorrhoea and infertility associated with hyperprolactinaemia and to suppress lactation.

Despite extensive searching, the CEU could find no documented evidence of any drug interaction between bromocriptine and hormonal contraception, including the progestogen-only emergency contraceptive.

QUESTION

For women using combined oral contraception, is there evidence that contraceptive efficacy is reduced by interaction with vitamin C?

POPULATION: Women using combined oral contraception.
INTERVENTION: Vitamin C.
OUTCOME: Contraceptive efficacy.

ANSWER

Vitamin C (ascorbic acid) and ethinylestradiol both undergo sulphation in the liver and potential interaction due to competition for sites in the liver may occur. A small study in 37 women using a combined oral contraceptive pill containing 30 micrograms ethinylestradiol and 150 micrograms levonorgestrel found that use of vitamin C did not lead to an increase in the bioavailability of ethinylestradiol.[2] There was no alteration in ethinylestradiol concentration when high doses (1 g) of vitamin C were discontinued.

Grapefruit juice may reduce the metabolism of ethinylestradiol and increase its bioavailability.[3] However, this effect was thought to be due to the naringin content rather than vitamin C.

The CEU was unable to find any other studies investigating effects of ascorbic acid on the bioavailability of ethinylestradiol or contraceptive efficacy.

QUESTION

For women using diclofenac sodium with misoprostol (Arthrotec®, Pharmacia) and methotrexate, which contraceptive options may provide safe and effective contraception?

POPULATION: Women using Arthrotec and methotrexate.
INTERVENTION: Hormonal contraception.
OUTCOME: Reduction in contraceptive efficacy and adverse events.

ANSWER

Diclofenac sodium (50–75 mg) with misoprostol 200 micrograms (marketed as Arthrotec) is indicated for pain and inflammation in rheumatic disease and other musculoskeletal disorders, acute gout and postoperative pain.

Misoprostol is a synthetic prostaglandin analogue with antisecretory and protective properties, promoting healing of gastric and duodenal ulcers. The prostaglandin misoprostol is given by mouth or by vaginal administration to induce medical abortion [unlicensed indication]; intravaginal use ripens the cervix before surgical abortion [unlicensed indication]. Manufacturers advise misoprostol should not be used in women of childbearing age unless the patient requires NSAID therapy and is at high risk of complications from non-steroidal induced ulceration. In such patients it is advised that misoprostol should only be used if the patient takes effective contraceptive measures and has been advised of the risks of taking misoprostol if pregnant.

Methotrexate is a suspected teratogen and women using this drug should avoid pregnancy in the 3 months following its discontinuation. Effective contraception is essential.

There are no known drug interactions between Arthrotec (which contains diclofenac sodium and misoprostol), methotrexate and contraceptive hormones. There is no evidence that the efficacy of hormonal contraception is reduced with use of Arthrotec.

QUESTION

For young women taking sibutramine hydrochloride (Reductil®, Abbot), does combined hormonal contraception or the progestogen-only pill provide safe and effective contraception?

POPULATION: Young women taking sibutramine hydrochloride (Reductil).

INTERVENTION: Combined oral contraceptive pill or progesterone-only pill.
OUTCOME: Efficacy and safety.

ANSWER

Sibutramine hydrochloride is indicated for women who find it difficult to achieve or maintain more than 5% weight loss within 3 months and have a BMI of over 30 or have a BMI of 27 and complications such as type II diabetes. Sibutramine hydrochloride is recommended only for those aged 18–65 years of age. Hypertension is a common adverse effect and blood pressure and pulse should be measured every 2 weeks for the first 3 months, every month for the next 3 months and then every 3 months.[4] Sibutramine hydrochloride should be discontinued if blood pressure increases above 145/90 mmHg or by more than 10 mmHg from baseline. The Summary of Product Characteristics advises that there is no interaction between Reductil and hormonal contraception.

Coexisting medical conditions, in particular risk of VTE, associated with raised BMI should be considered for women using sibutramine hydrochloride who require contraception.

The *WHO Medical Eligibility Criteria* has stated that for women with a BMI greater than 30 kg/m², the benefits of using combined hormonal contraception generally outweigh the risks (WHO category 2). However, obesity is a risk factor for VTE. Progestogen-only methods may be a more suitable option for women who are obese. Progestogen-only contraceptives have unrestricted use (WHO category 1) by women with a BMI over 30 kg/m².

QUESTION

For young women taking sibutramine hydrochloride (Reductil) who smoke and have a family history of hypertension, is the combined oral contraceptive pill a safe and effective method of contraception?

POPULATION: Women taking sibutramine hydrochloride (Reductil) who smoke and have a family history of hypertension.
INTERVENTION: Combined oral contraceptive pill.
OUTCOME: Efficacy of contraception.

ANSWER

Sibutramine hydrochloride is indicated for women who find it difficult to achieve or maintain more than 5% weight loss within 3 months and have a BMI of over 30; or have a BMI of 27 and complications such as type II diabetes.

Sibutramine hydrochloride is recommended only for those aged 18–65 years of age. Hypertension is a common adverse effect and blood pressure and pulse should be measured every 2 weeks for the first 3 months, every month for the next 3 months and then every 3 months.[4] Sibutramine hydrochloride should be discontinued if blood pressure increases above 145/90 mmHg or by more than 10 mmHg from baseline. The Summary of Product Characteristics advises that there is no interaction between Reductil and hormonal contraception.

The *WHO Medical Eligibility Criteria* recommends that for women under the age of 35 years who smoke the benefits of using combined hormonal contraception generally outweigh the risks (WHO category 2). A WHO category 2 is also given for women with a BMI greater than 30 kg/m². Obesity is a risk factor for VTE and case–control studies suggest that venous thromboembolic risk increases with increasing BMI. Progestogen-only methods may be a more suitable option for women who are obese.

QUESTION

For women using a progestogen-only pill, does use of orlistat (Xenical®, Roche) have any effect on contraceptive efficacy?

POPULATION: Women using progestogen-only pill.
INTERVENTION: Orlistat (Xenical)
OUTCOME: Contraceptive efficacy.

ANSWER

Orlistat is used in the management of obesity. There are no interactions noted in BNF between orlistat and contraceptive hormones. Orlistat may impair the absorption of fat-soluble vitamins so these vitamins should be taken at least 2 hours after a dose. This advice may also be given for other oral medication, such as oral contraceptives which may also be taken 2 hours after orlistat.

Adverse effects of orlistat include liquid oily stools, faecal urgency, faecal incontinence, flatulence, abdominal pain and rectal pain. It is unlikely that these gastrointestinal adverse effects would interfere with the absorption of a progestogen-only pill. There is no enterohepatic circulation of progestogens.

The *WHO Medical Eligibility Criteria* states that, for women with a BMI greater than 30 kg/m², use of progestogen-only pills is unrestricted (WHO category 1).

The CEU recommends the use of two progestogen-only pills daily for women who weigh over 70 kg.[5]

The CEU advises that there is no evidence that use of orlistat interferes with the efficacy of progestogen-only pills. Women who weigh over 70 kg, however, should consider use of two progestogen-only pills taken together daily.

QUESTION

For women with a personal history of VTE in pregnancy who are taking warfarin, can the desogestrel-only pill be used safely and does it interact with warfarin?

POPULATION: Women with previous VTE in pregnancy now on warfarin.
INTERVENTION: Use of desogestrel-only pill (Cerazette®, Organon).
OUTCOME: Risk of VTE and interactions with warfarin.

ANSWER

The desogestrel-only pill should be considered in all respects as any other progestogen-only pill. A critical review on drug interactions among commonly used medications found no interaction between progestogens and warfarin.[6] The CEU identified no studies to support an interaction between the desogestrel-only pill and warfarin.[7]

Progestogens may be important in the risk of VTE in women using combined oral contraceptives. However, when considering progestogen-only contraceptives, there is no evidence of an association with increased risk of VTE. The WHO Collaborative Study found no increase in VTE in women using progestogen-only oral contraception.[8] The WHO *Medical Eligibility Criteria* classifies all progestogen-only methods of contraception (pills, injectables, implants and intrauterine system) as WHO category 2 (advantages generally outweigh risks) for women with a personal history of VTE.

The CEU concludes that the desogestrel-only pill is a safe and effective method of contraception for women with previous VTE who are taking warfarin.

References

1. McCann MF, Potter LS. Progestin-only oral contraception: A comprehensive review. *Contraception* 1994;50:S159–88.
2. Zamah NM, Hümpel M, Kuhnz W, Louton T, Rafferty J. Absence of an effect of high vitamin C dosage on the systemic availability of ethinyl estradiol in women using a combination oral contraceptive. *Contraception* 1993;48:377–91.
3. Weber A, Jäger R, Börner A, Klinger G, Vollanth R, Matthey SK, *et al.* Can grapefruit

juice influence ethinylestradiol bioavailability? *Contraception* 1996;53:41–7.

4.   Department of Health. *Prodigy Guidance Obesity*. London: DOH; 2000 [www.prodigy.nhs.uk/guidance.asp?gt=Obesity].

5.   Faculty of Family Planning and Reproductive Health Care Clinical Effectiveness Unit. The use of contraception outside the terms of the product licence. *J Fam Plann Reprod Health Care* 2005;31:225–41.

6.   Crowther NR, Holbrook AM, Kenwright R, Kenwright M. Drug interactions among commonly used medications. *Can Fam Phys* 1997;43:1972–81.

7.   Faculty of Family Planning and Reproductive Health Care Clinical Effectiveness Unit. New product review desogestrel-only pill (Cerazette). *J Fam Plann Reprod Health Care* 2003;29: 162–5.

8.   World Health Organization Collaborative Study of Cardiovascular Disease and Steroid Hormone Contraception. Cardiovascular disease and use of oral and injectable progestogen-only contraceptives and combined injectable contraceptives. *Contraception* 1998;57:315–24.

Illegal 'recreational' drugs

QUESTION

For women using illegal 'recreational' drugs, which contraceptive methods can be used safely?

POPULATION: Women using illegal recreational drugs.

INTERVENTION: Contraception.

OUTCOME: Safety.

ANSWER

The UK Report to the European Monitoring Centre for Drugs and Drug Addiction identified that up to one-third of adults in England and Wales aged between 16 and 59 years have used illicit drugs or solvents at some point in their lives, and this rose to half of 16–24 year olds.[1] Around one in three 15-year-olds in England, and two in five in Scotland, report ever using drugs. Despite this high recreational drug use particularly in young women, the CEU could find little evidence of drug effects on contraceptive use, efficacy and safety.

BNF states that barbiturates accelerate metabolism of estrogens and progestogens, thus potentially reducing the contraceptive efficacy of hormonal contraception.

A small study investigated the effect that combined oral contraceptives have on the acute effects of cocaine.[2] No differences in cocaine-induced subjective, physiological responses or plasma cocaine and metabolite concentrations during the times equivalent to the follicular and luteal phases of the menstrual cycle were noted. A triphasic combined oral contraceptive pill did not present an added risk of cocaine-induced cardiovascular events. Exogenous administration of estrogen and progestogen in combined oral contraception did not alter the subjective responses to acute cocaine.

Cocaine exposure has been shown to induce platelet activation.[3] Even at low doses and among occasional users, cocaine may promote thrombosis and predispose healthy individuals to ischaemic events.[3] This may suggest that estrogen-containing preparations should not be used in this risk group or at least should be used with caution. Indeed the *WHO Medical Eligibility Criteria* gives a category 4 (unacceptable health risk) for use of combined hormonal contraception by women with a predisposition to thrombosis.

Progestogen-only hormonal contraception does not have a significant effect on thrombotic risk and long acting progestogen-only methods (injectables, implants or intrauterine) or a copper IUD may be suitable options, particularly if poor compliance in this vulnerable group of women is an issue.

The CEU suggests that women who use recreational drugs should have their contraceptive needs and preferences assessed individually. Use of combined hormonal contraceptives may be inappropriate if the risk of thrombosis is increased. Alterative methods (progestogen-only and non-hormonal) which avoid daily pill-taking and use of estrogen may be considered.

QUESTION

For women who are ecstasy users and require contraception, is it safe to use combined oral contraception?

POPULATION: Women who are ecstasy users.
INTERVENTION: Combined oral contraception.
OUTCOME: Safety.

ANSWER

Ecstasy (3–4 methylenedioxymethamphetamine) is a synthetic psychoactive drug with both stimulant and hallucinogenic properties. Ecstasy affects the serotonin system by which neurones communicate and regulate mood, aggression, sexual activity, sleep and pain sensitivity.

The UK Report to the European Monitoring Centre for Drugs and Drug Addiction identified that up to one third of adults in England and Wales aged between 16 and 59 years have used illicit drugs and solvents at some point in their lives and this rose to half of 16–24 year olds.[1] Also, around one in three 15-year-olds in England, and two in five in Scotland, report ever using drugs.

Despite this high recreational drug use particularly in young women, the CEU could find no evidence of any interaction between ecstasy and hormonal contraception.

QUESTION

For young women who are using hormonal contraception, does use of recreational drugs cocaine and ecstasy have an effect on safe contraceptive use?

POPULATION:	Young women using hormonal contraception.
INTERVENTION:	Recreational drug use: cocaine and ecstasy.
OUTCOME:	Safety and efficacy.

ANSWER

The CEU was unable to find any studies investigating interaction between cocaine or ecstasy and hormonal contraception. Evidence suggests that cocaine use can induce platelet activation which may predispose even healthy individuals to thrombosis and ischaemic events.[3]

The *WHO Medical Eligibility Criteria* suggest that for women with a predisposition to thrombosis (specifically known thrombogenic mutations), the use of combined hormonal contraception poses an unacceptable health risk (WHO category 4).

In view of this potential risk of thrombosis, the CEU suggests that alternatives to estrogen-containing contraceptives should be considered.

QUESTION

For women who are cocaine or ecstasy users and require contraception, would the etonogestrel implant, Implanon, be effective?

POPULATION:	Women who are cocaine or ecstasy users and require contraception.

INTERVENTION: The etonogestrel implant (Implanon).
OUTCOME: Efficacy.

ANSWER

The CEU has been unable to find any evidence suggesting an interaction between cocaine or ecstasy use and the etonogestrel implant (Implanon). The Summary of Product Characteristics for Implanon states that no specific interaction studies have been conducted. The long acting etonogestrel implant may be a good option for women using cocaine and ecstasy who may find it difficult to comply with other contraceptive methods.

References

1. Department of Health. *UK Drug Situation 2000: The UK report to the European Monitoring Centre for Drugs and Drug Addiction (EMCDDA)*. 2001 [www.dh.gov.uk/PolicyAndGuidance/HealthAndSocialCareTopics/].
2. Kouri EM, Lundahl LH, Borden KN, McNeil JF, Lukas SE. Effects of oral contraceptives on acute cocaine response in female volunteers. *Pharmacol Biochem Behav* 2002;74:173–80.
3. Heesch CM, Wilhelm CR, Ristich J, Adnane J, Bontempo FA, Wagner WR. Cocaine activates platelets and increases the formation of circulating platelet containing microaggregates in humans. *Heart* 2000;83:688–95.

11 NEUROLOGICAL AND CEREBROVASCULAR DISORDERS

Epilepsy

QUESTION

For women with epilepsy, can hormones or hormonal contraception increase seizure frequency?

POPULATION: Women with epilepsy.
INTERVENTION: Hormonal contraception.
OUTCOME: Seizure frequency.

ANSWER

Safe and effective contraception is particularly important for women with epilepsy, so that pregnancy can be a planned event and anti-epileptic monotherapy used prior to conception where possible. The effects of hormones and hormonal contraception on epilepsy are unclear, though the *WHO Medical Eligibility Criteria for Contraceptive Use* recommends that all methods of contraception can be used safely by women with epilepsy (WHO category 1).

A review article summarised available evidence on the hormonal considerations of epilepsy in adolescents.[1] Catamenial epilepsy refers to an increased seizure frequency in association with the menstrual cycle. Research has provided conflicting evidence on the influences of hormones on seizures. However, exogenous hormones have been used to treat catamenial epilepsy, though none are licensed for this indication. Parenteral medroxyprogesterone acetate has been shown to reduce seizure frequency when given in doses sufficient to inhibit ovulation.

The CEU supports the WHO recommendation that there is no restriction *per se* on the use of hormonal contraception in women with epilepsy. However, caution is advised when liver enzyme-inducing anti-epileptic drugs are used due to their potential to reduce contraceptive efficacy.

QUESTION

For women with epilepsy, does using liver enzyme-inducers reduce the effectiveness of all contraceptive options? (Five similar enquiries.)

POPULATION: Women with epilepsy.

INTERVENTIONS: Liver enzyme-inducing anticonvulsant treatment.

OUTCOMES: Efficacy of contraception.

ANSWER

The anti-epileptic liver enzyme-inducers reduce the contraceptive efficacy of progestogen-only pills, combined oral contraception and subdermal progestogens.[2-4] If combined oral contraception is to be used then at least 50 micrograms ethinylestradiol daily is required to maintain efficacy. Guidance from the Scottish Intercollegiate Guideline Network on the management of women with epilepsy suggests using condoms in addition to a 50-microgram pill.[5] There is no evidence that breakthrough bleeding is a marker of serum levels of hormones or of risk of ovulation.

There is little evidence to support a reduction in contraceptive efficacy of injectable progestogen and no evidence to support giving injectable medroxy-progesterone acetate more frequently in women using liver enzyme-inducers. Although the evidence is limited, there does not appear to be a reduction in the efficacy of LNG-IUS with liver enzyme-inducers due to the high-dose local effects of progestogen on the reproductive tract. Enzyme-inducers do not affect non-hormonal contraceptives such as the copper IUD.

Current FFPRHC guidance[6] and BNF recommend that the dose of progestogen-only emergency contraception is increased by 50% for women taking anti-epileptic liver enzyme-inducers. These should be viewed as consensus recommendations for which there is no strong evidence base.

Update to Answer

Subsequent to preparing this response, the 0.75-mg tablet of levonorgestrel emergency contraception has been discontinued and replaced by a 1.5-mg tablet. Thus, the option of giving a total dose of 2.25 mg is no longer available. Advice from the FFPRHC is to give 3 mg as a single dose if only 1.5-mg tablets are available.

QUESTION

For a women taking the enzyme-inducing anti-epileptic drug topiramate, which methods of contraception would best provide efficacy and acceptability? (Two similar enquiries.)

POPULATION:	**Women with epilepsy using topiramate.**
INTERVENTIONS:	**Contraceptive methods.**
OUTCOMES:	**Efficacy and acceptability.**

ANSWER

Guidance from both the CEU and the WHO suggests that women on enzyme-inducing drugs should be counselled that methods other than oral hormonal preparations represent their first-line methods of choice.[7] For reversible contraception, a copper-containing IUD or the LNG-IUS would be appropriate. On theoretical grounds supported by evidence from a small case series, enzyme-inducers are unlikely to interfere with the largely local effects of the LNG-IUS. Progestogen-only pills and the etonogestrel implant are both considered unsuitable.

Women with epilepsy who are taking liver enzyme-inducing medication should be counselled regarding the risks of reduced efficacy of combined oral contraception. If, after counselling, a women still wishes to use the combined pill, she should be advised to use a regimen containing at least 50 micrograms ethinylestradiol or mestranol daily.

In accordance with guidance from the Scottish Intercollegiate Guidelines Network, additional barrier contraception should be advised along with the high-dose pill regimen. Barrier methods should be continued for 4 weeks after discontinuation of the liver enzyme-inducing drug (as enzyme-induction persists for this length of time after the medication is withdrawn).[5]

QUESTION

For women with epilepsy, which regimen of combined oral contraception provides best efficacy and acceptability? (Nine similar enquiries.)

POPULATION: Women with epilepsy.
INTERVENTIONS: Combined oral contraception regimens.
OUTCOMES: Efficacy and acceptability.

ANSWER

Many women with epilepsy are taking enzyme-inducing anticonvulsant drugs. Previous guidance from the CEU provides summary information on anticonvulsants which are, or are not, enzyme-inducers.[7,8] If such a woman chooses to used combined oral contraception, then it is established UK practice to use a regimen containing at least 50 micrograms estrogen daily. Traditionally, Ovran® (Wyeth), which contained 50 micrograms ethinylestradiol, was used for this purpose. This preparation was discontinued in 2002. A preparation containing 50 micrograms of a different estrogen, mestranol, remains available in the UK (Norinyl-1,® Pharmacia). Authorities differ as to the bioequivalence of ethinylestradiol and mestranol.[9,10] Differences in bioactivity between women and in the same woman at different times are probably greater than differences between formulations.[9]

On balance, if a woman taking enzyme-inducing anticonvulsants chooses combined oral contraception as her method, there seems little to choose between the mestranol formulation and use of two lower-dose ethinylestradiol pills in combination. For low-dose pills used in combination, the CEU found no evidence regarding relative benefits of taking the two pills separately or together. Similarly, we found no evidence regarding any advantage offered by taking the contraceptive pills at a different time from the enzyme-inducing anticonvulsant. Thus, the dosage schedule should be according to the woman's choice and convenience.

QUESTION

For a woman with epilepsy who uses non-enzyme-inducing medication, is DMPA a safe method of contraception and when should the repeat injection be given?

POPULATION: Women with epilepsy using non-liver enzyme-inducers.
INTERVENTION: Depot medroxyprogesterone with varying injection intervals.
OUTCOMES: Safety and efficacy.

ANSWER

Epilepsy is a neurological disorder with a lifetime prevalence of between 2% and 5% of the population and an annual incidence rate of 80/100 000, with the highest rates being among children and the elderly. Some anti-epileptics such as benzodiazepines (such as clonazepam), lamotrigine and levetiracetam are non-enzyme-inducers. These do not induce the hepatic microsomal enzyme system and therefore do not increase the rate of metabolism of hormonal contraceptives.

The *WHO Medical Eligibility Criteria for Contraceptive Use* advises that women with epilepsy may have unrestricted use (WHO category 1) of DMPA. Even for women using liver enzyme-inducers, WHO assigns a category 2 for DMPA (benefits generally outweigh risks).

The *WHO Selected Practice Recommendations for Contraceptive Use* advises that women in general should have repeat injections of DMPA every 3 months. A repeat injection may safely be given up to 2 weeks early (if a woman presents early) or up to 2 weeks late without the need for additional contraceptive measures. These exact same recommendations can be applied to a woman with epilepsy who is using non-enzyme-inducing anticonvulsants (and indeed, to women using enzyme-inducers).

QUESTION

For a women with epilepsy who uses lamotrigine (a non-enzyme-inducing anticonvulsant) is the effectiveness of hormonal contraception reduced? (Three similar enquiries.)

POPULATION: Women with epilepsy using lamotrigine.
INTERVENTIONS: Hormonal contraception.
OUTCOME: Efficacy.

ANSWER

Some anti-epileptic drugs are liver enzyme-inducers and can reduce the contraceptive efficacy of combined oral contraceptives and of progestogen-only pills and implants. They do not affect progestogen-only injectables and there is little evidence that they reduce the effect of the LNG-IUS.

Lamotrigine, like sodium valproate and other newer anti-epileptics (clobazam, vigabactrin, gabapentin, tiagabine, levetiracetam, zonisamide), is not a liver enzyme-inducer. Lamotrigine has no effect on sex steroid metabolism and will not increase the metabolism of sex steroids nor reduce the efficacy of hormonal contraception. The CEU advises that women using lamotrigine may use any method of contraception without reduction in efficacy.

Update to Answer

In June 2005 (subsequent to the preparation of these responses), the Summary of Product Characteristics for Lamictal® (GSK) (lamotrigine) was updated to reflect the findings of three small studies. The CEU reviewed these studies and concluded:

The CEU could find no evidence that use of lamotrigine leads to ovulation in combined pill users. There is no good evidence to suggest that non-hormonal methods should be used in favour of hormonal methods. After counselling, women may choose to continue with, or initiate, a hormonal method.

There is evidence from case series that seizure control worsens in some women when starting a combined pill and that adverse effects associated with lamo-trigine can increase in some women when the combined pill is discontinued. Clinicians should monitor any such clinical effects when initiating or discon-tinuing combined hormonal contraception in women using lamotrigine.

The usual escalation regimen for lamotrigine is recommended for combined pill users when starting lamotrigine. The maintenance dose of lamotrigine may need to be increased up to two-fold according to clinical response when a combined pill is started. For women stopping a combined pill while taking lamotrigine, the daily dose may need to be reduced by as much as 50% according to clinical response in order to minimise adverse effects.

QUESTION

For women who are taking anti-epileptic medication, is either the etonogestrel implant or DMPA an effective form of contraception?

POPULATION: Women taking anti-epileptic drugs.
INTERVENTIONS: Etonogestrel implant or DMPA.
OUTCOME: Efficacy.

ANSWER

All the evidence found related to levonorgestrel implants, although drug information on the etonogestrel implant indicates that interaction may occur with enzyme-inducing drugs also. After reviewing the evidence, the CEU recommends that women who use antiepileptic drugs that induce hepatic microsomal enzymes (such as phenobarbital) should not use etonogestrel implants as contraceptive efficacy may be reduced. However, DMPA can be used. Some clinicians give repeat injections at 10-week rather than 12-week intervals. However, the Summary of Product Characteristics for DMPA does not suggest shortening the injection interval as the clearance of medroxyprogesterone acetate is approximately equal to the rate of hepatic blood flow, and it is unlikely that drugs which induce hepatic enzymes will affect the kinetics of medroxyprogesterone acetate.

Women who use anti-epileptic drugs that are not enzyme-inducers, such as valproic acid, can use DMPA, levonorgestrel implants, and (presumably) etonogestrel implants at their normal doses.

References

1. Logsdon-Pokorny VK. Epilepsy in adolescents: hormonal considerations. *J Pediatr Adolesc Gynecol* 2000;13:9–13.
2. Guberman, A. Hormonal contraception and epilepsy. *Neurology* 1999;53:S38–S40.
3. Haukkamaa M. Contraception by Norplant subdermal capsules is not reliable in epileptic patients on anticonvulsant treatment. *Contraception* 1986;33:559–65.
4. Odlind V, Olsson SE. Enhanced metabolism of levonorgestrel during phenytoin treatment in a woman with Norplant contraception. *Contraception* 1986;33:257–61.
5. Scottish Intercollegiate Guidelines Network. *Diagnosis and Management of Epilepsy in Adults*. National Clinical Guideline No. 70. Edinburgh: SIGN; 2003.
6. Faculty of Family Planning and Reproductive Health Care Clinical Effectiveness Unit. Emergency contraception: Recommendations for clinical practice. *J Fam Plann Reprod Health Care* 2003;29:9–16.
7. Faculty of Family Planning and Reproductive Health Care. First prescription of combined oral contraception. *J Fam Plann Reprod Health Care* 2003;29:209–23.
8. Faculty of Family Planning and Reproductive Health Care Clinical Effectiveness Unit. Drug interactions with hormonal contraception. *J Fam Plann Reprod Health Care* 2005;31:139–50.
9. Goldzieher JW. Selected aspects of the pharmacokinetics and metabolism of ethinyl estrogens and their clinical implications. *Am J Obstet Gynecol* 1990;163:S318–22.
10. Kisicki J. Bioequivalence of Norethin and Ortho-Novum in health females. *Adv Ther* 1989;6:261–8.

Migraine

QUESTION

For women with migraine, can combined oral contraception be used safely? (Two similar enquiries.)

POPULATION:	Women with migraine.
INTERVENTION:	Combined oral contraception.
OUTCOME:	Safety.

ANSWER

The risk of ischaemic stroke is increased in combined oral contraceptive users (relative to non-users), however the absolute risk remains very low.[1] There may be a further increased risk of stroke in combined pill users with migraine (particularly migraine with aura). Aura includes: homonymous visual disturbances, unilateral paraesthia and/or numbness, unilateral weakness and aphasia or unclassifiable speech disorder. Sensory symptoms (pins and needles, numbness) occur in only one-third of people with migraine with aura. Visual disturbances such as generalised 'spots before the eyes', 'flashing lights', blurring of vision or photophobia of variable duration before or with headaches are not suggestive of focal ischaemia. The association between migraine and ischaemic stroke is limited to women under 45 years, the risk being greater for women suffering from migraine with aura.[2]

The *WHO Medical Eligibility Criteria for Contraceptive Use* recommends that in women under the age of 35 years suffering from migraine without aura, the benefits of **initiating** combined oral contraception generally outweigh the risks (WHO category 2). However, for women already using combined oral contraception who develop migraine without aura, the risks of **continuing** the method generally outweigh the benefits (WHO category 3). For women over the age of 35 years with migraine without aura, the risks of **initiating** combined oral contraception generally outweigh the benefits (WHO category 3) and **continuation** poses an unacceptable health risk (WHO category 4). WHO recommends that for women of any age suffering from migraine with aura, combined oral contraception should not be used (WHO category 4).

The CEU endorse the WHO recommendations on the use of combined oral contraception by women with migraine.

QUESTION

For women with abdominal migraine, can combined oral contraception be used safely?

POPULATION: Women with abdominal migraine.

INTERVENTION: Combined oral contraception.

OUTCOME: Safety.

ANSWER

Migraine with focal symptoms indicates ischaemia, which increases the risk of ischaemic stroke three-fold.[3] Case–control studies support an increased risk of stroke in combined oral contraceptive users with migraine, compared to users without migraine.[4,5] There is evidence in children that episodic abdominal pain occurring in the absence of headache may be a migrainous phenomenon.[6] Abdominal migraine is rare in adults. It is unclear if abdominal migraine is classed as a focal symptom.

The *WHO Medical Eligibility Criteria for Contraceptive Use* recommends that women with migraine with focal symptoms should be advised against the use of combined oral contraception (WHO category 4). Women over the age of 35 years with non-focal migraine should also be advised that the risks of combined pill use generally outweigh benefits (WHO category 3).

The CEU was unable to identify any evidence regarding the initiation or continuation of combined oral contraception in women with a diagnosis of abdominal migraine. Alternative contraceptive options, such as progestogen-only methods, may be more appropriate and should be discussed.

QUESTION

For women who suffer from migraine and from occasional facial numbness, without any other symptoms of focal migraine, can combined oral contraception be used safely?

POPULATION: Women who suffer from migraine and from occasional facial numbness.

INTERVENTION: Combined oral contraception.

OUTCOME: Safety.

ANSWER

The risk of ischaemic stroke is increased in oral contraceptive users but the absolute risk is low because of the low stroke incidence in this age category.[1,7] However, there may be a further increased risk of stroke in combined oral contraceptive users with migraine (particularly migraine with focal symptoms). Focal symptoms are described as: homonymous visual disturbances, unilateral paraestheia and/or numbness, unilateral weakness and aphasia or unclassifiable speech disorder.[8] Sensory symptoms include 'positive' features, for instance pins and needles, and/or 'negative' features, such as numbness.[9] Numbness usually occurs after the headache. Sensory symptoms occur in only one-third of people with migraine with focal symptoms, are usually 'positive' and are usually in association with visual symptoms. Headache usually follows focal symptoms, however, less commonly, the headache can lack migrainous features, or be completely absent.

It is unclear whether women experiencing facial numbness, without any other symptoms, are suffering from migraine with focal symptoms. The CEU advises erring on the side of caution and that such a woman should be counselled on the increased risk of ischaemic stroke associated with migraine with focal symptoms and combined pill use. A progestogen-only method, or an IUD may be a safer form of contraception for such a woman.

QUESTION

For women who suffer from migraine during the pill-free interval, can combined oral contraception be used safely?

POPULATION: Women who suffer from migraine during the pill-free interval.
INTERVENTION: Combined oral contraception.
OUTCOME: Safety.

ANSWER

The relative risk of ischaemic stroke is increased in combined oral contraceptive users, however the absolute risk remains very low.[1,7] There may be an increased risk of stroke in combined pill users with migraine (particularly migraine with focal symptoms).

Migraine attacks occurring in the pill-free week seem to be associated with falling levels of estrogen.[10] Women using combined oral contraception who have migraine (without focal symptoms) during the pill-free week can advised to run two or three pill packets together ('bicycling' or 'tricycling'). This avoids the pill-free week, maintains hormone levels and prevents the onset of headache.[10] Small studies have shown that the use of natural estrogen,[10] injections of estradiol valerate,[11] percutaneous gel,[12,13] or transdermal patches[14-16] may be of benefit in preventing headache in the pill-free week.

The *WHO Medical Eligibility Criteria for Contraceptive Use* recommends that, in women under the age of 35 years suffering from migraine (without focal symptoms), the benefits of **initiating** combined oral contraception generally outweigh the risks (WHO category 2). However, for women already using combined pills who develop migraine without focal symptoms, the risks of **continuing** the method generally outweigh the benefits (WHO category 3). For women suffering from migraine with focal symptoms, combined oral contraception should not be used (WHO category 4).

Women suffering from migraine with focal symptoms, or those suffering from migraine without focal symptoms but with multiple risk factors for ischaemic stroke, should be counselled on the risks of stroke, and should consider the use of non-estrogen methods of contraception.

QUESTION

For women who suffer from migraine with focal symptoms, can progestogen-only contraception be used safely?

POPULATION: Women who suffer from migraine with focal symptoms.
INTERVENTION: Progestogen-only contraception.
OUTCOME: Safety.

ANSWER

The *WHO Medical Eligibility Criteria for Contraceptive Use* recommends that for women with migraine with focal symptoms, the benefits of **initiating** progestogen-only pills, implants, injectables or the LNG-IUS generally outweigh the risks (WHO category 2). For women already using these methods who develop migraine with focal symptoms during use, the risks of **continuing** their use generally outweigh the benefits (WHO category 3).

If migraine with focal symptoms develops as a new feature in women using progestogen-only pills, implants, injectables or the LNG-IUS, the CEU recommends that the migraine is investigated, and consideration is given to ~opping the method.

QUESTION

For women who suffer from migraine with focal symptoms and hypermobility syndrome, can progestogen-only contraception be used safely?

POPULATION: Women who suffer from migraine with focal symptoms and hypermobility syndrome.

INTERVENTION: Progestogen-only contraception.

OUTCOME: Safety.

ANSWER

Hypermobility syndrome is characterised by extremely mobile joints as a consequence of joint laxity. Patients are often referred to as being 'double jointed'.[17]

The Summary of Product Characteristics for the etonogestrel implant, Implanon, advises that arthralgia (joint pain), skeletal pain, and myalgia (muscle pain) are uncommon adverse effects of its use. Leg cramps have been reported in users of DMPA and back pain has been reported in DMPA and LNG-IUS users. Despite extensive searching, the CEU could find no direct evidence on the use of progestogen-only contraception in women with hypermobility syndrome.

The *WHO Medical Eligibility Criteria for Contraceptive Use* recommends that progestogen-only contraception can be used in women with migraine (with or without focal symptoms). A WHO category 2 is given for the **initiation** of progestogen-only pills, implants, DMPA and the LNG-IUS. A WHO category 3 is given for the **continuation** of these methods if migraine with focal symptoms develops while using the method. An IUD is given a WHO category 1 (unrestricted use).

The CEU advises that women with migraine and focal symptoms may use progestogen-only contraception, however they should be informed that joint, skeletal and muscle pain can occur with the use of these methods. Consideration may also be given to the use of a non-hormonal method of contraception.

QUESTION

For women who develop focal migraine while using DMPA, should the injectable be discontinued?

POPULATION: Women who develop focal migraine while using DMPA.
INTERVENTION: Continuation of DMPA.
OUTCOME: Safety.

ANSWER

Migraine affects 25% of women at some time in their lives.[18] Migraine with aura (or focal migraine) accounts for 30% of total migraine attacks.[8]

The *WHO Medical Eligibility Criteria for Contraceptive Use* notes that any new headaches or marked changes in headaches should be evaluated. The categories indicated below apply only to women without other risk factors for stroke. The risk of stroke increases with age, hypertension and smoking.

WHO recommends that for women of any age with pre-existing migraine with aura, the benefits of **initiating** DMPA generally outweigh the risks (WHO category 2). For women of any age who develop migraine with aura, the risks of **continuing** DMPA generally outweigh the benefits (WHO category 3).

The CEU recommends that migraine with aura is investigated in these women and that for most a switch to a non-hormonal method is advised.

QUESTION

For women who develop focal migraine while using a LNG-IUS, should the device be removed? (Two similar enquiries.)

POPULATION: Women who develop focal migraine while using a LNG-IUS.
INTERVENTION: Continuation of the contraceptive method.
OUTCOME: Safety.

ANSWER

The annual incidence of ischaemic stroke in women aged under 35 years is low (around 3/100 000).[19] Migraine is an independent risk factor for ischaemic stroke (odds ratio 3.45; 95% CI 1.3–9.61).[20] Progestogen-only methods of contraception can be used in women with migraine (with or without focal neurological symptoms). A WHO category 2 is given for the **initiation** of progestogen-only methods, including the LNG-IUS, in women with pre-existing migraine with focal symptoms. However, a WHO category 3 is given for the **continuation** of these methods if focal migraine develops while using the method. A copper-bearing IUD is given a WHO category 1 in this circumstance.

Systemic levels of levonorgestrel are lower with the LNG-IUS than following oral, injectable, or subdermal administration. The CEU recommends that when a woman develops focal migraine as a new symptom while using the LNG-IUS, her symptoms should be investigated. The woman should be counselled regarding alternative methods of contraception, but if these are unacceptable she may continue with the LNG-IUS.

QUESTION

For women who suffer from migraine with focal symptoms and have a previous history of haemolytic-uraemic syndrome, which methods of contraception can be used safely?

POPULATION: Women who suffer from migraine with focal symptoms and have a history of haemolytic-uraemic syndrome.

INTERVENTIONS: Methods of contraception.

OUTCOME: Safety.

ANSWER

Haemolytic-uraemic syndrome is a triad characterised by acute renal failure, microangiopathic haemolytic anaemia, and thrombocytopenia.[21] The *WHO Medical Eligibility Criteria for Contraceptive Use* does not address this syndrome. Women who have made a good, permanent recovery and have no nephropathy can be treated as normal. For women with nephropathy, WHO advises that combined oral contraception should not be used (WHO category 4) and that the risks of DMPA generally outweigh the benefits (WHO category 3). The benefits of the progestogen-only pill, the progestogen-only implant and the LNG-IUS generally outweigh the risks (WHO category 2). Unrestricted use of the copper IUD is permitted (WHO category 1).

The International Headache Society classifies migraine with focal symptoms as indicating ischaemia.[8] WHO advises that women who experience migraine with focal neurological symptoms should not use combined oral contraception (WHO category 4). The benefits of the progestogen-only pill, the progestogen-only implant and the LNG-IUS generally outweigh the risks (WHO category 2) and unrestricted use (WHO category 1) of the IUD is permitted.

CEU guidance on first prescription of combined oral contraception[22] supports the WHO recommendation that women with focal migraine should not use a combined pill. Women with past history of haemolytic uraemic syndrome with no residual nephropathy who experience focal migraines therefore have choice between progestogen-only or non-hormonal methods of contracept

QUESTION

For women who suffer from migraine with focal symptoms and are using an etonogestrel implant or DMPA for contraception, can natural estrogen be used to manage problematic bleeding?

POPULATION: Women who suffer from migraine with focal symptoms and are using an etonogestrel implant or DMPA.

INTERVENTIONS: Natural estrogen.

OUTCOME: Safety and control of problematic bleeding.

ANSWER

The management of unacceptable bleeding in women using long-term progestogen-only methods of contraception is a frequent clinical challenge. Use of combined oral contraception is considered WHO category 4 (unacceptable health risk) for women with migraine with aura.

Summaries of Product Characteristics do not list migraine with aura as a contra-indication to the use of estrogen-only HRT. The CEU could not identify any evidence that estrogen replacement is effective in improving the bleeding pattern in women using progestogen-only implants or injectables.

There is insufficient evidence available to recommend the use of natural estrogen in women who have a history of migraine with aura who have bleeding problems with progestogen-only implants or injectables.

The WHO *Selected Practice Recommendations for Contraceptive Use* states that NSAIDs can be used in this group of patients, with the usual contraindications.

QUESTION

Are conjugated estrogens a safe and useful treatment for women with focal migraine using DMPA who are found to be hypoestrogenic?

POPULATION: Women with focal migraine using DMPA.

INTERVENTIONS: Conjugated estrogens.

OUTCOME: Safety and bone protection.

ANSWER

Most of the concerns about long-term use of DMPA relate to its hypoestrogenic effects and possible consequences on bone mineral density. However, most women using injectable DMPA have normal follicular phase levels of estradiol.[23-25] Some women have lower levels of estradiol but this does not appear to correlate with the risk of osteopenia or osteoporosis.[25] There is no evidence to support routine assessment of serum estradiol or the use of estrogen replacement in women using DMPA. There appears to be a reduction in bone loss in the first 5 years of use, little loss thereafter and a return to normal density after discontinuation. The clinical significance of reduced bone mineral density is unclear. Care should be taken when using DMPA in women with risk factors for low bone density such as smoking, family history, low BMI, corticosteroid therapy or thyroid disease. Bone densitometry may be considered if it will help in counselling and decision making.

The *WHO Medical Eligibility Criteria for Contraceptive Use* recommends that women aged 18–45 years can have unrestricted use (WHO category 1) of DMPA. The use of DMPA by women under 18 years or over 45 years of age is classified as a WHO category 2, which means that the benefits of using the contraceptive usually outweigh any theoretical risks. WHO recommends that for women with migraine with aura, the benefits generally outweigh the risks (WHO category 2) for **initiation** of DMPA. No evidence was identified in the literature regarding whether the use of conjugated estrogens is contraindicated in women with migraine with focal aura. However, there is no evidence to support the use of estrogen for bone protection by women using DMPA.

References

1. Gillum LA, Mamidipudi SK, Johnston SC. Ischemic stroke risk with oral contraceptives: a meta-analysis. *JAMA* 2000;284:72–8.
2. Carolei A, Marini C, De Matteis G, Italian National Research Council Study group on Stroke in the Young. History of migraine and risk of cerebral ischaemia in young adults. *Lancet* 1996;347:1503–6.
3. The International Headache Society Task Force on Combined Oral Contraceptives and Hormone replacement Therapy. Recommendations on the risk of ischaemic stroke associated with use of combined oral contraceptives and hormone replacement therapy in women with migraine. *Cephalagia* 2000;20:155–6.
4. Lidegaard O. Oral contraception and risk of cerebral thromboembolic attack: results of a case–control study. *BMJ* 1993;306:956–63.
5. Chang CL, Donaghy M, Poulter NR, WHO Collaborative Study of Cardiovascular Disease and Steroid Hormone Contraception. Migraine and stroke in young women: case–control study. *BMJ* 1999;318:13–8.
6. Russell, G, Abu-Arafeh, I, Symon, DN. Abdominal migraine: evidence for existence and treatment options. *Paediatr Drug* 2002;4: 1–8.
7. Giroud M, Creisson E, Fayolle H, Andre N, Becker F, Martin D, *et al*. Risk factors for primary cerebral hemorrhage: A population based study: the Stroke Registry of Dijon. *Neuroepidemiology* 1995;14:20–6.
8. Headache Classification Committee of the International Headache Society. Classificatio

and diagnostic criteria for headache disorders, cranial neuralgias and facial pain. *Cephalalgia* 1988;8 Suppl 7:1–96.

9. Troost, T. Migraine with aura [IMigraine.net].

10. MacGregor EA, Hackshaw A. Prevention of migraine in the pill-free interval of combined oral contraceptives: A double-blind, placebo-controlled pilot study using natural estrogen supplements. *J Fam Plann Reprod Health Care* 2002;28:27–31.

11. Somerville BW. Estrogen-withdrawal migraine II. Attempted prophylaxis by continuous estradiol administration. *Neurology* 1975;25:245–50.

12. de Lignieres B, Vincens M, Mauvais-Jarvis P, Mas JL, Touboul PJ, Bousser MG. Prevention of menstrual migraine by percutaneous oestradiol. *BMJ* 1986;293:1450.

13. Dennerstein L, Morse C, Burrows G, Oats J, Brown J, Smith M. Menstrual migraine: A double-blind trial of percutaneous estradiol. *Gynecol Endocrinol* 1988;2:113–20.

14. Pfaffenrath V. Efficacy and safety of percutaneous estradiol vs placebo in menstrual migraine. *Cephalagia* 1993;13:244.

15. Pradalier A, Vincent D, Beaulieu PH, Baudesson G, Launay JM. Correlation between oestradiol plasma level and therapeutic effect on menstrual migraine. In: Clifford-Rose F, editor. *New Advances in Headache Research: 4.* London: Smith-Gordon; 1994. p. 129–32.

16. Smiths MG, van der Meer YG, Pfeil JPJM, *et al.* Perimenstrual migraine: effect of Estraderm TTSS and the value of cognitive negative variation and exteroceptive temporalis muscle suppression test. *Headache* 1994;34:103–6.

17. Gotlieb, D. Hypermobility syndrome [drdoc on-line].

18. Rasmussen BK, Jensen R, Schroll M, Olesen J. Epidemiology of headache in a general Population: a prevalence study. *J Clin Epidemiol* 1991;44:1147–57.

19. MacGregor EA, Guillebaud J. Recommendations for clinical practice. Combined oral contraceptives, migraine and ischaemic stroke. *Br J Fam Plann* 1998;24:55–60.

20. Gupta S, Hannaford P. Combined Oral Contraceptives: myocardial infarction, stroke and venous thromboembolism. *J Fam Plann Reprod Health Care* 2001;99:1–7.

21. Hemolytic uraemic syndrome [www.gpnotebook.co.uk/simplepage.cfm?ID=-422576121].

22. Faculty of Family Planning and Reproductive Health Care Clinical Effectiveness Unit. First prescription of combined oral contraception. *J Fam Plann Reprod Health Care* 2003;29:209–22.

23. Gbolade BA, Ellis S, Murby B, Randall S, Kirkman R. Bone density in long term users of depot medroxyprogesterone acetate. *Br J Obstet Gynaecol* 1998;105:790–94.

24. Ryan PJ, Guillebaud J. Depot medroxyprogesterone and bone mineral density. *J Fam Plann Reprod Health Care* 2002;28:12–15.

25. Tang OS, Tang G, Yip PS, Li B. Further evaluation on long-term depot-medroxyprogesterone acetate use and bone mineral density: a longitudinal cohort study. *Contraception* 2000;62:161–4.

Benign intracranial hypertension

QUESTION

Does the use of hormonal contraception exacerbate benign intracranial hypertension? (Twelve similar enquiries.)

POPULATION: Women with benign intracranial hypertension.
INTERVENTION: Hormonal contraception.
OUTCOME: Exacerbation of benign intracranial hypertension.

ANSWER

Benign intracranial hypertension (also known as pseudotumour cerebri or idiopathic intracranial hypertension) is an uncommon condition, which presents most often in women of reproductive age. It is characterised by raised intracranial pressure in the absence of a focal space-occupying lesion. The incidence in women aged 15–44 years is 3.5/100 000.[1] The pathophysiology is unknown but benign intracranial hypertension has been associated with: certain drugs including hormones such as estrogen; systemic illnesses such as disseminated lupus erythematosus, sarcoidosis, infectious diseases including AIDS; chronic renal failure; and obesity. Importantly, it has also been associated with underlying coagulation disorders such as antiphospholipid syndrome and anti-thrombin III deficiency.[2] Benign intracranial hypertension can present with symptoms resulting from a rise in intracranial pressure: headache, visual disturbances, vomiting, confusion and sensorimotor disturbances. It is important to distinguish benign intracranial hypertension from migraine with focal symptoms and from intracranial lesions.

Benign intracranial hypertension is not included among the medical conditions addressed within the *WHO Medical Eligibility Criteria for Contraceptive Use*. However, since estrogens have been implicated in the aetiology of the disorder and are associated with an increased thrombotic risk, it is likely that estrogen-containing contraceptives should be WHO category 4 (unacceptable health risk). Although there have been reports to the WHO Collaborating Centre for International Drug Monitoring of benign intracranial hypertension in women using progestogen-only contraception (levonorgestrel subdermal implants)[3] no causal relationship has been established. There is no evidence available on the effects of progestogen-only contraception on the symptoms or clinical course of benign intracranial hypertension.

QUESTION

Is the progestogen-only pill a safe and effective method of contraception for women with benign intracranial hypertension?

POPULATION: Women with benign intracranial hypertension.
INTERVENTION: Progestogen-only pills.
OUTCOME: Exacerbation of benign intracranial hypertension.

ANSWER

Benign intracranial hypertension is a rare condition characterised by raised intracranial pressure in the absence of a focal space-occupying lesion. It is associated with a range of underlying causes. The CEU has been unable to find any published evidence indicating that the progestogen-only pill is contra-indicated in women with this condition. We suggest that a progestogen-only pill may be prescribed, with regular follow-up and monitoring of the optic fundi.

QUESTION

Is the desogestrel-only pill associated with weight gain or fluid retention which might exacerbate benign intracranial hypertension?

POPULATION: Women with benign intracranial hypertension.
INTERVENTION: Desogestrel-only pills.
OUTCOME: Safety and efficacy.

ANSWER

Benign intracranial hypertension, or pseudotumour cerebri, is a condition which most commonly affects women of childbearing age who are obese or who have experienced recent weight gain.

The CEU published a New Product Review on the desogestrel-only pill Cerazette.[4] It quoted a randomised trial which investigated the most commonly reported adverse effects of Cerazette: weight gain was not included among them.[5] Nevertheless, the Summary of Product Characteristics for Cerazette suggests that weight increase is a common adverse effect of Cerazette use, occurring in more than 1/100 women. Despite extensive searching, the CEU could find no other evidence in the literature relating to weight gain and Cerazette use.

Although there have been reports to the WHO Collaborating Centre for International Drug Monitoring of benign intracranial hypertension in women using progestogen-only contraception (levonorgestrel subdermal implants),[3] no causal relationship has been established. There is no evidence available on the effects of progestogen-only contraception on the symptoms or clinical course of benign intracranial hypertension. We suggest that a progestogen-only pill (including the desogestrel pill) may be prescribed, with regular follow-up and monitoring of the optic fundi.

QUESTION

Have progestogen-only pills (including the desogestrel-only pill) been shown to exacerbate benign intracranial hypertension; and is the LNG-IUS a suitable alternative?

POPULATION: Women with benign intracranial hypertension.

INTERVENTIONS: Progestogen-only pills; LNG-IUS.

OUTCOME: Exacerbation of benign intracranial hypertension.

ANSWER

Benign intracranial hypertension is a rare condition characterised by raised intracranial pressure in the absence of a focal space-occupying lesion. Although there have been reports to the WHO Collaborating Centre for International Drug Monitoring of benign intracranial hypertension in women using progestogen-only contraception (levonorgestrel subdermal implants)[3] no causal relationship has been established. There is no evidence available on the effects of progestogen-only contraception (including the desogestrel-only pill) on the symptoms or clinical course of benign intracranial hypertension.

Benign intracranial hypertension may be estrogen-associated, but is not thought to be progestogen-associated. It would be reasonable to prescribe any progestogen-only method of contraception (including the LNG-IUS) for a woman with benign intracranial hypertension. Monitoring of the condition would be required with a view to discontinuing the contraceptive method if signs and symptoms of raised intracranial pressure were exacerbated.

QUESTION

Is the LNG-IUS a safe and effective method of contraception for a woman with a cerebrospinal fluid shunt in place for benign intracranial hypertension?

POPULATION: Women with a cerebrospinal fluid shunt for benign intracranial hypertension.

INTERVENTIONS: LNG-IUS.

OUTCOME: Safety and efficacy.

ANSWER

The CEU identified no evidence directly relating to contraceptive choices f women with cerebrospinal fluid shunts in place. Cerebrospinal fluid shunts are used for a variety of indications, including benign intracranial hypertension.[6] Benign intracranial hypertension itself has a range of aetiological causes, including previous sagittal sinus thrombosis. Contraceptive choices must be governed by the underlying indication for shunt insertion. On theoretical grounds, the LNG-IUS would appear to be an appropriate contraceptive method for a woman with a cerebrospinal fluid shunt. We were able to identify no evidence suggesting otherwise.

References

1. Radhakrishnan K, Ahlskog JE, Cross SA, Kurland LT, O'Fallon WM. Idiopathic intracranial hypertension (pseudotumour cerebri): descriptive epidemiology in Rochester, Minn, 1976–1990. *Arch Neurol* 1993;50:78–80.
2. Gwan Go K. Pseudotumour Cerebri: Incidence, management and prevention. *CNS Drugs* 2000;14:33–49.
3. Alder JB, Fraunfelder FT, Edwards R, Weber M, Rofsky HE, Deitch MW. Levonorgestrel implants and intracranial hypertension. *N Engl J Med* 1995;332:1720–1.
4. Faculty of Family Planning and Reproductive Health Care Clinical Effectiveness Unit. New Product Review. Desogestrel-only pill (Cerazette). *J Fam Plann Reprod Health Care* 2003;29:162–4.
5. Collaborative Study Group on the Desogestrel-containing Progestogen-only Pill. A double-blind study comparing the contraceptive efficacy, acceptability and safety of two progestogen-only pills containing desogestrel 75 µg/day or levonorgestrel 30 µg/day. *Eur J Contracept Reprod Health Care* 1998;3:169–78.
6. Johnston I, Teo C. Disorders of CSF hydrodynamics. *Childs Nerv Syst* 2000;16,10–11.

Pituitary tumours

QUESTION

For a woman with a pituitary microadenoma (prolactinoma) and who has heavy periods, would use of the LNG-IUS affect prolactin levels? (Two similar enquiries.)

POPULATION: Women with prolactinoma and heavy periods.

INTERVENTION: LNG-IUS.

OUTCOME: Effect on prolactin levels.

ANSWER

The pituitary microadenoma is an intracellar, intrapituitary benign tumour of less than 10 mm in diameter. Most frequently these tumours are prolactin-secreting (prolactinoma) and, in women, amenorrhoea and galactorrhoea result from the hormones secreted. Common symptoms of high prolactin levels include changes in menstruation, loss of libido and painful intercourse due to vaginal dryness.

Medical treatment aims to return prolactin levels to normal, reduce the size of the tumour, correct any visual abnormalities and restore normal pituitary function. Drugs such as bromocriptine or cabergoline, which are dopamine agonists, are able to shrink tumours and restore normal prolactin levels in approximately 80% of patients. Surgery is considered if patients cannot tolerate medical treatment or if it fails to reduce prolactin levels. Studies suggest that, depending on the size of the tumour and how much is removed surgically, 20–50% will recur in 5 years.[1]

The CEU was unable to identify any direct evidence on use of the LNG-IUS by women with prolactinoma. The Summary of Product Characteristics for the LNG-IUS indicates that the levonorgestrel is released directly into the uterine cavity and thus results in low plasma concentrations of progestogen. The LNG-IUS may be a good option for women with prolactinoma: it would provide effective contraception and also medical management of menorrhagia. It is unlikely to influence prolactin levels.

QUESTION

For a woman with hyperprolactinaemia due to macroprolactinaemia, would use of hormonal contraception affect prolactin levels?

POPULATION: **Women with hyperprolactinaemia due to macroprolactinaemia.**
INTERVENTION: **Hormonal contraception.**
OUTCOME: **Effect on prolactin levels.**

ANSWER

A high molecular mass form of prolactin, macroprolactin, accumulates in the sera of some individuals. Although macroprolactin exhibits limited bioavailability *in vivo*, it retains immunoreactivity. Macroprolactinaemia is a clinically and biologically heterogeneous condition. The predominance of macroprolactin (macroprolactinaemia) has long been known in hyperprolactinaemic patien whose fertility is not reduced. In a prospective study among 1106 patients with hyperprolactinaemia, serum prolactin chromatography was performed in 368 cases because of discordant clinical, biological and neuroradiological findings.[2] The 106 patients who were shown to have macroprolactinaemia were investigated prospectively (96 women, 6 men and 4 children). These were compared with 262 hyperprolactinaemic patients with normal prolactin elution patterns. This observational study identified a 10% incidence of macro-prolactinaemia in hyperprolactinaemic patients. Many conceived and achieved a successful pregnancy outcome. Prolactin levels usually stabilised over time and, with dopamine therapy, prolactin levels returned to the normal range in just under 50% of patients. Magnetic resonance imaging of the pituitary was normal in 78% of patients. The authors concluded that a diagnostic method for macroprolactinaemia should be available in all centres to avoid unnecessary hormonal or radiological investigations.

The CEU could find no evidence on the effect of hormonal contraception on prolactin or macroprolactin levels. Women with macroprolactinaemia are usually fertile and successful pregnancies are reported, therefore contraception is required to avoid unintended pregnancy.

QUESTION

For a woman with hyperprolactinaemia due to a pituitary macroadenoma, would use of DMPA affect prolactin levels? (Two similar enquiries.)

POPULATION: Women with hyperprolactinaemia due to macroadenoma.
INTERVENTION: DMPA.
OUTCOME: Effect on prolactin levels.

ANSWER

The use of DMPA does not increase basal levels of prolactin.[3,4] However, no evidence was identified on the effect of DMPA on prolactin levels specifically in women with hyperprolactinaemia.

In lactating women, DMPA has been shown to improve the quantity of breast milk and its protein concentration.[5] Basal levels of prolactin are increased in lactating women when DMPA is started 6 weeks postpartum, compared with IUD users.[6] This increase is apparent 3–6 weeks after starting DMPA.

ral medroxyprogesterone acetate (20 mg) (Provera®, Pharmacia) used to treat vasomotor flushes in postmenopausal women slightly increases serum prolactin levels.[7]

The CEU could find no evidence to show how DMPA affects prolactin levels in women who have a macroprolactinoma and increased prolactin.

QUESTION

For a woman who has had an adrenocorticotrophic hormone-secreting pituitary tumour removed surgically, which contraceptive methods can be used safely?

POPULATION: Women with previous adrenocorticotrophic hormone-secreting tumours.
INTERVENTION: Contraceptive methods.
OUTCOME: Safety.

ANSWER

A review article on brain neoplasms in women includes a useful overview of pituitary tumours, including those secreting adrenocorticotrophic hormone (ACTH).[8] Approximately 15% of all pituitary tumours secrete ACTH, resulting in classic Cushing's disease with hypertension, moon face, central obesity and a 'buffalo hump'. Excess endogenous cortisol production predisposes to osteoporosis. The preferred treatment is transsphenoidal resection, if feasible.

The CEU searched EMBASE, 1980–2003 and Medline 1966–2003 and found no publications addressing Cushing's disease or ACTH and contraception. Contraceptive choices must therefore be guided by the general *Medical Eligibility Criteria for Contraceptive Use* as outlined by the WHO. If an ACTH-secreting pituitary tumour has been fully resected, with normal endocrinology, then a woman can be offered the same range of contraceptive choices as any other woman. However, resection does not always result in cure. Where there are residual features of Cushing's disease, include hypertension, then general WHO eligibility criteria should be applied.

QUESTION

For a woman with an asymptomatic microprolactinoma and a cyst of Rathkes pouch, can combined oral contraception be used safely?

POPULATION: Women with asymptomatic microprolactinoma and a cyst of Rathkes pouch.

INTERVENTION: Combined oral contraception.

OUTCOME: Safety.

ANSWER

Rathkes pouch is a component of normal embryonic development, which eventually forms parts of the pituitary gland. This pouch normally closes early in fetal development but often a remnant persists as a cleft that lies within the pituitary gland. This remnant can give rise to a large cyst, the Rathkes cleft cyst, that may cause symptoms. Symptomatic Rathke cysts are relatively uncommon, and account for less than 1% of all primary masses within the brain.[9] Despite extensive searching, the CEU could find no direct evidence in the literature on the use of combined oral contraceptives in women with a cyst of Rathkes pouch.

A microprolactinoma is a prolactin-secreting pituitary tumour which is less than 10 mm in diameter.[1] Symptoms include amenorrhoea, infertility and excess breast milk production (galactorrhoea), which may cause the breasts to leak spontaneously. The UK Pituitary Foundation states that women with microprolactinoma may use combined oral contraception.[10] A prospective study followed up women with hyperprolactinaemia using combined oral contraceptives for 2 years. There was a nonsignificant decrease in serum prolactin levels, and the women did not experience any radiological changes.[11]

References

1. National Institute of Diabetes and Digestive and Kidney Diseases of the National Institutes of Health. *Prolactinoma*. NIH Publication No.02–3294; 2002 [www.niddk.nih.gov/health/endo/pubs/prolact/prolact.htm].
2. Vallette-Kasic S, Morange-Ramos I, Selim A, Gunz G, Morange S, Enjalbert A, *et al*. Macroprolactinemia revisited; a study on 106 patients. *J Clin Endocrinol Metab* 2002;87:581–8.
3. Mukasa FR, Sekadde-Kigondu CB, Mati JK, Njoronge JK. The pituitary reserve for gonadotrophins and prolactin in women under long-term use of depomedroxyprogesterone acetate (DMPA) as a contraceptive. *J Obstet Gynaecol East Cent Africa* 1982;1:160–3.
4. Spellacy WN, Buhi WC, Birk SA. Stimulated plasma prolactin levels in women using medroxyprogesterone acetate or an intrauterine device for contraception. *Fertil Steril* 1975;26:970–2.
5. Badraoui MHH, Hefnawi F, Bahgat R, Fawzig GE, Ismail H, Hegab M. Contraception during lactation. *Reproduction* 1982;6:9–18.
6. Ratchanon S, Taneepanichskul S. Depot medroxyprogesterone acetate and basal serum

prolactin levels in lactating women. *Obstet Gynecol* 2000;96:926–8.

7. Schiff I, Tulchinsky D, Cramer D, Ryan KJ. Oral medroxyprogesterone in the treatment of postmenopausal symptoms. *JAMA* 1980;244:1443–5.

8. Swensen R, Kirsch W. Brain neoplasms in women: a review. *Clin Obstet Gynecol* 2002;45:904–27.

9. Cushings Help and Support. Rathke Cleft Cyst. 2005 [www.cushing-help.com/rathke.htm].

10. The Pituitary Foundation. Prolactinoma. 2004 [www.pituitary.org.uk/resources/prolactinoma.htm].

11. Testa G, Vegetti W, Motta T, Alagna F, Bianchedi D, Carlucci C, *et al*. Two-year treatment with oral contraceptives in hyperprolactinemic patients. *Contraception* 1998;58:69–73.

Miscellaneous neurological disorders

QUESTION

For a woman with a past history of acoustic neuroma who has acne and is 7 weeks postpartum, can she use combined oral contraception safely?

POPULATION: **Postpartum women with past history of acoustic neuroma and acne.**
INTERVENTION: **Combined oral contraception.**
OUTCOME: **Safety.**

ANSWER

Despite extensive searching, the CEU could find no information in the literature on the use of combined oral contraception in women with a history of acoustic neuroma.

FFPRHC CEU guidance recommends that breastfeeding women should be advised that combined oral contraception is not generally recommended between 6 weeks and 6 months postpartum. However, if breastfeeding is established, combined oral contraception may be considered if other contraceptive methods are unacceptable.[1] The *WHO Medical Eligibility Criteria for Contraceptive Use* recommends that women who are more than 21 days postpartum and are not breastfeeding, can use combined oral contraception without restriction (WHO category 1).

The CEU recommends that, generally, a woman with a past history of acoustic neuroma who has acne is around 7 weeks postpartum and is breastfeeding, should not use combined oral contraception until she is 6 months postpartum. However, if breastfeeding is established and other methods of contraception are unacceptable, combined oral contraception might be initiated after counselling.

The CEU recommends that that if such a woman is not breastfeeding, she may use combined oral contraception. She should be advised that there is no evidence on the use of combined oral contraception in women with a past history of acoustic neuroma. Dianette (35 micrograms ethinylestradiol and 2 mg cyproterone acetate) can be used for the treatment of acne and as contraception. However, it should be stopped 3–4 months after the acne has resolved or if there is no improvement in lesions. 'Second-generation' combined pills (such as those containing levonorgestrel or desogestrel) have been shown to significantly reduce the number of acne lesions, and are thought to be associated with a smaller risk of VTE than Dianette. These pills should be considered by women needing both contraception and treatment for acne.

QUESTION

For women with acute macular neuroretinopathy, are hormonal contraceptives associated with the onset of, or deterioration in, this condition?

POPULATION:	Women with acute macular neuroretinopathy.
INTERVENTION:	Hormonal contraception.
OUTCOME:	Effects on acute macular neuroretinopathy.

ANSWER

A review article summarises the entire experience of the English-speaking world with the condition of acute macular neuroretinopathy (AMNR).[2] The condition was first described in 1975 and since then, only 41 cases have been described in the English-language medical literature. Symptoms usually include temporary or permanent vision loss associated with uni- or bilateral paracentral scotomas. Typical lesions are seen biomicroscopically in a flower-petal arrangement around the centre of the macula. The lesions are thought to lie in the outer sensory retinal layers. Lesions and visual loss may resolve spontaneously, or may persist. The pathophysiology of AMNR is unclear, the causes uncertain and there is no specific treatment.

Full details of all 41 reported cases are provided in the review. Thirty-four of the cases were female, aged between 20 and 53 years, mean age 27 years. Oral contraceptive use was reported by 17/34 female patients. However, the review authors point out that this rate of contraceptive use in women of this age group is unsurprising and no conclusions can be drawn about causality.

The review authors consider an infectious process to be a promising aetiological association; 18/41 cases had a history of influenza-like illness less than one week prior to their ocular events.

QUESTION

For women with cerebral palsy, can combined oral contraception be used safely?

POPULATION:	**Women with cerebral palsy.**
INTERVENTION:	**Combined oral contraception.**
OUTCOME:	**Safety.**

ANSWER

Cerebral palsy comprises a group of motor or postural abnormalities observed during early development that may be due to varying prenatal, perinatal or postnatal events.[3] Evidence suggests that prenatal factors (genetic abnormalities, toxins, infections or vascular insufficiency) are associated with 70–80% of cases of cerebral palsy. Although multiple gestation may not increase the risk of cerebral palsy, if one twin dies *in utero*, the surviving twin has a higher chance than a singleton pregnancy of developing the condition. In 10% or fewer cases, the cause of cerebral palsy may be birth asphyxia. Even in these instances however, prenatal factors such as congenital brain malformations or intrauterine growth restriction may have caused perinatal fetal distress. Classification systems divide patients into mild, moderate and severe types depending on their disabilities and these include spastic hemiplegia, spastic diplegia, dyskinesia (extrapyramidal) and spastic quadriplegia. Complications associated with the condition include cognitive difficulties, gastrointestinal problems, dental caries, sensory limitations and seizures.[3]

The *WHO Medical Eligibility Criteria for Contraceptive Use* has not addressed contraceptive choices for women with cerebral palsy. It does address the issue of prolonged immobilisation, but in relation to major surgery, and advises that for women with major immobilisation, combined oral contraception should not be used (WHO category 4).

The CEU could find no evidence in the literature that a combined oral contraceptive would not be a safe option for a woman with cerebral palsy provided that she is not severely immobilised, which may indicate an increased risk of VTE.

QUESTION

For a woman aged over 40 years with Charcot Marie Tooth syndrome, what methods of contraception can be used safely?

POPULATION: Women aged over 40 years with Charcot Marie Tooth syndrome.
INTERVENTION: Contraception.
OUTCOME: Safety.

ANSWER

Charcot Marie Tooth syndrome is a neurological disease which affects around 40/100 000 people in the UK. The disease usually progresses slowly and can cause degeneration of the muscles of the foot, lower leg, hand and forearm.[4]

Despite extensive searching, the CEU could find no information in the literature on the use of contraception by women with Charcot Marie Tooth syndrome.

FFPRHC CEU Guidance on *Contraception for Women Aged Over 40 Years*[5] advises that women aged over 40 years should be informed that, although a natural decline in fertility occurs from the age of 37 years, effective contraception is still required to prevent unplanned pregnancy. No contraceptive method is contraindicated by age alone and women should be advised of risks and non-contraceptive benefits of all contraceptive methods.

If women are immobilised due to Charcot Marie Tooth disease, progestogen-only methods or an IUD may be more suitable than estrogen-containing contraception.

QUESTION

For women with congenital glaucoma, can combined oral contraception be used safely?

POPULATION: Women with congenital glaucoma.
INTERVENTION: Combined oral contraception.
OUTCOME: Safety.

ANSWER

Glaucoma refers to eye diseases associated with an increase in intraocular pressure and is classified into primary open-angle glaucoma, acute angle-closure glaucoma and the much rarer congenital form.[6] About 1–2% of adults over the age of 40 years in the UK have primary open-angle glaucoma and this increases to about 7% in those over the age of 75 years.[6] The prevalence of acute angle-closure glaucoma is low; it occurs in about 1/1000 people over the age of 40 years.

After a detailed literature search, the CEU was only able to find studies that examined the risk of developing different eye diseases associated with oral contraceptive use. Clinicians should therefore be guided by the advice of an ophthalmologist about the risk of an increase in intraocular pressure if a woman who has congenital glaucoma chooses to use the combined oral contraceptive pill.

Two cohort studies, the Royal College of General Practitioners' oral contraception study[7] and the Oxford Family Planning Association contraceptive study[8] investigated the relationship between oral contraceptive use and certain eye diseases. The General Practitioners' study followed 23 000 users of oral contraception (who were divided into current users and former users) and a similar number of never-users over a 14-month period. The Oxford study recruited 17 032 white, married women aged 25–39 years from 17 family planning clinics in England and Scotland; 90% of these were followed up after reaching age 45 years and divided into never-users, those who had used oral contraceptives for eight years or longer and other durations of use (which were excluded from the analysis).

In their analyses, these studies considered conjunctivitis, keratitis, iritis, lacrimal disease, strabismus, cataract, glaucoma, retinal detachment and retinal vascular lesions. There was a two-fold increase in the risk of retinal vascular lesions in recent pill users in both studies but the increase was statistically significant only in the General Practitioners' study.[9] The conclusion reached was that oral contraceptive use does not appear to increase the risk of eye disease although there is a possible increase in the risk of retinal vascular lesions.[9]

QUESTION

For women with multiple sclerosis (MS), is the use of hormonal contraception associated with any particular benefits or adverse effects?

POPULATION: Women with multiple sclerosis.
INTERVENTION: Hormonal contraception.
OUTCOME: Specific benefits and adverse effects.

ANSWER

A review article provides a useful overview of MS.[10] MS is an inflammatory, autoimmune disorder of the central nervous system with a lifetime risk of 1/400. It is characterised by acute, focal, inflammatory demyelination. Limited remyelination occurs, culminating in the chronic, multifocal, sclerotic plaques from which the disease gets its name. The symptoms and signs of multiple sclerosis reflect disordered neural conduction at the affected sites. The cause of multiple sclerosis is said to be an interplay between genes and the environment, with an increased rate among first-degree relatives of sufferers. Attempts to implicate specific environmental agents have been frustrating, but infections with *Chlamydia pneumoniae* and herpes virus are among the suggestions. Although generally comprehensive, this review makes no mention of a possible role for hormonal contraception in causing or exacerbating MS.

One cohort study examined the influence of oral contraceptives on the risk of multiple sclerosis.[11] The authors point out that a national Handbook of Contraceptive Practice, MIMS and individual Summaries of Product Characteristics all state that MS is a 'relative contraindication', a 'special precaution' or a 'condition requiring careful observation' for use of combined oral contraception. However, the reasons behind these cautions are unclear. In a cohort study of 46 000 women, these authors found no significant difference in the incidence of MS among current users, ever-users and never-users of combined oral contraception. Similarly, among women with MS in the cohort, there were no significant differences in survival between current users, ever-users and never-users. The authors concluded that neither their own study, nor others published in the literature, provided an explanation for the precautionary notes in prescribing advice.

A more recent paper summarised two cohort studies examining oral contraceptives and the incidence of MS.[12] Oral contraceptive use was not associated with the risk of MS. This paper provided no data on the impact of oral contraception on established MS.

A further paper described the proceedings of an interdisciplinary workshop on the effects of sex steroids on neurological diseases.[13] Only the abstract was accessible by the CEU but it included the statement that 'manifestation and course of multiple sclerosis are not substantially affected by sex steroids'.

The abstract only of a further review was accessed by the CEU.[14] This included the statement 'it has been conclusively demonstrated that susceptibility to multiple sclerosis in women is not influenced by the use of oral contraceptives'. It also indicated that 'a trial of estrogens in the treatment of multiple sclerosis is ongoing', suggesting a hypothesis that sex steroids might have a beneficial effect. A further article aimed 'to clarify interactions between oral contraception and the main neurological diseases'[15] and stated that 'oral contraception has no influence in other diseases such as multiple sclerosis'.

A case report summarised details of four patients with MS suffering cerebral venous thrombosis.[16] Two of these patients were current, or past, users of oral contraceptives. The conclusion of the report was that the association of cerebral venous thrombosis and MS was probably fortuitous. There was no suggestion that MS and hormonal contraception were acting as independent risk factors for the condition.

Thus, the CEU literature search identified little research evidence to guide contraceptive choices for women with MS. However, the limited evidence available provides reassurance that hormonal contraception has little, if any, influence on the incidence or course of multiple sclerosis . Thus, the CEU advises that women with MS be offered the same range of contraceptive choices as other women. Standard good practice, including assessment of medical eligibility and enquiry about possible drug interactions, should be applied.

QUESTION

For women with neurofibromatosis and a ventriculoperitoneal shunt, is the progestogen-only pill a suitable contraceptive?

POPULATION: Women with neurofibromatosis and ventriculoperitoneal shunt.
INTERVENTION: Progestogen-only contraception.
OUTCOME: Safety and appropriateness.

ANSWER

Neurofibromatosis (NF) is a neurocutaneous disorder consisting of two types. NF-1 (also referred to as von Recklinghausen's disease) occurs in 1/3000 people and accounts for 97% of all cases and NF-2 accounts for the rest. Neurofibromatosis is inherited in an autosomal dominant fashion. Approximately 30–50% of cases are attributable to spontaneous new mutations. Skin involvement may be focal (*café au lait* macules) or diffuse. The macules can occur on most sites of the body. In patients with NF-1, the most common benign

tumour is the neurofibroma. Neurofibromas arise indiscriminately along a nerve, either cutaneously or subcutaneously. Plexiform neurofibromas wrap in and around vital structures and may cause pronounced disfigurement. Rate of progression cannot be predicted. Recognised central nervous tumours include schwannomas, astrocytomas and meningiomas. Central nervous system manifestations of NF-1 include aqueduct stenosis, hydrocephalus and seizures. Of patients with NF-1, 25–40% may have learning disabilities. Hypertension may occur, either essential hypertension or secondary hypertension due to phaeochromocytoma, renal artery stenosis, neurofibromas that compress the kidneys and renal arteries, renal artery dysplasia, Wilm's tumour, or coarctation of the abdominal or thoracic aorta. Other features include loss of vision or hearing, skeletal problems and constipation.[17,18] Fertility is not affected. Avoiding pregnancy until preconception counselling can assess the woman's general health and provide appropriate genetic assessment is desirable.

A ventriculoperitoneal shunt is a small tube that is placed inside the cerebral ventricle and tunnelled underneath the skin to the peritoneum. It reduces the amount of cerebral spinal fluid in the brain by draining it into the peritoneal space. Complications include obstruction of the shunt. This can lead to vomiting, vision problems, irritability and tiredness, loss of coordination or balance, difficulty in waking up or staying awake, seizures and decline in work performance. A shunt infection can also cause the shunt to fail.

The CEU was unable to identify any papers referring specifically to neuro-fibromatosis or ventriculoperitoneal shunts and contraceptive options.

Regarding existing hypertension, the progestogen-only pill, injectable, implant or intrauterine systems are all suitable options when blood pressure is adequately controlled (WHO categories 1 and 2). Only when the systolic blood pressure is over 160 mmHg or diastolic blood pressure is over 100 mmHg do the risks of progestogen-only injectables generally outweigh the benefits (WHO category 3). For other progestogen-only methods, the benefits still generally outweigh any risks (WHO category 2).

Regarding epilepsy, all progestogen-only methods are suitable (WHO category 1).

Pragmatically, there may be problems with the progestogen-only pill if learning disabilities or visual impairment are present and medication is not administered by carers. The presence of macules or neurofibromas may make insertion or removal of progestogen-only implants problematic. The progestogen-only pill, injectable progestogen and implants may worsen pre-existing constipation. There is no evidence regarding need for antibiotics to prevent shunt infection following IUD insertion.

QUESTION

For women using combined oral contraception, progestogen-only contraception or HRT, is there any association with deterioration of otosclerosis? (Two similar enquiries.)

POPULATION: Women with otosclerosis.

INTERVENTION: Using combined oral contraception, progestogen-only contraception or HRT.

OUTCOME: Deterioration of otosclerosis.

ANSWER

Otosclerosis is a disorder of hardening of the bones of the middle ear, causing progressive hearing loss that is often reversible.[19] Most cases of otosclerosis involve the smallest bone, the stapes, which becomes calcified or hardened by overgrowth of new bone. About three-quarters of patients with otosclerosis develop tinnitus, while in 25–30% of patients balance problems including unsteadiness, dizziness or vertigo may also occur. The primary treatment for otosclerosis is surgical stapedectomy, where the top portion of the stapes is removed and a small prosthesis inserted.[19]

Many cases of otosclerosis are genetic and the disorder affects women twice as often as men and often worsens rapidly during pregnancy. Even though heredity plays an important role, a significant number of cases arise from non-genetic causes, which are currently unknown.[20]

The Summaries of Product Characteristics for various combined oral contraceptives state that the use of combined oral contraception is contra-indicated if a woman has experienced deterioration of otosclerosis during pregnancy or with previous steroid use. Some Summaries advise that with the deterioration or first appearance of otosclerosis, combined oral contraception should be strictly medically supervised or discontinued.

Data from the Oxford Family Planning Association contraceptive cohort study, which included 17 032 women who were followed up for up to 26 years, was analysed by Vessey and Painter for evidence of an association between combined oral contraceptives and ear disease. Thirty-one subjects were identified who had otosclerosis. The relative risk of having otosclerosis in subjects who were ever-users of combined oral contraceptives was 1.0 (95% CI 0.4–2.2); for current or recent users was 0.8 (95% CI 0.3–2.4); and for past users was 1.0 (95% CI 0.6–1.8). Therefore they did not find any significant association between combined oral contraceptives and otosclerosis.[21]

The Summary of Product Characteristics for the contraceptive implant, Implanon, states that an association between the use of progestogens and otosclerosis has not been established.

A study by Strachan in 1996 reported the case of one woman who developed tinnitus and hearing loss in one ear, two days after taking estradiol (Climaval®, Novartis) as HRT.[22] The tinnitus and hearing loss disappeared when the preparation was stopped and she began taking corticosteroids.

Hartmann and Huber conducted a systematic review of the literature on contra-indications contained in pharmaceutical Summaries of Product Characteristics of five estrogen replacement preparations.[23] The conclusion reached, contrary to the Summaries of Product Characteristics, was that otosclerosis, among other conditions, is not a contraindication to HRT.

The CEU was unable to find any evidence that progestogen-only contraceptives can increase the risk of deterioration of otosclerosis. It is known that otosclerosis reacts to hormonal changes and worsens during pregnancy. There have been suggestions that the combined pill and HRT can worsen the condition, but there is no evidence to support this.[24] Women who are anxious about using a hormonal method of contraception may wish to consider use of an IUD or a barrier method.

QUESTION

For women with retinoblastoma, can DMPA be used safely?

POPULATION:	Women with retinoblastoma.
INTERVENTION:	DMPA.
OUTCOME:	Safety.

ANSWER

Retinoblastoma is the most common malignant ocular tumour in children, occurring in 1/20 000 live births.[25–28] Children are usually affected between birth and the age of 7 years.[25,28] In the majority of cases, retinoblastoma is a sporadic non-heritable malignancy with no increased risk of further malignancies in the affected child.[25] However in 40% of cases, retinoblastoma can be due to a heritable mutation in the RB1 gene. Heritable retinoblastoma may be bilateral or unilateral and is associated with a predisposition to develop other malignancies in later life.[25,26,28,29]

The Summary of Product Characteristics for DMPA advises that the history or emergence of acute visual disturbances of any kind requires careful consideration and appropriate investigation before using DMPA.

Despite extensive searching, the CEU could find no other information in the literature regarding the use of DMPA in women with a history of retinoblastoma.

QUESTION

For women with Sydenham's chorea, can hormonal contraception be used safely?

POPULATION: Women with Sydenham's chorea.
INTERVENTION: Hormonal contraception.
OUTCOME: Safety.

ANSWER

The CEU identified one review article which provides an overview of Sydenham's chorea.[30] Sydenham's chorea is a major manifestation of rheumatic fever, characterised by a range of neuropsychiatric symptoms. Some of the symptoms are similar to those seen in Tourette syndrome and in childhood-onset obsessive-compulsive disorder. Sydenham's chorea is thought to arise when antibodies directed against group A beta-haemolytic streptococcus cross-react with epitopes in various brain areas, causing motor and behavioural disturbances.

Motor symptoms typically associated with Sydenham's chorea include frank chorea, ballismus, facial grimacing, tongue fasciculations and disturbances of gait and speech. The movements of typical chorea are described as brief, arrhythmic and to 'dance' over the body.

We were able to access only the abstracts of further useful review articles.[31–34] The first of these[31] indicates that chronic treatment with penicillin is required to prevent future attacks. Some adult disorders (including chorea gravidarum, obsessive-compulsive disorder, Tourette syndrome and schizophrenia) may sometimes have their origins in previous Sydenham's chorea.

We also identified a case report and literature review on chorea and contraceptives.[35] This paper indicates that more than 50 cases of oral contraceptive-induced chorea have been described. In most cases, patients gave a past history of basal ganglia abnormalities including Sydenham's chorea and chorea gravidarum. In a few cases, the contraceptive-induced chorea appeared to have arisen *de novo*.

A further paper on oral contraceptive-induced chorea indicated that 'use of oral contraceptives is a recognised but infrequent cause of chorea.[36] This type of chorea has usually been considered a reactivation of Sydenham's chorea by an unknown mechanism'.

The Summary of Product Characteristics for a typical combined oral contraceptive (Microgynon) lists Sydenham's chorea among conditions which 'require strict medical supervision during medication with oral contraceptives. Deterioration or first appearance of the condition may indicate that use of the oral contraceptive should be discontinued'.

Thus, oral contraceptives have been described both as inducing re-activation of Sydenham's chorea and of inducing chorea *de novo*. However, these adverse effects are very rare (around 50 cases in the world literature). The Summary of Product Characteristics for a typical combined oral contraceptive indicates that it may be used under strict medical supervision for a woman with Sydenham's chorea. The CEU supports this view and suggests that either a combined, or progestogen-only, pill may be used. If deterioration of the symptoms of Sydenham's chorea occurs, then clearly the method should be stopped and a non-hormonal method of contraception substituted.

QUESTION

For women with Takayasu arteritis and other medical problems, what methods of contraception can be used safely?

POPULATION: Women with Takayasu arteritis.

INTERVENTION: Contraception.

OUTCOME: Safety.

ANSWER

Takayasu's arteritis is a chronic systemic inflammatory disease that affects the aorta, its primary branches and sometimes the pulmonary and coronary arteries.[37]

Despite extensive searching, the CEU could find no specific information on the use of contraceptive methods in women with Takayasu's arteritis.

Takayasu's arteritis may be associated with stroke. The *WHO Medical Eligibility Criteria for Contraceptive Use* recommends that combined oral contraception is contraindicated in women with stroke (history of cerebrovascular accident) (WHO category 4). The risks of using DMPA generally outweigh the benefits (WHO category 3). For use of the progestogen-only pill, implant and the LNG-IUS, the benefits generally outweigh the risks (WHO category 2). The IUD can be used without restriction (WHO category 1). The Summaries of Product Characteristics for some combined pills, progestogen-only pills, and the LNG-IUS also recommend that they are contraindicated in women with a history of stroke.

Smoking acts as an additional risk factor for arterial disease. The *WHO Medical Eligibility Criteria for Contraceptive Use* recommends that in women aged less than 35 years, the benefits of using combined pills outweigh the risks in women who smoke (WHO category 2). However, in women aged over 35 years who smoke more than 15 cigarettes a day, combined pills should not be used (WHO category 4).

FFPRHC CEU guidance on first prescription of combined oral contraception[38] advises that in heavy smokers (more than 15 cigarettes/day), the risk of myocardial infarction is increased with combined pill use (relative risk 20.8; 95% CI 5.2–83.1), as is the risk of ischaemic stroke (odds ratio 7.2; 95% CI 3.23–16.1),[39] and VTE (odds ratio 2.0; 95% CI 1.3–3.3).[40,41] As the risks of stroke, myocardial infarction and VTE increase with age, smokers over the age of 35 years are advised against the use of combined oral contraception.[38]

The *WHO Medical Eligibility Criteria for Contraceptive Use* recommends that the progestogen-only pill, DMPA, progestogen implant, LNG-IUS and IUD can all be used without restriction in women of any age who smoke (WHO category 1).

Patients with Takayasu's arteritis are often taking anti-inflammatory and immunosuppressive drugs. BNF states that combined oral contraceptives increase plasma concentrations of corticosteroids (prednisolone).

FFPRHC CEU guidance on drug interactions with hormonal contraception[42] advises that the bioactive pool of some drugs (corticosteroids, ciclosporin, theophylline and ropinirole) can be increased by concomitant hormonal contraceptive use. Depending on the nature and clinical effect of the drug concerned, potentially toxic effects can result. An increase in corticosteroid concentrations has little if any clinical effect.

It is important that patients with Takayasu's arteritis recognise the effects of anti-inflammatory and immunosuppressive drugs on pregnancy and fertility.[43] Prednisolone and other glucocorticoids are generally considered safe for a developing fetus but may cause, or worsen, diabetes mellitus in pregnant women. BNF states that corticosteroids and aspirin reduce the excretion of methotrexate (increased risk of toxicity).[43] Methotrexate is a folate antagonist and folic acid supplementation prevents methotrexate toxicity.[44] Women taking methotrexate who wish to become pregnant should discontinue treatment under medical supervision at least 3 months before stopping contraception and continue the use of folic acid.[45]

From the evidence available, the CEU recommends that combined oral contraception is contraindicated in women who are heavy smokers and have a history of stroke, even if due to Takayasu arteritis. Therefore, in women who are heavy smokers with Takayasu arteritis, a history of stroke, memory problems and a history of bilateral cortical infarcts (as illustrated by the patient prompting this particular enquiry), long-acting progestogen-only methods (implants, injectables) or intrauterine contraception may be used, and are likely to be manageable by women with memory problems.

References

1. Faculty of Family Planning and Reproductive Health Care Clinical Effectiveness Unit. Contraceptive choices for breastfeeding women. *J Fam Plann Reprod Health Care* 2004;30:181–9.
2. Turbeville SD, Cowan LD, Gass DM. Acute Macular Neuroretinopathy: A review of the Literature. *Surv Ophthalmol* 2003;48:1–11.
3. Ratanawongsa B. Cerebral palsy [www.emedicine.com/topic533.htm.].
4. Charcot Marie Tooth Association. United Kingdom. An overview of Charcot-Marie-Tooth-Disorders. 2004 [www.charcot-marie-tooth.org/about_cmt/overview.php].
5. Faculty of Family Planning and Reproductive Healthcare Clinical Effectiveness Unit. Contraception for women aged over 40 years. *J Fam Plann Reprod Health Care* 2005;31:51–64.
6. Department of Health. *Prodigy Guidance. Glaucoma.* London: DH; 2001 [www.prodigy.nhs.uk/guidance.asp?gt=Glaucoma].
7. Royal College of General Practitioners. *Oral Contraceptives and Health.* London: Pitman Medical; 2004.
8. Vessey MP, Doll R, Peto R, Johnson B, Wiggins P, *et al*. A long-term follow-up study of women using different methods of contraception- an interim report. *J Biosoc Sci* 1976;8:337–427.
9. Vessey MP, Hannaford P, Mant J, Painter R, Frith P, Chappel D. Oral contraception and eye disease: findings in two large cohort studies. *Br J Ophthalmol* 1998;82:538–42.
10. Compston A, Coles A. Multiple sclerosis. *Lancet* 2002;359:1221–31.
11. Thorogood M, Hannaford P. The influence of oral contraceptives on the risk of multiple sclerosis. *Br J Obstet Gynaecol* 1998;105:1296–9.
12. Hernan MA, Hohol MJ, Olek MJ, Spiegelman D, Ascherio A. Oral contraceptives and the incidence of multiple sclerosis. *Neurology* 2000;55:848–53.
13. Hufnagel A, Breckwoldt M, Hosli I, Ried S, Tettenborn B, Kuhl H. Influence exercised by estrogens and gestagens on neurological diseases. *Aktuelle Neurol* 2000;27:106–9.

14. Duquette P. Hormonal factors in multiple sclerosis. *International Multiple Sclerosis Journal* 2002;9:17–25.

15. Combs C, Redondo A, Rey A. Contraception and neurology. *Ann Med Int* 2002;153:363–7.

16. Vandenberghe N, Debouverie M, Anxionnat R, Clavelou P, Bouuly S, Weber M. Cerebral venous thrombosis in four patients with multiple sclerosis. *Eur J Neurol* 2003;10:63–6.

17. Gutmann D, Aylsworth A, Carey JC, Korf B, Marks J, Pyeritz RE, *et al*. The diagnostic evaluation and multidisciplinary management of neurofibromatosis 1 and neurofibromatosis 2. *JAMA* 1997;278:51–7.

18. Karnes P. Neurofibromatosis: a common neurocutaneous disorder. *Mayo Clin Proc* 1998;73:1071–6.

19. Harris JP. Otosclerosis [www.surgery.ucsd.edu/ent/PatientInfo/info_otosclerosis.html].

20. Sabitha R, Ramalingam R, Ramalingam KK, Sivakumaran TA, Ramash A. Genetics of otosclerosis. *J Laryngol Otolaryngol* 1997;111:109–12.

21. Vessey M, Painter R. Oral contraception and ear disease: Findings in a large cohort study. *Contraception* 2001;63:61–3.

22. Curtis B. Hormones and tinnitus [www.tinnitusformula.com/info/articles/cond/hormones.asp].

23. Hartmann BW, Huber JC. The mythology of hormone replacement therapy (comment). (Review) *Br J Obstet Gynaecol* 1997;104:163–8.

24. Mcferran D. British Tinnitus Association. Otosclerosis. 2001 [www.tinnitus.org.uk/information/info%20sheets/front%20page/otosclerosis.htm].

25. Chen CS, Suthers G, Carroll J, Rudzki Z, Muecke J. Sarcoma and familial retinoblastoma. *Clin Exp Ophthamol* 2003;31:392–6.

26. Gallie BL, Muncaster M, Cohen BL, Gill RM, Hamel PA, Phillips RA. Retinoblastoma mutations: initiation versus progression of cancer. In Novak JF, editor. *Osterosarcoma Research Conference 1991.* Pittsburgh: Hogrefe and Huber: 1993. p. 367–73.

27. Dunn JM, Phillips RA, Zhu X, Becker A, Gallie BL. Mutation in the RB1 gene and their effects on transcription. *Mol Cell Biol* 1989;9:4594–604.

28. Sanders BM, Draper GJ, Kingston JE. Retinoblastoma in Great Britain 1969–80: Incidences, treatment and survival. *Br J Ophthalmol* 1988;72:576–83.

29. Kudson AG. Hereditary cancer: two hits revisited. *J Cancer Res Clin Oncol* 1996;122:135–40.

30. Murphy TK, Goodman WK, Ayoub EM, Voeller KK. On defining Sydenham's chorea: where do we draw the line? *Biol Psychiatr* 2000;47:851–7.

31. Moore, DP. Neuropsychiatic aspects of Sydenham's chorea: a comprehensive review. *J Clin Psych* 1996;57:407–414.

32. Marques-Dias MJ, Mercadante MT, Tucker D, Lombroso P. Sydenham's chorea. *Psychiatr Clin North Am* 1997;20:809–820.

33. Van der Merwe PL, Kalis NN. Sydenham's chorea – analysis of 27 patients and a review of the literature. *S Afr Med J* 1997;87:C157–60.

34. Bonthius, DJ, Karacay B. Sydenham's chorea: not gone and not forgotten. *Semin Pediatr Neurol* 2003;10:11–19.

35. Vela L, Sfakianakis GN, Heros D, Koller W, Singer C. Chorea and Contraceptives: case report with pet study and review of the literature. *Mov Disord* 2004;19:349–52.

36. Miranda, M, Cardoso, F, Giovannoni, G, and Church, A. Oral contraceptive induced chorea: another condition associated with anti-basal ganglia antibodies. *J Neurol Neurosurg Psychiatr* 2004;75:327–328.

37. Neidhart B, Kosek R, Bachmann LM, Stey C. Exertional dyspnea as initial manifestation of Takayasu's arteritis- A case report and literature review. *BMC Pulm Med* 2001;1:3.

38. Faculty of Family Planning and Reproductive Health Care Clinical Effectiveness Unit. First prescription of combined oral contraception. *J Fam Plann Reprod Health Care* 2003;29:209–22.
39. World Health Organization. WHO Collaborative Study of Cardiovascular Disease and Sex Steroid Contraception. Ischaemic stroke and combined oral contraception: results of an international, multicentre, case–control study. *Lancet* 1996;348:498–505.
40. Jick H, Kaye JA, Vasilakis-Scaramozza C, Jick SS. Risk of venous thromboembolism among users of third generation oral contraceptives compared with users of oral contraceptives with levonorgestrel before and after 1995: cohort and case–control analysis. *BMJ* 2000;321:1190–5.
41. Farmer RDT, Lawrenson RA, Todd JC, Williams TJ, MacRae KD, Tyrer F, *et al.* A comparison of the risks of venous thromboembolic disease in association with different combined oral contraceptives. *Br J Pharmacol* 2000;49:580–90.
42. Faculty of Family Planning and Reproductive Health Care Clinical Effectiveness Unit. Drug interactions with hormonal contraception. *J Fam Plann Reprod Health Care* 2005;31:139–50.
43. Merkel PA. Fertility, contraception and pregnancy in patients with Takayasu's arteritis [www.takayasus.com/merkel.html].
44. Morgan SL, Baggott JE, Lee JY, Alarcon GS. Folic acid supplementation prevents deficient blood folate levels and hyperhomocysteinemai during longterm, low dose methotrexate therapy for rheumatoid arthritis: implications for cardiovascular disease prevention. *J Rheumatol* 1998;25:441–6.
45. Janssen NM, Genta MS. The effects of immunosuppressive and anti-inflammatory medications on fertility, pregnancy, and lactation. *Arch Intern Med* 2000;160:610–19.

Cerebrovascular disorders

QUESTION

Can women who have suffered a brain haemorrhage use hormonal contraception safely? (Two similar enquiries.)

POPULATION: Women who have suffered a brain haemorrhage.

INTERVENTION: Hormonal contraception.

OUTCOME: Safety.

ANSWER

About 80% of subarachnoid haemorrhages are a result of rupture of a berry aneurysm. Berry aneurysms are localised dilatations of an intracranial artery and are common, affecting approximately 5% of the population. The incidence of asymptomatic unruptured cerebral aneurysms is greater among people who have a first or second-degree relative with a history of subarachnoid haemorrhage than among people with no family history. An intracranial aneurysm may be detected by non-invasive magnetic resonance angiography but even if an aneurysm is detected, this does not mean that rupture is likely.

Little evidence was available directly investigating hormonal contraceptive use in women with a family history of berry aneurysm. A population-based case–control study,[1] which investigated the relationship between subarachnoid haemorrhage and hormonal factors, found that premenopausal women who did not smoke or have a history of hypertension (which are independent risk factors for haemorrhagic stroke) had a reduced risk of subarachnoid haemorrhage compared with age-matched postmenopausal women (odds ratio 0.24; 95% CI 0.09–0.68).

There is no increased risk of haemorrhagic stroke in normotensive non-smokers under the age of 35 years who are current combined pill users. Most studies suggest there is no increased risk of haemorrhagic stroke in relation to duration of combined oral contraceptive use or past use. Neither estrogen nor progestogen appears to affect the risk of haemorrhagic stroke.

The *WHO Medical Eligibility Criteria* suggests, for women with a personal history of cerebrovascular event: combined oral contraception should not be used (WHO category 4); progestogen-only pills and implants can be used as benefits generally outweigh risks (WHO category 2); and injectable progestogens are not recommended as risks generally outweigh benefits (WHO category 3).

Contraceptive choice should be based on individual risk factors for subarachnoid haemorrhage such as age, smoking, hypertension, family history of haemorrhage and berry aneurysm and patient choice.

QUESTION

For a young woman aged under 16 years who has had a brain haemorrhage, can progestogen-only contraception be used safely.

POPULATION:	Women aged under 16 years who have suffered brain haemorrhage.
INTERVENTION:	Progestogen-only contraception.
OUTCOME:	Safety.

ANSWER

The *WHO Medical Eligibility Criteria for Contraceptive Use* recommends that for women with a history of stroke, the risks of using DMPA generally out-weigh the benefits (WHO category 3). On the other hand, the benefits of using the progestogen-only pill, the etonogestrel implant or the LNG-IUS generally outweigh the risks (WHO category 2).

Any competent young person, regardless of age, can give valid (voluntary) consent to medical treatment. For young people under the age of 16 years, competence to consent to contraceptive treatment has to be demonstrated. Competence is demonstrated if the young person is able to understand the treatment, its purpose and nature and why it is being proposed; is able to understand its benefits, risks, and alternatives; is able to understand in broader terms what the consequences of the treatment will be; and is able to retain the information for long enough to use it and weigh it up in order to arrive at a decision.

Following the case of Gillick versus West Norfolk and Wisbech Area Health Authority (1986), the Department of Health provided guidance for clinicians specifically relating to contraceptive provision for those aged less than 16 years. The Law Lords' ruling (the Fraser ruling) states that a clinician may provide contraceptive advice and treatment to a young person under the age of 16 years without parental consent provided he has confirmed that the young person is competent and that the Fraser criteria are met.

The CEU published comprehensive guidance on contraceptive choices for young people in October 2004.[2]

QUESTION

For women with a history of stroke, can the LNG-IUS be used safely?

POPULATION: Women with a history of stroke.
INTERVENTION: LNG-IUS.
OUTCOME: Safety.

ANSWER

The *WHO Medical Eligibility Criteria for Contraceptive Use* recommends that the benefits for women with stroke (history of a cerebrovascular accident) using the LNG-IUS generally outweigh any risks (WHO category 2). However, the Summary of Product Characteristics for the LNG-IUS recommends that it is contraindicated in women with previous arterial disease, such as stroke or myocardial infarction.

Despite extensive searching, the CEU could find no other information on the use of the LNG-IUS in women with a history of stroke. The CEU recommends that women with a history of stroke may use the LNG-IUS, but should be informed that there is a lack of evidence on this topic.

QUESTION

For women with a history of stroke while taking the combined oral contraceptive pill, can the LNG-IUS be used safely? (Two similar enquiries.)

POPULATION: Women with a history of stroke while taking combined oral contraception.

INTERVENTION: LNG-IUS.

OUTCOME: Safety.

ANSWER

The third edition of the *WHO Medical Eligibility Criteria for Contraceptive Use* recommends that for women with a past history of stroke (cerebrovascular accident), the benefits of using the LNG-IUS generally outweigh the risks (WHO category 2).

An international, multicentre, case–control trial by WHO[3] identified no significant changes in the odds ratio for stroke, VTE or acute myocardial infarction in association with use of oral or injectable progestogen-only methods. This should be reassuring for LNG-IUS users who have an even lower dose of progestogen in the systemic circulation.

Despite extensive searching, the CEU could find no other information on the use of the LNG-IUS in women with a past history of stroke.

QUESTION

For women who have had a cerebral infarction, does use of DMPA carry an increased risk of arterial cardiovascular disease?

POPULATION: Women with a history of cerebral infarction.

INTERVENTION: DMPA.

OUTCOME: Risk of arterial cardiovascular disease.

ANSWER

There are few data available on the incidence, prognosis and cause of stroke associated with pregnancy or the puerperium.[4] Some estimates state that pregnancy increases the likelihood of cerebral infarction by 13 times the rate expected outside pregnancy. Other data suggest that the rate of arterial ischaemic stroke associated with pregnancy or the early puerperium does not differ greatly from that of all women of childbearing age.[4]

The *WHO Medical Eligibility Criteria for Contraceptive Use* advises that combined oral contraception should not be used by women who have had a stroke or cerebrovascular accident (WHO category 4). The risks of using DMPA generally outweigh the benefits (WHO category 3) for these women. However, the benefits of using the progestogen-only pill, implant (specifically Norplant) or the LNG-IUS generally outweigh the risks in this case (WHO category 2). Unrestricted use of the copper IUD is advised (WHO category 1).

A WHO collaborative study on cardiovascular disease[5] recruited 3697 cases: 2196 with stroke, 1137 with VTE and 364 with acute myocardial infarction. A total of 9997 control subjects were also recruited from a hospital population. The cases and controls were matched for mean age, BMI and numbers of live births, and cases were more likely to have had a history of cardiovascular risk factors such as hypertension, diabetes, rheumatic heart disease or smoking. This study was limited by small numbers and potential biases in the study design have also been discussed.[6] The data suggest that there is little or no increase in risk of VTE, stroke or acute myocardial infarction associated with use of oral or injectable progestogen-only methods or, indeed, of combined injectables. However, progestogen-only contraceptive users with hypertension were found to have twice the risk of haemorrhagic stroke compared with non-users. These findings must be interpreted with caution however, as numbers were small and confidence intervals wide. It is unlikely that larger studies will be conducted to evaluate the risk of cardiovascular disease associated with the use of progestogen-only contraceptives. Firstly, there is a low incidence of cardiovascular morbidity in women of childbearing age and secondly, progestogen-only contraceptives have limited use worldwide.

The Summary of Product Characteristics for DMPA advises that women with thromboembolic or coronary vascular disease should be carefully evaluated before using the injectable, and if cerebrovascular disease is experienced while receiving DMPA, the drug should not be readministered. In the light of the Summary of Product Characteristics and WHO recommendations, the CEU advises that for a woman who has had a cerebral infarction, a non-hormonal or progestogen-only method other than DMPA should be considered.

QUESTION

For a woman with attention deficit disorder who has had a stroke, can the etonogestrel implant be used safely?

POPULATION: Women with attention deficit disorder and history of stroke.
INTERVENTION: Etonogestrel implant.
OUTCOME: Safety.

ANSWER

The *WHO Medical Eligibility Criteria for Contraceptive Use* recommends that for women with stroke (history of cerebrovascular accident), the benefits of initiating the use of the etonogestrel implant (Implanon) generally outweigh the risks (WHO category 2).

Despite extensive searching, the CEU could find no evidence in the literature specifically on the use of the etonogestrel implant in women with attention deficit disorder who have had a stroke. The CEU recommends that the etonogestrel implant can be used, and it likely to be an acceptable method of contraception for women with attention deficit disorder.

QUESTION

For a woman with a history of transient ischaemic attack, is the LNG-IUS a safe method of contraception?

POPULATION: Women with a history of transient ischaemic attack.
INTERVENTION: LNG-IUS.
OUTCOME: Safety.

ANSWER

One review article defines transient ischaemic attack (TIA) as 'a syndrome characterised by the sudden onset of discrete neurological symptoms that resolves completely within 24 hours'.[7] A patient presenting with TIA is at high risk of subsequent adverse events. The 90-day risk of stroke is greater than 10%, with the highest risk occurring in the first 2 days. TIAs generally represent 'mini ischaemic strokes' with the vascular aetiology being atherosclerotic or embolic. However, some TIAs may be caused by micro-haemorrhages rather than ischaemia. Thus, accurate diagnosis is important in determining appropriate secondary prevention therapy. Patients with a history of TIA may be taking various secondary prevention treatments including statins to reduce serum cholesterol, aspirin or other anti-platelet agents, or warfarin.[8]

The CEU Medline search identified no publications specifically relating to TIAs and contraception. One paper addressed the relationships between migraine, combined oral contraception and stroke.[9] The study specifically excluded women with TIA (an event lasting less than 24 hours) and provided no guidance regarding contraceptive choices.

FFPRHC guidance published in April 2004 addressed the LNG-IUS in contraception and reproductive health.[10] This guidance summarises and endorses the WHO recommendations on medical eligibility for use of LNG-IUS.

The third edition of the *WHO Medical Eligibility Criteria for Contraceptive Use* does not specifically include TIA among the conditions for which it provides recommendations. However, it assigns category 2 to use of an LNG-IUS in a woman with a history of stroke. The same categorisation is given for use of LNG-IUS in a woman with valvular heart disease complicated by atrial fibrillation (a situation which predisposes to TIA). For women with migraine with aura (a condition which may be confused with TIA and which also predisposes to stroke), use of an LNG-IUS is given a WHO category 3. In contrast, a copper IUD is given a WHO category 1 in this circumstance.

The manufacturer's Summary of Product Characteristics for the LNG-IUS indicates that a history of stroke represents a contraindication but that the method may be used with caution in a woman with migraine or with a history suggestive of transient cerebral ischaemia.

The CEU endorses the recommendation of WHO relating to use of an LNG-IUS in a woman with a history of true stroke, that 'the advantages of using the method generally outweigh the theoretical or proven risks'. Thus, for a woman with the 'lesser' condition of TIA, the LNG-IUS would also be permissible. Nevertheless, it would be appropriate to discuss use of a copper IUD with such a woman, as this method of contraception has an 'unrestricted' categorisation from WHO.

QUESTION

For a woman who has paralysis of her left arm and leg, can the etonogestrel implant or the LNG-IUS be used safely?

POPULATION: Women with hemiparesis.
INTERVENTIONS: Progestogen-only methods of contraception.
OUTCOME: Safety.

ANSWER

One-sided paralysis of the body (hemiparesis) may be caused by brain disorder, head injury, stroke or transient ischaemic attack. The International Headache Society classifies migraine with focal symptoms as indicating ischaemia, and hemiparesis can occur due to focal migraine.

The *WHO Medical Eligibility Criteria for Contraceptive Use* recommends that for women with stroke (history of cerebrovascular accident), the benefits of initiating the use of the etonogestrel implant, Implanon, generally outweigh the risks (WHO category 2). Also, the benefits of using the LNG-IUS generally outweigh the risks (WHO category 2). For women with migraine with focal symptoms, the benefits of initiating Implanon or the LNG-IUS also generally outweigh the risks (WHO category 2).

The CEU recommends that the etonogestrel implant or the LNG-IUS may be used in women who have had paralysis in their left leg or arm. However, women must be advised that there is a lack of evidence for the use of Implanon or LNG-IUS in women with a history of stroke or focal migraine.

QUESTION

For women with post-meningitic cerebral infarcts, is it safe to use combined oral contraception?

POPULATION: Women with post-meningitic cerebral infarcts.

INTERVENTIONS: Combined oral contraception.

OUTCOME: Safety.

ANSWER

In survivors of childhood bacterial meningitis, cerebral infarcts are relatively common.[11] Various studies have found that they can occur in anything between 4 and 47% of cases. Infarctions are most frequently located in the circle of Willis. The CEU could find no information in the literature about the use of combined oral contraception in women with post-meningitic cerebral infarcts.

QUESTION

For a woman who has had a cerebral venous sinus thrombosis with residual neurological signs, which methods of contraception can be used safely and effectively?

POPULATION: Women who have had cerebral venous sinus thrombosis with residual neurological signs.

INTERVENTION: Methods of contraception.

OUTCOME: Safety and efficacy.

ANSWER

Cerebral venous sinus thrombosis is a rare condition associated with predisposing conditions (such as pregnancy and coagulopathies) similar to those for other forms of VTE. Women who have suffered cerebral venous sinus thrombosis may have residual neurological problems requiring long-term anticonvulsant medication. The CEU identified no publications specifically related to cerebral venous sinus thrombosis and contraception. Clinical decisions must therefore be based on guidance relating to VTE generally, and to enzyme-inducing anticonvulsants if relevant. In line with *WHO Medical Eligibility Criteria for Contraceptive Use* recommendations, combined oral contraception would generally be considered unsuitable for any woman with a personal history of VTE. For such a woman who is also taking an enzyme-inducing anticonvulsant, the use of any systemic hormonal method would be problematic. An IUD or levonorgestrel IUS would represent an appropriate contraceptive choice, providing high efficacy, no association with VTE and no interaction with liver enzyme-inducers.

QUESTION

For a woman with a recent postnatal saggital sinus thrombosis treated with warfarin, does use of the IUS for contraception convey increased risk of thrombosis?

POPULATION:	**Women with recent postnatal saggital sinus thrombosis treated with warfarin.**
INTERVENTION:	**LNG-IUS.**
OUTCOME:	**Risk of subsequent thrombosis.**

ANSWER

Dural sinus thrombosis is a lesion found among central nervous system diseases and the most common site of venous occlusion is the sagittal sinus.[12] The superior sagittal and lateral sinuses are most commonly involved in central venous thrombosis and local factors important in the aetiology include infection, particularly of the bony structures of the head and neck (middle ear, sinuses), head injury, neurosurgical procedures and neoplasia. Patients may be asymptomatic with spontaneous resolution or present with a wide array of symptoms from headaches and seizures to severe coma and death. Treatment usually involves the use of heparin and phenytoin.[12]

Risk factors for the condition include pregnancy, the puerperium, oral contraceptives, haematological disorders associated with an increased risk of thrombosis (sickle cell disease, polycythaemia, clotting disorders, platelet disorders), severe dehydration, inflammation, connective tissue disorders and congestive or congenital cardiac disease.

It would appear that the best contraceptive choice for a woman with a recent postnatal sagittal sinus thrombosis is the copper IUD. This is based on the WHO recommendation that women with current DVT or pulmonary embolism may have unrestricted use of the method. In addition, women who are at or more than 4 weeks postpartum may have unrestricted use of this method, even if breastfeeding.

WHO has also advised that, for women with past thromboembolism, contraceptive benefits are generally greater than risks when they use the progestogen-only pill, DMPA, progestogen implants or the IUS. Any of these methods may thus be chosen by a woman when warfarin therapy has ceased. However, the IUS should not be inserted until 6 weeks postpartum if the woman is breastfeeding.

QUESTION

For a woman aged 45 years with high cholesterol, who has a family history of cerebrovascular accident (stroke), can combined oral contraception be used safely?

POPULATION: Women aged 45 years with high cholesterol and family history of stroke.

INTERVENTION: Combined oral contraception.

OUTCOME: Safety.

ANSWER

The British Heart Foundation recommends that total blood cholesterol levels should be below 5.0 mmol/l and in particular low density lipoprotein (LDL) should be below 3.0 mmol/l and high density lipoprotein (HDL) above 1.0 mmol/l. The American Heart Association states that the total cholesterol to HDL ratio should stay below 5:1, however the optimum ratio is 3.5:1. Hypercholesterolaemia is a dominantly inherited genetic condition that results in high LDL cholesterol levels beginning at birth. High levels of cholesterol can increase the risk of cardiovascular disease, which can lead to stroke or heart attack.

The *WHO Medical Eligibility Criteria for Contraceptive Use* recommends that for women with known hyperlipidaemias, the risk of combined oral contraceptive use may or may not outweigh the benefits (WHO category 2/3) depending on other risk factors. However, the FFPRHC CEU Guidance on first prescription of combined oral contraception[13] assigned a WHO category 2 for women with known hyperlipidaemias. (In the process of developing the guidance, expert group members decided that the WHO 2/3 categorisation was unhelpful.) If multiple risk factors such as smoking, hypertension, or obesity are present, the risks of combined pill use may outweigh the benefits (WHO category 3).

In most observational studies that have investigated the association between hypercholesterolaemia and stroke, a weak or unclear association has been found. An international, multicentre, case–control trial by WHO found that in users of combined oral contraception in Europe, the odds ratio of ischaemic stroke associated with low-dose pills (less than 50 micrograms estrogen) was 1.53 (95% CI 0.71–3.31).

Combined oral contraception may be contraindicated if a woman has more than one additional risk factor for stroke. These risk factors include age over 35 years, diabetes mellitus, close family history of arterial disease under 45 years, hyperlipidaemia, hypertension, migraine, obesity (BMI greater than 30) and smoking. It is recommended that women with one additional risk factor for stroke (which does not in itself contraindicate combined oral contraception) may use combined pills with caution. Otherwise, for women with more than one additional risk factor, progestogen-only contraceptives or non-hormonal methods of contraception should be considered, as they are not associated with an increased risk of ischaemic stroke.

References

1. Longstreth WT, Nelson LM, Koepsell TD, van Belle G. Subarachnoid haemorrhage and hormonal factors in women. *Ann Intern Med* 1994;121:168–73.
2. Faculty of Family Planning and Reproductive Health Care Clinical Effectiveness Unit. Contraceptive choices for young people. *J Fam Plann Reprod Health Care* 2004;30:237–51.
3. World Health Organization. Cardiovascular disease and use of oral and injectable progestagen only contraceptives and combine injectable contraceptives. Results of an international, multicentre, case control study. *Contraception* 1998;57:315–24.
4. Lamy C, Sharshar T, Mas JL. Cerebrovascular diseases in pregnancy and puerperium. *Rev Neurol* 1996;152:422–40.
5. World Health Organization. Cardiovascular disease and use of oral and injectable progestagen only contraceptives and combine injectable contraceptives. Results of an international, multicentre, case control study. *Contraception* 1998;57:315–24.
6. World Health Organization. Cardiovascular disease and use of steroid hormonal

contraception, venous thromboembolic disease and combined oral contraceptives: results of a multicentre case–control study. *Lancet* 1996;345:1575–82.

7. Johnson DCC, Hill MD. The patient with transient cerebral ischemia: a golden opportunity for stroke prevention. *JAMA* 2004;170:1134–7.

8. Lees KR, Bath PMW, Naylor AR. Secondary prevention of transient ischaemic attack and stroke. *BMJ* 2000;320:991–4.

9. Chang CL, Donaghy M, Poulter NR, WHO Collaborative Study of Cardiovascular Disease and Steroid Hormone Contraception. Migraine and stroke in young women: case–control study. *BMJ* 1999;318:13–8.

10. Faculty of Family Planning and Reproductive Health Care Clinical Effectiveness Unit. The levonorgestrel-releasing intrauterine system (LNG-IUS) in contraception and reproductive health. *J Fam Plann Reprod Health Care* 2004;30:99–109.

11. Jan W, Zimmerman RA, Bilaniuk LT, Hunter JV, Simon EM, Haselgrove J. Diffusion-weighted imaging in acute bacterial meningitis in infancy. *Neuroradiology* 2003;45:634–9.

12. Altamirano AC, Gonzalez VA, Cuervo OJ. Sagittal sinus thrombosis. A report of two cases. *Cir Cir* 1999;67:213–7.

13. Faculty of Family Planning and Reproductive Health Care Clinical Effectiveness Unit. First prescription of combined oral contraception. *J Fam Plann Reprod Health Care* 2003;29:209–22.

12 CONGENITAL AND ACQUIRED CARDIOVASCULAR DISORDERS

Congenital heart disease

QUESTION

For women with tetralogy of Fallot, which methods of contraception are safe?

POPULATION: Women with tetralogy of Fallot.
INTERVENTION: Contraception.
OUTCOME: Safety.

ANSWER

Tetralogy of Fallot is a congenital heart defect whereby a combination of four abnormalities allows oxygenated and deoxygenated blood to mix.[1] In 1888, Fallot described the anatomy as consisting of a subaortic ventricular septal defect, right ventricular infundibular stenosis, aortic valve positioned to override the right ventricle and right ventricular hypertrophy.[2] Infants with this condition usually have a heart murmur, cyanosis and may experience breathlessness on exertion. Long-term effects may include infective endocarditis, damage to the pulmonary valve, thromboses, stroke and abscess. Open-heart surgery involves closing the defect in the septum, removing extra heart muscle and repairing the pulmonary valve.[1]

The *WHO Medical Eligibility Criteria for Contraceptive Use* recommends that for women with uncomplicated valvular heart disease the benefits of using combined oral contraception generally outweigh any risks (WHO category 2). These women also have unrestricted use of DMPA, the implant (specifically Norplant), the progestogen-only pill, the IUD and the LNG-IUS (WHO category 1).

WHO advises that women with valvular heart disease complicated by pulmonary hypertension, risk of arterial fibrillation, on anticoagulant treatment, or with history of subacute bacterial endocarditis should not use combined oral contraception as it may further increase the risk of arterial thrombosis (WHO category 4). These women may have unrestricted use of DMPA, the implant (specifically Norplant) and the progestogen-only pill (WHO category 1). The benefits of using the IUD or the LNG-IUS generally outweigh any risks (WHO category 2).

Systematic studies on the use of contraception by women with congenital heart disease are lacking in the literature. Guidelines from the European Society of Cardiology advise that the risks of pregnancy vary greatly among the different forms of congenital heart disease and must be measured against the risks of contraception.[3] Clinicians should consider patient compliance and sexual behaviour on an individual basis and choose the least hazardous method of contraception. These guidelines advise that combined pills are contraindicated for women at risk of paradoxical embolism, unless they are also receiving anticoagulants, and women with pulmonary or systemic hypertension. The use of progestogen-only methods should be considered individually. Although it has been suggested that the insertion of IUDs carries a risk of bacterial endocarditis for cyanotic women, those with artificial valves and shunts, and those with previous endocarditis, the number of women who develop endocarditis is low. Both the IUD and the LNG-IUS may be used if antibiotic prophylaxis is given at insertion.

QUESTION

For women with aortic stenosis which contraceptive methods can be safely used?

POPULATION: Women with aortic stenosis.
INTERVENTION: Contraception.
OUTCOME: Safety of use.

ANSWER

Cardiac disease is one of the most common causes of maternal death reported in the confidential enquiry into maternal deaths.[4] Severe aortic stenosis is uncommon in pregnancy but is associated with a maternal mortality of 17%.[5] Consequently, safe and effective contraception is warranted.

The *WHO Medical Eligibility Criteria for Contraceptive Use* distinguishes valvular heart disease into 'uncomplicated' and 'complicated' (pulmonary hypertension, atrial fibrillation, history of subacute bacterial endocarditis). The *WHO Medical Eligibility Criteria* are summarised in Table 7.

Table 7. The *WHO Medical Eligibility Criteria* classification for women with valvular heart disease

Contraceptive method	WHO classification for uncomplicated valvular heart disease	WHO classification for complicated valvular heart disease
Low-dose combined oral contraceptive	2	4
Progestogen-only pill	1	1
DMPA	1	1
Progestogen-only implants (Norplant)	1	1
Copper containing IUD	1	2
LNG-IUS	1	2
Condom	1	1
Spermicide	1	1
Diaphragm	1	2

1 = unrestricted use; 2 = benefits generally outweigh risks; 3 = risks generally outweigh benefits; 4 = unacceptable health risk

WHO makes specific mention of the use of combined oral contraception, IUD and diaphragm in women with valvular heart disease. Among women with valvular heart disease, combined pill use may further increase the risk of arterial thrombosis; women with complicated valvular heart disease are at greatest risk. Prophylactic antibiotics should be used to prevent endocarditis for insertion of an IUD or IUS. BNF advice regarding prevention of endo-carditis states that for obstetric and gynaecological procedures, prophylaxis is required only for women with prosthetic heart valves or those who have previously had endocarditis. It has been common practice to use 3 g amoxicillin orally 1 hour prior to IUD insertion for women who require antibiotic cover. The risk of urinary tract infection with the diaphragm may increase the risk of subacute bacterial endocarditis and caution is advised if considering this option.

The *WHO Medical Eligibility Criteria for Contraceptive Use* also provides recommendations for female sterilisation. For women with uncomplicated valvular heart disease the procedure may be conducted in a routine setting but with extra preparation and precautions. The woman requires prophylactic antibiotics. For women with complicated valvular heart disease, the procedure should be undertaken in a setting with an experienced surgeon and staff, equipment needed to provide general anaesthesia, and other back up medical support. For these conditions, the capacity to decide on the most appropriate procedure and anaesthetic regimen is also needed. Alternative temporary methods of contraception should be provided if referral is required or there is otherwise any delay. The woman is at high risk for complications associated with anaesthesia and surgery. If she has unstable atrial fibrillation or current subacute bacterial endocarditis, the procedure should be delayed.

Within the Medline and EMBASE databases, the CEU was able to identify only a single paper that had relevance to the member's enquiry.[6] This review paper discusses women with congenital heart disease and has a small discussion with regard to contraception. It does not discuss each form of heart disease along with contraceptive choices and so little further advice can be added to the recommendations described above from WHO.

QUESTION

For women with mitral valve prolapse, can combined oral contraception be used safely?

POPULATION: Women with mitral valve prolapse.
INTERVENTION: Combined oral contraception.
OUTCOME: Safety.

ANSWER

Mitral valve prolapse is an abnormality of the mitral valve in which one or both valve flaps close incompletely, often producing either a click or murmur.[7] It occurs when the left ventricular size is small in comparison to an enlarged mitral annulus, leaflets, or chordae tendineae. It can happen in healthy women with typical body habitus following dehydration that is reversed with rehydration. Often mitral valve prolapse does not occur as a single disease, but in association with a number of different disorders, including Marfan syndrome, Ehlers-Danlos syndrome, polycystic kidney disease, SLE, Wolff-Parkinson-White syndrome, and Von Willebrand disease. Mitral valve prolapse patients are at risk of endocarditis, stroke, mitral valve surgery and sudden death.[8]

The *WHO Medical Eligibility Criteria for Contraceptive Use* recommends that combined oral contraception is contraindicated for women with complicated valvular heart disease (such as pulmonary hypertension, atrial fibrillation or a history of subacute bacterial endocarditis) (WHO category 4). For women with uncomplicated valvular heart disease, the benefits of combined oral contraception generally outweigh the risks (WHO category 2).

Despite extensive searching, the CEU could find no direct evidence on the use of combined oral contraception in women with mitral valve prolapse. However, the CEU recommends that women should be counselled on the risks of stroke with mitral valve prolapse, and the increased risk of stroke with combined oral contraception.[9] Consideration should be given to the use of progestogen-only or non-hormonal methods.

QUESTION

Can women with Marfan syndrome use combined oral contraception safely?

POPULATION: Women with Marfan syndrome.
INTERVENTION: Combined oral contraception.
OUTCOME: Safety.

ANSWER

Marfan syndrome is an heritable condition caused by a mutation in the gene coding for the structure of fibrillin, a protein found in connective tissue.[10] This condition has been found among people of all ethnic backgrounds and affects children and adults, although symptoms usually progress with age. Systems most affected by Marfan syndrome include the skeleton (individuals may be tall, slender and loose-jointed with a protruding or indented sternum, scoliosis or flat feet); eyes (the lenses of the eyes may be dislocated, there is a risk of myopia, early glaucoma or cataracts); cardiovascular system (aortic dilatation causing an increased risk of aortic dissection, defects in heart valves causing heart murmurs and palpitations); nervous system (risk of dural ectasia); skin (frequent stretch marks, risk of abdominal or inguinal hernias) and lungs (snoring or sleep apnoea and increased risk of lung collapse).

One study looked at maternal and fetal outcomes of pregnancy and gynae-cological problems in 14 women with Marfan syndrome.[11] The authors concluded that women with this condition are at high risk of aortic dissection in pregnancy, even if they did not exhibit aortic root dilatation prior to conception. Women with Marfan syndrome should ideally only undertake a pregnancy after consultation with obstetricians and other specialists familiar with the condition.

The *WHO Medical Eligibility Criteria for Contraceptive Use* does not refer specifically to Marfan syndrome. Women with uncomplicated valvular heart disease may have unrestricted use (WHO category 1) of the progestogen-only pill, DMPA, the implant (Norplant), the LNG-IUS and the copper IUD. The benefits of combined oral contraception generally outweigh the risks in these cases (WHO category 2). Women with complicated valvular heart disease (pulmonary hypertension, atrial fibrillation or history of subacute bacterial endocarditis) may have unrestricted use (WHO category 1) of the progestogen-only pill, DMPA and Norplant. The benefits of the LNG-IUS and the IUD generally outweigh the risks for these women (WHO category 2), but WHO advises that antimicrobial prophylaxis is considered. Use of the combined oral contraceptive pill is not advised (WHO category 4).

After an extensive literature search, the CEU has been unable to find any further evidence on the use of combined oral contraception by women with Marfan syndrome or on the effects of estrogen, if any, on this condition. If progestogen-only methods are acceptable these are likely to be the most suitable first line option.

QUESTION

For young women with various forms of congenital heart disease (specifically, atrial septal defect, pulmonary stenosis, or bicuspid aortic valve), is use of combined oral contraception associated with any increased risks or adverse effects?

POPULATION: Young women with congenital heart disease (specifically, atrial septal defect, pulmonary stenosis or bicuspid aortic valve).

INTERVENTION: Combined oral contraception.

OUTCOME: Risks and adverse effects.

ANSWER

The CEU literature searches identified no primary research publications specifically relating to contraceptive use in women with congenital heart disease. We identified a number of expert statements and editorials.[3,12] All provided similar guidance. There appears to be a consensus that combined oral contraception can safely be used in women with uncomplicated congenital heart disease. Because of its thrombogenic effect, combined oral contraception is better avoided in women with complicated congenital heart disease which, in itself, predisposes to thromboembolism. The various publications list different complications which should be viewed as contraindications to combined oral contraception. These include pulmonary hypertension, atrial fibrillation/flutter, history of subacute bacterial endocarditis, cyanosis, low cardiac output, dilated cardiac chambers, following a fontan procedure, Eisenmenger reaction, or arterial hypertension (such as coarctation). A copper IUD or levonorgestrel IUS may represent a better contraceptive choice for many women with congenital heart disease.

QUESTION

For adolescents who have a small asymptomatic ventricular septal defect and smoke, does use of the combined oral contraceptive have any adverse effects?

POPULATION: Adolescents who have a small asymptomatic ventricular septal defect (VSD) and smoke.

INTERVENTION: The combined oral contraceptive.

OUTCOME: Adverse effects of the contraceptive.

ANSWER

A VSD is a developmental defect of the interventricular septum whereby communication exists between the cavities of the two ventricles.[13] Isolated VSDs constitute over 20% of all congenital heart diseases (approximately 2–6 of every 1000 live births). The first clinical description is given in an article published by Roger in 1879 and the phrase *maladie de Roger* is still used today for small asymptomatic VSD. For women with congenital heart disease, the inherent dangers of pregnancy should be weighed against the possible adverse effects of the contraceptive method being considered.

The FFPRHC guideline on first prescription of the combined oral contraceptive pill states that the clinical history of a patient provides details on medical conditions or treatments, which may require special precautions for oral contraceptive use or are contraindications.[9] The clinical history should include details of heart disease and valvular and septal defects as well as cigarettes smoked per day.

The *WHO Medical Eligibility Criteria for Contraceptive Use* states that complicated valvular disease or significant septal defect is classified as an unacceptable health risk (WHO category 4). The use of combined pills by women with uncomplicated valvular disease, and presumably small septal defect, is classified as WHO category 2.

The WHO classifies the use of the combined oral contraceptive pill by women under 35 years of age who smoke as category 2. WHO has noted however, that the risk of cardiovascular events increases with increasing age and an increase in the number of cigarettes smoked daily. When two problems (such as a woman under 35 years who smokes and has uncomplicated valvular disease) coexist then the classification is revised to category 3. Alternative contraceptive methods should be recommended and the potential risks of the combined pill should be explained to these women.

The CEU therefore feels that, for an adolescent with a small asymptomatic ventricular septal defect, the combined oral contraceptive pill may be used and it is highly advisable that the woman is counselled to stop smoking. This patient would then fall under WHO category 2, where the benefits of using the method generally outweigh the risks. Nevertheless, women with congenital heart defects would require ongoing medical evaluation to detect possible complications such as pulmonary hypertension.

QUESTION

For women with PCOS, and postoperative congenital heart disease, can Dianette be used safely?

POPULATION: Women with PCOS and postoperative congenital heart disease.
INTERVENTION: Dianette.
OUTCOME: Safety.

ANSWER

The *WHO Medical Eligibility Criteria for Contraceptive Use* does not specifically mention congenital heart disease. With uncomplicated valvular heart disease, the benefits of combined oral contraceptives generally outweigh the risks (WHO category 2). Combined pills should not be used (WHO category 4) with complicated valvular heart disease (pulmonary hypertension, atrial fibrillation or history of subacute bacterial endocarditis).

CEU guidance advises that there is no specific indication for Dianette in women with PCOS, unless they exhibit symptoms of androgen excess; for example, acne or hirsuitism.[9] All combined pills will increase sex hormone binding globulin, decrease free testosterone, and improve acne and hirsutism. Given the higher risk of VTE with Dianette, the CEU advises that other combined pills may be used instead for women with PCOS and postoperative congenital heart disease.

The Medicines Control Agency (MCA)[14] reviewed two epidemiological studies demonstrating that the incidence of VTE in Dianette users is higher than in users of low-dose estrogen combined oral contraceptives.[15,16] This higher risk of VTE may occur during the first year of use due to the potential 'unmasking' of underlying thrombophilia, and may not be associated with duration of use, but evidence to confirm this is lacking.

A guideline from the RCOG on PCOS mentions that oligomenorrhoeic or amenorrhoeic women with PCOS have an increased risk of endometrial hyperplasia and malignancy.[17] Polycystic ovary syndrome can be managed with any combined oral contraceptive to regulate menstruation, provide contraception and reduce the risk of endometrial malignancy. An alternative treatment involves use of progestogen to induce a withdrawal bleed at least every 3–4 months.

QUESTION

For women with anatomical heart defects who are having the etonogestrel implant inserted or removed, should antibiotic prophylaxis be given?

POPULATION: Women with anatomical heart defects who are having the etonogestrel implant inserted or removed.

INTERVENTION: Antibiotic prophylaxis.

OUTCOME: Risk of bacterial endocarditis.

ANSWER

Bacterial endocarditis is a potentially life-threatening condition caused by the infection of susceptible cardiac structures following bacteraemia. There are a variety of diagnostic and therapeutic procedures that can cause transient bacteraemia and the benefits of antimicrobial prophylaxis have been shown in trials on animal models but it is unlikely that there will ever be trials in humans.[18] Systemic antibiotics rely on a finite window of time to fight infection at the time of inoculation of potential pathogens.[19] Infective endocarditis has a mortality rate of 20–30% and in the UK there are approximately 200 deaths/ year from this disease. Although antibiotic prophylaxis is effective in reducing bacteraemia, there are no prescriptive data to confirm that it prevents endocarditis. Only 50% of patients with endocarditis have a known predisposing lesion[20] and the majority of episodes (about 80%) of endocarditis occur without a known specific preceding episode of instrumentation that might have caused bacteraemia.[21]

The *WHO Medical Eligibility Criteria for Contraceptive Use* recommends that the etonogestrel implant can be used without restriction in women with complicated (pulmonary hypertension, atrial fibrillation, or history of subacute bacterial endocarditis) or uncomplicated valvular heart disease (WHO category 1). No mention was made on the need for prophylactic antibiotics for women undergoing implant insertion or removal.

Despite extensive searching, the CEU could find no further information in the literature on the use of antibiotic prophylaxis in women with anatomical heart defects who are having implants inserted or removed. Furthermore, no information could be identified on the detection of bacteraemia or bacterial endocarditis in women who have had an implant inserted or removed.

BNF provides information on antibiotic prophylaxis. It focuses on antibiotic prophylaxis in the prevention of endocarditis in patients with heart-valve lesions, septal defects, patent ductus or prosthetic valves. Prophylactic antibiotic regimens provided in the BNF pertain to women undergoing gynaecological or genitourinary procedures. There is no advice specific to implant insertion, nor indeed IUD insertion.

The committee of the British Society for Dermatological Surgery have reviewed the literature summarised above and found no strong evidence to support antibiotic prophylaxis for routine dermatological surgery even in the presence of a pre-existing heart lesion. In addition, the Therapy Guidelines and Audit Sub-Committee have surveyed members of the British Association of Dermatologists and no responders have seen endocarditis as a direct result of dermatological surgery. The British Society for Dermatological Surgery, in agreement with the British Society for Antimicrobial Chemotherapy, therefore believes that antibiotic prophylaxis for endocarditis is not required for routine dermatological surgery even in the presence of a pre-existing heart lesion.[22]

The CEU advises that when inserting or removing a contraceptive implant in a woman with a prosthetic heart valve, or who has a history of endocarditis, prophylactic antibiotics are not required.

QUESTION

For young women with Carpenter syndrome and a history of tetralogy of Fallot (with continuing atrial septal defect), what methods of progestogen-only contraception can be used safely?

POPULATION: Young women with Carpenter syndrome and a history of tetralogy of Fallot with continuing atrial septal defect.

INTERVENTION: Progestogen-only contraception.

OUTCOME: Safety.

ANSWER

Carpenter syndrome is a very rare (40 cases reported to date) craniofacial condition; the cause is unknown.[23] People with Carpenter syndrome often have a tower-shaped skull, they can have additional or fused fingers and toes, be of reduced height, become obese, have problems with speech, or experience mental deficiency. Growth is limited by the syndrome. No evidence was identified on estrogen use and Carpenter syndrome.

Tetralogy of Fallot is a congenital heart defect whereby a combination of four abnormalities allows oxygenated and deoxygenated blood to mix. Infants with this condition usually have a heart murmur, cyanosis and may experience breathlessness on exertion. The long-term effects of the condition may include infective endocarditis, damage to the pulmonary valve, blood clots, stroke and abscess.

The *WHO Medical Eligibility Criteria for Contraceptive Use* advises that women with uncomplicated valvular heart disease can have unrestricted use of DMPA, progestogen-only implants, the progestogen-only pill and the LNG-IUS (WHO category 1). Women with complicated valvular heart disease (pulmonary hypertension, risk of arterial fibrillation, on anti-coagulant treatment or with history of subacute bacterial endocarditis) may have unrestricted use of DMPA, the implant, and the progestogen-only pill (WHO category 1) and the benefits of using the LNG-IUS generally outweigh any risks (WHO category 2).

Guidelines from the European Society of Cardiology advise that the risks of pregnancy vary greatly among the different forms of congenital heart disease and must be measured against the risks of contraception. These guidelines advise that the use of progestogen-only methods should be considered individually. Although it has been suggested that IUDs carry a risk of bacterial endocarditis for cyanotic women, those with artificial valves and shunts, and those with previous endocarditis, the number of women who develop endocarditis is low and both the IUD and the LNG-IUS may be used if antibiotic prophylaxis is given at insertion.

Despite extensive searching, the CEU could find no other information in the literature on the use of progestogen-only methods of contraception in young women with Carpenter's syndrome and a history of tetralogy of Fallot. All progestogen-only methods may be advised if congenital heart disease is complicated; however, the woman should be able to select a method which is both safe and acceptable to avoid unplanned pregnancy.

QUESTION

For women who have valvular heart disease and previous stroke which progestogen-only contraceptive methods would be suitable and provide amenorrhoea?

POPULATION: Women with valvular heart disease and previous stroke who also have menorrhagia.

INTERVENTION: Progestogen-only contraception.

OUTCOME: Amenorrhoea.

ANSWER

Contraceptive advice for women with complex problems should take account of each medical condition. Drug interaction information can be obtained from BNF. Contraceptive choices should be tailored to the individual's needs and take account of the risks and benefits of each method, as outlined in the *WHO Medical Eligibility Criteria for Contraceptive Use*.

No method of contraception can be relied upon to produce amenorrhoea, although the LNG-IUS, DMPA, and continuous use of the combined oral contraceptive pill are all likely to do so. Women should be counselled regarding bleeding patterns to be expected.

WHO advises that women with a past history of stroke can use any progestogen-only method with the exception of DMPA (for which the risks are felt generally to outweigh the benefits, WHO category 3). WHO advises that women with complicated valvular heart disease (with pulmonary hypertension, risk of atrial fibrillation and subacute endocarditis) can use any progestogen-only method. Combined hormonal contraceptives should not be used by women with a history of stroke or complicated valvular heart disease.

QUESTION

For women with valvular heart disease (with or without a prosthetic valve), a history of endocarditis or of tetralogy of Fallot, which regimen of antibiotic prophylaxis is recommended for insertion or removal of an IUD?

POPULATION:	Women with valvular heart disease or a history of endocarditis.
INTERVENTION:	Antibiotic prophylaxis for insertion or removal of the IUD.
OUTCOME:	Risk of bacterial endocarditis.

ANSWER

Bacterial endocarditis is a potentially life-threatening condition caused by the infection of susceptible cardiac structures following bacteraemia.[18] There are a variety of diagnostic and therapeutic procedures that can cause transient bacteraemia and the benefits of antimicrobial prophylaxis have been shown in trials on animal models but it is unlikely that there will ever be trials on humans. Systemic antibiotics rely on a finite window of time to fight infection at the time of inoculation of potential pathogens.[20]

The *WHO Medical Eligibility Criteria for Contraceptive Use* advises that women with uncomplicated valvular heart disease may have unrestricted use of an IUD or LNG-IUS (WHO category 1). For women with complicated valvular heart disease (pulmonary hypertension, atrial fibrillation, history of subacute bacterial endocarditis), the benefits of using an IUD/IUS generally outweigh the risks (WHO category 2).

Guidelines on prevention of bacterial endocarditis were produced by the American Heart Association in 1997 and these classify cardiac conditions into negligible, moderate and high-risk categories.[18] Particular cardiac conditions are known to be more susceptible to endocarditis. The risk of bacteraemia and the organisms which may cause endocarditis vary depending on the procedure being performed. All these factors influence the clinician's decision on whether prophylaxis is required and if so, which antibiotics would be the most suitable.

Complex cyanotic congenital heart disease and surgically constructed systemic pulmonary shunts are classified as cardiac conditions with a high risk for which antimicrobial prophylaxis is required.[18] It is advised that patients at high risk who are undergoing genitourinary procedures are given a single dose of ampicillin 2 g (intravenously or intramuscularly) plus gentamicin 1.5 mg/kg (up to 120 mg) within 30 minutes of starting the procedure followed by ampicillin 1 g (intravenously or intramuscularly) or amoxicillin 1 g orally 6 hours later.

High-risk patients who are allergic to ampicillin are advised to receive vancomycin 1 g intravenously over 1–2 hours plus gentamicin 1.5 mg/kg (intravenously or intramuscularly) (up to 120 mg), to be completed within 30 minutes of starting the procedure.

Most cardiac conditions requiring prophylaxis fall into the moderate risk category. Patients at moderate risk who are undergoing genitourinary procedures are advised to take amoxicillin 2 g orally 1 hour before the procedure or ampicillin 1 g (intravenously or intramuscularly) within 30 minutes of starting the procedure. Patients in this category who are allergic to ampicillin are advised to take vancomycin 1g intravenously over 1–2 hours to be completed within 30 minutes of starting the procedure.

Guidance on antibiotic prophylaxis for insertion of IUDs is covered in CEU guidance on the copper IUD as long-term contraception.[24] An expert group for the FFPRHC considered the advice in BNF and interpreted that prophylactic antibiotics are not recommended for routine IUD insertion. However, women with previous endocarditis or with prosthetic heart valve require intravenous antibiotic prophylaxis during IUD insertion or removal. As a good practice point, the guidance advises that when prophylaxis against bacterial endocarditis is required, clinicians should refer to BNF for the most up-to-date regimen and ensure the IUD procedure takes place in an appropriate setting (which may mean theatre, day surgery or a clinic with facilities for intravenous administration).

References

1. Berlin E. Tetralogy of Fallot. 2003
    [http://andatoz.iqhealth.com/HealthAnswers/encyclopedia/HTMLfiles/63.html].
2. Greenberg SB. Tetralogy of Fallot 2004 [www.emedicine.com/radio/topic685.htm].
3. The Task Force on the Management of Grown Up Congenital Heart Disease of the European Society of Cardiology. Management of grown up congenital heart disease. *Eur Heart J* 2003;24:1035–84.
4. De Swiet. Cardiac disease. In: Lewis G, Drife J, editors. *Why Mothers Die 1997–1999: Fifth Report on Confidential Enquiries into Maternal Deaths in the United Kingdom*. London: RCOG Press; 2001. p. 153–64.
5. Chia P, Chia H, Subramaniam R. A clinical approach to heart disease in pregnancy. *The Obstetrician & Gynaecologist* 2002;4:212–16.
6. Somerville J. The woman with congenital heart disease. *Eur Heart J* 1998; 19:1766–75.
7. Simmons, S. Mitral Valve Prolapse. What Causes It? Can Diet Changes Help? Connective Tissue Disorder Site. 2004 [www.ctds.info/mvp1.html].
8. Venugopalan P. Mitral Valve Prolapse. eMedicine. 2004 [www.emedicine.com/ped/topic1465.htm].
9. Faculty of Family Planning and Reproductive Health Care Clinical Effectiveness Unit. First prescription of combined oral contraception. *J Fam Plann Reprod Health Care* 2003;29:209–22.

10. National Institute of Arthritis and Musculoskeletal and Skin Diseases. Questions and answers about Marfan syndrome. 2001 [www.niams.nih.gov/hi/topics/marfan/marfan.htm].

11. Rahman J, Rahman FZ, Rahman W, al-Suleiman SA, Rahman MS. Obstetric and gynecologic complications in women with Marfan syndrome. *J Reprod Med* 2003;48:723–8.

12. Swan L, Hillis WS, Cameron A. Family planning requirements of adults with congenital heart disease. *BMJ Heart* 1997;78:9–11.

13. Anbumani P, Srinivasan K, Ramaswamy P, Srinivasan A, Natesan V, Srinivasan S. Ventricular Septal Defect, General Concepts. September 2001 [www.emedicine.com].

14. Committee on Safety of Medicines. Cyproterone acetate (Dianette): Risk of venous thromboembolism (VTE). *Curr Probl Pharmacovigil* 2002;28:9–10.

15. Vasilakis-Scaramozza C, Jick H. Risk of venous thromboembolism with cyproterone or levonorgestrel contraceptives. *Lancet* 2001;358:1427–9.

16. Parkin L, Skegg DCG, Wilson M, Herbison GP, Paul C. Oral contraceptives and fatal pulmonary embolism. *Lancet* 2000;355:2088.

17. Royal College of Obstetricians and Gynaecologists. *Long-Term Consequences of Polycystic Ovary Syndrome.* Guideline No. 33. London: RCOG; 2003.

18. American Heart Association. Prevention of bacterial endocarditis. *JAMA* 1997;277:794–801.

19. American College of Obstetricians and Gynecologists Practice Bulletin. Antibiotic Prophylaxis for Gynecologic Procedures. *Obstet Gynecol* 2001;23:1–9.

20. Bayliss R, Clarke C, Oakley CM, Somerville W, Whitfield AGW. The teeth and infective endocarditis. *Br Heart J* 1983;50:506–12.

21. Child JS. Risks for and prevention of infective endocarditis. *Cardiol Clin* 1996;14:327–43.

22. Therapy Guidelines and Audit Sub-Committee (TGASC) of the British Association of Dermatologists and the British Society for Dermatological Surgery (BSDS). *Antibiotic Prophylaxis for Endocarditis in Dermatological Surgery.* 2004 [www.bad.org.uk/doctors/guidelines/surgery.asp].

23. World Craniofacial Foundation. Carpenter's Syndrome. 2004 [www.worldcf.org].

24. Faculty of Family Planning and Reproductive Health Care Clinical Effectiveness Unit. Copper intrauterine device as long-term contraception. *J Fam Plann Reprod Health Care* 2004;30:29–42.

Acquired heart disease

QUESTION

For women with pulmonary hypertension, can combined oral contraception be used safely?

POPULATION:	Women with pulmonary hypertension.
INTERVENTION:	Combined oral contraception.
OUTCOME:	Safety.

ANSWER

No evidence was identified directly relating to the use of hormonal contraception by women with pulmonary hypertension. The *WHO Medical Eligibility Criteria for Contraceptive Use* does not specifically include pulmonary hypertension as a category. However, if a patient has complicated valvular heart disease with pulmonary hypertension, WHO indicates that combined oral contraception should not be used (WHO category 4). The CEU supports a similar category for women with primary pulmonary hypertension.

The benefits of progestogen-only methods (pills, injectables, implants or IUS) for women with pulmonary hypertension generally outweigh the risks. The CEU upholds these recommendations and advises that women with primary pulmonary hypertension could also use non-hormonal contraceptive methods.

QUESTION

For women with dilated cardiomyopathy, can the combined oral contraceptive, Cilest or the progestogen-only pill be used safely?

POPULATION: Women with dilated cardiomyopathy.
INTERVENTION: The combined oral contraceptive, Cilest, or the progestogen-only pill.
OUTCOME: Safety.

ANSWER

Cardiomyopathies are defined by the WHO as diseases of the myocardium associated with ventricular dysfunction. They are classified as dilated cardiomyopathy, hypertrophic cardiomyopathy, and restrictive cardiomyopathy.[1] Dilated cardiomyopathy causes the heart to become enlarged, and the heart muscle becomes weak, thin and floppy, and unable to pump blood around the body efficiently. This causes pulmonary oedema and breathlessness. For most individuals with dilated cardiomyopathy, the symptoms will not affect the quality or duration of life; however, a small minority may experience significant symptoms and be at risk of sudden death. It is recommended that all individuals with dilated cardiomyopathy have regular follow-up appointments.[2]

The *WHO Medical Eligibility Criteria for Contraceptive Use* does not specifically address contraceptive choice for women with familial cardiomyopathy. However, for women with multiple risk factors for arterial cardiovascular disease (such as older age, smoking, diabetes and hypertension) WHO advises that combined oral contraception should not be used (WHO category 3/4).

For women with uncomplicated valvular heart disease, the benefits of using the combined pill generally outweigh the risks (WHO category 2), while women with complicated valvular heart disease (pulmonary hypertension, atrial fibrillation, history of subacute bacterial endocarditis) are advised not to use it (WHO category 4).

For women with multiple risk factors for arterial cardiovascular disease, the benefits of using the progestogen-only pill generally outweigh the risks (WHO category 2). The progestogen-only pill can be used without restriction in women with uncomplicated or complicated valvular heart disease (WHO category 1).

Veille and Zaccaro surveyed clinicians about their treatment of women with peripartum cardiomyopathy.[3] Clinicians were asked about the contraceptive methods they usually recommend to these women. Combined oral contraceptives were recommended by 41%, progestogen-only pills by 23%, and IUDs or foam and condoms were recommended by 58%.[3]

Despite extensive searching, the CEU could find no other information regarding the use of hormonal contraception in women with cardiomyopathy. As a woman with cardiomyopathy requires continuing evaluation, it seems reasonable to equate this condition to that of a woman with complicated valvular heart disease, which implies that combined oral contraception would not be advised. Women should be counselled on the possible increased risk of cardiovascular disease with combined oral contraception and consideration should be given to other methods of contraception. As the risk of cardiovascular disease with the progestogen-only pill is small and it is not contraindicated in women with valvular heart disease, women with cardiomyopathy can safely use the progestogen-only pill.

QUESTION

For women with cardiomyopathy stable on warfarin, is the etonogestrel implant a safe and effective method of contraception?

POPULATION: Women with cardiomyopathy stable on warfarin.
INTERVENTION: The etonogestrel implant.
OUTCOME: Safety and efficacy.

ANSWER

Cardiomyopathies are defined by the WHO as diseases of the myocardium associated with ventricular dysfunction. They are classified as dilated, hypertrophic and restrictive.[1] Familial cardiomyopathy of various kinds occurs with autosomal dominant inheritance. There is also an asymmetrical form affecting the ventricles and the interventricular septum.[4]

Oral anticoagulants such as warfarin are teratogenic and carry a risk of placental and fetal haemorrhage. The BNF advises that they should be avoided in pregnancy, especially in the first and third trimesters.

The *WHO Medical Eligibility Criteria for Contraceptive Use* does not address contraceptive choice for women with cardiomyopathy. However, for women with multiple risk factors for arterial cardiovascular disease (such as older age, smoking, diabetes and hypertension) WHO advises that the benefits of using the implant (specifically Norplant) generally outweigh the risks (WHO category 2). Both women with uncomplicated valvular heart disease and women with complicated valvular heart disease (pulmonary hypertension, atrial fibrillation, history of subacute bacterial endocarditis) may have unrestricted use (WHO category 1) of the implant (Norplant).

As WHO has advised that women with complicated valvular heart disease may have unrestricted use of Norplant, it seems reasonable to extrapolate that women with cardiomyopathy, stable on warfarin, may safely use the etonogestrel implant (Implanon). Insertion and removal of the implant may be associated with localised bleeding and bruising and this risk may be slightly increased in women on warfarin.

QUESTION

Can women with Wolff-Parkinson-White syndrome use combined oral contraception safely?

POPULATION: Women with Wolff-Parkinson-White syndrome.
INTERVENTION: Combined oral contraception.
OUTCOME: Safety.

ANSWER

Wolff-Parkinson-White syndrome is a pre-excitation syndrome whereby the ventricle receives a stimulus from the atrium earlier than would be expected if the impulse arrived via the normal pathway only.[5] This pre-excitation is caused by the development of bypass accessory connections between the atrium and ventricle during embryonic development. Wolff-Parkinson-White syndrome affects approximately 0.15–0.2% of the population, and is more common in men (60–70%) than in women. Symptoms may range from mild chest pain to severe distress or cardiac arrest, and mortality is frequently due to associated arrhythmias. The two most common arrhythmias are circus movement tachycardias and atrial fibrillation. Atrial fibrillation has an incidence of 11–38% in patients with Wolff-Parkinson-White syndrome and may be fatal if it leads to subsequent ventricular fibrillation.[5]

Evidence in the literature suggests that asymptomatic women with Wolff-Parkinson-White syndrome may be at higher risk of supraventricular tachycardia if they become pregnant. A prospective study looked at the cardiac status of six women between the ages of 18 and 33 years with Wolff-Parkinson-White syndrome and found that three to seven supraventricular tachycardias were reported during each pregnancy.[6] These episodes occurred most frequently between 20 weeks and 35 weeks of gestation. A case report of the collaborative management of pregnancy and delivery of a patient with Wolff-Parkinson-White syndrome has also been described.[7]

The *WHO Medical Eligibility Criteria for Contraceptive Use* does not refer to Wolff-Parkinson-White syndrome. Women with uncomplicated valvular heart disease may have unrestricted use (WHO category 1) of the progestogen-only pill, DMPA, progestogen implant, LNG-IUS and the IUD. The benefits of combined oral contraception generally outweigh the risks (WHO category 2).

Women with complicated valvular heart disease (pulmonary hypertension, atrial fibrillation or history of subacute bacterial endocarditis) may have unrestricted use (WHO category 1) of the progestogen-only pill, DMPA and progestogen implant. The benefits of the LNG-IUS and the IUD generally outweigh the risks for these women (WHO category 2), but WHO advises that antimicrobial prophylaxis is considered. Use of the combined oral contraceptive pill is not advised (WHO category 4).

The CEU was unable to find any specific evidence relating to combined oral contraceptive use by women with Wolff-Parkinson-White syndrome. However, as WHO advises that women with atrial fibrillation should not use the combined pill, it seems prudent that a woman at risk of arrhythmias such as atrial fibrillation should consider use of a method other than the combined pill.

QUESTION

For women with arrhythmia who take flecainide acetate, is the combined oral contraceptive pill a safe form of contraception?

POPULATION: Women with arrhythmia who take flecainide acetate.

INTERVENTION: The combined oral contraceptive pill.

OUTCOME: Safety.

ANSWER

An arrhythmia is any deviation from, or disturbance of, the normal heart rhythm.[8] The heart's intrinsic pacemaker is the sinoatrial node located in the right atrium. This emits an impulse to trigger the heartbeat. There are different types of arrhythmia including: ventricular tachycardia, atrial tachycardia, and atrial fibrillation or flutter.

Ventricular tachycardia originates in the ventricles, frequently in the aftermath of a myocardial infarct when scar tissue alters many local electrical properties. Atrial tachycardia originates in the atria, and may be related to a structural problem. Atrial fibrillation is a rapid chaotic rhythm originating from multiple sites within both atria in a dynamic, changing pattern. Atrial flutter also involves the rapid firing of electrical impulses but the heartbeat will be more regular than with atrial fibrillation.[8]

One study by Marchlinski *et al.* attempted to investigate sex-specific triggers for right ventricular outflow tract tachycardia.[9] Symptomatic tachycardia was found to coincide with exercise, stress, caffeine, fatigue and (in women) with periods of hormonal flux. Periods of hormonal flux included premenstrual, gestational, and perimenopausal states as well as administration of birth control pills.

The *WHO Medical Eligibility Criteria for Contraceptive Use* does not specifically address contraceptive choices for women with arrhythmia. However, WHO includes atrial fibrillation as an indication of complicated valvular heart disease and advises that women with complicated valvular heart disease should not use the combined oral contraceptive pill (WHO category 4). Women with complicated valvular heart disease and atrial fibrillation may have unrestricted use of the progestogen-only pill, DMPA and the implant (specifically Norplant) (WHO category 1). The contraceptive benefits of using the IUD or LNG-IUS generally outweigh the risks (WHO category 2). WHO has noted that antimicrobial prophylaxis should be considered for individuals with valvular heart disease at risk of bacterial endocarditis following IUD insertion.

No evidence was identified on the use of combined oral contraception in young healthy women with isolated arrhythmia. The benefits of using progestogen-only contraceptives generally outweigh the risks in women with complex arrhythmias. There are no drug interactions between flecainide acetate and combined pills, however, the use of combined oral contraception would need to be considered on an individual basis.

QUESTION

For women who have had cardiac laser therapy, can the combined oral contraceptive pill be used safely?

POPULATION: Women who have had cardiac laser therapy.
INTERVENTION: Combined oral contraception.
OUTCOME: Safety.

ANSWER

Cardiac laser surgery is performed to remove or coagulate diseased tissue, by using short pulsed lasers producing shockwaves to mechanically injure tissue. Laser coagulation has the same effect as radio frequency or microwave applications.[10]

The *WHO Medical Eligibility Criteria for Contraceptive Use* does not specifically mention cardiac laser therapy. However, WHO recommends that in cases of uncomplicated valvular heart disease, the benefits of using combined oral contraception generally outweigh the risks (WHO category 2). However, among women with complicated valvular heart disease (suffering from pulmonary hypertension, atrial fibrillation, or history of subacute bacterial endocarditis), the combined pill should not be used (WHO category 4). This is because its use may further increase the risk of arterial thrombosis.

Progestogen-only methods of contraception, such as pills, implants or DMPA, are classified as WHO category 1 (unrestricted use) for women with complicated and uncomplicated valvular heart disease.

The IUD or LNG-IUS may be used without restriction in women with uncomplicated valvular heart disease. In cases of complicated valvular heart disease, women should be advised that the benefits of using either the IUD or LNG-IUS generally outweigh the risks (WHO category 2).

Within the Medline and EMBASE databases, the CEU could not identify any literature regarding combined oral contraception, or any other method of contraception, and cardiac laser therapy. Therefore no further advice can be added to the recommendations described above from WHO.

QUESTION

For women who have had cardiac transplants, are contraceptive methods associated with any specific adverse effects?

POPULATION: **Women who have had cardiac transplant.**
INTERVENTION: **Contraceptive methods.**
OUTCOME: **Specific adverse effects.**

ANSWER

The CEU systematic literature search identified only two relevant publications.[11,12] At least 24 pregnancies in heart transplant recipients have been reported in the world literature, 18 with a successful outcome. The authors of one of the reviews report on their own experience with one heart transplant recipient whose contraceptive needs were successfully managed with a low dose combined oral contraceptive.[12] To their knowledge, their own patient represents the only case reported in the literature of successful use of a combined oral contraceptive before a pregnancy.

In choosing a contraceptive method for a heart transplant recipient, all the usual medical eligibility criteria and drug interactions should be considered. In particular, some immunosuppressive agents may interact with hormonal contraceptives. The CEU has previously reviewed contraceptive choices for women taking the agent tacrolimus, and recommended non-hormonal methods. However, this agent is generally used for liver and kidney, rather than cardiac, transplant recipients.

References

1. Kasper EK. Cardiomyopathy and Heart Failure Practice. Definitions [www.hopkinsmedicine.org/cardiology/heart/definitions.html].
2. The Cardiomyopathy Association. Dilated Cardiomyopathy. 2004 [www.cardiomyopathy.org/docs/dialated.pdf].
3. Veille JC, Zaccaro D. Peripartum cardiomyopathy: summary of an international survey on peripartum cardiomyopathy. *Am J Obstet Gynecol* 1999;181:315–19.
4. Familial Hypertrophic Cardiomyopathy [www.books.md/F/dic/familialhypertrophiccardiomyopathy.php].
5. Herbert M, Tully G. Wolff-Parkinson-White Syndrome [www.emedicine.com/emerg/topic644.htm].
6. Kounis NG, Zavras GM, Papadaki PJ, Soufras GD, Kitrou MP, Poulos EA. Pregnancy-induced increase of supraventricular arrhythmias in Wolff-Parkinson-White syndrome. *Clin Cardiol* 1994:18:137–40.
7. Gray M, D'Amato L. Medically complex pregnancy: A case report illustrating CNM/MD collaborative management. *J Midwifery Womens Health* 2000:45:552–7.
8. The Arrhythmia Service. What is arrhythmia? [www/more_rythmns.html].
9. Marchlinski FE, Deely MP, Zado ES. Sex-specific triggers for right ventricular outflow tract tachycardia. *Am Heart J* 2000;139:1009–13.
10. Dorschuler K, Muller G. The role of laser in cardiac surgery. *Thorac Cardiovasc Surg* 1999;47 Suppl 3:385–7.

11. Cupples SA. Cardiac transplantation. *Crit Care Nurs Clin North Am* 1997;9:521–33.
12. Spina V, Aleandri V, Salvi M. Contraccezione dopo trapianto cardiaco. *Minerva Ginecol* 1998;50:539–43.

Ischaemic heart disease

QUESTION

For women with hypertension which is being treated, can combined oral contraception be used safely?

POPULATION: Women with treated hypertension.

INTERVENTION: Combined oral contraception.

OUTCOME: Safety.

ANSWER

The FFPRHC produced guidelines on the first prescription of combined oral contraception.[1] The guidance advises that combined pill users with hypertension have an increased risk of myocardial infarction,[2] ischaemic stroke[3] and haemorrhagic stroke,[4] compared with normotensive users. According to pooled data from four large phase III clinical trials,[1–5] combined oral contraception has a negligible effect on blood pressure itself.

The *WHO Medical Eligibility Criteria for Contraceptive Use* recommends that, for women with adequately controlled hypertension, the risks of using combined oral contraception generally outweigh the benefits (WHO category 3). In these women, the benefits of using DMPA generally outweigh the risks (WHO category 2) and the progestogen-only pill, progestogen implant, LNG-IUS or the IUD can be used without restriction (WHO category 1).

The CEU recommends that women with adequately controlled hypertension should be counselled on the risks of cardiovascular disease with combined pill use and should use a progestogen-only or non-hormonal contraceptive method.

QUESTION

In asymptomatic women with a family history of coronary heart disease, will use of the combined oral contraceptive pill increase their risk of coronary heart disease?

POPULATION:	Asymptomatic women with a family history of coronary heart disease.
INTERVENTION:	Use of the combined oral contraceptive pill.
OUTCOME:	Increased personal risk of coronary heart disease.

ANSWER

Coronary heart disease is a major cause of morbidity and mortality in the Western world. The Framingham Heart Study looked at men and women in the 1970s and further research has been carried out in this population-based sample.[6] Blood pressure, total cholesterol and low density cholesterol can effectively predict the risk of coronary heart disease in a middle-aged white population. The contribution of a family history of heart disease, physical activity and obesity to the prediction of risk is difficult to quantify. The strength of a positive family history will vary, depending on the number of relatives affected, the background risk of disease and the age distribution of affected individuals. A family history of coronary heart disease is felt to be 'strong' if there are two or more first-degree relatives or a first-degree relative under the age of 50 years with coronary heart disease.

The FFPRHC has published a Faculty Aid to CPD Topics (FACT) on combined oral contraceptives: myocardial infarction, stroke and venous thrombo-embolism.[7] This review summarised findings from a number of important studies but no reference was made regarding family history.

Within the *WHO Medical Eligibility Criteria for Contraceptive Use*, there is no recommendation regarding a family history of cardiovascular disease. Personal risk factors for heart disease include hypertension, smoking and hyper-lipidaemias and these conditions are reviewed independently within the *Medical Eligibility Criteria* for each type of contraceptive. Multiple personal risk factors for cardiovascular disease (such as older age, smoking, diabetes and hypertension) are given a WHO category 3 or 4. However, it is noted that a combination of two risk factors each assigned WHO category 2 may not necessarily warrant a higher category. Family history in first-degree relatives of DVT or pulmonary embolism is given a WHO category 2.

QUESTION

For a woman with coronary artery disease treated by bypass and stenting, which contraceptive method would best provide efficacy and safety?

POPULATION: Women with severe coronary artery disease who have undergone bypass or other coronary surgery.

INTERVENTION: Long-term contraception.

OUTCOME: Efficacy and safety.

ANSWER

Our literature searches identified no guidelines, systematic reviews or individual studies directly related to contraception for women with severe coronary artery disease. Since the avoidance of unintended pregnancy is vital for women with heart disease, effective contraception is essential. The CEU advises therefore that prescribers are guided by the *WHO Medical Eligibility Criteria*. On this basis, combined oral contraception would be unsuitable but any of the progestogen-only methods or a copper IUD would be acceptable. On pragmatic grounds, for a woman on anti-platelet drugs with a resulting bleeding tendency, an implant or IUD might be considered less suitable. Thus, the LNG-IUS or the most effective progestogen-only pill (theoretically, the desogestrel pill, Cerazette) appear to be the methods of choice.

QUESTION

For women at increased risk of cardiovascular disease (on the basis of age or other risk factors), do combined oral contraceptives containing 'newer' progestogens have any particular benefits?

POPULATION: Women at increased risk of cardiovascular disease (on the basis of age or other risk factors).

INTERVENTION: Combined oral contraceptives containing 'newer' progestogens.

OUTCOME: Risks and benefits.

ANSWER

The risk of myocardial infarction in women of reproductive age is low but increases exponentially with age. Combined oral contraceptive use has no impact on the risk of myocardial infarction in women of any age in the absence of additional recognised risk factors (such as smoking, family history, diabetes and hypertension).[8] However, combined pill use aggravates the increased risk associated with smoking such that the risks of combined oral contraception in smokers aged over 35 years are judged (by the *WHO Medical Eligibility Criteria for Contraceptive Use*) as unacceptable. On an individual basis, and as guided by WHO, clinicians may consider that combinations of other risk factors also render combined pill use unacceptably risky.

The balance of current evidence suggests that combined pills containing the 'newer' progestogens, desogestrel or gestodene, are associated with higher risks of VTE than pills containing levonorgestrel or norethisterone.[9] The evidence is more conflicting regarding myocardial infarction risk and progestogen type.[8] However, there is no convincing evidence that the 'newer' progestogens carry any advantage in terms of myocardial infarction risk.[10]

The CEU recommends that the choice of combined oral contraceptive for an individual woman is based on clinician experience and preference, price and acceptability to the woman of the adverse-effect profile. In general, the CEU recommends that, for women starting the pill for the first time, a monophasic pill containing 30–35 micrograms of estrogen with either norethisterone or levonorgestrel is chosen.[10] The prescription may be altered subsequently depending on the woman's response to this first choice. However, the CEU is unable to recommend any particular pill formulation for women with a 'borderline' elevated risk of cardiovascular disease. (In line with WHO and Faculty guidance, women with a substantially increased risk should be advised to choose contraception other than combined oral contraception.)

QUESTION

For women with risk factors (hyperlipidaemia or family history) for arterial cardiovascular disease, is combined oral contraception a safe contraceptive choice?

POPULATION: Women with risk factors for arterial cardiovascular disease (specifically hyperlipidaemia) or family history.

INTERVENTION: Combined oral contraception.

OUTCOME: Safety.

ANSWER

A search of Medline (1996–2004) identified three reviews on cardiovascular risk factors. The first of these identified nine variables which independently contribute to coronary heart disease risk (age, smoking, personal angina history, family history of myocardial infarction, diabetes, systolic blood pressure, levels of cholesterol and triglyceride). These data were derived from an 8-year cohort study of German middle-aged men.[11]

A second review article focused specifically on myocardial infarction in young patients (aged under 45 years).[12] This review highlighted the two types of myocardial infarction occurring in younger people, atherosclerotic and nonatherosclerotic (approximately 20%). Overall risk factors included smoking, lipid abnormalities, hypertension, diabetes, obesity, cocaine abuse, congenital coronary anomalies, hypercoagulable states and family history. A positive family history of premature coronary disease in a first-degree relative was identified as a major risk factor for myocardial infarction in young patients. Siblings of a young patient with myocardial infarction have up to a ten-fold increased risk of developing coronary artery disease.

The third review specifically addressed oral contraceptives and thrombosis.[13] It focused on relative risks associated with different types of progestogen, rather than on risk factors *per se*. Among the final conclusions was the statement: 'If oral contraceptives are prescribed to women with a risk factor for arterial thrombotic diseases (smoking, diabetes, controlled hypertension, migraine without aura, family disposition for acute myocardial infarction or thrombotic stroke) a low-dose pill with a third generation progestogen seems to be preferable. The woman should be informed about the relative and absolute risk of thrombosis by taking oral contraceptives'.[13]

FFPRHC guidance on first prescription of combined oral contraception[1] provides summary recommendations on medical eligibility for combined oral contraception based on previous recommendations from the *WHO Medical Eligibility Criteria for Contraceptive Use*. The WHO guidance regarding hyperlipidaemia was considered ambiguous by the FFPRHC expert group. A consensus decision was reached by our group to assign a WHO category 2 for women with known hyperlipidaemias.

Neither our own guidance, nor the WHO recommendations on which it was based, specifically include family history among the listed risk factors for arterial cardiovascular disease which should be taken into account when assessing a woman's suitability for use of combined oral contraception. However, there is good evidence that a history of myocardial infarction or thrombotic stroke in a first-degree relative aged under 45 years increases the risk of such disease by as much as ten-fold. Therefore, family history is undoubtedly one of the risk factors which must be included in an assessment of any individual woman's suitability for combined oral contraception.

QUESTION

For women with high cholesterol (total blood cholesterol 9.5 mmol/l, HDL 2.5 mmol/l and LDL 6.7 mmol/l), can combined oral contraception be used safely?

POPULATION: Women with high cholesterol.

INTERVENTION: Low-dose combined oral contraception.

OUTCOME: Safety.

ANSWER

Cholesterol is an endogenous fatty substance. Proteins carry cholesterol around the circulation, and the combinations of cholesterol and proteins are called lipoproteins. LDLs carry cholesterol from the liver to the cells. HDLs return extra cholesterol that is not needed to the liver. If individuals have high levels of lipoproteins and triglycerides, they are at a greater risk of coronary heart disease.[14] The risk of coronary heart disease is especially high if an individual has a low level of HDL cholesterol and a high level of LDL cholesterol.

Hypercholesterolaemia is a dominantly inherited genetic condition that results in high LDL cholesterol levels beginning at birth.[15] The British Heart Foundation recommends that total blood cholesterol levels should be below 5.0 mmol/l, LDL below 3.0 mmol/l and HDL above 1.0 mmol/l.[16] The American Heart Association states that the total cholesterol to HDL ratio should stay below 5:1, however the optimum ratio is 3.5:1.0.[17] Guidelines on the treatment of hyperlipidaemia from the Finnish Medical Society also advise that triglyceride levels should be under 2.0 mmol/l.[18]

The *WHO Medical Eligibility Criteria for Contraceptive Use* recommends that, for women with known hyperlipidaemias, the risk of combined oral contraceptive use may or may not outweigh the benefits (WHO category 2/3) depending on other risk factors. However, the FFPRHC guidance on first prescription of combined oral contraception assigned a WHO category 2 for women with known hyperlipidaemias (as in the process of developing the guidance, expert group members decided that the WHO 2/3 categorisation was unhelpful).[1] If multiple risk factors are present, (such as smoking, hypertension, or obesity) the risks of combined pill use generally outweigh the benefits (WHO category 3).

In most observational studies that have investigated the association between hypercholesterolaemia and stroke, a weak or unclear association has been found.[19] An international, multicentre, case–control study by WHO found that the odds ratio for ischaemic stroke associated with low-dose combined pills (less than 50 micrograms estrogen) was 1.53 (95% CI 0.71–3.31) and 5.30 (95% CI 2.56–11.0) for higher-dose preparations.[20] Studies have shown that the risk of ischaemic stroke is lower in women using a lower-dose combined pill.

The CEU advises that low-dose combined oral contraception (less than 50 micrograms ethinylestradiol) may be used with caution in women with high cholesterol and no other risk factors for stroke. Progestogen-only methods (pills, injectables, implants, or the intrauterine system) or non-hormonal methods may all be used.

QUESTION

In women with hypercholesterolaemia treated with fenofibrate, what is the risk of using progestogen-only contraception, particularly upon cardiovascular outcome?

POPULATION: Women with hypercholesterolaemia.
INTERVENTION: Progestogen-only contraception.
OUTCOME: Risk of cardiovascular disease.

ANSWER

Fenofibrate is a lipid-reducing agent which primarily reduces triglycerides. It does not act by inducing a gastrointestinal malabsorption process. It is not an enzyme-inducer and does not interact with any contraceptive methods.

WHO Medical Eligibility Criteria for Contraceptive Use classifies all progestogen-only methods of contraception as category 2 for use in women with hyperlipidaemias. No articles were identified which discussed the effects of progestogen-only injectables, implants or the desogestrel-only pill upon lipid profile.

The CEU supports the use of progestogen-only methods, including the LNG-IUS, for women with treated hypercholesterolaemia.

QUESTION

For women with familial hypercholesterolaemia, can combined oral contraception be used safely, or what are the alternatives?

POPULATION: Women with familial hypercholesterolaemia.
INTERVENTION: Combined oral contraception and alternatives.
OUTCOME: Safety.

ANSWER

Familial hypercholesterolaemia is a dominantly inherited genetic condition that results in high LDL cholesterol levels beginning at birth.[15] High levels of cholesterol can increase the risk of cardiovascular disease, which can lead to stroke or heart attack.

The *WHO Medical Eligibility Criteria for Contraceptive Use* recommends that, for women with known hyperlipidaemias, the risks of combined oral contraception may or may not outweigh the benefits (WHO category 2/3) depending on other risk factors.

Observational studies have shown a weak or unclear association between hypercholesterolaemia and stroke. The CEU advises that the combined oral contraceptive pill may be used with caution in women with familial hypercholesterolaemia and no other risk factors for stroke. Progestogen-only methods (pills, injectables, implants or the intrauterine system) or non-hormonal methods may all be used.

QUESTION

For women with ischaemic heart disease, can progestogen-only methods of contraception be used safely?

POPULATION: Women with ischaemic heart disease.
INTERVENTION: Use of progestogen-only contraceptives.
OUTCOME: Risk of cardiovascular event.

ANSWER

Few studies have been large enough to evaluate the risk of cardiovascular disease associated with progestogen-only contraception. This is in part because there is a low incidence of cardiovascular morbidity in women of childbearing age and also because of the relatively limited use of progestogen-only contraception worldwide. The WHO Collaborative Study collected data from Africa, Asia, Europe and Latin America and evaluated the risks of cardiovascular disease with the use of oral and injectable progestogen-only contraceptives.[20] Although limited by the small numbers of women using these methods, the data suggest that there is little or no increase in risk of VTE, stroke or acute myocardial infarction associated with use of oral or injectable progestogen-only methods.

In summary, this large WHO study recruited 3697 cases (2196 with stroke, 1137 with VTE and 364 with acute myocardial infarction); 9997 control subjects were also recruited from a hospital population. The cases and controls were matched for age, BMI and number of live births. As expected, cases were more likely to have a history of other cardiovascular risk factors: hypertension, diabetes, rheumatic heart disease or to be smokers. No significant increase in odds ratio for VTE was identified in association with the use of all oral progestogen-only methods. There was also no increase in odds ratio for stroke in progestogen-only users without a prior history of hypertension. However, progestogen-only contraceptive users with hypertension had twice the risk of haemorrhagic stroke compared to non-users. Findings must be interpreted with caution as numbers were small and confidence intervals are wide.

The *WHO Medical Eligibility Criteria* recommends that the progestogen-only pill, implant or LNG-IUS can be initiated in women with ischaemic heart disease (WHO category 2). However, DMPA should not generally be used (WHO category 3); this is because there is particular concern regarding reduced HDLs among depot-users, which may persist for some time after discontinuation.

QUESTION

For a woman with a history of acute myocardial infarction and postoperative pulmonary embolism, benign intracranial hypertension with lumboperitoneal shunt and epilepsy treated with the liver enzyme inducer phenytoin, is subdermal progestogen-only contraception an appropriate method?

POPULATION: Women with multiple diseases (acute myocardial infarction, postoperative pulmonary embolism, benign intracranial hypertension with lumboperitoneal shunt and epilepsy treated with a liver enzyme inducer).

INTERVENTION: Subdermal progestogen-only contraception.

OUTCOME: Safe and effective contraception.

ANSWER

Women with multiple pathologies must be considered individually in terms of their contraceptive requirements. The *WHO Medical Eligibility Criteria for Contraceptive Use* can be used to guide health professionals in contraceptive decision-making. Consideration should be given to the effect of contraception on the disease and the effect of the disease and its management on contraceptive use. Consideration must also be given to the importance of pregnancy prevention.

Myocardial infarction

The use of estrogen-containing contraceptives should be avoided in women with current or previous ischaemic heart disease (WHO category 4). If myocardial infarction occurs in a woman already using progestogen-only methods, the risks of continuing the method theoretically outweigh the benefits (WHO category 3). Progestogen-only pills and progestogen-only implants may be initiated (WHO category 2). The IUD is given a WHO category 1 classification and the LNG-IUS is classified as WHO category 2. There is specific concern regarding the hypoestrogenic effects of DMPA and its reduction in HDL cholesterol, which may persist after cessation.

Pulmonary embolism

The use of estrogen-containing contraception should be avoided in women with previous or current pulmonary embolism (WHO category 4). The benefits of progestogen-only methods in women with a history of pulmonary embolism generally outweigh the risks (WHO category 2). The IUD is given a WHO category 1 classification and the LNG-IUS receives a WHO category 2 classification for previous pulmonary embolism.

Benign intracranial hypertension

Since estrogens have been implicated in the aetiology of benign intracranial hypertension and are associated with an increased thrombotic risk, it is likely they should be given a WHO category 4 classification. Although there have been reports to the WHO Collaborating Centre for International Drug Monitoring of benign intracranial hypertension in women using progestogen-only contraception (levonorgestrel subdermal implants), no strong causal relationship has been identified. There is no evidence available on the effects of progestogen-only contraception and the symptoms or clinical course of benign intracranial hypertension. In cases where a treatable or self-limiting cause of benign intracranial hypertension is identified and where thrombotic associations have been excluded, a history of benign intracranial hypertension would not necessarily contraindicate the use of progestogen contraception.

A report published in 1995 reviewed the National Registry of Drug-induced Ocular Side-effects (Casey Eye Institute, Portland, USA), the Food and Drug Administration's Spontaneous Reporting System (Rockville, USA) and the WHO Collaborating Centre for International Drug Monitoring (Uppsala, Sweden) for a possible association between levonorgestrel use and benign intracranial hypertension.[21] A total of 56 cases of benign intracranial hypertension have been reported; all patients were female with a mean age of 22 years (range 16–34 years). Visual field defects and diplopia were the most common presentations. Headaches are a common presentation for women with benign intracranial hypertension but are also one of the most common adverse effects associated with levonorgestrel implants. The manufacturers advise screening for papilloedema if headaches of a different type, pattern or severity occur and persist. Levonorgestrel may have been associated with benign intracranial hypertension but this association may not be causal. Until more information is available, the ocular fundus should be inspected in women with visual symptoms or a change in pattern of headache and the implant removed in women in whom intracranial pressure increases.

Epilepsy

The anti-epileptic liver enzyme-inducers reduce the contraceptive efficacy of progestogen-only pills, combined oral contraception and subdermal progestogens. The anticonvulsants carbamazepine, phenytoin, phenobarbitone, oxcarbazepine, felbamate and topiramate increase the metabolism of estradiol and progestogens. Other anticonvulsants (sodium valproate, clobazam, vigabactrin, gabapentin, tiagabine, levetiracetam, zonisamide and lamotrigine) have no effect on sex steroid metabolism. It is important that women with epilepsy are provided with safe and effective contraception, as a pregnancy should be a planned event. The FFPRHC has published a Faculty Aid to Continuing Professional Development Topics on interactions with hormonal contraception.[22] The FACT concluded that enzyme-inducers reduce the contraceptive efficacy of implants and another form of contraception is suggested.[23,24]

QUESTION

For women with multiple risk factors for cardiovascular disease, is DMPA a safe method of contraception?

POPULATION:	Women with multiple risk factors for cardiovascular disease.
INTERVENTION:	DMPA.
OUTCOME:	Safety.

ANSWER

The *WHO Medical Eligibility Criteria for Contraceptive Use* classifies the use of DMPA as Category 3 for individuals with multiple risk factors for arterial cardiovascular disease (such as older age, smoking, diabetes and hypertension).

WHO mentions that some progestogen-only contraceptives may increase the risk of thrombosis (although this risk is substantially less than with combined oral contraceptives) and the effects of DMPA may persist for some time.

For women with a history of hypertension, including hypertension during pregnancy or adequately controlled hypertension, WHO classifies the use of DMPA as category 2. Specifically for women with systolic blood pressure ≥ 160 mmHg or diastolic ≥ 100 mmHg, WHO applies a category 3 for DMPA. WHO also classifies DMPA use by women with vascular disease as category 3.

The CEU recommends that, for women with cardiovascular disease, the benefits and risks of all contraceptive methods should be considered. Decisions on contraceptive use should be made individually and should be based on the severity of disease and any co-existing risk factors.

Update to Answer

The UK version of the *Medical Eligibility Criteria for Contraceptive Use*, which has been developed by the FFPRHC, has modified the recommendations relating to use of DMPA in women with hypertension. For women with systolic blood pressure between 140 mmHg and 159 mmHg or diastolic between 90 mmHg and 94 mmHg, a category 1 (unrestricted use) applies. For women with systolic blood pressure of 160 mmHg or above or diastolic of 95 mmHg or above, a category 2 (benefits generally outweigh risks) applies. Only for women with hypertensive vascular disease has a category 3 (risks generally outweigh benefits) been allocated.

QUESTION

In women with cardiovascular and/or cerebrovascular disease, does use of the LNG-IUS for contraception have any adverse effects on the underlying disease?

POPULATION: **Women with cardiovascular and/or cerebrovascular disease.**

INTERVENTION: **Use of the LNG-IUS for contraception.**

OUTCOME: **Adverse effect on the underlying disease.**

ANSWER

For women with significant cardiovascular or cerebrovascular disease, effective contraception is important to avoid unintended pregnancy which may worsen the condition. The LNG-IUS is a very effective method of contraception which can also be effective in reducing menstrual blood loss.

The *WHO Medical Eligibility Criteria for Contraceptive Use* provides guidance to allow clinicians to provide contraception for women safely and without unnecessarily limiting their contraceptive choice.

Decisions regarding contraceptive use in women with significant cardiovascular or cerebrovascular disease should be made on the basis of the individual's risks and the potential benefits of contraception and after discussion with the physicians involve in their medical care.

QUESTION

For women with a recent myocardial infarction on warfarin, is an IUD a safe method of contraception?

POPULATION: Women with recent myocardial infarction on warfarin.
INTERVENTION: IUD.
OUTCOME: Safety.

ANSWER

The *WHO Medical Eligibility Criteria for Contraceptive Use* advises that women with current, or a history of, ischaemic heart disease may have unrestricted use of a copper-bearing IUD (WHO category 1).

Based on guidelines produced by the American Heart Association, a woman who has had a myocardial infarction does not fall into any of the risk categories for bacterial endocarditis and therefore does not require antibiotic prophylaxis prior to IUD insertion.

The CEU was unable to find any information on the potential effects of warfarin therapy on the increase in menstrual bleeding that accompanies copper IUD use in healthy women.

QUESTION

For women with angina, is a copper IUD the safest method of contraception?

POPULATION: Women with angina.

INTERVENTION: The intrauterine contraceptive device.

OUTCOME: Safety.

ANSWER

The *WHO Medical Eligibility Criteria for Contraceptive Use* does not specifically address contraceptive use for women with angina. However, women with current, or a history of, ischaemic heart disease may have unrestricted use of a copper-bearing IUD (WHO category 1).

For these women, the contraceptive benefits of the progestogen-only pill, LNG-IUS, or implant (Norplant) generally outweigh the possible risks (WHO category 2) and these methods may be considered. The risks of using DMPA generally outweigh the contraceptive benefits for these women (WHO category 3) and the combined oral contraceptive pill should not be used (WHO category 4).

Ultimately, the safest method of contraception for a woman with angina is the copper IUD. Women who cannot tolerate the bleeding and cramping that occurs following insertion may choose to use the progestogen-only pill or implant instead.

QUESTION

For a woman with a personal history of myocardial infarction, and a coronary artery stent in place, is intrauterine contraception appropriate, and, if so, would antibiotic prophylaxis be required for insertion?

POPULATION: Women with a personal history of myocardial infarction and a coronary artery stent in place.

INTERVENTION: Intrauterine contraception (IUD or IUS).

OUTCOME: Safety and efficacy; special precautions required.

ANSWER

WHO Medical Eligibility Criteria for Contraceptive Use assigns a category 1 for copper IUDs in women with a history of ischaemic heart disease. Category 2 is assigned for initiation of contraception with the LNG-IUS. However, a category 3 is assigned for continuation of contraception with an IUS in a woman who was using the method at the time of developing ischaemic heart disease.

No publications specifically relating to coronary artery stents and contraception were identified by CEU searches. A review on coronary artery stent infection was identified.[25] This indicated that stent infection is rare, but life-threatening. This review specifically stated: 'the complication rate at the present time does not warrant the use of prophylactic antibiotics prior to high-risk procedures.' A further review on stents specifically relates to their implications for dentists.[26] Again, it is reassuring that antibiotic prophylaxis is not considered necessary for patients with stents undergoing minor procedures: 'literature indicates that antibiotic prophylaxis, if required, may only be needed during the first few weeks after stent placement'.

The manufacturer's Summary of Product Characteristics for Mirena, the LNG-IUS, lists 'active or previous severe arterial disease, such as stroke or myocardial infarction' as a contraindication.

The CEU advises that a copper IUD would be a suitable contraceptive choice for a woman with a coronary artery stent in place. Published literature suggests that antibiotic prophylaxis is not required for insertion or removal.

References

1.   Faculty of Family Planning and Reproductive Health Care Clinical Effectiveness Unit. First prescription of combined oral contraception. *J Fam Plann Reprod Health Care* 2003;29:209–22.
2.   Croft P, Hannaford P. Risk factors for adults myocardial infarction in women –evidence from RCGP Oral Contraceptive Study. *BMJ* 1989;298:165–8.
3.   World Health Organization. WHO Collaborative Study of Cardiovascular Disease and Sex Steroid Contraception. Ischaemic stroke and combined oral contraception: results of an international, multicentre, case–control study. *Lancet* 1996;348:498–505.
4.   World Health Organization. WHO Collaborative Study of Cardiovascular Disease and Steroid Hormone Contraception. Haemorrhagic stroke, overall stroke risk, and combined oral contraceptives: results of an international, multicentre, case–control study. *Lancet* 1996;346:505–10.
5.   Endrikat J, Gerlinger C, Cronin M, Ruebig A, Schmidt W, Dusterberg B. Blood pressure stability in a normotensive population during intake of monophasic oral contraceptive intake containing 20 microgram ethinyl oestradiol and 75 microgram desogestrel. *Eur J Contracept Reprod Health Care* 2001;6:159–66.
6.   Wilson PWF, D'Agostino RB, Levy D, Belanger AM, Silbershatz H, Kannel WB. Prediction of coronary heart disease using risk factor categories. *Circulation* 1998;97:1837–47.
7.   Gupta S, Hannaford P. *Combined oral contraceptive: myocardial infarction, stroke and venous thromboembolism: a CPD self-assessment test: review*. Review no. 99/01. London: Faculty of Family Planning and Reproductive Health Care of the Royal College of Obstetricians and Gynaecologists; 1999.
8.   Lewis MA, Heinemann LAJ, Spitzer WO, MacRae KD, Bruppacher R. The use of oral

contraceptives and the occurrence of acute myocardial infarction in young women. *Contraception* 1997;56:129–40.

9. WHO Collaborative Study of Cardiovascular Disease and Steroid Hormone Contraception. Acute myocardial infarction and combined oral contraceptives: results of an international multicentre case–control study. *Lancet* 1997;349:1202–9.

10. Dunn N, Thorogood M, Faragher B, de Caestecker L, MacDonald T, McCollum C, *et al.* Oral contraceptives and myocardial infarction: results of the MICA case–control study. *BMJ* 1999;318:1579–84.

11. Cullen P, VonEckardstein A, Assmann G. Diagnosis and management of new cardiovascular risk factors. *Eur Heart J* 1998;19:13–19.

12. Choudhury L, Marsh JD. Myocardial infarction in young patients. *Am J Med* 1999;107:254–61.

13. Lidegaard O, Bygdeman M, Milsom I, Neshiem B, I, Skjeldestad FE, Toivonen J. Oral contraceptives and thrombosis. From risk estimates to health impact. *Acta Obstet Gynecol Scand* 1999;78:142–9.

14. British Heart Foundation. *What are Cholesterol, Lipoproteins and Blood Lipids*. London: British Heart Foundation; 2004.

15. Medline Plus. Medical Encyclopedia: Familial Hypercholesterolemia. 2003 [www2.merriam-webster.com/cgi-bin/mwmednlm?book=Medical&va=familial%20hypercholesterolemia].

16. British Heart Foundation. *Any questions? Cholesterol Absorption Inhibition (Ezetimbe)*. London: British Heart Foundation; 2004.

17. American Heart Association. *Cholesterol ratio*. 2004 [www.americanheart.org/presenter.jhtml?identifier=4503].

18. Finnish Medical Socet Duodecim. Treatment of hyperlipidaemia: Aims and selection. 2004 [www.guideline.gov/summary/summary.aspx?doc_id=3380] (Now withdrawn).

19. Leys D, Deplanque D, Mounier-Vehier C, Mackowiak-Cordoliani M, Lucas C, Bordet R. Stroke prevention. Management of modifiable vascular risk factors. *J Neurol* 2002;249:507–17.

20. World Health Organization. Cardiovascular disease and use of oral and injectable progestagen only contraceptives and combined injectable contraceptives. Results of an international, multicentre, case control study. *Contraception* 1998;57:315–24.

21. Alder JB, Fraunfelder FT, Edwards R, Weber M, Rofsky HE, Deitch MW. Levonorgestrel implants and intracranial hypertension. *N Engl J Med* 1995;332:1720–1.

22. Elliman A. Interactions with hormonal contraception. *J Fam Plann Reprod Health Care* 2000;26:109–11.

23. Haukkamaa M. Contraception by Norplant subdermal capsules is not reliable in epileptic patients on anticonvulsant treatment. *Contraception* 1986;33:559–65.

24. Odlind V, Olsson SE. Enhanced metabolism of levonorgestrel during phenytoin treatment in a woman with Norplant Contraception. *Contraception* 1986;33:257–61.

25. Dieter RS. Coronary artery stent infection. *Clin Cardiol* 2000; 23:808–10.

26. Roberts HW, Redding SW. Coronary artery stents: review and patient-management recommendations. *J Am Dental Assoc* 2000;131:797–801.

Venous thromboembolism and associated disorders

Current VTE and use of anticoagulants

QUESTION

For women with recent DVT and/or pulmonary embolism being actively treated with anticoagulants, which methods of contraception can be used safely? (Three similar enquiries.)

POPULATION: Women with a recent deep vein thrombosis on anticoagulants.
INTERVENTION: Contraception.
OUTCOME: Safety.

ANSWER

The WHO Collaborative Study of Cardiovascular Disease and Steroid Hormone Contraception collected data from women recruited in Africa, Asia, Europe and Latin America. The risks of VTE associated with the use of oral and injectable progestogen-only contraception were evaluated.[1] Data from this study suggest that there is little or no increase in risk of VTE associated with use of oral or injectable progestogen-only contraceptives.

The *WHO Medical Eligibility Criteria* provides recommendations for use of contraception by women with current DVT or pulmonary embolism. 'Current' disease is not defined by WHO. The CEU suggests that this refers to DVT or pulmonary embolism where anticoagulants are currently being used. The use of combined hormonal contraception by women with current DVT or pulmonary embolism poses an unacceptable health risk (WHO category 4). The risks of using progestogen-only contraception (pill, implant, injectable or the LNG-IUS) generally outweigh the benefits (WHO category 3). The use of progestogen-only methods is not usually recommended unless other methods are unacceptable or unavailable. WHO recommends that non-hormonal methods (copper IUD or barrier method) may be used without restriction (WHO category 1). WHO does not provide recommendations on use of progestogen-only emergency contraception for women with current DVT or pulmonary embolism.

The UK *Medical Eligibility Criteria* defines women with 'current' DVT or pulmonary embolism as those currently using anticoagulants. The UK recommendations are somewhat less cautious than those of WHO with regard to progestogen-only methods in women with current VTE. The UK version recommends that the benefits of progestogen-only pill use by women with current DVT or pulmonary embolism generally outweigh the risks (UK category 2). The risks of using a progestogen-only implant, injectable or the LNG-IUS generally outweigh the benefits (UK category 3). This category 3 is given not because of the progestogen content but because of the potential risk of haematoma formation with insertion of a subcutaneous implant, when giving an intramuscular injection, or when using a tenaculum to aid insertion of intrauterine contraception. Use of these methods may be delayed until anticoagulants are stopped. After counselling and with clinical judgement, these methods may be considered during anticoagulant treatment if other methods are unacceptable or unavailable. The CEU supports these UK recommendations.

QUESTION

For women with current DVT on warfarin and with heavy periods, can intrauterine contraception be used safely?

POPULATION: Women with current DVT and heavy periods.
INTERVENTION: Intrauterine contraception.
OUTCOME: Safety.

ANSWER

The *WHO Medical Eligibility Criteria* recommends that for women with current DVT, the risks of using the LNG-IUS generally outweigh the benefits (WHO category 3). WHO recommends that a copper IUD may be used without restriction (WHO category 1).

The UK *Medical Eligibility Criteria* suggests that 'current' DVT refers to disease for which anticoagulant is being used. The risks associated with use of intrauterine contraception are therefore related to risk of haemorrhage during insertion of the device, rather than the progestogen content. The UK *Medical Eligibility Criteria* therefore suggest that, for women with DVT and using anticoagulant, the risks associated with intrauterine contraception (LNG-IUS or the copper IUD) generally outweigh the benefits (UK category 3). After counselling and with clinical judgement, these intrauterine methods can be used if other methods are unacceptable or not available.

The WHO Collaborative Study found no increased risk of VTE with oral or injectable progestogen-only contraception.[1] No data were identified on risk of VTE with use of the LNG-IUS but it is likely that there would be no increased risk. The Summary of Product Characteristics for the LNG-IUS suggests that the device can be used in women with VTE.

The use of a copper IUD is associated with increased menstrual bleeding.[2] Women with menorrhagia may prefer the option of a LNG-IUS which is licensed to treat idiopathic menorrhagia.

The CEU advises that while receiving anticoagulant treatment for DVT or pulmonary embolism, women may, after counselling, consider the use of the LNG-IUS to improve menorrhagia.

References

1. World Health Organization Collaborative Study of Cardiovascular Disease and Steroid Hormone Contraception. Cardiovascular disease and use of oral and injectable progestogen-only contraceptives and combined injectable contraceptives. *Contraception* 1998;57:315–24.
2. Faculty of Family Planning and Reproductive Health Care Clinical Effectiveness Unit. The copper intrauterine device as long-term contraception. *J Fam Plann Reprod Health Care* 2004;30:29–42.

Past history of venous thromboembolism

QUESTION

For women who have a history of VTE, can progestogen-only contraception be used safely? (Seven similar enquiries.)

POPULATION: Women with a history of VTE.
INTERVENTION: Progestogen-only contraception.
OUTCOME: Safety.

ANSWER

The *WHO Medical Eligibility Criteria* recommends that the benefits of using progestogen-only contraception (pills, implant, injectable or the LNG-IUS) for women with a past history of VTE generally outweigh the risks (WHO category 2). This was supported by the UK *Medical Eligibility Criteria*.

Few studies have been large enough to evaluate the risks of VTE associated with the use of any progestogen-only contraceptives. This is in part due to the low incidence of VTE in women of reproductive age and the relatively limited use of progestogen-only contraception worldwide. There is however, no biological reason to suggest that progestogen-only contraceptives increase the risk of VTE. The WHO Collaborative Study collected data from women in Africa, Asia, Europe and Latin America.[1] Data from this study suggest that there is little, or no, increase in risk of VTE associated with use of oral or injectable progestogen-only contraceptives. There are no data on the risk of VTE with use of progestogen-only implants or the LNG-IUS.

The CEU supports the use of progestogen-only contraception or non-hormonal contraception by women with a past history of VTE.

Reference

1. World Health Organization Collaborative Study of Cardiovascular Disease and Steroid Hormone Contraception. Cardiovascular disease and use of oral and injectable progestogen-only contraceptives and combined injectable contraceptives. *Contraception* 1998;57:315–24.

Family history of venous thromboembolism

QUESTION

For women with a family history of pulmonary embolism, should the age and sex of the first-degree relative be taken into consideration when assessing the safety of combined oral contraceptive use?

POPULATION: Women with a family history of pulmonary embolism.
INTERVENTION: Combined oral contraception.
OUTCOME: Safety.

ANSWER

A family history of VTE can alert clinicians to women who may have an increased personal risk of VTE. Nevertheless, many women with a family history, or even a proven genetic thrombophilia, will never develop VTE.

The *WHO Medical Eligibility Criteria for Contraceptive Use* recommends that for women with a family history (first-degree relative, age not specified) with

VTE, the benefits of using combined oral contraception generally outweigh the risks (WHO category 2).

The UK *Medical Eligibility Criteria* recommends that the benefits of using combined hormonal contraception (pills or patch) by women with a family history of VTE in a first-degree relative over the age of 45 years generally outweigh the risks (UK category 2). The risks of using combined hormonal contraception by women with a family history of VTE in a first-degree relative under the age of 45 years generally outweigh the benefits (UK category 3). Other contraceptive options (progestogen-only or non-hormonal) should be considered.

No evidence was identified that the sex of the first-degree relative was important. Some young women considering combined hormonal contraception may not yet have a first-degree relative aged over 45 years. Even when a family history of VTE is identified, many women will never develop VTE. A thrombophilia screen may be considered, but a negative screen does not necessarily exclude an underlying thrombophilia.[1]

The CEU recommends that the risks of using combined hormonal contraception for women with a first-degree relative aged under 45 years with a VTE generally outweigh the benefits. If after counselling about the preferred use of progestogen-only or non-hormonal methods, these are unacceptable, combined hormonal contraception may be considered with clinical judgement (UK category 3).

Reference

1. Faculty of Family Planning and Reproductive Health Care. First prescription of combined oral contraception. *J Fam Plann Reprod Health Care* 2003;29:209–23.

Known thrombophilias

QUESTION

For a woman with factor V Leiden deficiency, which contraceptive methods can be used safely? (Two similar enquiries)

POPULATION: Women with factor V Leiden deficiency.

INTERVENTION: Contraception.

OUTCOME: Safety.

ANSWER

Some individuals have a mutation affecting production of a protein called factor V Leiden. Women who are heterozygous for factor V Leiden have a three- to seven-fold increase in risk of VTE; those who are homozygous have an 80-fold increase in risk compared to those without the mutation.[1] This increased risk of VTE is further increased with combined oral contraceptive use.[2] It has been estimated that the seven-fold increased risk of VTE for women with factor V Leiden deficiency compared with the general population is increased to a 20- to 30-fold increased risk if combined oral contraception is used. Nevertheless, the absolute risk of VTE remains low and many women with factor V Leiden will never develop DVT or pulmonary embolism.

A case–control study found little evidence that progestogens alone increase the risk of VTE.[3]

The CEU supports the *WHO Medical Eligibility Criteria* recommendations that combined hormonal contraceptive use poses an unacceptable health risk if a woman has a known thrombophilia (such as factor V Leiden). The benefits of using progestogen-only contraception by women with factor V Leiden deficiency generally outweigh the risks (WHO category 2).

QUESTION

For women using heparin for factor V Leiden deficiency, can progestogen-only contraceptive implants be inserted before heparin is discontinued, or is there a risk of haematoma formation?

POPULATION: Women using heparin for factor V Leiden deficiency.

INTERVENTION: Insertion of progestogen-only contraceptive implant.

OUTCOME: Haematoma formation.

ANSWER

The *WHO Medical Eligibility Criteria* recommends that the benefits of using progestogen-only contraception by women with factor V Leiden deficiency generally outweigh the risks (WHO category 2). There is no specific reference to women with factor V Leiden deficiency who are currently using anticoagulants.

The Summary of Product Characteristics for the etonogestrel implant (Implanon) does not indicate any drug interaction between the implant and heparin. Subcutaneous unfractionated heparin has a half-life of approximately 10 hours. Heparin may need to be discontinued temporarily prior to insertion to reduce risk of haematoma and this should be done in consultation with expert advice (such as the woman's haematologist).

The UK *Medical Eligibility Criteria* recommends that the risks of using a progestogen-only implant by women currently using anticoagulants (for treatment of current VTE) generally outweigh the benefits (UK category 3). This is primarily because of the risk of haematoma formation associated with insertion of an implant, rather than increased risk of VTE. Nevertheless, the insertion of a progestogen-only implant may be considered after counselling and with clinical judgement if other methods are unacceptable.

The CEU suggests that women with a known thrombophilia (such as factor V Leiden deficiency) may use progestogen-only contraception without increased risk of VTE. If heparin is being used and insertion of an implant cannot be delayed, advice should be sought from an appropriate expert on temporarily discontinuing heparin until the implant is inserted to reduce the risk of haematoma formation.

QUESTION

For women with antiphospholipid syndrome, does the combined oral contraceptive pill increase the risk of thrombosis?

POPULATION: Women with antiphospholipid syndrome.

INTERVENTION: Combined oral contraceptive pill.

OUTCOME: Risk of thrombosis.

ANSWER

Women with antiphospholipid syndrome have raised concentrations of lupus anticoagulant and anticardiolipin antibody. Antiphospholipid syndrome is associated with an increased risk of venous or arterial thrombosis and of recurrent miscarriage.

The *WHO Medical Eligibility Criteria* recommends that use of combined hormonal contraception (pills or patch) poses an unacceptable health risk if a woman has a known thrombophilia (such as antiphospholipid syndrome) (WHO category 4). Alternative contraceptive options (progestogen-only and non-hormonal) should be considered.

The CEU supports the WHO recommendation that combined hormonal contraception may increase the already increased risk of VTE in women with antiphospholipid syndrome and alternative contraceptive options should be considered.

QUESTION

For women with antiphospholipid syndrome, are there any contraindications to the use of progestogen-only contraception?

POPULATION: Women with antiphospholipid syndrome.
INTERVENTION: Progestogen-only contraception.
OUTCOME: Safety.

ANSWER

Women with antiphospholipid syndrome have raised concentrations of lupus anticoagulant and anticardiolipin antibody. Antiphospholipid syndrome is associated with venous or arterial thrombosis and recurrent miscarriage.

The *WHO Medical Eligibility Criteria* recommends that the benefits of using progestogen-only contraception (pill, implant, injectable and the LNG-IUS) by women with a known thrombophilia (such as antiphospholipid syndrome) generally outweigh the risks (WHO category 2). Non-hormonal methods (copper IUD and barrier methods) may be use without restriction (WHO category 1).

The CEU advises that there are no contraindications to the use of progestogen-only contraception by women with antiphospholipid syndrome.

QUESTION

For women with systemic lupus erythematosus, which contraceptive methods can be used safely? (Two similar enquiries.)

POPULATION: Women with SLE.
INTERVENTION: Contraception.
OUTCOME: Safety.

ANSWER

Systemic lupus erythematosus is an autoimmune disease, which occurs in approximately 1/1000 people. It is more common in women than men (ratio 15:1).[4] Some evidence suggests that exacerbations of systemic lupus can occur in pregnancy.[5] A prospective cohort study in 121 645 women investigated the relationship between combined oral contraceptive use and development of SLE.[6] There was no significant association found. A small prospective study identified exacerbations of systemic lupus in five out of 20 women using a combined oral contraceptive.[7] Nevertheless, a similar number of exacerbations occurred in 20 women not using combined oral contraception.

Women with systemic lupus may have an associated underlying thrombophilia. The antiphospholipid syndrome (with elevated lupus anticoagulant and anticardiolipin antibody) is commonly found in association with systemic lupus.[8] The choice of contraceptive will be determined by the presence or absence of this underlying thrombophilia which predisposes to arterial and VTE.

The *WHO Medical Eligibility Criteria* recommends that use of combined hormonal contraception by women with a known thrombophilia poses an unacceptable health risk (WHO category 4).

The CEU recommends that women with SLE and an underlying thrombophilia should avoid combined hormonal contraception but progestogen-only and non-hormonal methods can be used.

QUESTION

For women with antithrombin III deficiency, can progestogen-only contraception be used safely?

POPULATION: Women with antithrombin III deficiency.
INTERVENTION: Progestogen-only contraception.
OUTCOME: Risk of VTE.

ANSWER

Approximately one person in 3000 has reduced levels of the natural anticoagulants, anti-thrombin III, protein C or protein S. This predisposes them to VTE. Antithrombin III deficiency is rare (0.02–0.05% of the population).[9] There are few data on associations between antithrombin III deficiency and hormonal contraception.

The *WHO Medical Eligibility Criteria* advises that use of combined hormonal contraception for women with known thrombophilias poses an unacceptable health risk (WHO category 4). The benefits of using progestogen-only methods (pills, implant, injectables or the LNG-IUS) by women with known thrombophilias generally outweigh the risks (WHO category 2). These recommendations were supported in the UK *Medical Eligibility Criteria*.

The CEU recommends that women with antithrombin III deficiency can use progestogen-only contraception without further increasing their risk of VTE.

QUESTION

> **For women with a previous VTE and antithrombin III deficiency on long-term warfarin, is use of combined oral contraception associated with unacceptable risks of VTE?**

POPULATION: Women with previous DVT and antithrombin III deficiency on long-term warfarin.

INTERVENTION: Combined oral contraception.

OUTCOME: Risk of VTE.

ANSWER

The *WHO Medical Eligibility Criteria* recommends that use of combined hormonal contraception by women with known thrombophilias (such as antithrombin III deficiency) and/or a previous VTE poses an unacceptable health risk (WHO category 4). The benefits of using progestogen-only contraception by women with known thrombophilias and/or a previous VTE generally outweigh the risks (WHO category 2).

The concurrent use of warfarin may increase the risk of haematoma formation during insertion of a progestogen-only implant or intramuscular progestogen-only injection or during insertion of a copper IUD or LNG-IUS.

The UK *Medical Eligibility Criteria* recommends that the benefits of using a progestogen-only pill by women using anticoagulants for current VTE generally outweigh the risks (UK category 2). However, the risks of using a progestogen-only implant, injectable or the LNG-IUS generally outweigh the benefits (UK category 3). The principal risk is haematoma formation with insertion of a subcutaneous implant, giving an intramuscular injection, or with the insertion of intrauterine contraception, rather than any risk due to the progestogen content.

The CEU recommends that a progestogen-only pill or barrier contraception may be most appropriate for a woman using warfarin for a past history of VTE and with antithrombin III deficiency. The progestogen-only injectable may be unsuitable due to the need for repeat injections. After counselling and with clinical judgement, the progestogen-only implant or intrauterine contraception may be considered (UK category 3). Warfarin may be temporarily discontinued for insertion but this should be discussed with the woman's haematologist.

QUESTION

For women with protein C or protein S deficiency, can the LNG-IUS be used safely? (Two similar enquiries.)

POPULATION: Women with protein C or protein S deficiency.
INTERVENTION: LNG-IUS.
OUTCOME: Risk of thrombosis.

ANSWER

There appears to be no direct evidence in the literature about the likelihood of thromboembolism in women with protein C or protein S deficiency who use the LNG-IUS. Few studies have been large enough to evaluate the risks of VTE associated with the use of progestogen-only contraceptives. This is in part due to the low incidence of VTE in women of reproductive age and the relatively limited use of progestogen-only contraception worldwide. There is no biological plausibility to suggest that progestogen-only contraceptives increase the risk of VTE (deep vein thrombosis and/or pulmonary embolism). The WHO Collaborative Study[10] suggests that there is little or no increase in risk of VTE associated with use of oral or injectable progestogen-only contraceptives. There are no data on the risk of VTE with use of a progestogen-only implant or the LNG-IUS.

The *WHO Medical Eligibility Criteria* recommends that, for women with a known thrombophilia (such as protein C or protein S deficiency), the benefits of using of progestogen-only contraception (pills, implant, injectable or the LNG-IUS) generally outweigh the risks (WHO category 2).

The CEU found no evidence to suggest that use of a LNG-IUS for women with protein C or protein S deficiency increases the risk of VTE.

QUESTION

For women with a prothrombin gene mutation, is the combined oral contraceptive a safe method of contraception?

POPULATION: Women with a prothrombin gene mutation.
INTERVENTION: Combined oral contraception.
OUTCOME: Safety and risk of VTE.

ANSWER

The prevalence of prothrombin G20210A gene mutation is low (0.7% to 4.0%) but those affected are at increased risk of recurrent thrombosis at a young age.[11-13] Studies have suggested that women with prothrombin G20210A mutations who use combined oral contraceptives may have a four- to eight-fold increase in the risk of venous thrombosis.[14]

The *WHO Medical Eligibility Criteria* recommends that combined hormonal contraceptives pose an unacceptable health risk if a woman has a known thrombophilia (such as a prothrombin gene mutation). Women with a prothrombin gene mutation may however use progestogen-only contraception (WHO category 2) or non-hormonal methods (WHO category 1).

The CEU recommends against the use of combined hormonal contraception for a woman with prothrombin G20210A gene mutation because of an increased risk of VTE.

QUESTION

For women with a prothrombin gene mutation, is subdermal progestogen-only contraception a safe option?

POPULATION: Women with a prothrombin gene mutation.
INTERVENTION: Subdermal progestogen-only implants.
OUTCOME: Safety.

ANSWER

Studies have suggested that women with prothrombin G20210A mutations who use combined oral contraceptives may have a four- to eight-fold increase in the risk of venous thrombosis.[14] No direct evidence was identified on the risk of VTE with use of progestogen-only implants in women with a prothrombin gene mutation. Progestogen-only contraceptives for which data are available (pills and injectables) are not associated with an increased risk of VTE.[10]

The *WHO Medical Eligibility Criteria* recommends that the benefits of using a progestogen-only implant by women with a prothrombin gene mutation generally outweigh the risks (WHO category 2).

The CEU recommends that women with a prothrombin gene mutation may safely use progestogen-only implants.

QUESTION

For women with a history of Klippel-Trenaunay-Weber syndrome who require contraception, does use of hormonal contraception carry an increased risk of adverse effects?

POPULATION: Women with a history of Klippel-Trenaunay-Weber syndrome.
INTERVENTION: Hormonal contraceptives.
OUTCOME: Increased risk of adverse effects.

ANSWER

Klippel-Trenaunay-Weber syndrome presents with three features: port-wine stain, varicose veins and bony and soft tissue hypertrophy. Research has shown that people with this condition are at increased risk of venous thrombosis. One study has estimated that the incidence of pulmonary embolism in people with Klippel-Trenaunay-Weber syndrome is 14–22% and that they also have a ten-fold increase in the rate of postoperative thromboembolism compared with other surgical patients.[15]

A specific thrombophilia to account for the increased risk of VTE has not been identified in patients with Klippel-Trenaunay-Weber syndrome. However, because of the increased risk, it may be appropriate to consider contraceptive options as for women with known thrombophilia. The *WHO Medical Eligibility Criteria* recommends that combined hormonal contraception poses an unacceptable health risk if a woman has a known thrombophilia. Women with a known thrombophilia may use progestogen-only contraception (WHO category 2) or non-hormonal methods (WHO category 1).

The CEU recommends that patients with Klippel-Trenaunay-Weber syndrome should avoid combined hormonal contraception because of increased risk of VTE and consider use of progestogen-only methods (pill, implant, injectable, or the LNG-IUS) or non-hormonal methods.

References

1. Lee R. Factor V Leiden: a clinical review. *Am J Med Sci* 2001;322:88–102.
2. Rosendaal FR. Venous thrombosis: a multicausal disease. *Lancet* 1993;353:1167–73.
3. Vasilakis C, Jick H, del Mar Melero-Montes M. Risk of idiopathic venous thromboembolism in users of progestagens alone. *Lancet* 1999;354:1610–11.

4. Cervera R, Khamashta MA, Font J, Sebastiani GD, Gil A, Lavilla P, *et al*. Systemic lupus erythematosus: clinical and immunologic patterns of disease expression in a cohort of 1000 patients. *Medicine* 1993;72:113–24.

5. Ruiz-Irastorza G, Lima F, Alves J, Khamastita MA, Simpson J, Hughes GR, *et al*. Increased rate of lupus flare during pregnancy and the puerperium: a prospective study of 78 pregnancies. *Br J Rheumatol* 1996;35:133–8.

6. Sanchez-Guerrero J, Karlson EW, Liang MH, Hunter DJ, Speizer FE, Colditz GA. Past use of oral contraceptives and the risk of developing systemic lupus erythematosus. *Arthritis Rheum* 1997;40:804–8.

7. Rampone A, Rampone B, Tirabasso S, Panariello S, Rampone N, Vozza A, *et al*. Contraception with the latest estroprogestogens in women suffering from systemic lupus erythematosus. *Minerva Ginecol* 2001;53:75–7.

8. Lakasing L, Khamashta M. Contraceptive practices in women with systemic lupus erythematosus and/or antiphospholipid syndrome: What advice should we be giving? *J Fam Plann Reprod Health Care* 2001;27:7–12.

9. Bauersachs R, Lindhoff-Last F, Ehrly AM, Kuhl H. The significance of hereditary thrombophlebia for the risk of thrombosis associated with oral contraception. *Zentralbl Gynakol* 1996;118:262–70.

10. World Health Organization Collaborative Study of Cardiovascular Disease and Steroid Hormone Contraception. Cardiovascular disease and use of oral and injectable progestogen-only contraceptives and combined injectable contraceptives. *Contraception* 1998;57:315–24.

11. De Stefano V, Rossi E, Leone G. Inherited thrombophilia, pregnancy, and oral contraceptive use: clinical implications. *Semin Vasc Med* 2003;3:47–59.

12. Aznar J, Vayá A, Estellés A, Mira Y, Segui R, Villa P, *et al*. Risk of venous thrombosis in carriers of the prothrombin G20210A variant and factor V Leiden and their interaction with oral contraceptives. *Haematologica* 2000;85:1271–6.

13. Rosendaal FR, Doggen CJ, Zivelin A, Arruda VR, Aiach M, Siscovick DS, *et al*. Geographic distribution of the 20210 G to A prothrombin variant. *Thromb Haemost* 1998;79:706–8.

14. Lindqvist PG, Svensson P, Marsaal K, Grennert L, Luterkort M, Dahlback B. Activated protein B resistance (FV:Q506) and pregnancy. *Thromb Haemost* 1999;81:532–7.

15. Baskerville PA, Ackroyd JS, Thomas ML. The Klippel-Trenaunay syndrome: clinical, radiological and haemodynamic features and management. *Br J Surg* 1985;72:232–6.

13 LIVER DISEASE AND ASSOCIATED DISORDERS

Gall bladder disease

QUESTION

For women who have had gallstones removed by cholecystectomy, can the progestogen-only pill or combined oral contraception be used safely? (Two similar enquiries.)

POPULATION: Women who have had gallstones removed by cholecystectomy.
INTERVENTION: Progestogen-only pill or combined oral contraception.
OUTCOME: Safety.

ANSWER

The *WHO Medical Eligibility Criteria for Contraceptive Use* recommends that the benefits of combined oral contraception or the progestogen-only pill generally outweigh the risks in women with gall-bladder disease treated by cholecystectomy (WHO category 2). The CEU endorses this recommendation.

QUESTION

For women with gallstones awaiting surgery, is it safe to use combined oral contraception?

POPULATION: Women with gall stones awaiting surgery.
INTERVENTION: Combined oral contraception.
OUTCOME: Safety.

ANSWER

The *WHO Medical Eligibility Criteria for Contraceptive Use* suggests that the risks of using combined hormonal contraception with current symptomatic gallstones generally outweigh the benefits (WHO category 3). After the removal of gallstones by cholecystectomy, combined pill use is considered a WHO category 2. The benefits of using the LNG-IUS, or other progestogen-only methods of contraception, generally outweigh the risks (WHO category 2), and this classification is no different after cholecystectomy. The use of a copper IUD is unrestricted (WHO category 1) before and after cholecystectomy.

The risk of postoperative VTE is increased from 0.5% to 1.0% for pill users compared with non-pill users. The Scottish Intercollegiate Guidelines Network recognises that the decision to discontinue combined oral contraception preoperatively is controversial. SIGN recommends that women using combined pills who are undergoing surgery should be counselled regarding the use of hormones preoperatively.[1] WHO suggests that combined pills should not be used in women undergoing major surgery with prolonged immobilisation (WHO category 4). Progestogen-only methods however, do not need to be discontinued prior to surgery, even with prolonged immobilisation.

The CEU recommends that, for women with symptomatic gallstones awaiting surgery, an IUD or a progestogen-only method of contraception are the most suitable options.

QUESTION

For a woman awaiting gallbladder surgery who also has polymyositis, SLE, osteoporosis, colitis and hypothyroidism, can the etonogestrel implant be used safely after gallbladder surgery, when liver function tests have returned to normal?

POPULATION: Women post-gallbladder surgery when liver function has returned to normal (who also have polymyositis, SLE, osteoporosis, colitis and hypothyroidism).

INTERVENTION: Etonogestrel-only implant.

OUTCOME: Safety.

ANSWER

The *WHO Medical Eligibility Criteria for Contraceptive Use* recommends that the etonogestrel implant (Implanon) can be used without restriction in women with thyroid disorders (WHO category 1). The UK version of the *Medical Eligibility Criteria* suggests that women with inflammatory bowel disease can use the etonogestrel implant (UK category 1). The benefits of the etonogestrel implant in symptomatic women awaiting gallbladder surgery generally outweigh the risks (WHO category 2).

Despite extensive searching, the CEU could find no information in the literature on the initiation of an etonogestrel implant in women specifically with polymyositis, SLE, osteoporosis or colitis. Randomised trials have shown that progestogen-only implants have no detrimental effect on liver function. No information was found on the use of an etonogestrel implant in women with abnormal liver function tests. The CEU recommends that women with polymyositis, SLE, osteoporosis, colitis and hypothyroidism, who have normal liver function tests after gallbladder surgery, can use an etonogestrel implant or non-hormonal methods of contraception, such as the IUD.

Reference

1. Scottish Intercollegiate Guidelines Network. *Prophylaxis of Venous Thromboembolism*. SIGN Publication No. 62. Edinburgh: SIGN; 2002 [www.sign.ac.uk/guidelines/fulltext/62/index.html].

Pregnancy-related cholestasis

QUESTION

For women with a history of pregnancy-related cholestasis, can combined oral contraception be used safely? (Four similar enquiries.)

POPULATION: **Women with a history of pregnancy-related cholestasis.**

INTERVENTION: **Combined oral contraception.**

OUTCOME: **Safety.**

ANSWER

Cholestasis of pregnancy is a multifactorial disorder with genetic, environmental and hormonal factors (estrogen and progesterone) implicated in its aetiology. It can lead to preterm delivery in up to 60% of pregnancies affected and intrauterine death in 2%. It usually presents in the second or third trimester of pregnancy. Pruritus and elevated serum bile acids usually resolve within hours of delivery. In severe cases, serum transaminases and bilirubin are also elevated. These abnormalities can recur in a subsequent pregnancy or when taking hormonal contraception.

In practice, women with previous pregnancy-related cholestasis are generally advised to avoid hormonal contraception because of the high risk of recurrence following exposure to estrogen or progestogen.[1] BNF also recommends that women with a history of cholestasis during pregnancy should avoid using combined oral contraception. The *WHO Medical Eligibility Criteria for Contraceptive Use* however, recommends that women with a history of pregnancy-related cholestasis may use combined oral contraception (WHO category 2).

The CEU advises that women with a history of pregnancy-related cholestasis should be counselled on the potential risks of using combined hormonal contraception and consideration should be given to the use of non-hormonal methods.

QUESTION

> **For women who have had pregnancy-related cholestasis and are heterozygous for alpha-1 antitrypsin deficiency, does use of hormonal contraception result in disease recurrence? (Two similar enquiries.)**

POPULATION: Women who have had pregnancy-related cholestasis and are heterozygous for alpha-1 antitrypsin deficiency.

INTERVENTION: Hormonal contraception.

OUTCOME: Disease recurrence.

ANSWER

Pregnancy-related cholestasis complicates 0.1–1.5% of pregnancies and can lead to preterm delivery or intrauterine death.. In severe cases, transaminases and bilirubin are elevated. Symptoms and signs can recur in subsequent pregnancies or when using hormonal contraception.[2]

Homozygotes for Z α_1-antitrypsin have plasma α_1-antitrypsin levels which are 10–15% of the levels seen in the general population. The abnormal protein accumulates and can lead to juvenile hepatitis, cirrhosis and hepatocellular carcinoma.[3]

Previous pregnancy-related cholestasis might predict an increased risk of developing combined pill-associated cholestasis. The *WHO Medical Eligibility Criteria for Contraceptive Use* recommends that women with previous pregnancy-related cholestasis may still use combined oral contraception, giving it a WHO category 2. Progestogen-only methods can be used by women who have had previous pregnancy-related cholestasis (WHO category 1). Women with cirrhosis who have normal liver function tests can use progestogen-only methods (WHO category 2). For women with severe decompensated cirrhosis with abnormal liver function test the risks of using progestogen-only methods generally outweigh the benefits (WHO category 3).

QUESTION

For women with previous liver disease (including previous pregnancy-related cholestasis), can DMPA be safely used?

POPULATION: Women with past liver disease or past cholestasis.

INTERVENTION: DMPA.

OUTCOME: Safety.

ANSWER

The *WHO Medical Eligibility Criteria for Contraceptive Use* advises that for women with mild cirrhosis the benefits of using progestogen-only contraceptives (pill, implant, injectables or the LNG-IUS) generally outweigh the risks (WHO category 2). For women with severe cirrhosis or active viral hepatitis, the risks of using progestogen-only contraceptives generally outweigh the benefits (WHO category 3). There is no restriction on the use of the copper IUD for women with active viral hepatitis (WHO category 1). Women who are carriers of viral hepatitis may have unrestricted use of progestogen-only methods (WHO category 1).

Women with a history of pregnancy-related cholestasis may have unrestricted use of progestogen-only contraceptives (WHO category 1). For women with a history of cholestasis related to previous use of combined oral contraception, the benefits of progestogen-only contraceptives generally outweigh the risks (WHO category 2).

The CEU advises that if liver function tests are normal, progestogen-only contraceptive can be used without restriction in women with previous liver disease.

References

1.   Lindberg MC. Hepatobiliary complications of oral contraceptives. *J Gen Intern Med* 1992;2:199–209.
2.   Milkiewicz P, Elias A, Williamson C, Weaver J. Obstetric cholestasis. *BMJ* 2002;324:123–4.
3.   Lomas DA, Mahadeva R. Antitrypsin polymerization and the serpinopathies: pathobiology and prospects for therapy. *J Clin Invest* 2002;110:1585–90.

HELLP syndrome

QUESTION

For a woman who has had HELLP syndrome in a recent pregnancy, can the combined oral contraceptive pill be used safely?

POPULATION: Women who have had HELLP syndrome.
INTERVENTION: Combined oral contraception.
OUTCOME: Safety.

ANSWER

HELLP syndrome (haemolysis, elevated liver enzymes and low platelets) is a rare and serious complication of the hypertensive disorder of pregnancy, pre-eclampsia. Elevated liver enzymes usually begin to return to normal within 24 hours of delivery.[1]

A case series of 98 women with previous HELLP showed no complications with subsequent oral contraceptive use.[2]

The CEU considers that a woman with previous HELLP syndrome may safely use combined oral contraception if liver function tests have returned to normal.

QUESTION

For women who have had HELLP syndrome in a recent pregnancy, can progestogen-only contraceptives be used safely?

POPULATION: Women who have had HELLP syndrome in a recent pregnancy.
INTERVENTION: Progestogen-only contraception.
OUTCOME: Safety.

ANSWER

HELLP syndrome is a rare and serious complication of pre-eclampsia. The Summaries of Product Characteristics for the etonogestrel implant (Implanon) and some progestogen-only pills state that they are contraindicated in women with current, or a history of, severe hepatic disease if liver function tests have not returned to normal. The Summary of Product Characteristics for the

LNG-IUS recommends that it may be used with caution in women with hepatic jaundice or other acute or severe liver disease.

The CEU advises that women who have had HELLP syndrome in a recent pregnancy can use progestogen-only contraception if liver function has returned to normal.

References

1. Anumba DO, Dilly OC, Robson SC. Management of pre-eclampsia and haemolysis, elevated liver enzymes, and low platelets syndrome. *Curr Opin Obstet Gynaecol* 1999;11:149–56.
2. Sibai BM, Ramadan MK, Chari RS, Friedman SA. Pregnancies complicated by HELLP syndrome (hemolysis, elevated liver enzymes, and low platelets): subsequent pregnancy outcome and long-term prognosis. *Am J Obstet Gynecol* 1995;172:125–9.

Cirrhosis

QUESTION

For women with liver cirrhosis requiring contraception, which methods are safe to use?

POPULATION:	**Women with liver cirrhosis.**
INTERVENTION:	**Contraception.**
OUTCOME:	**Safety.**

ANSWER

The use of combined hormonal contraception in women with cirrhosis may increase the risk of other liver diseases (hepatocellular carcinoma, hepatic adenoma, focal nodular hyperplasia, cholestasis, gallstone formation and hepatic vein thrombosis).[1]

The *WHO Medical Eligibility Criteria for Contraceptive Use* recommends that, for women with mild (compensated) cirrhosis, the risks of using combined hormonal contraception generally outweigh the benefits (WHO category 3). Combined hormonal contraceptive use by women with severe (decompensated) cirrhosis poses an unacceptable health risk (WHO category 4). WHO recommends that the benefits of using progestogen-only methods (pill, implant, injectable and LNG-IUS) generally outweigh the risks in women with mild (compensated) cirrhosis (WHO category 2); for women with severe (decompensated) cirrhosis, the risks generally outweigh the benefits (WHO category 3).

Barrier methods and the copper IUD can be used without restriction (WHO category 1) in women with both mild (compensated) and severe (decompensated) cirrhosis.

Despite extensive searching, the CEU could find no other literature on the use of contraception in women with cirrhosis. The CEU supports WHO recommendations that for women with mild cirrhosis, progestogen-only methods or non-hormonal methods are suitable; and for severe cirrhosis, non-hormonal methods such as an IUD are preferable.

QUESTION

For women with primary biliary cirrhosis, what contraceptive options are suitable?

POPULATION: Women with primary biliary cirrhosis.
INTERVENTION: Contraceptive options.
OUTCOME: Safe and effective contraception.

ANSWER

Primary biliary cirrhosis is characterised by inflammatory destruction of the small bile ducts, which leads to cirrhosis of the liver. The cause is unknown, but an autoimmune aetiology is likely. The worldwide prevalence is 5/100 000 and about 90% of cases are women. The disease is most commonly diagnosed between the ages of 40 and 60 years. Osteomalacia and osteoporosis can occur. Although fertility is often reduced in women with chronic liver disease, pregnancy may occur even with advanced primary biliary cirrhosis and women will require contraceptive advice and appropriate contraception.

There is little direct evidence on the effects of hormonal contraception on primary biliary cirrhosis. Two small studies in women with primary biliary cirrhosis given ethinylestradiol[2] or injectable medroxyprogesterone acetate[3] showed improved liver function.

WHO Medical Eligibility Criteria recommends that that there is no restriction in the use of copper IUD or barrier methods (WHO category 1) by women with cirrhosis (compensated or decompensated). In mild (compensated) cirrhosis, the benefits of using progestogen-only methods (pill, implant, injectable and the LNG-IUS) generally outweigh risks (WHO category 2). For women with severe (decompensated) cirrhosis, the risks of progestogen-only methods are thought to outweigh the benefits (WHO category 3). Combined hormonal contraceptives are classed as WHO category 3 for women with mild cirrhosis and WHO category 4 in women with severe (decompensated) cirrhosis. Sterilisation may be appropriate for women who have completed their families.

The CEU recommends that progestogen-only or non-hormonal methods are appropriate for women with cirrhosis and normal liver function. Liver function test may be monitored after initiation of progestogen-only methods. Women with primary biliary cirrhosis are at increased risk of osteoporosis and should consider alternatives to injectable progestogen-only methods. Advice should be given in consultation with the woman's physician.

References

1. Fagiuoli S, Van Thiel DH. The liver in endocrine disorders. In: *The Liver in Systematic Diseases*. Rustgi VK, Van Thiel DH, editors. New York: Raven Press; 1993. p. 294–5.
2. Guattery JM, Faloon WW. Effects of estradiol upon serum enzymes in primary biliary cirrhosis. *Hepatology* 1987;7:737–42.
3. Sotaniemi EA, Flynnynen T, Ahlqvist J. Effects of medroxyprogesterone on the liver function and drug metabolism of patients with primary biliary cirrhosis and chronic active hepatitis. *J Med* 1978;9:117–28.

Gilbert's disease

QUESTION

For women with a history of Gilbert's disease, will the combined oral contraceptive pill affect liver function and bilirubin?

POPULATION: Women with Gilbert's disease.

INTERVENTION: Combined oral contraceptive pill.

OUTCOME: Effect on liver function tests and bilirubin.

ANSWER

Gilbert's disease is an asymptomatic liver disease where raised bilirubin is identified, often incidentally. Approximately 5% of the population is affected by

Gilbert's disease which is caused by a deficiency of a liver enzyme involved in the metabolism of bilirubin. Serum bilirubin concentrations are elevated and this can lead to jaundice. No treatment is required and life expectancy is normal.

Small randomised controlled trials have investigated the effects of combined oral contraceptive pills on liver function.[1,2] In both trials, bilirubin concentrations were reduced with combined oral contraceptive use. Although monitoring serum bilirubin after initiating combined oral contraception has been advocated for women with Gilbert's disease, there is little evidence to support this.

QUESTION

For women with Gilbert's disease, does the etonogestrel implant have an effect on bilirubin concentrations?

POPULATION:	**Women with Gilbert's disease.**
INTERVENTION:	**The etonogestrel-only implant.**
OUTCOME:	**Effect on bilirubin concentration.**

ANSWER

Gilbert's disease is caused by a deficiency of a liver enzyme involved in the metabolism of bilirubin. No treatment is required and life expectancy is normal.

A prospective randomised controlled trial investigated the effects of progestogen implants (Implanon and Norplant) on haemostasis and liver function in 86 healthy women.[3] Total bilirubin and gamma-glutamyl transferase were increased in the two women using Implanon and all women using Norplant. However, neither implant adversely affected liver function to a clinically significant degree.

Based on this evidence, it would appear that women with Gilbert's disease may use the etonogestrel implant. Monitoring serum bilirubin concentration may be considered during the first few months of use.

References

1. Sadik W, Kovacs L, Pretnar- Darovec A, Mateo de Acosta O, Toddywalla VS, Dhall GI. A randomized double-blind study of the effects of two low-dose combined oral contraceptives on biochemical aspects. Report from a seven-centred study. *Contraception* 1985;32:223–36.
2. Loke DFM, Ng CSA, Holck S, Hall PE, Ratnam SS. Lipid and biochemical changes after low-dose oral contraception. *Contraception* 1992;46:227–41.

3. Egberg N, van Beek A, Gunnervik C, Hulkko S, Hirvonen E, Larsson-Cohn U, *et al.* Effects on the hemostatic system and liver function in relation to Implanon and Norplant. A prospective randomised clinical trial. *Contraception* 1998;58:93–8.

Wilson's disease

QUESTION

For women with Wilson's disease requesting long-term contraception, which method would best provide efficacy and acceptability? (Four similar enquiries.)

POPULATION:	**Women with Wilson's disease.**
INTERVENTION:	**Long-term contraception.**
OUTCOME:	**Efficacy, acceptability and safety.**

ANSWER

Wilson's disease is an autosomal recessive disorder of copper metabolism. Copper initially accumulates in the liver and subsequently other tissues. The main clinical manifestations are hepatic (hepatitis, cirrhosis or fulminant liver failure) and neurological. With modern treatment, it is compatible with pregnancy.

The *WHO Medical Eligibility Criteria* advises against combined oral contraception for women with cirrhosis (WHO category 3 or 4). The benefits of using progestogen-only contraception generally outweigh the risks with compensated cirrhosis (WHO category 2) and the risks generally outweigh the benefits with decompensated cirrhosis (WHO category 3). One research paper was identified which advised against combined oral contraceptive use in women with Wilson's disease.[1]

The CEU advises that, for women with Wilson's disease, combined hormonal contraception is usually best avoided; the use of progestogen-only methods may be considered if liver function is normal; and non-hormonal methods can be used without restriction.

Reference

1. Haimov-Kockman R, Ackerman Z, Anteby EY. The contraceptive choice for a Wilson's disease patient with chronic liver disease. *Contraception* 1997;56:241–4.

Hepatitis

QUESTION

For women who have had acute hepatitis following combined oral contraceptive use, can progestogen-only methods be used safely?

POPULATION: Women who have had acute hepatitis following combined oral contraceptive use.

INTERVENTION: Progestogen-only methods of contraception.

OUTCOME: Disease recurrence.

ANSWER

Serious hepatobiliary complications associated with combined hormonal contraceptive use are rare.[1] A history of cholestasis related to combined hormonal contraceptive use may predict risk of subsequent cholestasis with progestogen-only methods, but this has never been documented. The *WHO Medical Eligibility Criteria* recommends that women with a history of cholestasis related to combined oral contraceptive use should not use this method again (WHO category 3). However, the benefits of progestogen-only methods (pill, implant, injectable or the LNG-IUS) by women with cholestasis related to combined hormonal contraceptive use generally outweigh the risks (WHO category 2).

QUESTION

For women with hepatitis A, should the etonogestrel implant be removed early and when can it be reinserted?

POPULATION: Women with hepatitis A.

INTERVENTION: The etonogestrel implant.

OUTCOME: Early removal and insertion of a new implant.

ANSWER

Hepatitis A infection is usually self-resolving and management conservative. A small number of patients may develop profound cholestatic illness and remain jaundiced for several months.

The *WHO Medical Eligibility Criteria for Contraceptive Use* recommends that for women with active viral hepatitis the risks of using a progestogen-only implant generally outweigh the benefits (WHO category 3). However, viral hepatitis carriers may have unrestricted use of this method (WHO category 1).

The Summary of Product Characteristics for the etonogestrel implant (Implanon) states that use is contraindicated in women with the presence, or history, of severe hepatic disease if liver function is abnormal. Once liver function is normal, the implant may be inserted between day 1 and day 5 of the menstrual cycle without the need for additional contraceptive protection.

The CEU advises that for women using the etonogestrel implant who develop hepatitis A infection, the implant may be retained in place with monitoring of liver function. If liver function is abnormal and/ or worsening, the implant should be removed and a non-hormonal method of contraception used. For women with previous hepatitis A when liver function has returned to normal, the etonogestrel implant can be inserted.

QUESTION

For women with hepatitis B, is an IUD an appropriate contraceptive option?

POPULATION: Women with hepatitis B.
INTERVENTION: Copper IUD.
OUTCOME: Adverse effects for patient or professional.

ANSWER

Hepatitis B is one of the most common chronic viral infections with a prevalence in the UK of approximately 1/550. Chronic infection causes abnormal liver function with increases in alanine transaminases to a level two or three times normal values. A non-randomised comparative trial investigated combined oral contraceptive use in asymptomatic carriers of hepatitis B.[2] Seventy-eight women used a combined oral contraceptive pill and 81 women were included as controls. No differences in liver function were identified between combined oral contraceptive users and non-users.

The *WHO Medical Eligibility Criteria* recommends that hormonal and non-hormonal contraception are suitable for asymptomatic carriers of acute viral hepatitis. For women with active viral hepatitis (abnormal liver function), hormonal methods are not recommended (WHO category 3 for progestogen-only methods or WHO category 4 for combined hormonal methods). Non-hormonal contraception can be used by women with acute viral hepatitis.

There is no evidence published on the risk of hepatitis B transmission with IUD insertion. All health care professionals should adopt appropriate infection control procedures such as hand washing, wearing of gloves and avoidance of glove/skin punctures for all patient contacts and procedures. All professionals undertaking clinical procedures should have been vaccinated against hepatitis B.

QUESTION

For women with hepatitis C, what methods of contraception can be safely used? (Four similar enquiries.)

POPULATION: **Women with hepatitis C.**
INTERVENTION: **Contraception.**
OUTCOME: **Safety.**

ANSWER

The *WHO Medical Eligibility Criteria* recommends that women who are carriers of hepatitis can have unrestricted use of combined hormonal contraception and progestogen-only methods (WHO category 1). For women with active viral hepatitis, combined hormonal methods pose an unacceptable health risk (WHO category 4) and the risk of using progestogen-only methods may outweigh the benefits (WHO category 3). There is no restriction on the use of the copper IUD for women who are carriers of viral hepatitis or who have active viral hepatitis (WHO category 1).

Ribavirin (tribavirin) and interferon are drugs licensed to be used in the treatment of women with hepatitis C. Ribavirin is associated with birth defects in animals and can cause embryotoxicity after exposure of either the male or female parent. Adequate contraception is advised when either partner is using this drug and for up to 7 months after treatment is discontinued.

In conclusion, it is not recommended that women with active viral hepatitis use hormonal contraception and they should consider use of the IUD. Clinicians must carefully evaluate and exercise their judgement for those patients who do not wish to use the IUD. Viral hepatitis carriers may have unrestricted use of any method.

References

1. Lindberg, M. C. Hepatobiliary complications of oral contraceptives. *J Gen Intern Med* 1992;2:199–209.

2. Wang P, Lai Z, Tang J, Xu W, Mi X, Ma F. Safety of hormonal steroid contraceptive use for hepatitis B virus carrier women. *Pharmacoepidemiol Drug Saf* 2000;9:245–6.

Liver transplants and immunosuppressants

QUESTION

For women who have had liver transplant and take immunosuppressants, which contraceptive methods are safe?

POPULATION: Women who have had liver transplant and take immunosuppressants.
INTERVENTION: Contraception.
OUTCOME: Safety.

ANSWER

Two immunosuppressant drugs used to prevent transplant rejection are tacrolimus (Prograf®, Astellas) and mycophenolate mofetil (CellCept®, Roche). BNF advises that if individuals using tacrolimus require contraception, non-hormonal methods should be used. Pregnancy should be excluded before using mycophenolate mofetil and continued until 6 weeks after the drug is discontinued. The *WHO Medical Eligibility Criteria* does not address contraceptive choices for women who have undergone organ transplantation.

Specialist supervision is required for women following organ transplantation. Women using the immunosuppressant tacrolimus should consider the use of non-hormonal methods of contraception, such as a copper IUD. Barrier methods may also be used but failure rates may be unacceptably high.

Miscellaneous liver disorders

QUESTION

For women with focal nodular hyperplasia of the liver, can progestogen-only pills be used safely?

POPULATION: Women with focal nodular hyperplasia of the liver.
INTERVENTION: Progestogen-only pill.
OUTCOME: Safety.

ANSWER

Focal nodular hyperplasia of the liver is the second most common benign hepatic tumour (after haemangioma). Between 80% and 95% of cases of focal nodular hyperplasia occur in women aged 30–40 years.

The Summaries of Product Characteristics for progestogen-only pills do not recommend use in women with previous, or existing, liver tumours, hepatic adenomas or liver disease.

A small comparative study investigated 216 women diagnosed with focal nodular hyperplasia who continued to use hormonal contraception (combined hormonal contraception or progestogen-only pills) or used no hormonal contraception. Changes in the size of focal aggregates over 9 years were rare and were not associated with hormonal contraceptive use.[1]

The *WHO Medical Eligibility Criteria for Contraceptive Use* recommends that the risks of using a progestogen-only pill generally outweigh the benefits in women with benign liver tumours (adenoma) (WHO category 3). This is also the case for the other progestogen-only methods (implant, injectable and the LNG-IUS).

Reference

1. Mathieu D, Kobeiter H, Maison P, Rahmouni A, Cherqui D, Zafrani ES, *et al*. Oral contraceptive use and focal nodular hyperplasia of the liver. *Gastroenterology* 2000;118:560–4.

14 RENAL DISORDERS

QUESTION

For women with renal failure, can combined oral contraception be used safely?

POPULATION: Women with renal failure.
INTERVENTION: Combined oral contraception.
OUTCOME: Safety.

ANSWER

The UK National Kidney Federation[1] advises that combined oral contraception can be used in women with kidney diseases and that a low dose of ethinylestradiol (less than 35 micrograms) is generally preferred. Hypertension is common in women with kidney disease and the UK National Kidney Federation advises that blood pressure should be monitored and that the dose of antihypertensive drugs may need to be increased. According to the WHO, the risks of using combined oral contraception in women with hypertension generally outweigh the benefits (WHO category 3). The CEU suggests that progestogen-only methods would be more appropriate for women with renal disease and hypertension. The UK National Kidney Federation states that the LNG-IUS, the IUD and barrier methods can be used in women with kidney diseases. Despite extensive searching, the CEU could find no other information in the literature on the use of combined oral contraception in women with renal failure.

QUESTION

For women on haemodialysis, are progestogen-only contraceptives safe methods to use?

POPULATION: Women on haemodialysis.
INTERVENTION: Progestogen-only contraceptives.
OUTCOME: Safety.

ANSWER

Renal failure may be associated with a risk of cardiovascular complications arising from severe hyperlipidaemia. Chronic renal failure is associated with neuroendocrine disturbances, menstrual disorders and sexual dysfunction[2] and many women undergoing long-term haemodialysis are amenorrhoeic.[3,4]

Fertility is markedly decreased in women on chronic haemodialysis.[5] Successful outcomes were seen in only a small fraction of pregnancies of haemodialysis patients (for example about 25% in Europe)[6] before the introduction of erythropoietin; subsequently the success rate has increased to about 40%.[4] Transplantation restores fertility[7] and improves the likelihood of a successful pregnancy.[8] Effective contraception is required if pregnancy is not desired.

The *WHO Medical Eligibility Criteria for Contraceptive Use* does not address contraceptive choices for women with renal problems. WHO advises that for women with known hyperlipidaemias, the benefits of using the progestogen-only pill, DMPA, progestogen-only implants and the LNG-IUS generally outweigh the risks (WHO category 2). Women with known hyperlipidaemias may have unrestricted use (WHO category 1) of the IUD.

The pharmacokinetics of ethinylestradiol and progestogens are unlikely to be significantly affected by haemodialysis. Absorption, distribution and metabolism (in the gastrointestinal tract and liver) will be unaffected. Excretion may be affected, but most progestogen and some ethinylestradiol is excreted in faeces rather than in urine.

QUESTION

For women who have had renal transplants, are hypertensive, and are on various medications, can the progestogen-only pill, Cerazette or the LNG-IUS be used safely?

POPULATION: Women who have had a renal transplant, are hypertensive and are on various medications.

INTERVENTION: Progestogen-only pill or LNG-IUS.

OUTCOME: Safety.

ANSWER

The *WHO Medical Eligibility Criteria for Contraceptive Use* recommends that the progestogen-only pill or the LNG-IUS can be used without restriction in women with adequately controlled hypertension. BNF states that progestogens may inhibit the metabolism of the immunosuppressant drug, ciclosporin, resulting in increased plasma concentration. BNF does not mention any interactions between progestogens and atenolol, perindopril, prednisolone, or cefalexin. Antibiotics such as cefalexin may affect gut bacteria, which are important for enterohepatic circulation of ethinylestradiol but do not affect progestogen-only methods.

A large, WHO multicentre case–control study found that among women with a history of hypertension the risk of stroke is lower in those who do not use any form of steroid hormone contraceptive compared to those who use progestogen-only pills.[9] However, evidence is limited and the confidence interval for progestogen-only pill users was wide.

A case report has described a significant reduction in menorrhagia, dysmenorrhoea and uterine myoma size with the use of the LNG-IUS in a woman who had a renal transplant[10] The LNG-IUS has also been shown to reduce abnormal uterine bleeding in women who have had renal transplants and continue to experience abnormal bleeding after hysteroscopic endometrial ablation.[11]

Women can be immunocompromised because of disease (HIV) or drugs (ciclosporin, tacrolimus). The CEU was unable to identify any evidence on the risk of infection with IUD-use for immunocompromised women.

Despite extensive searching, the CEU could find no other information on the use of the progestogen-only pill or LNG-IUS in women who have had a renal transplant, are hypertensive and who are on various medications. The CEU advises that women who have had a renal transplant and are hypertensive can use the progestogen-only pill, LNG-IUS or IUD; however, they should be advised on the lack of good evidence of the safety of the methods.

QUESTION

For women with nephrotic syndrome (with normal renal function and cholesterol while on azathioprine), who also have menorrhagia and dysmenorrhoea, can combined oral contraception be used safely?

POPULATION: Women with nephrotic syndrome, menorrhagia and dysmenorrhoea.

INTERVENTION: Combined oral contraception.

OUTCOME: Safety.

ANSWER

Nephrotic syndrome results from damage to the glomeruli causing proteinuria, hypoproteinaemia with swelling (especially around the eyes, feet, and hands) and hypercholesterolaemia.[12]

The Summary of Product Characteristics for Norimin® (Pharmacia) states that it should be used with caution in women with kidney disease. No other Summaries of Product Characteristics for combined oral contraceptives mention kidney disease.

The patient referred to in this enquiry was aged 32 years, a non-smoker, with a BMI of less than 28, with normal blood pressure and with normal cholesterol and renal function. She was taking azathioprine for previous nephrotic syndrome. According to BNF, there is no interaction between azathioprine and combined pills.

Despite extensive searching, the CEU could find no other relevant information on the use of combined oral contraception in women with nephrotic syndrome. If progestogen-only contraception, including the LNG-IUS, is unacceptable to this woman, combined oral contraception could be used.

A Cochrane review concluded that there is insufficient evidence to confirm that combined pills reduce menstrual blood loss;[13] however, one small, randomised trial cited in the review found a 43% reduction in measured menstrual blood loss with combined pill use over two cycles. Anecdotally, women commonly describe less bleeding with combined pill use.[14]

The RCOG has published national evidence-based clinical guidance for the initial management of menorrhagia.[15] Further RCOG guidance on drug treatments for managing menorrhagia in secondary care[16] advises that the LNG-IUS can reduce menstrual blood loss and should be considered prior to surgical treatment. The LNG-IUS has a product licence in the UK for the treatment of idiopathic menorrhagia. Guidance from the FFPRHC CEU[17] advises that women should be informed that the LNG-IUS may reduce menstrual blood loss by over 90%.

DMPA induces amenorrhoea in almost half of users (46%) at 3 months, 53% at 6 months and 58% at 12 months.[18] This retrospective study, which investigated bleeding patterns in 536 users of DMPA in urban populations in the USA, also found that bleeding was frequent and prolonged in a number of women. Periods were reported as longer than usual by 18% of women at 12 months. Frequent bleeding was reported by 15% of women in the first 3 months of use but this fell to 6% at 12 months. However, 16% of women reported lighter bleeding at 12 months.

The available evidence indicates that combined pill use is not contraindicated in women with nephrotic syndrome. Although combined pills might reduce menstrual blood loss, the LNG-IUS or DMPA might be more effective in the management of menorrhagia and provide effective contraception.

QUESTION

For young women with polycystic kidney disease and hypertension treated with atenolol, are long-acting progestogen-only methods a safe contraceptive option?

POPULATION: Young women with polycystic kidney disease who are hypertensive.

INTERVENTION: Long acting progestogen-only contraceptives, excluding LNG-IUS.

OUTCOME: Safety.

ANSWER

Polycystic kidney disease is of unknown aetiology. Thirty percent of cases are inherited as an autosomal dominant trait. Autosomal dominant polycystic kidney disease is a systemic disorder characterised by multiple renal cysts causing chronic flank pain, haematuria, hypertension, renal stones, urinary tract infections and renal failure. Extra-renal manifestations include cardiovascular anomalies such as valve prolapse and ventricular septal hypertrophy, intracranial aneurysms and hepatic cysts. A prospective imaging study suggests that ovarian cysts are not more common in women with autosomal dominant polycystic kidney disease compared with women in the general population.[19]

Fertility rates among women with autosomal dominant polycystic kidney disease are not substantially different from those of the general population.[20] Pregnancy does not usually adversely affect renal function in normotensive women with autosomal dominant polycystic kidney disease, but there is increased risk of developing hypertension, pre-eclampsia, preterm delivery, renal stones, urinary tract infections, renal cyst infections and acute renal failure.[21] A case of a woman with hypertension and polycystic kidney disease suffering a fatal subarachnoid haemorrhage during sexual intercourse has been reported.[22]

Limited evidence suggests that DMPA use by women with hypertension may be associated with an increased risk of cardiovascular events (WHO category 2). This does not apply to subdermal progestogen-only implants (WHO category 1).

Research has raised concerns that women may experience a decrease in bone density with use of DMPA. As the attainment of peak bone density appears to be the single most useful measure to prevent osteoporosis and fractures in later life, it would seem prudent to avoid drugs that would prevent attainment of peak bone density during adolescence in young women with other risk factors for osteoporosis. There is a paucity of data about the effect of long-term use of DMPA in adolescents on bone density but three small studies have addressed this issue.[23-5] All suggest a negative impact on bone density/mineralisation in this group of women but larger studies in adolescents are needed to confirm these findings. The WHO classifies the use of DMPA from the menarche to 18 years as category 2.

As there are no hypoestrogenic effects with subdermal implants, they are suitable for contraception from the menarche to 18 years (WHO category 1).

Progestogen-only contraceptives do not protect against STIs. As there is an increased risk of *C. trachomatis* infection in women under 20 years of age, correct and consistent use of condoms is recommended.

QUESTION

For a young women aged 17 years with a family history of polycystic kidney disease, can the etonogestrel implant be used safely?

POPULATION: **Young women with family history of polycystic kidney disease.**
INTERVENTION: **Etonogestrel implant.**
OUTCOME: **Safety.**

ANSWER

Polycystic kidney disease is of unknown aetiology; 30% of cases are inherited as an autosomal dominant trait. Despite extensive searching, the CEU could find no evidence that the etonogestrel implant (Implanon) may not be used in young women with a family history of polycystic kidney disease, or young women with polycystic kidney disease. The CEU recommends that the etonogestrel implant is a highly effective method for young women and can remain in place for up to 3 years.

QUESTION

For women with Alport syndrome, is the combined oral contraceptive pill a safe choice?

POPULATION:	Women with Alport syndrome.
INTERVENTION:	Combined oral contraception.
OUTCOME:	Safety.

ANSWER

Alport syndrome is an inherited nephropathy characterised by alterations in the glomerular basement membrane as a result of mutations in type IV collagen.[26] The pathophysiology of the disease is unclear. Patients may present with a family history, microhaematuria or extra-renal abnormalities involving the ear. Renal biopsy has been the gold standard for the diagnosis of Alport's disease,[27] although skin biopsies and genetic testing have a role.[28] Characteristic histological findings are thickening of the glomerular basement membrane due to reduplication of the lamina densa. Alport syndrome is uncommon, occurring in approximately 1/5000 to 1/10 000 in the general population. There are no specific therapies. Renal failure may require dialysis or renal transplant. Deafness and eye problems may also occur. No evidence was identified by CEU searches on contraception for women with Alport's syndrome. The *WHO Medical Eligibility Criteria for Contraceptive Use* does not specifically mentioned Alport syndrome but there is information regarding use of combined oral contraception by women with hypertension and diabetic nephropathy. WHO recommends that the risks of combined oral contraception by women with hypertension (even when adequately controlled) generally outweigh the benefits (WHO category 3). For women with diabetic nephropathy, combined oral contraception is given a WHO category 3 or category 4, depending on the severity of the condition.

No evidence was identified by CEU searches on contraception for women with Alport's syndrome. Thus, the CEU would suggest that, for women with Alport syndrome with normal renal function and blood pressure, combined oral contraception might be considered. However, owing to the likely deterioration of renal function, a progestogen-only method may be more appropriate.

References

1. UK National Kidney Federation. Contraception. 2002 [www.kidney.org.uk/medical-info/sex-problems/contraction.html].
2. Lim VS, Henriquez C, Sievertsen G, Frohman LA. Erythropoietin causes hormonal changes in haemodialysis patients? *Ann Intern Med* 1980;93:21–7.
3. Perez RJ, Lipner H, Abdulla N. Menstrual dysfunction of patients undergoing chronic haemodialysis. *Obstet Gynecol* 1978;51:552–5.
4. Lim VS, Henriquez C, Sievertsen G, Frohman LA. Ovarian function in chronic renal failure: evidence suggesting hypothalamic anovulation. *Ann Intern Med* 1980;93:21–7.

5. Okundaye I, Abrinko P, Hou S. Registry of pregnancy in dialysis patients. *Am J Kidney Dis* 1998;31:766–73.

6. Anonymous. Successful pregnancies in women treated by dialysis and kidney transplantation. Report from the registration committee of the European Dialysis and Transplant Association. *Br J Obstet Gynaecol* 1980;87:839–45.

7. Sturgiss SN, Davison JM. Effect of pregnancy on long-term function of renal allografts. *Am J Kidney Dis* 1992;19:167–72.

8. Davison JM. Dialysis, transplantation, and pregnancy. *Am J Kidney Dis* 1991;17:127–32.

9. Debert-Ribeiro M, Medina E, Artigas J, He S, Zhong YH, De-Wei Z, *et al*. Cardiovascular disease and use of oral and injectable progestogen-only contraceptives and combined injectable contraceptives: Results of an international, multicenter, case–control study. *Contraception* 1998;57:315–24.

10. Fong FY, Singh K. Effect of the levonorgestrel-releasing intrauterine system on uterine myomas in a renal transplant patient. *Contraception* 1999;60:51–3.

11. Jeong KA, Park KH, Chung DJ, Shin JS, Bai SW, Lee BS, *et al*. Hysteroscopic endometrial ablation as a treatment for abnormal uterine bleeding in patients with renal transplants. *J Am Assoc Gynecol Laparosc* 2004;11:252–5.

12. National Kidney and Urologic Diseases Information Clearinghouse. Nephrotic Syndrome in Adults. 2003 [www.kidney.niddk.nih.gov/Kudiseases/Pubs/nephrotic].

13. Iyer V, Farquhar C, Jepson R. Oral contraceptive pills for heavy menstrual bleeding. *Cochrane Database Syst Rev* 2003;(2):1–2.

14. Fraser I, McCarron G. Randomised trial of two hormonal and two prostaglandin inhibiting agents in women with a complaint of menorrhagia. *Aust N Z J Obstet Gynaecol* 1991;31:66–70.

15. Royal College of Obstetricians and Gynaecologists. *The Initial Management of Menorrhagia*. National Evidence- Based Clinical Guidelines. London: RCOG Press;1998.

16. Royal College of Obstetricians and Gynaecologists. *The Management of Menorrhagia in Secondary Care*. National Evidence-Based Clinical Guidelines. London: RCOG Press; 1999.

17. Faculty of Family Planning and Reproductive Health Care Clinical Effectiveness Unit. The levonorgestrel-releasing intrauterine system (LNG-IUS) in contraception and reproductive health. *J Fam Plann Reprod Health Care* 2004;30:99–109.

18. Sangi-Haghpeykar H, Poindexter AN, Bateman L, Ditmore Jr. Experiences of injectable contraceptive users in an urban setting. *Obstet Gynecol* 1996;88:227–33.

19. Stamm ER, Townsend RR, Johnson AM, Garg K, Manco-Johnson M, Gabow PA. Frequency of ovarian cysts in patients with autosomal dominant polycystic kidney disease. *Am J Kidney Dis* 1999;34:120–124.

20. Mulutinovic J, Fialkow P, Agodoa L, Phillips LA, Bryant JL *et al*. Fertility and pregnancy complications in women with autosomal dominant polycystic kidney disease. *Obstet Gynecol* 1983;61:566–70.

21. Chapman AB. Cystic disease in women: Clinical characteristics and medical management. *Adv Ren Replace Ther* 2003;10:24–30.

22. Raschka C, Parzeller M, Muller E, Bratzke, H. Intracerebral hemorrhage during sexual intercourse of a woman with polycystic kidney disease. *Herz Kreislauf* 1999;31:259–61.

23. Scholes D, LaCroix AZ, Ott SM, Ichikawn LE, Barlows WE, *et al*. Bone mineral density in women using depot medroxyprogesterone acetate for contraception. *Obstet Gynecol* 1999;93:233–8.

24. Cromer BA, McArdle Blair J, Mahan J, Zibners L, Naumovski Z. A prospective comparison of bone density in adolescent girls receiving depot medroxyprogesterone

acetate (Depo-Provera), levonorgestrel (Norplant), or oral contraceptives. *J Pediatr* 1996;129:671–5.

25. Schwingl P, Visness CM, Weber T. Does depot-medroxyprogesterone acetate reduce bone mineral density in adolescent users? Contraception Online 1999;10(5):4–7 [www.contraceptiononline.org/contrareport/pdfs/10_05.pdf].

26. Heidet L, Cai Y, Guicharnaud L, Antignac C, Gubler MC. Glomerular expression of type IV collagen chains in normal and X-linked Alport syndrome kidneys. *Am J Pathol* 2004;156:1901–10.

27. Meleg-Smith S. Alport Disease: A review of the diagnostic difficulties. *Ultrastruct Pathol* 2001;25:193–200.

28. Grunfeld JP. Contemporary diagnostic approach in Alport's syndrome. *Ren Fail* 2000;22:759–63.

15 SKIN DISORDERS

QUESTION

For women with chloasma can combined oral contraception be used safely?

POPULATION: Women with chloasma.

INTERVENTION: Combined oral contraception.

OUTCOME: Safety.

ANSWER

Chloasma is a term used to describe the occurrence of melasma during pregnancy. Melasma occurs as symmetrical hyperpigmented areas usually on the cheeks, upper lip, chin or forehead and is much more common in women than men. It is more common in constitutionally darker skin types and the major contributing factor is sunlight exposure. There does appear to be a genetic predisposition to developing this hyperpigmentation. Hormones play a role and some women will develop the condition during pregnancy or while using hormonal contraception.[1]

The Summaries of Product Characteristics for various combined oral contraceptive pills advise that melasma may occur during use, especially in women with a history of chloasma during pregnancy. It is recommended that the condition requires strict medical supervision, and that women should avoid exposure to sunlight or ultraviolet radiation. The same advice is given in the Summaries of Product Characteristics for some progestogen-only pills, DMPA and the etonogestrel implant, Implanon.

Katsmabas and Antoniou[2] conducted a review of the classification and treatment of melasma. Both natural and synthetic estrogen and progesterone hormones have been implicated in the pathogenesis. They advise that if melasma is being treated, oral contraceptives should be discontinued. A cohort study of men and women with hyperpigmented skin lesions in Bangladesh found a high prevalence of melasma in women. More than 50% of the women with melasma had a history of pregnancy or oral contraceptive use.[3]

Furthermore, a comparative study of two combined pills (containing 20 micrograms ethinylestradiol and 75 micrograms gestodene or 30 micrograms ethinylestradiol and 75 micrograms gestodene) found that melasma was one of the most commonly reported adverse effects in both treatment groups.[4] Melasma was also a reported reason for discontinuing the levonorgestrel implant, Norplant, in a cohort study examining its effectiveness.[5] However, in all studies melasma only occurred in a small number of participants and it may be that the incidence in these studies is related to it being more common in constitutionally darker skin types. Despite extensive searching, the CEU could find no information on the occurrence of melasma in caucasian women in the UK.

The CEU advises that women with chloasma/melasma can use hormonal contraception. However, they should use a broad-spectrum sunscreen and avoid sunlight exposure. If the condition worsens, the use of non-hormonal methods of contraception should be considered.

QUESTION

If women with a history of chloasma use the progestogen-only pill, is there a risk of recurrence?

POPULATION: **Women with chloasma who require contraception.**
INTERVENTION: **The progestogen-only pill.**
OUTCOME: **Risk of recurrence of chloasma.**

ANSWER

After an extensive search, the CEU was unable to determine if there is a risk of chloasma recurring if a woman uses progestogen-only pills. Most of the literature has focused on treatment of the condition. Certainly, both estrogens and progestogens have been implicated in the initial development of the condition in conjunction with sunlight and genetic predisposition. However, the exact pathway leading to development of chloasma is unknown. Expert opinion suggests that the progestogen-only pill will not worsen melasma which occurred when a woman was taking the combined pill.[6]

The CEU advises that women with a past history of chloasma can take the progestogen-only pill. However, they should use a broad-spectrum sunscreen and avoid sunlight exposure, which is the main catalyst for the condition.

QUESTION

In women with dermatomyositis, does use of the combined oral contraceptive pill provide an additional increase in thromboembolic risk?

POPULATION: Women with dermatomyositis.

INTERVENTION: Use of combined oral contraception.

OUTCOME: Thromboembolic risk.

ANSWER

Dermatomyositis is a rare inflammatory myopathy caused by an autoimmune response of unknown aetiology. Around 1400 new cases are identified each year in the USA. It may appear at any age but usually presents between the ages of 40 and 60 years. Dermatomyositis is twice as common in women as men. A juvenile form may occur in adolescence. Dermatomyositis causes voluntary muscle weakness, pain and fatigue. It can develop gradually over years. There is an associated skin rash on the face, eyelids, neck, chest, knees or elbows which can precede the muscle weakness by months or years. Hard nodules of calcium can deposit under the skin in juvenile dermatomyositis. Arthitis, Raynaud's phenomenon, SLE and interstitial lung disease are found in association with dermatomyositis. Mild cardiac problems can occur, the most common being rhythm defects and myocarditis; however, these rarely lead to complications.

There is no evidence, however, to support an increased thrombotic risk *per se*. Fist-line treatments include corticosteroids and in some cases other immuno-suppressive drugs may be required. The most common are azathioprine and methotrexate. Most patients with dermatomyositis respond well to treatment but relapses can occur. Morbidity and mortality are increased in association with cancer, significant cardiac disease, dysphagia and interstitial lung disease. The condition may worsen during pregnancy and is associated with preterm delivery.

The *WHO Medical Eligibility Criteria for Contraceptive Use* states that the degree of cardiac involvement determines the WHO category for combined oral contraceptive use in women with dermatomyositis. Cardiac involvement does not appear to lead to valve damage. Women with uncomplicated valvular heart disease can use the combined pill, a WHO category 2. In women with complicated valvular heart disease, the combined pill is not advised, WHO category 4. If systemic lupus, with its increase in thrombotic risk, is associated with dermatomyositis, then use of the combined pill would be given a WHO category 3/4.

QUESTION

For women with Stevens–Johnson syndrome, is the combined oral contraceptive pill a safe method of contraception?

POPULATION: Women with Stevens–Johnson syndrome.
INTERVENTION: The combined oral contraceptive pill.
OUTCOME: Safety.

ANSWER

Stevens–Johnson syndrome and toxic epidermal necrolysis are severe, sometimes fatal, skin reactions, which are frequently drug-induced by sulphonamides, antibiotics, anticonvulsants, NSAIDS[7] or cocaine.[8] Stevens–Johnson syndrome is now known also as erythema multiforme major. The incidence of Stevens–Johnson syndrome and its variants is estimated to be approximately 1.89 cases/million/year. A mortality rate of more than 40% has been calculated for toxic epidermal necrolysis sufferers; mortality increases with age and the amount of skin detachment related to the body surface area.[7] No specific drug treatment exists for Stevens–Johnson syndrome and the choice of antibiotic depends on the associated infection. High doses of corticosteroids may be used early in the reaction but their use is controversial as morbidity and mortality may increase in association with their use.[8]

After an extensive search of the literature, the CEU has been unable to find any studies that have investigated the relationship between the combined oral contraceptive and Stevens–Johnson syndrome.

The *WHO Medical Eligibility Criteria for Contraceptive Use* states that if the initial episode of Stevens–Johnson syndrome is combined pill-associated, this may reasonably be given a WHO category 4 classification. A clinician should therefore establish the cause of the Stevens–Johnson syndrome episode while keeping in mind that the syndrome may also be idiopathic. Women may be advised to choose a different method of contraception if it is established that the combined pill contributed to the Stevens–Johnson syndrome episode.

QUESTION

For women with non-neoplastic vulvar epithelial disorders, which methods of contraception would be safe and effective?

POPULATION:	Women with non-neoplastic vulvar epithelial disorders.
INTERVENTION:	Contraception.
OUTCOME:	Safety and efficacy.

ANSWER

A standard CEU search of Medline and Embase from 1996–2004 using search terms 'vulva' and 'contraception' identified few directly relevant papers. The search was therefore extended back to 1966; again, few papers were found.

Two review articles provide comprehensive overviews of benign vulvar disorders.[9,10] Since 1987, the preferred term for this group of disorders has been non-neoplastic epithelial disorders. Previously, the term vulvar dystrophies was generally used. The principal disorder within the group is lichen sclerosus. It is characterised by whitish lesions of the vulva; histological appearances vary but typically include hyperkeratosis. Treatment of lichen sclerosus has evolved over the years. Currently, potent topical steroids provide the best outcomes.[9] Accurate diagnosis of chronic vulvar lesions is important to exclude those with neoplastic potential.

A study published in 1991 quantified estrogen and progesterone receptors in HPV-related (premalignant) lesions of the cervix, vulva, and penis. High levels of receptors were found in cervical lesions, but not in lesions of the vulva or penis. The authors hypothesised that sex steroid hormones may act as cofactors in HPV-related cervical neoplasia; but that this would not be the case for vulvar lesions.[11]

A case–control study suggested that ever-use of combined oral contraception increases the risk of vulvar vestibulitis (a condition characterised by superficial dysparunia).[12]

QUESTION

For women with lichen sclerosus, is there evidence that hormonal contraception adversely affects this skin condition?

POPULATION:	Women with lichen sclerosus.
INTERVENTION:	Hormonal contraception.
OUTCOME:	Adverse effects on skin condition.

ANSWER

Lichen sclerosus is a chronic inflammatory dermatosis, aetiology is unknown, characterised by white plaques with epidermal atrophy.[13] The prevalence of the condition is unknown and it may occur either as genital or extragenital lichen sclerosus. The male to female ratio of the condition is 1:6 with the majority of cases presenting with genital lichen sclerosus. Treatment may involve the use of topical corticosteroids and some limited studies have also shown retinoids, such as isotretinion and acitretin, to be useful. Topical testosterone was the preferred treatment for female genital lichen sclerosus for decades although its efficacy is still contested.

Women with lichen sclerosus who are using retinoids for treatment should be counselled about the teratogenicity of these drugs. In the UK, the Summary of Product Characteristics for isotretinoin requires that women should use an effective method of contraception while using the drug. Primary methods of contraception for isotretinion-users include tubal ligation or partner's vasectomy, IUDs, oral contraceptives, and DMPA.[14] The Summary of Product Characteristics for acitretin states that this drug is contraindicated in women of childbearing potential unless an effective method of contraception is used for at least 1 month before treatment, during treatment and for at least 2 years after treatment is stopped.

After a review of the literature, the CEU was unable to find any evidence of the effects, if any, of hormonal contraception on lichen sclerosus. The citations below may be useful in the event that a woman with lichen sclerosus is using retinoid therapy and requires hormonal contraception.

A review of retinoids and contraceptives concludes that combined oral contraceptives provide a good contraceptive option for women using retinoids.[15] The Teratology Society of America recommends that women taking oral retinoids who have difficulty taking combined pills regularly should consider the use of an injectable contraceptive such as DMPA.[16] A study by Berbis et al. in 1998 mentioned that there may be an interaction between acitretin and the progestogen-only pill.[17] It has been suggested that oral retinoids reduce the efficacy of the progestogen-only pill by their effect on epithelial (including mucosal layer) differentiation.[18] BNF also advises that tretinoin reduces the contraceptive efficacy of low dose progestogens.

There is no evidence as to whether the efficacy of the etonogestrel implant or LNG-IUS is reduced by an interaction with retinoids. However, the contraceptive effects of the LNG-IUS are related to local effects rather than due to systemic absorption. Systemic progestogen metabolism is not expected to affect local efficacy.

QUESTION

For women with discoid lupus erythematosus, would combined oral contraception have any effect on coagulation?

POPULATION: Women with discoid lupus erythematosus.

INTERVENTION: Combined oral contraception.

OUTCOME: Effect on clotting.

ANSWER

Discoid lupus erythematosus is a photosensitive dermatosis whose lesions may result in scarring, atrophy and alopecia.[19] Discoid lupus erythematosus is thought to be genetically inherited and may also occur in patients with SLE. About 5% of those with discoid lupus erythematosus progress to SLE. The condition most often occurs in the 20–40 year age group following ultraviolet light exposure and the male to female ratio of discoid lupus erythematosus is 1:2.

Regular laboratory tests may be needed to evaluate if the disorder is progressing to SLE. Management of the condition aims to control existing lesions and prevent the occurrence of future lesions, usually by the use of corticosteroids (topical or by intralesional injection) and immunomodulatory antimalarials.[19] Other therapies may include auranofin, thalidomide, oral or topical retinoids, interferon and immunosuppressive agents such as methotrexate. The safety of many of these drugs during pregnancy has not been established; whereas some (such as thalidomide, isotretinion, acitretin and azathioprine) are contra-indicated during pregnancy. Women who are sexually active and using these drugs therefore require a reliable method of contraception.

The CEU was able to find only one study that looked at the influence of hormones on discoid lupus erythematosus. Other studies cited below have looked at the use of hormonal contraception by women with SLE. SLE frequently coexists with the acquired thrombophilia, antiphospholipid syndrome, typified by raised lupus anticoagulant and anticardiolipin, in young women.[20] Clinicians have been concerned in the past that barrier methods such as condoms lubricated with spermicide may exacerbate skin rashes for women with SLE and that, because they take steroids, these women may be at higher risk of pelvic infection with the use of IUDs.[20]

One study looked at systemic and discoid lupus under the influence of various hormonal states in 68 women.[21] Of 57 women whose lupus erythematosus had been diagnosed prior to the menopause, 20% described a premenstrual cutaneous exacerbation. Only three women had taken an estrogen-containing contraceptive.

Rampone et al.[22] performed a study to evaluate the effect of combined oral contraceptive use on women suffering from SLE. Twenty women of childbearing age with SLE taking low-dose combined pills containing 20 micrograms ethinylestradiol were followed up for 1 year. A control group of women with SLE who were not using any medication was also observed. Only five of the 20 women taking combined oral contraceptives experienced flares and had to discontinue the combined pill; a similar number in the control group also experienced flares. The authors concluded that modern low-dose pills do not produce immediate exacerbation of SLE and can be used under supervision.

Lakasing and Khamashta[20] performed an observational questionnaire-based study to determine the past and present contraceptive practices of 86 women with SLE and/or antiphospholipid syndrome, and to establish whether various contraceptives were associated with complications. Among women with SLE alone, one of nine using the combined pill at the time of diagnosis reported a severe flare. In women with primary or secondary antiphospholipid syndrome, seven of the 32 women using a combined pill (containing either a second- or third-generation progestogen) suffered thromboses during use. The women with SLE and/or antiphospholipid syndrome using other contraceptive methods did not report any specific problems. The authors concluded that most contraceptive methods are relatively safe for women with SLE but that women with antiphospholipid syndrome should be advised strongly against using combined oral contraception.

CEU guidance on first prescription of combined oral contraception[23] advises that for women with antiphospholipid syndrome, thrombophilia screening is warranted to identify their risk of VTE. As good practice, the interpretation of a thrombophilia screen should be undertaken in consultation with a haematologist or other expert and along with a detailed family history.

CEU guidance on the copper IUD as long-term contraception[24] mentions that there are no drugs which are known to effect IUD use and efficacy. No published evidence was identified of any effects of anti-inflammatory drugs (nonsteroidal, corticosteroids, cyclo-oxygenase inhibitors) on IUD efficacy. The risk of pelvic infection increases for all women in the 3 weeks following IUD insertion but returns to the same risk as the non-IUD-using population after this period.

The CEU was unable to identify any specific evidence on the effects if any of combined pill use on blood clotting in women with discoid lupus erythematosus. If a woman with discoid lupus progresses to SLE, in view of the possible associated thrombotic risk, a progestogen-only method or IUD would be more appropriate than combined oral contraception.

QUESTION

For women who have had pemphigoid gestationis and have heavy periods, can progestogen-only contraception be used safely?

POPULATION: Women who have had pemphigoid gestationis and have heavy periods.

INTERVENTION: Progestogen-only contraception.

OUTCOME: Safety.

ANSWER

Pemphigoid gestationis is a rare pregnancy-associated, autoimmune skin disease, most common during the second and third trimesters of pregnancy. It is characterised by an itchy rash that develops into blisters. It is also known as herpes gestationis, although it has no association with the herpes virus.[25] Pemphigoid gestationis may recur with subsequent pregnancies, resumption of menses, and use of oral contraception.[26]

Despite extensive searching, the CEU could find no information in the literature on the use of progestogen-only contraception in women who have had pemphigoid gestationis.

The RCOG has published national evidence-based clinical guidance for the initial management of menorrhagia. Treatment options include a variety of contraceptive methods.[27]

Pemphigoid gestationis may recur with oral contraceptive use and although non-hormonal methods such as an IUD might be advised, this may exacerbate heavy bleeding. Serum levels of progesterone are low with the LNG-IUS, it can be readily removed and can reduce menstrual blood loss. The CEU could find no evidence regarding LNG-IUS and recurrence of pemphigoid gestationis and, after counselling about options, clinicians and women may choose to try this method.

QUESTION

For women with erythema nodosum, do hormonal contraceptives contribute to exacerbation of the condition?

POPULATION: Women with erythema nodosum.

INTERVENTION: Hormonal contraception.

OUTCOME: Exacerbations of erythema nodosum.

ANSWER

Two comprehensive review articles were identified which provide a useful overview of erythema nodosum.[28,29] Erythema nodosum is an inflammatory cutaneous reaction producing tender, nodular lesions, usually on the front of the legs. The incidence has been estimated at 2.4/1000 population per year. In one series, 83% of cases were female.[30] Erythema nodosum is classified as a septal panniculitis, usually resolves spontaneously, and is associated with a wide range of trigger factors. Erythema nodosum usually resolves spontaneously within 6 weeks and relapses are exceptional. Serious complications of erythema nodosum are uncommon. In a published series of 110 cases, 28% were associated with sarcoidosis, 17% with infections (typically streptococcal), 6% with pregnancy and 4% with oral contraceptive use. In 35% no trigger factor could be identified.

Oral contraception is listed among the recognised trigger factors for erythema nodosum in all review articles. Evidence for the association comes only from small case series. For example, Salvatore and Lynch[31] reported five cases where erythema nodosum developed in association with either pregnancy or hormonal contraception. Published evidence did not distinguish between estrogen or non-estrogen-containing hormonal contraception.[32,33]

Investigation of erythema nodosum focuses on the exclusion of serious causes such as sarcoidosis. Infection is a much more common trigger factor than hormonal contraception. In a woman who develops erythema nodosum after being established on hormonal contraception for some time, it seems unlikely that the contraception is the trigger.

The CEU could find no direct evidence on the use of DMPA, the implant or progestogen-only pill by women with erythema nodosum. The CEU considers that it is reasonable to prescribe hormonal contraception to women who have had erythema nodosum, after thorough investigation to exclude a serious underlying cause.

QUESTION

For women with pityriasis versicolor, can the etonogestrel implant, Implanon, be inserted safety?

POPULATION: Women with pityriasis versicolor.

INTERVENTION: Insertion of the etonogestrel implant, Implanon.

OUTCOME: Safety.

ANSWER

Pityriasis versicolor is a common skin disease caused by an overgrowth of a yeast fungus called *Pityrosporum orbiculare* (*Malassezia furfur*). It is commonly seen on the upper part of the back and on the chest, but it can be found on the entire body.[34]

The Summary of Product Characteristics for the etonogestrel implant, Implanon, make no mention of insertion in the presence of pityriasis versicolor. Despite extensive searching, the CEU could find no information in the literature on the insertion of Implanon in women with pityriasis versicolor.

The CEU suggest that if no skin lesions exist at the site of insertion, it may be appropriate to proceed with insertion if risk of pregnancy is real and other methods of contraception are unacceptable.

References

1.   Montemarano, AD. eMedicine-Melasma. 2003 [www.medicines.org.uk].
2.   Katsambas A, Antoniou C. Melasma: classification and treatment. *J Eur Acad Dermatol Venereol* 1995;4:217–23.
3.   Ali E, Aziz A, Fatema F. Morphological pattern of hyperpigmented skin lesions reporting for dermatological consultation; a 5 years clinical eperience. *Bangladesh J Dermatol Venereol Leprol* 1999;16:32–5.
4.   Taneepanichskul S, Kriengsinyot R, Jaisamrarn U. A comparison of cycle control, efficacy, and adverse effects among health Thai women between two low-dose oral contraceptives containing 20 µg ethinylestradiol/75 micrograms gestodene (Meliane) and 30 micriograms ethinylestradiol/75 micrograms gestodene (Gynera). *Contraception* 2002;66:407–9.
5.   Chompootaweep S, Kochagarn E, Sirisumpan S, Tang-usaha J, Theppitaksak B, Dusitsin N. Effectiveness of Norplant implants among Thai women in Bangkok. *Contraception* 1996;53:33–6.
6.   Szarewski A, Guillebaud J. *Contraception: A User's Handbook*. London: Churchill-Livingstone; 1999.
7.   Mockenhaupt M, Schopf E. Epidemiology of drug-induced severe skin reactions. *Semin Cutan Med Surg* 1996;15:236–43.
8.   Parrillo S and Parrillo CV. Stevens-Johnson Syndrome 2002 [www.emedicine.com/EMERG/topic555.htm].
9.   Larrabee R, Kylander DJ. Benign vulvar disorders. *Postgrad Med* 2001;109:151–64.
10. Foster DC. Vulvar disease. *Obstet Gynecol* 2002;100:145–63.
11. Monsonego, J, Magdelenat H, Catalan F, Corcas Y, Zerat L, Sastre X. Estrogen and progesterone receptors in cervical human papillomavirus related lesions. *Int J Cancer* 1991;48:533–9.
12. Bouchard C, Brisson J, Fortier M, Morin C, Blanchette C. Use of oral contraceptive pills and vulvar vestibulitis: a case controlled study. *Am J Epidemiol* 2002;156:254–61.
13. Meffert J. Lichen sclerosus et atrophicus 2004 [www.emedicine.com/derm/topic234.htm].
14. Family Practice notebook.com a Family Medicine Resource. Isotretinon (Accutane). 2003 [www.fpnotebook.com/DER186.htm].

15. Ceyrac D L, Serfaty D, Lefrancq H. Retinoids and contraception. *Dermatology* 1992;184:161–70.
16. Teratology Society. Recommendations for isotretinoin use in women of childbearing potential. *Teratology* 1991;44:1–6.
17. Berbis P, Bun H, Geiger JM, Rognin C, Durand A, Serradimigni A, *et al*. Acitretin (RO10–1670) and oral contraceptives: interaction study. *Arch Dermatol Res* 1988;280:388–9.
18. Geiger JM, Baudin M, Saurat JH. Teratogenic risk with etretinate and acitretin treatment. *Dermatology* 1994;189:109–16.
19. Callen JP. Lupus erythematosus, discoid. 2004 [www.emedicine.com/derm/topic247.htm].
20. Lakasing L, Khamashta M. Contraceptive practices in women with systemic lupus erythematosus and/or antiphospholipid syndrome: What advice should we be giving? *J Fam Plann Reprod Health Care* 2001;27:7–12.
21. Yell JA, Burge SM. The effect of hormonal changes on cutaneous disease in lupus erythematosus. *Br J Dermatol* 1993;129:18–22.
22. Rampone A, Rampone B, Tirabasso S, Panariello S, Rampone N, Vozza A, *et al*. Contraception with the latest estroprogestogens in women suffering from systemic lupus erythematosus. *Minerva Ginecol* 2001;53:75–7.
23. Faculty of Family Planning and Reproductive Health Care. First prescription of combined oral contraception. *J Fam Plann Reprod Health Care* 2003;29:209–23.
24. Faculty of Family Planning and Reproductive Health Care Guidance. The copper intrauterine device as long-term contraception. *J Fam Plann Reprod Health Care* 2004;30:29–42.
25. DermNet NZ. Pemphigoid gestationis. 2004 [http://dermnetnz.org/immune/pemphigoid-gestationis.html].
26. eMedicine. Pemphigoid Gestationis. 2004 [www.emedicine.com/DERM/topic178.htm].
27. Royal College of Obstetricians and Gynaecologists. *The Initial Management of Menorrhagia*. National Evidence-Based Clinical Guidelines. London: RCOG Press; 1998.
28. Requena L, Requena C. Erythema nodosum. *Dermatol Online J* 2002;8:1–30.
29. Bordell RT, Mehrabi D. Underlying causes of erythema nodosum. *Postgrad Med Online* 2000;108:1–5.
30. Psychos DNVP, V, Skopouli FN, Drosos A, Moutsopoulos HM. Erythema nodosum: the underlying conditions. *Clin Rheumatol* 2000;19:212–6.
31. Salvatore MA, Lynch PJ. Erythema nodosums, estrogens, and pregnancy. *Arch Dermatol* 1980;116:557–8.
32. Darlington LG. Erythema nodosum. *Br J Dermatol* 1974;90:209–12.
33. Taaffe A, Finlay AY, Marks R. Erythema nodosum and oral contraceptives. *BMJ* 1977;2:1353.
34. Pityriasis versicolor. 2002 [www.netdoctor.co.uk/diseases/facts/pityriasisversicolor.htm].

16 BREAST CANCER

Personal history of breast cancer

QUESTION

For a woman with recently treated breast cancer taking tamoxifen, which method of contraception is appropriate?

POPULATION: Women with recent breast cancer taking tamoxifen.
INTERVENTION: Contraception.
OUTCOME: Adverse effects on breast cancer prognosis.

ANSWER

Many factors influence the risk of developing breast cancer: increasing age, family history (especially a first-degree relative under the age of 50 years), specific genetic tendency (*BRCA1* gene mutations), reproductive factors (early menarche, late menopause and late age at first childbirth), long-term postmenopausal estrogen and progestogen replacement therapy, lifestyle factors (such as obesity and weight gain after the menopause, alcohol consumption and physical inactivity), radiation therapy (to the chest especially in childhood), a previous history of breast cancer and specific breast changes (on biopsy).[1]

The *WHO Medical Eligibility Criteria* recommends that the use of combined hormonal contraception or progestogen-only contraception (pills, injectable, implant and LNG-IUS) pose an unacceptable health risk (WHO category 4) for women with current or recent breast cancer. Non-hormonal contraception can be used without restriction (WHO category 1). The CEU found no evidence to contradict these recommendations.

A systematic review[2] and randomised controlled trial[3] provide evidence that the LNG-IUS reduces the incidence of endometrial abnormalities (cysts, polyps and hyperplasia) which are associated with tamoxifen use.

The CEU considers that, for women with recently treated breast cancer taking tamoxifen, the use of non-hormonal methods is advised. The use of a LNG-

IUS may be considered individually and in consultation with the woman's breast surgeon, if other methods are unacceptable.[4]

QUESTION

For a woman with recently treated breast cancer and taking tamoxifen, are the progestogen-only pill or the LNG-IUS appropriate? (Five similar enquiries.)

POPULATION: Women with recently treated breast cancer taking tamoxifen therapy.

INTERVENTION: Progestogen-only pill or the LNG-IUS.

OUTCOME: Adverse effects on breast cancer prognosis, interaction with tamoxifen therapy.

ANSWER

The *WHO Medical Eligibility Criteria* recommends that, for women with current breast cancer the use of hormonal contraception (combined hormonal methods or progestogen-only pills, injectable, implant and the LNG-IUS) poses an unacceptable health risk (WHO category 4).

Tamoxifen is a nonsteroidal drug with estrogen antagonist and agonist effects in different tissues; and is used in the treatment of breast cancer. The Summary of Product Characteristics for tamoxifen advises that women should use non-hormonal contraception while using this drug. Abnormal endometrial changes (polyps, cysts and hyperplasia) can occur in women using tamoxifen. These abnormalities are not prevented by the use of systemic progestogens.[5] Moreover, systemic progestogens may reduce the efficacy of tamoxifen therapy in breast cancer patients. A small study supported the insertion of a LNG-IUS (to deliver high doses of progestogen to the uterus with low systemic absorption) when tamoxifen therapy is commenced to prevent abnormal endometrial changes and hyperplasia.[6] The use of the LNG-IUS to reduce the incidence of endometrial abnormalities associated with tamoxifen use was supported in a systematic review[7] and randomised controlled trial.[3]

The CEU considers that for women with recently treated breast cancer taking tamoxifen, the use of non-hormonal methods is advised. The use of a LNG-IUS may be considered individually and in consultation with the woman's breast surgeon if other methods are unacceptable.[4]

QUESTION

For women with estrogen receptor positive breast cancer, is it safe to continue using progestogen-only methods of contraception? (Two similar enquiries.)

POPULATION:	Women with estrogen receptor positive breast cancer.
INTERVENTION:	Progestogen-only contraception.
OUTCOME:	Safety.

ANSWER

No direct evidence was identified to suggest that estrogen receptor status influences the risk of breast cancer in women using progestogen-only contraception or influences contraceptive options following a diagnosis of breast cancer. Breast cancer is a hormone-sensitive tumour, and the prognosis for women with current or recent breast cancer may worsen with progestogen-only contraceptive use.

The *WHO Medical Eligibility Criteria* recommends that, for women with current breast cancer the use of progestogen-only pills, injectable, implant and the LNG-IUS pose an unacceptable health risk (WHO category 4). For women with previous breast cancer and no recurrence in the last five years, the risks of using progestogen-only contraception generally outweigh the benefits and these methods are not usually recommended unless other methods are not available or are not acceptable (WHO category 3).

The CEU could find no evidence to contradict WHO recommendations and the use of non-hormonal methods is generally advised.

QUESTION

For women with current breast cancer taking tamoxifen, does use of the LNG-IUS have adverse effects on breast cancer prognosis or any interaction with tamoxifen therapy?

POPULATION:	Women with current breast cancer on tamoxifen therapy.
INTERVENTION:	The LNG-IUS.
OUTCOME:	Adverse effects on breast cancer prognosis, interaction with tamoxifen therapy.

ANSWER

Many factors influence the risk of developing breast cancer. Reproductive factors (which relate to endogenous estrogen and progesterone) are important: early menarche; late menopause; late age at first childbirth. Exogenous hormones may increase the risk of breast cancer: combined oral contraception[8] and long-term postmenopausal estrogen and progestogen replacement therapy.[1] Breast cancer is a hormone-sensitive tumour and the prognosis of women with current or recent breast cancer may worsen with hormonal contraceptive use. No data were identified regarding the prognosis for women with breast cancer if they use a LNG-IUS.

The *WHO Medical Eligibility Criteria* recommends that use of the LNG-IUS poses an unacceptable health risk for women with current breast cancer (WHO category 4).

A Cochrane review[7] investigated the non-contraceptive benefits of the LNG-IUS. A randomised controlled trial[3] showed that the LNG-IUS reduces the incidence of endometrial abnormalities (cysts, polyps and hyperplasia) associated with tamoxifen use.

The CEU suggests that non-hormonal contraception is most suitable for a woman with a history of breast cancer. The LNG-IUS may be considered individually and in consultation with the woman's breast surgeon if other methods are unacceptable.[4]

QUESTION

For women with recently treated breast cancer taking tamoxifen and who have a failed attempt at insertion of a copper IUD, what contraceptive options are available?

POPULATION: Women with recently treated breast cancer taking tamoxifen, who have had a failed attempt at insertion of a copper IUD.

INTERVENTION: Contraception.

OUTCOME: Safety.

ANSWER

Although tamoxifen may itself inhibit ovulation it is not licensed as a contraceptive. The Summary of Product Characteristics for tamoxifen advises use of non-hormonal contraception.

The *WHO Medical Eligibility Criteria* recommends that, for women with current breast cancer the use of combined hormonal contraception or progestogen-only contraception (pills, injectable, implant and LNG-IUS) pose an unacceptable health risk (WHO category 4). Non-hormonal contraception (copper IUD, condoms, diaphragms and cervical caps) can be used without restriction (WHO category 1).

Case reports describe the successful use of prostaglandin for cervical priming prior to IUD insertion.[9] Small randomised controlled trials have suggested that in premenopausal[10] and nulliparous women[11] undergoing hysteroscopy, misoprostol increases the ease with which the cervix is dilated and reduces complications. Although evidence is indirect, cervical priming agents may be considered in women in whom an attempt at IUD insertion has failed or where the cervix is atrophic or stenosed.[12] Alternatively, a paracervical block or general anaesthetic may be considered. In addition, it may be prudent to consider an ultrasound scan to assess any reason for a failed insertion (such as a distorted uterine cavity).

The CEU suggests that clinicians can assist women with breast cancer to make informed choices about contraception by discussing: individual risk of pregnancy; the effects of pregnancy on breast cancer prognosis; the efficacy of non-hormonal contraception (other than the copper IUD) and any risks associated with further attempts at IUD insertion.

References

1.   National Cancer Institute. Genetics of Breast and Ovarian Cancer (PDQ). 2002 [www.cancer.gov/cancertopics/pdq/genetics/breast-andovarian/healthprofessional].
2.   Hubacher D, Grimes DA. Noncontraceptive health benefits of intrauterine devices: a systematic review. *Obstet Gynecol Surv* 2002;57:120–8.
3.   Gardner FJE, Konje JC, Abrams KR, Brown LJR, Khanna S, Al-Azzawi F, *et al.* Endometrial protection for tamoxifen-stimulated changes by a levonorgestrel-releasing intrauterine system: a randomised-controlled trial. *Lancet* 2000;356:1711–17.
4.   Faculty of Family Planning and Reproductive Health Care Clinical Effectiveness Unit. The levonorgestrel-releasing intrauterine system (LNG-IUS) in contraception and reproductive health. *J Fam Plann Reprod Health Care* 2004;30:99–109.
5.   Powles TJ, Bourne T, Athanasiou S, Chang J, Grubock K, Ashley S, *et al.* The effects of norethisterone on endometrial abnormalities identified by transvaginal ultrasound screening of healthy post-menopausal women on tamoxifen or placebo. *Br J Cancer* 1998;78:272–5.
6.   Van Liedekerke D, Gevers R, De Sutter PH, Bourgain C, Amy JJ. Use of levonorgestrel intrauterine device for prevention of endometrial changes induced by tamoxifen. *Eur J Cancer* 1988;34:S55.
7.   Hubacher D, Grimes DA. Noncontraceptive health benefits of intrauterine devices: A systematic review. *Obstet Gynecolog Surv* 2002;57:120–8.

8. WHO Collaborative Group on Hormonal Factors in Breast Cancer. Breast Cancer and hormonal contraceptives: collaborative reanalysis of individual data on 53 297 women with breast cancer and 100 239 women without breast cancer from 54 epidemiological studies. *Lancet* 1996;347:1713–27.

9. Lauersen NH, Kurkulos M, Graves ZR, Leeds L. A new IUD insertion technique utilizing cervical priming with prostagladin. *Contraception* 1982;26:59–63.

10. Thomas JA, Leyland N, Durand N, Windrim RC. The use of oral misoprostol as a cervical ripening agent in operative hysteroscopy: a double-blind, placebo-controlled trial. *Am J Obstet Gynecol* 2002;186:876–9.

11. Preutthipan S, Herabutya Y. Vaginal misoprostol for cervical priming before operative hysteroscopy: a randomized controlled trial. *Obstet Gynecol* 2000;96:890–4.

12. Faculty of Family Planning and Reproductive Health Care Clinical Effectiveness Unit. The copper intrauterine device as long-term contraception. *J Fam Plann Reprod Health Care* 2004;30:29–42.

Family history of breast cancer

QUESTION

For women with a family history of breast cancer, what are the risks associated with use of combined oral contraception? (Two similar enquiries.)

POPULATION: Women with a family history of breast cancer.

INTERVENTION: Combined oral contraception.

OUTCOME: Risk of breast cancer.

ANSWER

A family history of breast cancer may increase a woman's personal risk of developing breast cancer. The Nurses' Health Study found that 5–10% of women had a family history of breast cancer in a first-degree relative.[1] Twice as many had a second-degree relative with breast cancer. Nevertheless, most breast cancers are sporadic and not due to genetic mutations. A genetic contribution to breast cancer risk is indicated if multiple family members are affected with breast cancer and other cancers.[2] Highly penetrant genes such as *BRCA1* and *BRCA2* have been identified which increase the risk of breast cancer.

A cohort study found that ever-users of combined oral contraceptives (high dose) who had a first-degree relative with breast cancer had a three-fold increase in the risk of breast cancer compared with never-users.[3] The risk was less if second-degree relatives had the disease. Low-dose formulations (less than 50 micrograms ethinylestradiol) are now used in the UK and these are likely to have a smaller effect on risk of breast cancer in women with a family history, although this has not been proven.

A retrospective case–control study showed a small increased risk of developing breast cancer for women with *BRCA1* gene mutations with combined oral contraceptive use. No further increase in risk of breast cancer, above their increased background risk, was identified for women with *BRCA2* mutations when exposed to combined oral contraception.[4]

The *WHO Medical Eligibility Criteria* recommends that women with a family history of breast cancer may use combined hormonal contraception (pills, patch and vaginal ring) without restriction (WHO category 1). This was supported in the UK *Medical Eligibility Criteria*.

The CEU suggests that women using combined oral contraception should be advised that any increase in risk of breast cancer associated with use is small and is in addition to their own background risk.[5-7] Any excess risk associated with combined oral contraceptive use disappears 10 years after stopping. For women with *BRCA1* mutations, combined oral contraception increases the already increased background risk of breast cancer. Women with *BRCA2* mutations, or with a sporadic family history of breast cancer, are not at any further increased risk with combined oral contraceptive use.

QUESTION

> **Do women with a family history of breast cancer have an increased risk of developing breast cancer while using the progestogen-only pill and, if so, is the risk similar for combined oral contraception?**

POPULATION: Women with a family history of breast cancer.

INTERVENTION: Progestogen-only pill.

OUTCOME: Risk of developing breast cancer.

ANSWER

A family history of breast cancer may increase a woman's personal risk of developing breast cancer. A possible genetic contribution to breast cancer risk is indicated by the finding of multiple affected family members. However, for most women with a family history of breast cancer, cases are sporadic and not due to genetic mutations.[2]

A population-based case–control study investigated the influence of the progestogen-only pill on a woman's risk of breast cancer.[8] Overall, the risk of breast cancer in women who had ever-used a progestogen-only pill did not appear to be increased compared to never-users. However, for users aged 25–34 years, the relative risk of breast cancer increased two-fold (relative risk 2.3; 95% CI 1.2–4.3). Women who had used a progestogen-only pill within the last 10 years had an increased risk of breast cancer (relative risk 1.6; 95% CI 1.0–2.4) but those who had used a progestogen-only pill more than 10 years ago were not found to have an increased risk (relative risk 0.44; 95% CI 0.22–0.90). One-third of women in this study who had used a progestogen-only pill had also used the progestogen-only injectable, so it is difficult to identified risk, if any, associated with an individual contraceptive method.

A prospective cohort study[9] found that the risk of breast cancer with progestogen-only pills (relative risk, 1.6; 95% CI 1.0–2.4) was similar to the risk associated with combined oral contraceptives (Relative risk 1.5; 95% CI 1.0–2.0). However, prescribing bias may have influenced the results.

The large UK national case–control study[10] reported that use of progestogen-only pills did not appear to be associated with an increased risk of breast cancer.

The WHO Collaborative Group[5] found that the relative risk of developing breast cancer for recent combined oral contraceptive users (less than 5 years ago) was not significantly increased for women with a family history of breast cancer. The evidence did not allow a reliable observation of any differences in the effects associated with different types of estrogen or progestogen. Available evidence suggests that there were no major differences in the effects of specific types or estrogen or progestogen and that the pattern of risk associated with use of hormonal contraceptives containing progestogen alone may be similar to that observed for preparations with both estrogen and progestogen.

A case–control study found no increased risk, above the background risk, of developing breast cancer in women with *BRCA2* mutations when exposed to combined oral contraception. However, a small increase in risk was found in *BRCA1* carriers.[4]

The *WHO Medical Eligibility Criteria* recommends that women with a family history of breast cancer may have unrestricted use of progestogen-only contraception (pills, injectable, implant and the LNG-IUS) (WHO category 1). For women with known mutations which are associated with increased risk of breast cancer, the *UK Medical Eligibility Criteria* recommends that the benefits of using combined hormonal methods generally outweigh the risks (UK category 2).

The CEU advises that although small studies have suggested a possible increased risk of breast cancer with progestogen-only pill use, the available data are limited by small sample size, recall and prescriber bias. Evidence from the largest good quality study does not support an increased risk of breast cancer with progestogen-only pill use.

References

1. Colditz GA, Willett WC, Hunter DJ. Family history, age and the risk of breast cancer: a systematic review and meta-analysis. *JAMA* 1993;270:338–42.
2. National Cancer Institute. Genetics of Breast and Ovarian Cancer (PDQ). 2002 [www.cancer.gov/cancertopics/pdq/genetics/breast-andovarian/healthprofessional].
3. Grabrick DM, Hartmann LC, Cerhan JR, Vierkant RA, Therneau TM, Vachon CM, *et al*. Risk of breast cancer with oral contraceptive use in women with a family history of breast cancer. *JAMA* 2000;284:1791–9.
4. Narod SA, Dubé M, Klijn J, Lubinski J, Lynch HT, Ghadirian P, *et al*. Oral contraceptives and the risk of breast cancer in BRCA1 and BRCA2 mutation carriers. *J Natl Cancer Inst* 2002;94:1773–9.
5. WHO Collaborative Group on Hormonal Factors in Breast Cancer. Breast Cancer and hormonal contraceptives: collaborative reanalysis of individual data on 53 297 women with breast cancer and 100 239 women without breast cancer from 54 epidemiological studies. *Lancet* 1996;347:1713–27.
6. Marchbanks PA, McDonald JA, Wilson HG, Folger SG, Mandel MG, Daling JR, *et al*. Oral contraceptives and the risk of breast cancer. *N Engl J Med* 2002;346:2025–32.
7. Faculty of Family Planning and Reproductive Health Care Clinical Effectiveness Unit. First prescription of combined oral contraception. *J Fam Plann Reprod Health Care* 2003;29:209–22.
8. Skegg DCG, Paul C, Spears GF, Wiliams SM. Progestogen-only oral contraceptives and risk of breast cancer in New Zealand. *Cancer Causes Control* 1996;7:513–9.
9. Kumle M, Weiderpass E, Braaten T, Persson I, Adami H, Lund E. Use of oral contraceptives and breast cancer risk: The Norwegian-Swedish women's lifestyle and health cohort study. *Cancer Epidemiol Biomarkers Prev* 2002;11:1375–81.
10. UK National Case-Control Study Group. Oral contraceptive use and breast cancer risk in young women. *Lancet* 1989;1:973–82.

QUESTION

For women who are HIV-positive and using the antiretrovirals atazanavir and Combivir® (GSK), can the etonogestrel implant be used safely?

POPULATION: Women who are HIV-positive and using the antiretrovirals atazanavir and Combivir.

INTERVENTION: Etonogestrel implant.

OUTCOME: Safety.

ANSWER

The antiretroviral drug atazanavir is a protease inhibitor. Combivir contains non-nucleoside reverse transcriptase inhibitors. Combivir tablets contain zidovudine and lamivudine. Atazanavir is a liver enzyme-inducing drug. It can cause a reduction in bioavailable ethinylestradiol and progestogen. BNF states that zidovudine and lamivudine are not liver-enzyme-inducing drugs.

FFPRHC CEU guidance on drug interactions with hormonal contraception[1] states that there are theoretical concerns that the use of antiretroviral drugs may reduce efficacy of hormonal contraception. Some antiretroviral drugs (such as protease inhibitors and non-nucleoside reverse transcriptase inhibitors) are metabolised by the CYP3A4 liver enzyme system and can affect liver enzymes.

Women with HIV may use combination therapy where one or more drugs may induce liver enzymes. Readers can refer to the most recent BNF or to a useful website[2] for further information on interactions with antiretrovirals. Few studies have been published which investigated the pharmacokinetics of ethinylestradiol and progestogens with antiretroviral drugs and none on efficacy of hormonal contraception. Serum concentrations of ethinylestradiol were reduced when women using a 50-microgram pill were also taking ritonavir but no pregnancies have been documented.[3] The protease inhibitor, saquinavir, did not affect pharmacokinetics of a 30-microgram pill.[4]

FFPRHC advice[1] for the use of contraception in women using liver enzyme-inducers is included in Table 8.

Table 8. FFPRHC advice for the use of contraception in women using liver enzyme-inducers[1]

Method	Advice
Combined hormonal contraception:	
Combined oral contraception	■ Use at least 50 micrograms of ethinyl estradiol daily. This can be taken as a 30-microgram COC plus a 20-microgram COC or as two 30 microgram COCs ■ Additional contraceptive protection, such as condoms, is required when taking liver enzyme-inducers and for 4 weeks after they are stopped ■ Information should be given on the use of alternative methods which are unaffected by liver enzyme-inducers ■ If additional contraception fails or is not used emergency contraception may be indicated
Combined contraceptive patch	■ Use one patch/week as for women not using liver enzyme-inducers ■ Additional contraceptive protection, such as condoms, is required when taking liver enzyme-inducers and for 4 weeks after they are stopped ■ Information should be given on the use of alternative methods which are unaffected by liver enzyme-inducers ■ If additional contraception fails or is not used emergency contraception may be indicated
Progestogen-only contraception:	
Progestogen-only pills	Advise alternative contraceptive if liver enzyme drugs are used
Progestogen-only implants	May continue with progestogen-only implants with additional contraceptive protection, such as condoms when taking liver enzyme-inducers and for 4 weeks after they are stopped Information should be given on the use of alternative if liver enzyme drugs are to be used long term
Progestogen-only injectables	Progestogen-only injectables are unaffected by liver enzyme-inducers. Continued with the usual injection interval of 12 weeks for DMPA and 8 weeks for norethisterone enanthate
Progestogen-only emergency contraception	Take a total dose of 2.25 mg levonorgestrel as a single dose as soon as possible and within 72 hours of unprotected sex (50% increase in dose) Consider the use of a copper IUD, which is unaffected by liver enzyme-inducers
LNG-IUS	No additional contraceptive protection required
Non-hormonal methods:	
Copper-bearing IUD, barrier methods	No additional contraceptive protection required

Thus the CEU recommends that for women wishing to use the etonogestrel implant, Implanon, consideration should be given to the use of alternative methods of contraception if a liver enzyme drug is to be used long term. The progestogen-only injectable, the LNG-IUS, and all non-hormonal methods of contraception can be used in women using liver enzyme-inducing drugs.

QUESTION

For women with HIV/AIDS receiving highly active antiretroviral therapy (HAART), is DMPA a safe and effective method of contraception?

POPULATION: Women receiving HAART for HIV/AIDS.
INTERVENTION: DMPA for contraception.
OUTCOME: Safety and efficacy.

ANSWER

Highly active antiretroviral therapy is used in the management of HIV/AIDS and comprises three or more highly potent anti-HIV drugs used in combination. The antiretroviral 'cocktail' typically includes reverse transcriptase inhibitors (for example, zidovudine) and protease inhibitors (such as lopinovar with retonavir or amprenavir). Some members of both these groups of drugs are hepatic enzyme-inducers; others are not. Liver enzyme-inducers may reduce the efficacy of some forms of hormonal contraception (combined oral contraception, progestogen-only pills and implants) but do not appear to reduce the efficacy of progestogen-only injectables (including DMPA) or of the LNG-IUS.

Drug interactions with hormonal contraception is the topic of a CEU guidance document[1]. Table 9 summarises antiretroviral agents which are and are not inducers of hepatic enzymes. Counselling a woman on HAART therapy about her contraceptive options requires precise information on the cocktail of drugs she is taking. For some women, their version of HAART may not include liver enzyme-inducers.

Available evidence suggests that DMPA is unaffected by liver enzyme-inducers and can therefore be used by any woman receiving HAART, regardless of her individual 'cocktail' of drugs. No alteration in the standard dosage schedule is required.

Table 9. A summary of antiretroviral agents which are, and are not, inducers of hepatic enzymes[1]

Liver enzyme-inducers	Non-liver enzyme-inducers

Protease inhibitors:
    amprenavir
    atazanavir
    nelfinavir
    ritonavir
	Protease inhibitors:
	    indinavir
	    lopinavir
	    saquinavir

Non-nucleoside reverse
transcriptase inhibitors:
    efavirenz
    nevirapine
	Non-nucleoside reverse
	transcriptase inhibitors:
	    abacavir
	    didanosine
	    emtricitabine
	    lamivudine
	    stavudine
	    tenofovir
	    zalctabine
	    zidovudine

QUESTION

For women at risk of acquiring HIV or those who are HIV-positive, does the combined oral contraceptive pill affect the risk of acquiring or transmitting the infection respectively?

POPULATION: Women at risk of acquiring HIV or those who are HIV-positive.

INTERVENTION: The combined oral contraceptive pill.

OUTCOME: Risk of acquiring or transmitting the infection.

ANSWER

There is theoretical concern, but no consistent evidence, that combined oral contraceptive use may increase the risk of acquisition or transmission of HIV infection.

Acquisition

The association between hormonal contraceptive use and HIV acquisition was investigated in a Ugandan cohort study.[5] A total of 5117 sexually active HIV-negative women were surveyed at 10-month intervals between 1994 and 1999 and information on contraceptive use was obtained through interviews. After adjusting for age, condom use, number of sexual partners, marital status, education and history of genital ulcer disease, the incidence rate ratio of HIV infection was 1.12 (95% CI 0.48–2.56) with combined oral contraceptive use and 0.84 (95% CI 0.41–1.72) with use of injectables. The authors concluded that hormonal contraception is not associated with HIV acquisition after adjusting for behavioural confounding.

Transmission

Mostad *et al.*[6] carried out a cross-sectional study in Kenya to investigate whether hormonal contraception, vitamin A deficiency, and other variables were risk factors for cervical and vaginal shedding of HIV-infected cells. They enrolled 318 women attending a sexually transmitted diseases clinic who had previously tested positive for HIV-1. Cervical and vaginal shedding of HIV-infected cells was found to be highly associated with CD4 lymphocyte depletion. After adjusting for CD4 count, cervical and vaginal shedding was significantly associated with use of DMPA (odds ratio 2.9; 95% CI 1.5–5.7) and use of low-dose combined pills (odds ratio 3.8; 95% CI 1.4–9.9) and high dose combined pills (odds ratio 12.3; 95% CI 1.5–101). Duerr *et al.* point out that the presence of HIV DNA on an endocervical swab may not be representative of real-life shedding and transmission.[7]

A systematic review of hormonal contraception and risk of HIV transmission included seven prospective studies, whose quality has been debated, and found that combined oral contraceptive users had increased odds for HIV transmission.[8]

The *WHO Medical Eligibility Criteria for Contraceptive Use* advises that both women who are at high risk of HIV and those who are HIV-positive may have unrestricted use of the combined oral contraceptive pill. WHO mentions that there is theoretical concern, but no consistent evidence, that combined oral contraceptive use may increase the risk of HIV infection.

QUESTION

For women who are HIV-positive and at risk of low bone mineral density, should DMPA be used?

POPULATION: Women who are HIV-positive and at risk of low bone mineral density.

INTERVENTION: DMPA.

OUTCOME: Effect on bone mineral density.

ANSWER

Individuals with HIV infection undergoing antiretroviral treatment frequently show reduced bone mineral density.[9] However, because HIV-positive patients not on antiretroviral therapy also have a higher than expected prevalence of reduced bone density, the effects of HIV itself on the immune system may be a contributory factor.[9] The precise causes of osteopenia, osteoporosis and osteonecrosis in HIV-positive patients are still to be determined.

Dolan *et al.* performed a cohort study investigating bone density in HIV-positive women.[10] Bone density was measured by dual-energy X-ray absorptiometry in 84 HIV-positive women and 63 controls matched for age, BMI and racial background. Exclusion criteria included use of DMPA within the 3 months prior to the study. Bone density at the lumbar spine and hip was found to be reduced in HIV-positive women compared to the controls. HIV-positive women were found to be 2.5 times as likely to have osteopenia after adjusting for age, race, menstrual function and BMI. The authors concluded that lower bone density in HIV-positive women may be due to altered nutritional status, hormonal function, and body composition and advised that bone density testing in HIV-positive women with risk factors for osteopenia should be considered.

The *WHO Medical Eligibility Criteria for Contraceptive Use* advises that women who are HIV-positive may have unrestricted use (WHO category 1) of DMPA. It is likely however, that evidence on the possible effects of DMPA on bone mineral density in HIV-positive women with risk factors for osteopenia was not considered when making this classification.

CEU guidance on contraceptive choices for women with inflammatory bowel disease addresses the use of progestogen-only injectables by these women.[11] The CEU recommended that women with inflammatory bowel disease and low bone mineral density (or who have had repeat courses of corticosteroids or have malabsorption) should be advised against the use of DMPA. Similar advice may be relevant to women with HIV.

The precise causes of osteopenia in HIV-positive patients are still undetermined. The time elapsed since diagnosis with HIV, use of antiretroviral therapy and duration of use of DMPA are also factors that may contribute to changes in bone density. If HIV-positive women still choose to use DMPA after being counselled about their increased risk of low bone mineral density, clinicians may decide to refer them for bone densitometry prior to use.

QUESTION

For women who are HIV-positive using antiretrovirals, which method of contraception provides an effective option?

POPULATION: Women who are HIV-positive using antiretrovirals.
INTERVENTION: Contraception.
OUTCOME: Efficacy.

ANSWER

Women who are HIV-positive have few restrictions on their choice of contraception. The *WHO Medical Eligibility Criteria for Contraceptive Use* advises that HIV-positive women may have unrestricted use (WHO category 1) of combined oral contraceptives, the progestogen-only pill, DMPA and the progestogen-only implant (specifically Norplant). However, the use of the LNG-IUS or IUD is classified as category 3 for HIV-positive women. WHO mentions that with these methods there are theoretical concerns about increased risks of STIs and PID and increased risk of transmission to uninfected partners. In the main, it is the use of liver enzyme-inducing antiretrovirals or antibiotics which limit women's choices.

Drugs used in the management of HIV include: nucleoside reverse transcriptase inhibitors (zidovudine, abacavir, didanosine, lamivudine, stavudine and zalcitabine), protease inhibitors (amprenavir, indinavir, lopinavir with ritonavir, nelfinavir and saquinavir) and non-nucleoside reverse transcriptase inhibitors (efavirenz and nevirapine). BNF states that antimicrobials such as rifampicin, rifabutin and griseofulvin may also be prescribed for opportunistic infections associated with HIV, such as tuberculosis.

Some antiretrovirals are not liver enzyme-inducers but many women with HIV may be on combination therapy with both liver enzyme-inducers and non-liver enzyme-inducers.

There is little direct evidence on contraceptive efficacy and adverse effects in women using antiretrovirals and much of the available information relates to anti-epileptic liver enzyme-inducers. The mechanism of drug interactions however, is likely to be similar. Sex steroid hormones (estrogen and progestogen) are absorbed from the upper small intestine. They are transported to the liver in the hepatic portal vein, either free in the serum or bound to sex hormone binding globulin or albumin. Enzyme-inducers increase the metabolism of estradiol and progestogen and have the potential to reduce the efficacy of hormonal contraception.

General advice for women taking liver enzyme-inducers is:[1]

● **Combined oral contraceptives**

Guidance on first prescription of combined oral contraception from the FFPRHC CEU[12] supports the recommendations made in a SIGN guideline.[13] Women using liver enzyme-inducing drugs who, having considered other methods, still choose to use combined oral contraceptives should be prescribed a regimen containing 50 micrograms daily ethinylestradiol or mestranol. Additional barrier contraception is advised until 4 weeks after cessation of the liver enzyme-inducer. There is no evidence that 'tricycling' (by taking three consecutive packs of the pill with four pill-free days) is more effective than 'monocycling'.

As the combined pill containing 50 micrograms ethinylestradiol (Ovran) has been discontinued, an alternative regimen involving the use of two low-dose pills (providing a total daily dose of 50–60 micrograms ethinylestradiol) has been proposed in the CEU guidance. To date, however, no trials have compared the bioavailability of two low-dose pills taken daily with that of a single daily high-dose pill. There is no evidence that break-through bleeding is a marker of insufficient serum levels and risk of ovulation. Episodes of diarrhoea and vomiting may be more common in HIV-positive women, and standard advice is that the combined pill cannot be relied on after vomiting or severe diarrhoea until a week after recovery.

● **Progestogen-only contraceptives**

A FFPRHC Faculty Aid to Continuing Professional Development Topics on interactions with hormonal contraception advises that women using the progestogen-only pill who take enzyme-inducers should switch to injectables or another form of contraception.[14] This is recommended up to one month after termination of the liver enzyme-inducer. Users of progestogen implants who take enzyme-inducers are advised to switch to an alternative method or use barrier methods as well. There is no evidence identified to confirm or refute this.

The SIGN guideline advises that DMPA injections may be used with anti-epileptic liver enzyme-inducers, but should be given every 10 weeks since efficacy may be reduced.[13] This recommendation however, was based on non-analytic studies, expert opinion, and evidence extrapolated from higher quality studies. The Summary of Product Characteristics for DMPA suggests that no time adjustment is required for the injection interval since the contraceptive hormone is cleared at a rate equal to hepatic blood flow, and this clearance is not increased by liver enzyme-inducers.

● **Intrauterine contraception**

There is presently no evidence that liver enzyme-inducers reduce the contraceptive efficacy of the LNG-IUS. With the LNG-IUS, levonorgestrel is released in a constant dose into the uterine cavity at a dose 1000 times greater than that seen after subdermal administration and the contraceptive effects of the IUS are related to local effects rather than due to systemic absorption. Systemic progestogen metabolism will not affect local efficacy.

Guidance from the FFPRHC CEU on the copper IUD as long-term contraception[15] recommends that women who are HIV-positive may be offered an IUD after testing for bacterial STIs. Evidence from prospective observational studies suggests that the actual risks associated with IUD use in HIV-positive women may be less than feared. It is accepted that there is a small increased risk of pelvic infection in the first 3 weeks after insertion for all women. After this phase, the risk of infection is related to exposure to STIs rather than the presence of an IUD. Similar advice is given for the LNG-IUS.

References

1. Faculty of Family Planning and Reproductive Health Care Clinical Effectiveness Unit. Drug interactions with hormonal contraception. *J Fam Plann Reprod Health Care* 2005;31:139–50.
2. Liverpool HIV Pharmacology Group [www.HIV-druginteractions.org].
3. Quellet D, Hsu A, Qian J, Locke CS, Eason CJ, Cavanaugh JH, *et al.* Effects of ritonavir ion the pharmacokinetics of ethinyl oestradiol in healthy female volunteers. *Br J Clin Pharmacol* 1998;46:111–16.
4. Fröhlich M, Burhenne J, Martin-Facklam M, Weiss J, von Wolff M, Strowitzki T, *et al.* Oral contraception does not alter single dose saquinavir pharmacokinetics in women. *Br J Clin Pharmacol* 2004;57:244–52.
5. Kiddugavu MA, Makumbi FA, Maria JD, Serwadda DB, Sewankambo NKC, Wabwire-Mangen FB, *et al.* Hormonal contraceptive use and HIV-1 infection in a population-based cohort in Rakai, Uganda. *AIDS* 2003;17:233–40.
6. Mostad SB, Overbaugh J, DeVange DM, Welch MJ, Chohan B, Mandaliya K, *et al.* Hormonal contraception, vitamin A deficiency, and other risk factors for shedding of HIV-1 infected cells from the cervix and vagina. *Lancet* 1997;359:922–7.
7. Duerr A, Curtis K, Shelton JD, Meirik O. Hormonal contraception and genital-tract shedding of HIV-1-infected cells. *Lancet* 1998;351:294–5.
8. Stephenson JM. Systematic review of hormonal contraception and risk of HIV transmission. *AIDS* 1998;12:545–53.
9. Glesby MJ. Bone disorders in human immunodeficiency virus infection. *Clin Infect Dis* 2003;37:S91–5.
10. Dolan SE, Huang JS, Kililea MA, Sullivan MP, Allabadi N, Grinspoon S. Reduced bone density in HIV-infected women. *AIDS* 2004;18.
11. Faculty of Family Planning and Reproductive Health Care Clinical Effectiveness Unit.

Contraceptive choices for women with inflammatory bowel disease. *J Fam Plann Reprod Health Care* 2003;29:127–34.

12. Faculty of Family Planning and Reproductive Health Care Clinical Effectiveness Unit. First prescription of combined oral contraception *J Fam Plann Reprod Health Care* 2003;29:209–22.

13. Scottish Intercollegiate Guidelines Network. *Diagnosis and Management of Epilepsy in Adults.* A national clinical guideline No. 70. Edinburgh: SIGN; 2003.

14. Elliman A. Interactions with hormonal contraception. *J Fam Plann Reprod Health Care* 2000; 26:109–11.

15. Faculty of Family Planning and Reproductive Health Care Guidance. The copper intrauterine device as long-term contraception *J Fam Plann Reprod Health Care* 2004;30:29–42.

18 MISCELLANEOUS MEDICAL DISORDERS A–C

QUESTION

For women with achondroplasia, is use of the combined oral contraceptive pill associated with an increased risk of thromboembolism?

POPULATION: Women with achondroplasia.
INTERVENTION: Combined oral contraception.
OUTCOME: Thromboembolism.

ANSWER

A detailed literature search of the CEU routine data sources identified no guidelines, systematic reviews or individual papers relating to achondroplasia and risks of thromboembolism, or special issues relating to contraception. We were unable to provide an evidence-based response to this enquiry.

QUESTION

For women with acrocyanosis, will combined oral contraception worsen clinical symptoms?

POPULATION: Women with acrocyanosis.
INTERVENTION: Combined oral contraception.
OUTCOME: Clinical symptoms.

ANSWER

Acrocyanosis is a benign, painless disorder resulting when sympathetic nerves cause constriction or spasm in peripheral blood vessels in the extremities.[1] Clinical symptoms include lack of sensation of pain and persistent blue, sweaty and swollen hands and/or feet, which may worsen under stress or cold temperatures. Drugs including calcium channel blockers, alpha-one antagonists or vasodilators may help the disorder, and surgery performed on the sympathetic nerves is rarely indicated.

Only one review article was identified that mentioned acrocyanosis and described definitions and epidemiology of the acrosyndromes.[2] It states that there is no link between Raynaud's phenomenon and estrogen treatment. All the remaining evidence found by the CEU relates specifically to Raynaud's phenomenon, which is a similar condition. An article published in 1975[3] mentioned that women are more sensitive to the cold prior to ovulation and when they are taking the oral contraceptive pill. It is suggested that estrogen may make the peripheral vascular bed more sensitive to catecholamines and hormones like adrenaline and noradrenaline. Several investigators have reported that progesterone has little effect, or the opposite effect to estrogen, in animal models.[4,5]

Bartelink *et al.*[6] stated that no definite relationship has been found between systemic estrogens and progestogens and blood flow in the skin. The authors gave 17 healthy women and 12 women with Raynaud's a single dose of oral 17 beta-estradiol and progesterone and then exposed their fingers to different temperatures. The estrogen was shown to cause a marginal increase in finger-tip temperature and cutaneous blood flow. A further study showed that short-term estrogen administration can improve the endothelium-dependent and endothelium-independent vasodilation in patients with Raynaud's who also have systemic sclerosis.[7]

The CEU was unable to find any studies that have looked specifically at the effects of estrogens and progestogens on acrocyanosis, and therefore no evidence to suggest that combined oral contraception is contraindicated in this condition. Clinical judgement should be used to decide if a combined pill should be used, and if the symptoms of acrocyanosis worsen an alternative method can be tried.

QUESTION

In women with Addison's disease and using corticosteroid therapy, which contraceptive methods can be used safely?

POPULATION: Women with Addison's disease.
INTERVENTION: Contraception.
OUTCOME: Safety.

ANSWER

Addison's disease is a rare endocrine disorder characterised by insufficient production of cortisol and sometimes of aldosterone. It may either occur as an autoimmune condition (primary adrenal insufficiency) or as secondary adrenal insufficiency. The CEU was unable to find any evidence that directly examined the use of different methods of contraception by women with Addison's disease.

Studies have shown a correlation between long duration of Addison's disease with high cumulative corticosteroid dose and subsequent low bone mineral density.[8,9] A review from the FFPRHC[10] recommends that women with risk factors for low bone mineral density, such as smoking or long-term high-dose corticosteroid therapy, should not use DMPA but all other contraceptive methods may be used.

QUESTION

In women with anorexia nervosa is use of combined oral contraception associated with any particular adverse effects?

POPULATION: Women with anorexia nervosa.
INTERVENTION: Combined oral contraception.
OUTCOME: Adverse effects.

ANSWER

A US review article[11] provides a useful overview. Anorexia nervosa occurs in 0.5–1.0% of adolescents and is characterised by intense fear of weight gain and lack of self-esteem. Accepted diagnostic criteria have been developed. Principal among these is a body weight less than 85% of that expected for age and height. Amenorrhoea, induced by calorie restriction, is also a diagnostic criterion. The precise mechanism of amenorrhoea is incompletely understood; but there is dramatic suppression of pituitary production of luteinising hormone and follicle stimulating hormone. Secondary to the lack of gonadotrophins, circulating estrogen is also very low.

Women with anorexia are at high risk of osteopenia and frank osteoporosis. Oral contraceptives have been evaluated in the management of anorexia nervosa as a form of estrogen replacement aimed at improving bone mineral density. Unfortunately, two randomised trials have shown that combined oral contraception is ineffective in this respect.[12,13]

The US review article[11] indicated that some clinicians use the return of menses to demonstrate regained health in the patient and may not want to mask this outcome by use of combined oral contraception.

Two US guidelines (from the American Psychiatric Association[14] and the

American Academy of Pediatrics[15]) on treating eating disorders were identified. Neither guideline included any recommendations on contraceptive choices for young women with anorexia.

Although amenorrhoea and anovulation are features of anorexia nervosa, women with this condition may nevertheless require reliable contraception. Contraceptive choices for women with anorexia should be made in consultation with the clinician responsible for managing the anorexia. Unless the clinician is using return of natural menses as an essential element of monitoring disease progression, there appears to be no particular disadvantage in choosing combined oral contraception.

QUESTION

For a woman with an anovaginal fistula since birth can intrauterine contraception be used safely?

POPULATION: Women with congenital anovaginal fistulae.
INTERVENTION: Intrauterine contraception.
OUTCOME: Safety.

ANSWER

The main concern for a woman with an anovaginal fistula considering intrauterine contraception might be the risk of PID. The risk of PID is increased almost six-fold in the first 20 days following insertion of an IUD but remains low thereafter. It is unclear if a woman with an anovaginal fistula would be at increased risk of PID with an IUD in place (owing to contamination of the vaginal with faecal organisms). The CEU was unable to identify any publications in Medline or EMBASE, which discussed this situation. If other methods of contraception are unacceptable, intrauterine methods could be considered in a woman with an anovaginal fistula.

QUESTION

For women with a history of Asherman syndrome, can an IUD be used safely and effectively?

POPULATION: Women with Asherman syndrome.
INTERVENTION: Intrauterine contraception.
OUTCOME: Safety and efficacy.

ANSWER

For this enquiry, due to a paucity of directly relevant evidence, the CEU extended its usual literature search back to 1966. A paper from the Netherlands (1998) provides a useful overview of Asherman syndrome.[16] The syndrome of intrauterine adhesions was first described in 1948. It occurs secondary to uterine trauma by curettage (especially of the pregnant or puerperal uterus), local infection, or a combination of these. The prevalence of intrauterine adhesions after these predisposing circumstances is unknown; determining prevalence would require hysteroscopic studies of large numbers of women. Sequelae include menstrual disturbances, infertility, recurrent miscarriage, preterm labour, placenta praevia and placenta accreta. A grading scheme (grades 0 to IV) for the extent of intrauterine adhesions has been devised by the European Society of Hysteroscopy.

Currently, hysteroscopy is the usual method for confirmation of the diagnosis of Asherman syndrome, and for treatment.[17] Pregnancies can occur following a diagnosis of Asherman syndrome (either treated or untreated). It seems likely that the intrauterine adhesions themselves would be 'cured' by a pregnancy; however, the increased risk of abnormal placentation is thought to remain.[17]

In the 1980s, insertion of an IUD was recognised as a first-line treatment for Asherman syndrome.[18,19]

The CEU considers that it would be reasonable to insert an IUD for contraception in a woman who has had a pregnancy following a diagnosis of Asherman syndrome. Expansion of the uterine cavity during pregnancy would have disrupted any adhesions which might have impeded insertion of an IUD. We are unaware of any published advice that Asherman syndrome represents a contraindication to IUD insertion; and indeed it has been advocated as a treatment.

QUESTION

For young women aged 14 years old who have Asperger syndrome, can DMPA be used safely and competently?

POPULATION:	Women with Asperger syndrome.
INTERVENTION:	DMPA.
OUTCOME:	Safety and efficacy.

ANSWER

Asperger syndrome is a developmental disorder, and a form of autism. Individuals with Asperger syndrome have problems with two-way social interaction, and verbal and non-verbal communication. They have a reluctance to accept change, inflexibility of thought, and have absorbing, narrow areas of interest. Individuals are often extremely good at rote memory skills (facts, figures, dates, times, and so on) and many excel in mathematics and science. There is a range of severity of symptoms, the mildly affected child often goes undiagnosed and may just appear odd or eccentric.[20] In young women with Asperger syndrome, there may be concerns about their competency to use contraception.

The *WHO Medical Eligibility Criteria for Contraceptive Use* recommends that the benefits of using DMPA in women under 18 years generally outweigh the risks (WHO category 2). However, they comment that there are theoretical concerns regarding the hypoestrogenic effect of DMPA.

The Department of Health defines a child as 'a person who has not reached the age of 18 years'.[21] In Scotland, a child is defined as 'a person below the age of 16 years but for certain purposes such as legal hearings or welfare may include a person up to the age of 18 years'.[22] Regardless of age, any competent young person can consent to medical treatment. The criteria to establish if a young person has the capacity to consent to medical treatment are the same as for adults. An individual must have sufficient capacity to understand the procedure and its alternatives, their consent must be voluntary, and their decision must be based on sufficient and accurate information.[23–25] During a consultation, the clinician should determine if the young person has the ability to take in and retain information, to believe the information given, to weigh up the risks, benefits and needs and to express her own wishes.[26] After the case of Gillick versus West Norfolk and Wisbech Area Health Authority in 1986, the Law Lords ruling (Fraser ruling) stated that if a clinician believes a young women to be competent, then he may provide contraceptive advice and treatment to a young woman under the age of 16 years without parental consent. This contraceptive advice or treatment can be given if the clinician cannot persuade the young person to inform her parents; if the young person will continue to have intercourse; if the young person may suffer emotionally or psychologically by not providing advice or treatment; and when this is judged to be in her best interests. The young woman should be documented as 'Fraser ruling competent'.

If a young woman under 18 years is not believed to be competent to consent to treatment, only the holder of 'parental responsibility' can give consent to treatment on her behalf.[27,28] Conflict may arise if the holder of parental responsibility and the clinician do not agree that treatment is in the best interests of the young person. For adults with incapacity (aged over 18 years), only an appointed 'guardian' can consent to treatment on their behalf.

Despite extensive searching, the CEU could find no directly relevant information on the use of DMPA in young women with Asperger syndrome. DMPA can be safely used in young women in general, however each young woman's competency to consent to treatment, or the wishes of those with 'parental responsibility, must be assessed before contraception can be supplied.

QUESTION

For women with autoimmune cyclical neutropenia, is the combined oral contraceptive a safe method of contraception?

POPULATION: Women with autoimmune cyclical neutropenia.
INTERVENTION: Combined oral contraception.
OUTCOME: Safety.

ANSWER

Cyclical neutropenia[29] is a periodic haematological disorder that originates from a defect in one of the stem cell populations of the bone marrow. Circulating neutrophil numbers periodically decrease from normal values to very low values. This period ranges between 19 and 21 days. During those periods, patients can have symptoms of malaise and anorexia, and signs of fever, mouth ulcers and lymphadenopathy. The condition occurs either sporadically or as an autosomal dominantly inherited disorder.

The CEU was unable to identify any relevant data regarding the use of contraception in women with cyclical neutropenia.

QUESTION

In women with Behçet's disease does use of hormonal contraception increase the risk of venous thrombosis?

POPULATION: Women with Behçet's disease.
INTERVENTION: Hormonal contraception.
OUTCOME: VTE.

ANSWER

Behçet's disease is a chronic rheumatic illness, which is thought to be auto-immune in aetiology. Inflammation affects blood vessels and venous thrombosis can occur in between 10% and 25% of patients. Mouth ulcers occur in up to 95% of patients; ulcers also occur in the genital region. Other skin lesions can occur elsewhere on the body. Eye complications such as uveitits and iritis can occur. Other less common complications include: joint involvement; bowel disease; depression and fatigue; central nervous system involvement with stiff neck, headache, poor coordination and risk of stroke.

Thrombophilic factors do not appear to explain most of the thrombotic risk in patients with Behçet's disease.[30] A negative thrombophilia screen may not indicate a lack of increased risk of thrombosis. Our literature search identified no evidence directly relating to Behçet's disease and use of hormonal contraception.

Combined oral contraception is given a WHO category 4 for women with a past history of DVT or pulmonary embolism or who have a risk factor for these conditions. The *WHO Medical Eligibility Criteria for Contraceptive Use* gives progestogen-only contraceptives a WHO category 2 for women with a past history of DVT or pulmonary embolism or who have a risk factor for these conditions.

The CEU suggests that these WHO recommendations be applied when advising women with Behçet's disease.

QUESTION

For women with bipolar affective disorder, is DMPA a safe method of contraception?

POPULATION: Women with bipolar affective disorder.
INTERVENTION: DMPA.
OUTCOME: Safety.

ANSWER

Bipolar disorder or manic-depressive illness is a brain disorder characterised by unusual shifts in mood, energy and ability to function. There are episodes of mania and depression, which may also include psychotic symptoms.[31] Bipolar disorder typically develops in late adolescence or early adulthood but some people may experience the first symptoms in childhood. It cannot be identified physiologically and a diagnosis has to be made on the basis of symptoms, course of illness, and family history.[32] The classical form of the illness (bipolar I disorder) involves recurrent episodes of mania and depression. Some individuals develop milder episodes of mania (hypomania) that alternate with depression (bipolar II disorder). Individuals who experience four or more episodes of illness within 1 year are said to have rapid-cycling bipolar disorder.[31] Mood stabilisers are prescribed to control bipolar disorder and the most common medications include lithium, valproate and carbamazepine. Newer anticonvulsants such as lamotrigine, gabapentin and topiramate are also being studied for their effects on mood cycles.[33] Women with bipolar disorder should be aware of the possible harmful effects of mood stabilisers on the developing fetus or nursing infant.

The Summary of Product Characteristics for DMPA advises that this is a long-term contraceptive agent suitable for use in women who have been appropriately counselled concerning the likelihood of menstrual disturbance and the potential for delay in return to full fertility. Regarding psychiatric disorders, the Summary of Product Characteristics advises that women with a history of endogenous depression should be carefully monitored while using DMPA and that some women may complain of premenstrual-type depression.

The *WHO Medical Eligibility Criteria for Contraceptive Use* advises that for women using anticonvulsants such as carbamazepine, the benefits of using DMPA generally outweigh the risks (WHO category 2).

A review of the literature on DMPA in 1996 concluded that data regarding depression and mood changes in DMPA users are scanty and that current evidence did not support a causal relationship between use of the contraceptive and affective disorders.[33]

A subsequent review on long-acting hormonal contraception states that multicentre experience showed no increase in depressive symptoms after use of DMPA for one year.[34] This was true even among those users who had the highest mean depressive scores prior to initiating contraception.

Gupta *et al.* performed a case–control study in 2001 looking at the effects of DMPA on mood in 39 adolescent females compared with 24 adolescents not using any hormonal contraception.[35] Two standardised questionnaires were administered to all the adolescents at baseline and again at 3, 6 and 12 months. Adolescents using DMPA over a 12-month period did not show depressive symptoms and showed no significant changes in negative or positive affect.

A letter in the *British Journal of Psychiatry* highlights the importance of providing contraceptive advice to women with chronic psychotic illness (who are at increased risk of relapse after childbirth).[36] Pregnancies have been reported in women with chronic psychotic illness whose medication was changed from older drugs (chlorpromazine, haloperidol) which cause significant hyperprolactinaemia and provide a contraceptive effect to atypical anti-psychotics (olanzapine, quetiapine, clozapine) which have negligible effect on prolactin levels.

The CEU found no direct evidence on the use of DMPA by women with bipolar disorder. After counselling, this may be a suitable method of contraception.

QUESTION

For women who are using progestogen-only contraception and have cervical intraepithelial neoplasia (CIN), what advice should be given regarding initiation or continuation of their method?

POPULATION: Women with CIN.
INTERVENTION: Progestogen-only contraception.
OUTCOME: Safety.

ANSWER

The *WHO Medical Eligibility Criteria for Contraceptive Use* provides evidence-based recommendations on eligibility for various contraceptive methods.

WHO identifies CIN as category 1 (unrestricted use) or 2 (benefits generally outweigh risks). A WHO category 1 is given to the use of progestogen-only pills. DMPA, subdermal progestogen-only contraception (specifically Norplant), and the LNG-IUSare given a WHO category 2. Similar categories are given for cervical cancer and progestogen-only methods, with the exception of the initiation of an IUS which is not recommended (WHO category 4).

QUESTION

For women using progestogen-only contraception, is there any evidence that it can exacerbate or cause a flare up of Crohn's disease?

POPULATION: Women with Crohn's disease.
INTERVENTION: Progestogen-only contraception.
OUTCOME: Exacerbation of Crohn's symptoms.

ANSWER

FFPRHC CEU guidance on contraceptive choices for women with inflammatory bowel disease[37] reviewed the literature and found no trials relating to progestogen-only contraceptive use in women with inflammatory bowel disease.

A case report described a 38-year-old woman who experienced a relapse of Crohn's disease when she was fitted with a LNG-IUS.[38] The Crohn's disease flared up in the 2 weeks after LNG-IUS insertion but settled again by the time of her 6-week review. However, some 3 months after LNG-IUS insertion, she requested removal as her Crohn's disease was getting much worse. After removal of the LNG-IUS, Crohn's disease symptoms settled with medication over the following 3 months.

Another case report described a 30-year-old woman with Crohn's disease who had undergone total colectomy and had a permanent ileostomy.[39] Every time she had vaginal bleeding, she suffered a debilitating exacerbation of diarrhoea. She started using DMPA and after the first injection she had only slight spotting, and after the second, suffered no vaginal loss and thus no debilitating exacerbations of diarrhoea.[39]

No studies were identified which investigated the use of DMPA (and its effects on bone mineral density) by women with inflammatory bowel disease. Previous expert opinion[40] suggested that women who use DMPA may be referred for bone densitometry screening if they have risk factors for osteoporosis such as heavy smoking, low BMI, amenorrhoea, corticosteroid use, thyroid disease or family history. Women with inflammatory bowel disease are likely to fall into this category. A cross-sectional study[41] identified corticosteroid use as a predictor of low bone mineral density but a significant number of patients with inflammatory bowel disease who have never used corticosteroids also have osteopenia or osteoporosis. Malabsorption may also increase the risk of low bone mineral density.

Low bone mineral density is usually asymptomatic unless women present with fractures. Only one study has measured the burden of fracture in patients with inflammatory bowel disease.[42] This population-based, matched, cohort study compared patients with inflammatory bowel disease with age- and gender-matched patients without inflammatory bowel disease. A significant increase in the incidence of fractures in inflammatory bowel disease patients, similar in both men and women, was identified with an incidence rate ratio of 1.41 (95% CI 1.27–1.56).[42] If women with inflammatory bowel disease are considering the use of DMPA, measurement of bone mineral density is recommended.[37]

The CEU recommend that women with inflammatory bowel disease and low bone density (or who have had repeat courses of corticosteroids or malabsorption) should be advised against the use of DMPA. [37]

QUESTION

For women with Cushing syndrome (taking furosemide, hydrocortisone, aminoglutethimide, metyrapone and antibiotics), what contraceptive methods can be used safely?

POPULATION: Women with Cushing syndrome.
INTERVENTION: Contraception.
OUTCOME: Safety.

ANSWER

Cushing syndrome occurs when the body is exposed to excessive levels of cortisol for long periods of time. This can happen when people take glucocorticoid hormones, or because of an overproduction of cortisol by the body.

The BNF states that estrogens antagonise the effect of diuretics (furosemide). The plasma concentration of corticosteroids (hydrocortisone) is increased by estrogen. Aminoglutethimide reduces the plasma concentration of medroxyprogesterone.

The Summary of Product Characteristics for the LNG-IUS states that the LNG-IUS should be used with caution in women using chronic corticosteroid therapy. The Summary of Product Characteristics for a progestogen-only pill (Microval; now discontinued: BNF 51, 2006) advises that interactions have been reported between oral contraceptives and corticosteroids.

As estrogens interact with diuretics and corticosteroids, the CEU advises that women using these drugs do not use combined oral contraception. Progestogens may interact with these drugs but there is no confirmatory evidence. However, aminoglutethimide does reduce the plasma concentration of medroxyprogesterone. Women wishing to use the progestogen-only pill, etonogestrel implant, or the LNG-IUS should be counselled on the possible risk of interaction between treatment drugs and progestogen. Consideration should be given to the use of non-hormonal methods of contraception for women on treatment for Cushing syndrome.

QUESTION

For women with cystic fibrosis, which methods of contraception are effective and acceptable? (Six similar enquiries.)

POPULATION: Women with cystic fibrosis.

INTERVENTION: Contraception.

OUTCOME: Safety and efficacy.

ANSWER

Cystic fibrosis is an autosomal recessive condition which affects approximately 1/3000 live births. However, it has a carrier rate of 3% in caucasian populations. Cystic fibrosis is caused by a gene mutation which results in viscous mucus being produced by exocrine glands. Patients tend to suffer from lung disease and pancreatic enzyme insufficiency. With advances in management, patients with cystic fibrosis are now living into the reproductive years. Contraception and planning of pregnancy are now an issue for women with cystic fibrosis.

Cystic fibrosis is not mentioned directly under contraception in the BNF. However, the following comments appear to be relevant to these patients. The combined oral contraceptive is suitable for use (but is less effective) with enzyme-inducing medications and broad-spectrum antibiotics such as ampicillin and doxycycline. If antibiotics are used only for short-term treatment, then additional contraception should be used for the duration and for 7 days after the course. However, if the antibiotics are long-term (that is more than 3 weeks) additional methods are not required (after the initiation). Progestogen-only pills should be used with caution in malabsorption syndromes[43] and patients with cystic fibrosis may have a degree of malabsorption. Broad-spectrum antibiotics do not affect DMPA, the implant (Implanon) or the LNG-IUS. Intrauterine devices (IUDs) and barrier methods can be used in cystic fibrosis in the same way as the general population.

The CEU found no evidence in the literature on the use of the combined contraceptive patch (Evra) by women with cystic fibrosis.

There is no specific reference to cystic fibrosis in the *WHO Medical Eligibility Criteria for Contraceptive Use*. However, patients with cystic fibrosis may suffer from gall bladder disease due to the viscous secretions. WHO recommends that, for women with gall bladder problems who are asymptomatic, the benefits of the combined pill, progestogen-only pill, DMPA and LNG-IUS generally outweigh the risks (WHO category 2). For symptomatic women, who have current or medically treated gall-bladder disease, the risks of the combined pill generally outweigh the benefits (WHO category 3). Once a cholecystectomy has been performed, these women are again classified as WHO category 2. For symptomatic women with current or medically treated gall bladder disease, the benefits of the progestogen-only pill, DMPA and LNG-IUS generally outweigh the risks (WHO category 2). Both symptomatic and asymptomatic women with gall bladder disease may have unrestricted use of the IUD (WHO category 1).

One study identified through our Medline search suggested that many contraceptive options present a possible increased risk to women with cystic fibrosis.[44] Unfortunately, we were unable to obtain the full article. The authors do acknowledge however that pregnancy holds its own risks for these women and therefore contraception will be required.

A study into the attitudes of cystic fibrosis sufferers about fertility noted that some of the women were using contraception, such as the pill or IUD.[45] There was no reference as to the appropriateness of the method of contraception.

It seems from the literature that there is no particular method of contraception contraindicated or recommended for women with cystic fibrosis. Each method needs to be weighed up against the particular pathologies caused by cystic fibrosis that are present in the woman (as one would do for all patients).

References

1. Acrocyanosis [www.chclibrary.org/micromed/00035990.html].
2. Carpentier PH. Definition and epidemiology of acrosyndromes. *Rev Pract* 1998;48:1641–6.
3. Altura BM. Sex and estrogens and responsiveness of terminal arterioles to neurohypophyseal hormones and catecholamines. *Pharmacol Exp Ther* 1975;193:403–12.
4. Roberts JM, Insel PA, Goldfien A. Alpha adrenoreceptors but not beta adrenoreceptors increase in rabbit uterus with estrogen. *Nature* 2003;270:624–5.
5. Williams LT, Lefkowitz RJ. Regulation of rabbit myometrial alpha adrenergic receptors by estrogen and progesterone. *J Clin Invest* 2003;60:815–8.
6. Bartelink ML, Wollersheim H, Vemer H, Thomas CM, de Boo T, Thien T. The effects of single oral doses of 17 beta-oestradiol and progesterone on finger circulation in healthy women and in women with primary Raynaud's phenomenon. *Eur J Clin Pharmacol* 1994;46:557–60.
7. Lekakis J, Mavrikakis M, Papamichael C, Papazoglou S, Economou O, Scotiniotis I, *et al.* Short-term estrogen administration improves abnormal endothelial function in women with systemic sclerosis and Raynaud's phenomenon. *Am Heart J* 1998;136:905–12.
8. Braatvedt GD, Joyce M, Evans M, Clearwater J, Reid IR. Bone mineral density in patients with treated Addison's disease. *Osteoporosis Int* 1999;10:435–40.
9. Heureux F, Maiter D, Boutsen Y, Devogelaer JP, Jamart J, Donckier J. Evaluation of corticosteroid replacement therapy and its effects on bones in Addison's disease. *Ann Endocrinol* 2000;61:179–83.

10. Gbolade BA. Depo-Provera and bone density. Faculty Aid to CPD Topics (FACT). *J Fam Plann Reprod Health Care* 2002;28:7–11.

11. Kaplan SME, Rickert VI. Impact of anorexia, bulimia and obesity on the gynecologic health of adolescents. *Am Fam Phys* 2001;64:445–50.

12. Grinspoon S, Thomas L, Miller K, Herzog D, Klibanski A. Effects of recombinant human IGF-I and oral contraceptive administration on bone density in anorexia nervosa. *J Clin Endocrinol Metab* 2002;87:2883–91.

13. Golden NH, Lanzkowsky L, Schebendach J, Palestro CJ, Jacobson MS, Shenker IR. The effect of estrogen-progestin treatment on bone mineral density in anorexia nervosa. *J Pediatr Adolesc Gynecol* 2002;15:135–43.

14. American Psychiatric Association Work Group on Eating Disorders. Practice guideline for the treatment of patients with eating disorders. *Am J Psychiatr* 2000;157:1–39.

15. American Academy of Pediatrics. Identifying and treating eating disorders. Identifying and treating eating disorders. *Pediatrics* 2003;111:204–11.

16. Westendorp ICD, Ankum WM, Mol BWJ, Vonk J. Prevalence of Asherman's syndrome after secondary removal of placental remnants or repeat curettage for incomplete abortion. *Hum Reprod* 1998;13:3347–50.

17. Capella-Allouc S, Morsad F, Rongieres-Bertrand C, Taylor S, Fernandez H. Hysteroscopic treatment of severe Asherman's syndrome and subsequent fertility. *Hum Reprod* 1999;14:1230–3.

18. Sanfilippo JS, Fitzgerald MR, Badawy SZ, Nussbaum ML, Yussman MA. Asherman's syndrome. A comparison of therapeutic methods. *J Reprod Med* 1982;27:328–30.

19. Ismajovich B, Lidor A, Confino E, David MP. Treatment of minimal and moderate intrauterine adhesions (Asherman's syndrome). *J Reprod Med* 1985;30:769–72.

20. Lord R. *Asperger Syndrome* [www.aspennj.org/lord.html].

21. Department of Health. The Childrens Act 1989 – Guidance and Regulations [www.lbcma.org.uk/guidelines2.pdf].

22. Children (Scotland) Act. London: HMSO; 1995.

23. Stampfer M. Oral contraception and cardiovascular disease. *N Engl J Med* 2001;345:1841–2.

24. Tanis B, Vandebosch M, Kemmeren JM, Cats VM, Helmerhorst FM, Algra A, *et al.* Oral contraceptives and the risk of myocardial infarction. *N Engl J Med* 2001;345:1787–93.

25. Potts M, McDevitt J. A use-effectiveness trial of spermicidally lubricated condoms. *Contraception* 1975;11:701–10.

26. Affandi R. Injectable contraceptives: A worldwide perspective. *J Fam Plann Reprod Health Care* 2002;28:3–4.

27. Snell RS. The pigmentary changes occurring in the breast skin during pregnancy and following estrogen replacement. *J Invest Dermatol* 1964;43:181–6.

28. Katsambas A, Antoniou Ch. Melasma. Classification and treatment. *J Eur Acad Dermatol Venereol* 1995;4:217–23.

29. Haurie C, Dale DC, Mackey MC. Cyclical neutropenia and other periodic hematological disorders: a review of mechanisms and mathematical models. *Blood* 1998;92:2629–40.

30. Espinosa G, Font J, Tassies D, Vidaller A, Deulofeu R, *et al.* Vascular involvement in Behçet's disease: relation with thrombophilic factors, coagulation activation, and thrombomodulin. *Am J Med* 2002;112:37–43.

31. National Institute of Mental Health. *Bipolar disorder*. NIH Publication No 02–3679. Bethesda, MD: NIH; 2001.

32. American Psychiatric Association. *Diagnostic and Statistical Manual for Mental Disorders*. Washington, DC: American Psychiatric Press; 1994.

33. Westhoff C. Depot medroxyprogesterone acetate contraception. Metabolic parameters and mood changes. *J Reprod Med* 1996;41:401–6.

34. Kauntiz AM. Long-acting hormonal contraception: assessing impact on bone density, weight and mood. *Int J Fertil Womens Med* 1999;44:110–7.

35. Gupta N, O'Brien R, Jacobsen LJ, Davis A, Zuckerman A, Supran S, *et al*. Mood changes in adolescents using depot-medroxyprogesterone acetate for contraception: a prospective study. *J Pediat Adolesc Gynecol* 2001;14:71–6.

36. Gregoire A. Risk of pregnancy when changing to atypical antipsychotics. *Br J Psychiatr* 2002;180:83–4.

37. Faculty of Family Planning and Reproductive Health Care Clinical Effectiveness Unit. Contraceptive choices for women with inflammatory bowel disease. *J Fam Plann Reprod Health Care* 2003;29:127–34.

38. Wakeman J. Exacerbation of Crohn's disease after insertion of a LNG-IUS: a case report. *J Fam Plann Reprod Health Care* 2003;29:154.

39. Irvine C. Depo Provera use in Crohn's disease. *Br J Fam Plann* 1999;25:129.

40. Gbolade BA. Depo-Provera and bone density. *J Fam Plann Reprod Health Care* 2002;28:7–11.

41. Habtezion A, Silverberg MS, Parkes R, Mikolainis S, Steinhart AH. Risk factors for low bone density in Crohn's disease. *Inflamm Bowel Dis* 2002;8:87–92.

42. Bernstein CN, Blanchard JF, Leslie W, Wajda A, Yu BN. The incidence of fracture among patients with inflammatory bowel disease. *Ann Intern Med* 2000;133:795–9.

43. Faculty of Family Planning and Reproductive Health Care Clinical Effectiveness Unit. Contraceptice choices for women with inflammatory bowel disease. *J Fam Plann Reprod Health Care* 2003;29:127–34.

44. Owens K, Honebrink A. Gynecologic care of medically complicated adolescents. *Pediatr Clin North Am* 1999;46:631–42.

45. Fair A, Griffiths K, Osman LM. Attitudes to fertility issues amongst adults with cystic fibrosis in Scotland. *Thorax* 2000;55:672–7.

19 MISCELLANEOUS MEDICAL DISORDERS D–H

QUESTION

For women with Ehlers-Danlos syndrome, is use of hormonal contraception associated with an increased risk of cardiovascular complications? (Two similar enquiries.)

POPULATION: Women with Ehlers-Danlos syndrome.
INTERVENTION: Hormonal contraception.
OUTCOME: Cardiovascular risk.

ANSWER

The Ehlers-Danlos syndromes are inherited connective tissue disorders thought to result from defects in a collagen molecule which gives strength and adhesion to body tissues. Symptoms may include fragile and hyper-extensible skin, hypermobile joints, osteoarthritis and the tendency to bruise.[1] The walls of blood vessels, the gut, uterus and fetal membranes may be excessively fragile. There are at least ten different subtypes of the disorder. Types I–III are the most common while type IV (the vascular form) is rare and one of the most severe. Internationally, the incidence of Ehlers-Danlos syndrome is reported to be one case in about 400 000 people; but mild or incomplete forms are underdiagnosed and more common than other forms.[2]

A paper on the clinical and genetic features of Ehlers-Danlos syndrome type IV mentions that patients with the disorder are at risk for rupture of the arteries, bowel and the uterus.[3] In addition to a 50% chance of having an affected child, women with type IV have a much higher risk of pregnancy complications. Ehlers-Danlos syndrome type IV can potentially cause a stroke in young people,[4] and may present with extremely fragile arteries associated with multiple aneurysm formation, spontaneous rupture, and dissection.[5]

The CEU was unable to find any evidence in the literature specifically on the use of different methods of contraception by women with Ehlers-Danlos syndromes. Eligibility criteria for contraceptive use by women with vascular disease from the WHO are presented below.

The *WHO Medical Eligibility Criteria for Contraceptive Use* states that women with underlying vascular disease may have unrestricted use (WHO category 1) of the IUD. The benefits of using the progestogen-only pill, implant (specifically Norplant) and the LNG-IUS generally outweigh the risks (WHO category 2) for these women. The risks of using DMPA generally outweigh the benefits (WHO category 3). The increased risk associated with combined pill use is considered unacceptable (WHO category 4).

Clinical judgement should be used to determine a woman's suitability for a particular method based on the subtype of Ehlers-Danlos syndrome and the severity of symptoms. A woman who does not have the vascular or severe form of Ehlers-Danlos syndrome may be suitable to use DMPA.

QUESTION

For women with Ehlers-Danlos syndrome requesting contraception, does use of the LNG-IUS, Mirena, increase capillary fragility in the endometrium?

POPULATION:	Women with Ehlers-Danlos syndrome.
INTERVENTION:	LNG-IUS.
OUTCOME:	Endometrial capillary fragility.

ANSWER

The Ehlers-Danlos syndromes are inherited connective tissue disorders which are thought to result from defects in a collagen molecule which gives strength and adhesion to body tissues.

The *WHO Medical Eligibility Criteria for Contraceptive Use* has classified the use of the IUS by women with underlying vascular disease as category 2 (benefits generally outweigh risks).

The *WHO Medical Eligibility Criteria for Contraceptive Use* states that there is evidence that systemic progestogens cause changes in the endometrial vasculature predisposing to large, thin walled vessels which may lead to abnormal bleeding in women using progestogen-only implants (Norplant). Similar findings have also been described in a small case series of women using LNG-IUS prior to hysterectomy.[6]

The CEU could find no further information more specifically related to the issue of endometrial vascular fragility in women with Ehlers-Danlos syndrome.

QUESTION

For women with insulin-dependent diabetes and a high BMI experiencing irregular, heavy bleeding with DMPA, what management options are advised?

POPULATION: Women with diabetes and obesity with bleeding problems on DMPA.

INTERVENTION: Management options.

OUTCOME: Relief of bleeding problems.

ANSWER

The *WHO Medical Eligibility Criteria for Contraceptive Use* advises that women with a BMI of $30\,kg/m^2$ or above may have unrestricted use (WHO category 1) of the progestogen-only pill and IUD. The benefits of combined oral contraception, DMPA, the progestogen implant (specifically Norplant) and the LNG-IUS generally outweigh the risks for these women (WHO Category 2).

Women with uncomplicated insulin-dependent diabetes may have unrestricted use of the IUD (WHO category 1), and the benefits of combined oral contraception, progestogen-only pill, DMPA, implant (Norplant) and the LNG-IUS generally outweigh the risks (WHO category 2).

The UK Version of the WHO *Selected Practice Recommendations for Contraceptive Use* provides these recommendations on bleeding and DMPA:

● The repeat injection for DMPA should be provided every 12 weeks and can be given up to 2 weeks early. There is no evidence to suggest that shortening the injection interval improves irregular bleeding.

● Spotting, light bleeding, heavy and prolonged bleeding are all common in the first injection cycle. For persistent bleeding and spotting or bleeding after a period of amenorrhoea, gynaecological problems and STIs should be excluded and referral to a gynaecologist may be appropriate. If bleeding continues or the woman's health is threatened, DMPA should be discontinued for another method.

● Short-term use of a combined oral contraceptive can be considered individually to manage abnormal bleeding with DMPA.

QUESTION

For women aged 48 years, with type II diabetes and Down syndrome, who are using DMPA when may this method of contraception be discontinued?

POPULATION: Women with diabetes and Down syndrome.
INTERVENTION: DMPA.
OUTCOME: Discontinuation in the perimenopause.

ANSWER

Women with Down Syndrome are fertile and therefore require adequate and appropriate contraception until the menopause if they are sexually active. An assessment of FSH level is possible in a woman using DMPA; FSH levels are usually low and increase if menopausal. Monitoring of FSH levels may be used to assess the onset of menopause. If a random FSH is over 30 iu/l, contraception should be continued for at least 2 years if the woman is under the age of 50 years or for 1 year if over the age of 50 years. Women with Down syndrome tend to have an earlier onset of menopause than other women with learning disability and than women without learning disability. On average, women with Down syndrome have relatively high mean levels of FSH, which would represent a higher prevalence of gonadal dysfunction than in the general population. However, no studies were identified that considered the FSH levels in women with Down syndrome who had had a pregnancy.

The *WHO Medical Eligibility Criteria* recommends that the benefits of DMPA generally outweigh the risks for women over the age of 45 years; and for those who have had non-insulin dependent diabetes for less than 20 years (WHO category 2). Women with non-insulin dependent diabetes for over 20 years may be advised against the use of DMPA, as the risks usually outweigh any benefits (WHO category 3).

For perimenopausal women using DMPA a switch to progestogen-only pill or barrier methods is usually appropriate. However, for women where compliance is a particular issue the risks and benefits of all contraceptive methods and the pregnancy risk should be considered individually.

QUESTION

In women with insulin-dependent diabetes and Addison's disease, which contraceptive methods can be used safely?

POPULATION: Women with diabetes and Addison's disease.
INTERVENTION: Contraception.
OUTCOME: Safety.

ANSWER

The *WHO Medical Eligibility Criteria* recommends that women with insulin-dependent diabetes may have unrestricted use of the copper IUD (WHO category 1). Women with diabetes will have greater benefits from contraception than the risks involved (WHO category 2) if they use the combined pill, progestogen-only pill, DMPA, the progestogen implant or the LNG-IUS. However, WHO has noted that both the combined pill and progestogen-only contraceptives may cause changes in carbohydrate metabolism; thus diabetic control may need to be monitored closely following initiation of hormonal contraception.

Addison's disease is a rare endocrine disorder characterised by insufficient production of cortisol and sometimes aldosterone. This may either occur as an autoimmune condition (primary adrenal insufficiency) or as secondary adrenal insufficiency. The CEU was unable to find any evidence that directly examined the use of different methods of contraception by women with Addison's disease. Studies have shown a correlation between long duration of Addison's disease with high cumulative corticosteroid dose and subsequent low bone mineral density. A review from the FFPRHC recommends that women with risk factors for low bone mineral density (such as smoking or long-term high-dose corticosteroid therapy) should not use DMPA but all other contraceptive methods may be considered.[6]

QUESTION

For women who have had microwave endometrial ablation, can the IUD be used safely? (Three similar enquiries.)

POPULATION: Women after microwave endometrial ablation.
INTERVENTION: IUD.
OUTCOME: Safety.

ANSWER

Endometrial destructive techniques such as transcervical resection of endo-metrium, laser or microwave endometrial ablation, or hot balloon endometrial ablation are techniques used when medical management of menorrhagia has failed. The endometrium is destroyed in order to produce lighter or absent periods. Small areas of endometrium may persist. These procedures do not prevent pregnancy; therefore effective contraception is still required. Pregnancy following endometrial destruction is not advised and complications have been noted on occasions when pregnancy has occurred.

A paper from Australia reported a pregnancy in a woman following endometrial ablation.[7] The authors recommend that sterilisation is performed at the same time as the ablation procedure or that contraception is continued. They did not state which contraceptive method.

According to the BNF, IUDs should be used with caution in the severely scarred uterus, which includes following endometrial destructive techniques. The rationale behind this would be the reduced cavity size and intrauterine adhesions, which would complicate insertion and increase the risk of perforation. We found no other evidence for or against other methods of contraception (including the LNG-IUS) following endometrial ablation or resection.

The LNG-IUS can be used as an alternative to IUD for contraception and would also provide treatment of menorrhagia.[8]

QUESTION

> **For women with endometriosis (treated with GnRHs and add-back combined continuous HRT) when can progestogen-only injectables or implants be commenced?**

POPULATION:	Women with endometriosis treated with GnRHs and 'add-back'.
INTERVENTION:	Initiating progestogen-only implant or injection.
OUTCOME:	Contraceptive efficacy.

ANSWER

GnRH agonists, used in the management of endometriosis, suppress ovulation. A long-acting GnRH agonist, administered as a monthly injection starting in the luteal phase, results in a transient stimulation of gonadotrophin release 2 hours after the initial injection followed by a sustained suppression of luteinising hormone, while FSH levels return to the normal range. Plasma estradiol concentrations fall to early follicular phase values within 14 days. Twice-weekly monitoring of urinary oestrone glucuronide and pregnanediol demonstrated inhibition of ovulation and almost complete suppression of follicular activity throughout the course of treatment. After cessation of the depot injections, postovulatory menstruation occurred within 80 days of administration of the last injection.[9] Non-hormonal contraception is advised when using GnRH agonists. GnRH agonists are generally used for up to 6 months. If used for longer, replacement of estrogen in the form of a combined continuous HRT is advised to prevent bone loss.

The use of DMPA and progestogen-only implants (specifically Norplant) in women who have endometriosis is given a WHO category 1 (unrestricted use) in the *WHO Medical Eligibility Criteria*.

The WHO has produced an evidence-based document giving advice on contraceptive use: *Selected Practice Recommendations for Contraceptive Use*. For women who are amenorrhoeic, DMPA can be given at anytime if it is reasonably certain she is not pregnant. She should be advised to abstain from sex or use additional contraceptive protection for the next 7 days. If women are having menstrual cycles, DMPA can be commenced up to and including day 7 of the menstrual cycle. A UK version of this document, the FFPRHC *UK Selected Practice Recommendations for Contraceptive Use* advises staring DMPA up to and including day 5 without the need for additional contraceptive cover. If a woman is amenorrhoeic and not pregnant nor has been at risk of pregnancy, she may start DMPA or progestogen-implants at any time. Additional barrier contraception should be advised for 7 days.

Hormonal contraception should not be started concurrently with GnRH agonists. The 'add back' HRT can be stopped at anytime but probably before initiation of the contraceptive method.

QUESTION

For women with fibrodysplasia ossificans progressive, is the etonogestrel implant a safe method of contraception?

POPULATION: Women with fibrodysplasia ossificans.
INTERVENTION: Etonogestrel implant.
OUTCOME: Safety.

ANSWER

Fibrodysplasia ossificans progressive is an autosomal dominant disease, which usually begins in infancy, with recurring episodes of painful soft tissue swelling and tumours which develop in the subcutaneous and muscle tissue and may subsequently undergo ossification.[10] Congenital skeletal malformations of the hands and feet, such as a hallus valgus deformity with microdactyly, are also characteristic. Most individuals with fibrodysplasia ossificans suffer decreasing mobility due to ankylosis of the spine and rib cage and are commonly bedridden by the time they reach their 30s.[10] The condition may also be associated with alopecia and deafness. Prevalence is estimated to be 1/1.64 million persons in the UK. Fibrodysplasia ossificans is more common in females than in males and medical treatment may involve the use of steroids.[10]

The etonogestrel implant (Implanon) is a long-acting contraceptive, containing 68 mg etonogestrel, in a non-biodegradable flexible rod, which is inserted subdermally into the upper arm. The FFPRHC training framework covers both the theoretical and practical aspects of subdermal implant insertion and removal and all doctors carrying out this procedure should do so only after appropriate training. Insertion and removal of the implant is carried out under local anaesthesia, which is uncomplicated in the majority of women,[11] although localised bleeding may occur. The Summary of Product Characteristics for Implanon states that use is contraindicated in women with active venous thromboembolic disorder, progestogen-dependent tumours, current or a history of severe hepatic disease, known or suspected pregnancy, undiagnosed vaginal bleeding or hypersensitivity to any of the implant components.

After a literature search, the CEU was unable to find any evidence on the use of the implant by women with fibrodysplasia ossificans (who may already have muscle tissue swelling at the site of insertion). Difficulties with the procedures of insertion and removal seem more likely to arise in women with this condition. The CEU can only advise that other contraceptive methods may be preferable to a subdermal method in such cases.

QUESTION

For women with haemochromatosis, is combined oral contraception safe and effective?

POPULATION: **Women with haemochromatosis.**
INTERVENTION: **Combined oral contraception.**
OUTCOME: **Safety.**

ANSWER

Haemochromatosis is associated with a Mendelian recessive condition with a prevalence of around 1/200 among Northern Europeans. Iron overload results from increased absorption in the duodenum and small intestine. Excess iron is deposited in parenchymal organs, notably the liver. However, the genetic condition is often not expressed and clinical manifestations occur in only around 1% of individuals who are homozygous for the relevant genes.

The CEU found no relevant publications specifically relating to contraception for women with haemochromatosis. In women with cirrhosis or liver tumours secondary to haemochromatosis, combined oral contraception should not be used. However, combined oral contraception need not be denied to a woman known to carry the genetic predisposition to haemochromatosis but in whom the condition is not clinically expressed.

QUESTION

For women with haemophilia and menorrhagia, is the combined oral contraceptive pill or the combined patch (Evra) safe to use and will either reduce menstrual bleeding? (Two similar enquiries.)

POPULATION: Women with haemophilia.

INTERVENTION: Combined hormonal contraception.

OUTCOME: Safety and effect on menorrhagia.

ANSWER

The RCOG guidance for the initial management of menorrhagia[12] advises that both the combined oral contraceptive pill and the LNG-IUS are effective treatment options for menorrhagia, particularly if contraception is also required. Mefenamic acid and cyclokapron are also used as first line treatments for menorrhagia.

The *WHO Medical Eligibility Criteria for Contraceptive Use* does not refer specifically to contraceptive choices for women with haemophilia. WHO advises that the combined oral contraceptive pill may decrease menstrual blood loss. Women with iron deficiency anaemia, perhaps attributable to menorrhagia, may thus have unrestricted use of this method (WHO category 1).

A Cochrane review[13] concluded that there is insufficient evidence to confirm that combined pills reduce menstrual blood loss. One small, randomised trial cited in the review found a 43% reduction in measured menstrual blood loss with combined pill use over two cycles.[14] Clinically, women describe less bleeding with combined oral contraception.

There is no evidence presently that the contraceptive patch (Evra) is effective in the management of menorrhagia.

QUESTION

For young women with a past history of Henoch-Schönlein purpura, which contraceptive methods are contraindicated and/or could cause a recurrence.

POPULATION:	**Women with a history of Henoch-Schönlein purpura.**
INTERVENTION:	**Contraception.**
OUTCOME:	**Disease recurrence.**

ANSWER

Henoch-Schönlein purpura is a syndrome that primarily affects children. The dominant features are purpura, arthritis, abdominal pain, gastrointestinal bleeding and nephritis. The clinical features are a consequence of widespread leukocytoclastic vasculitis following IgA deposition in vessel walls. It can occur from age 6 months to adulthood, with 75% of cases occurring in children aged under 10 years. The incidence is approximately 13–18 cases/100 000 children/year. Despite extensive efforts, no single pathogen or environmental agent has been identified as the cause. While most episodes are acute and self limiting, lasting about 4 weeks, nephritis is the one manifestation that can become chronic. Approximately 30–50% of patients will have persistent urinary abnormalities but only 1% progress to end-stage renal disease[1.5–17]

A past history of Henoch-Schönlein purpura does not preclude the use of any contraceptive method, even if renal impairment is present. There is no evidence from BNF or a review article (comprising an extensive Medline database search)[18] that any contraceptive methods precipitate recurrence of Henoch-Schönlein purpura.

The CEU was unable to find any specific published evidence on contraceptive use for women with Henoch-Schönlein purpura. It is likely that most contraceptive options would be suitable.

References

1.   Yeowell HN, Pinnell SR. The Ehlers-Danlos syndromes. *Semin Dermatol* 1993;12:229–40.
2.   Ehlers-Danlos Syndrome [www.emedicine.com/topic696.htm].

3. Pepin MG, Schwarze U, Superti-Furga A, Byres PH. Clinical and genetic features of Ehlers-Danlos syndrome type IV, the vascular type. *N Engl J Med* 2000;342:673–80.

4. North KN, Whiteman DA, Pepin MG, Byres PH. Cerebrovascular complications in Ehlers-Danlos syndrome type IV. *Ann Neurol* 1995;38:960–4.

5. Mattar SG, Kumar AG, Lumsden AB. Vascular complications in Ehlers-Danlos syndrome. *Am Surg* 1994;60:827–31.

6. Gbolade BA. Depo-Provera and bone density. Faculty Aid to CPD Topics (FACT). *J Fam Plann Reprod Health Care* 2002;28:7–11.

7. Opperman J, Browning D, Child A, Laverty C, Fraser IS. Pregnancy following rollerball endometrial ablation. *Gynaecol Endosc* 1998;7:3–7.

8. Royal College of Obstetricians and Gynaecologists. *The Management of Menorrhagia in Secondary Care*. National Evidence-Based Clinical Guidelines. London: RCOG Press; 1999.

9. West CP, Baird DT. Suppression of ovarian activity by Zoladex depot (ICI 118630), a long acting luteinizing hormone releasing hormone agonist analogue. *Clin Endocrinol* 1987;26:213–20.

10. Majewski S. Fibrodysplasia Ossificans [www.emedicine.com/derm/topic609.htm].

11. Oloto E, Mascarenhas L. Subdermal contraceptive implants. *J Fam Plann Reprod Health Care* 2000;26:171–4.

12. Royal College of Obstetricians and Gynaecologists. *The Initial Management of Menorrhagia*. National Evidence-based Clinical Guidelines No. 28. London: RCOG Press; 2002.

13. Iyer V, Farquhar C, Jepson R. Oral contraceptive pills for heavy menstrual bleeding. *Cochrane Database Syst Rev* 2003;(2):1–2.

14. Fraser I, McCarron G. Randomised trial of two hormonal and two prostaglandin inhibiting agents in women with a complaint of menorrhagia. *Aust N Z J Obstet Gynaecol* 1991;31:66–70.

15. Saulsbury F. Henoch-Schonlein purpura in children: report of 100 patients and review of the literature. *Medicine* 1999;78:395–409.

16. Tizard EJ. Henoch-Schonlein purpura. *Arch Dis Child* 1999;80:380–3.

17. Saulsbury FT. Henoch-Schonlein purpura. *Curr Opin Rheumatol* 2001;13:35–40.

18. Holder SMT, Joy MS, Falk RJ. Cutaneous and systemic manifestations of drug-induced vasculitis. *Ann Pharmacother* 2002;36:130–46.

QUESTION

For women with idiopathic thrombocytopenic purpura, which contraceptive methods can be used safely?

POPULATION: Women with thrombocytopenic prurpura.
INTERVENTION: Contraception.
OUTCOME: Safety.

ANSWER

The dyscrasias are pathological conditions of the blood, usually involving the cellular elements. Thrombocytopenic purpura is one type of blood dyscrasia and is a disease of platelets. Characteristics of the disease include a decrease in the number of circulating platelets in the absence of toxic exposure.[1] Most commonly, thrombocytopenic purpura is idiopathic.[2] Acute idiopathic thrombocytopenic purpura occurs particularly in children. It usually improves spontaneously and, in children at least, rarely recurs. Chronic idiopathic thrombocytopenic purpura is more common in adults, and occurs in three times as many women as men.[3]

Thrombotic thrombocytopenic purpura is a rarer form of the condition which is most common among people aged 20–40 years. Women are twice as likely as men to acquire this condition. The condition is thought to be caused by a plasma protein called von Willebrand factor, which is a normal component of plasma. It is required for effective blood clotting and deficiency results in von Willebrand's disease, an inherited condition characterised by excessive bleeding.[4]

Physician prescribing information for DMPA in the USA concluded, from a large trial of almost 4000 women, that blood dyscrasia was an adverse reaction to DMPA in less than 1% of users.

Fraser *et al.*[5] reported on a case of thrombotic thrombocytopenic purpura in a user of the levonorgestrel implant, Norplant. Through the Freedom of Information Act in the USA, they were able to review all adverse events associated with Norplant as of the end of 1992. They found two additional cases, which they also report in their paper. However, they could not identify a causal relationship between thrombotic thrombocytopenic purpura and Norplant.

Despite extensive searching, no other evidence on any associations between other contraceptive methods and thrombocytopenic purpura could be identified. Also no information could be found on initiation of contraceptive methods in women with thrombocytopenic purpura.

DMPA requires an intramuscular injection and may increase the risk of haematoma formation. Insertion of subdermal implants may also increase potential for haematoma formation. Oral methods of contraception such as combined oral contraception or the progestogen-only pill do not carry this risk.

In a study by Khan *et al.*[6] on the clinical and haematological profiles of idiopathic thrombocytopenic purpura, it was found that in 50 cases of idiopathic thrombocytopenic purpura, 50% of the female patients had menorrhagia. Furthermore, in two studies of causes of adolescent menorrhagia, 13% and 16% of cases were in adolescents with thrombocytopenic purpura.[7,8] Therefore, as menorrhagia is associated with thrombocytopenic purpura, methods such as the IUD may not be suitable for women with this condition, whereas the LNG-IUS may be a more suitable option.

QUESTION

For young nulliparous women with idiopathic thrombocytopenic purpura, and a history of cerebrovascular accident in a first-degree relative under the age of 45 years, what method of contraception is recommended to minimise the risk of adverse effects?

POPULATION: Women with thrombocytopenic purpura and family history of cerebrovascular disease.

INTERVENTION: Contraception.

OUTCOME: Safety.

ANSWER

Published evidence has focused on the therapeutic use of oral contraceptives in the management of menorrhagia for women with idiopathic thrombocytopenic purpura. One source has stated that combined oral contraceptive use may improve platelet function for women with bleeding disorders. The current British Society for Haematology guidance[9] states that women with idiopathic thrombocytopenic purpura and menorrhagia may use either oral contraceptives or the LNG-IUS to control their symptoms.

The *WHO Medical Eligibility Criteria for Contraceptive Use* states that, for women under the age of 35 years who smoke, the benefits of using the combined oral contraceptive generally outweigh the risks. Women with a history of a parent or sibling who suffered a heart attack before the age of 45 years, are severely obese or have abnormal levels of blood lipids, may be at increased risk of arterial disease. These risk factors are cumulative and increase if the woman also smokes.

Therefore for a young nulliparous woman who is not obese, has a normal level of blood lipids and has been counselled to stop smoking, the CEU feels that the combined pill can be used with appropriate follow-up. Clinicians may choose pills containing newer progestogens such as desogestrel, gestodene and norgestimate, which may be associated with less risk of arterial disease.

QUESTION

For women who are immunocompromised by the use of ciclosporin/tacrolimus, is insertion of an IUD associated with an increased risk of infection? (Two similar enquiries.)

POPULATION: Women immunocompromised by use of ciclosporin.
INTERVENTION: IUD insertion.
OUTCOME: Risk of infection.

ANSWER

Women can be immunocompromised due to disease (such as HIV) or due to drug use (such as ciclosporin, tacrolimus). The CEU was unable to identify any evidence on the risk of infection with IUD use for women immuno-compromised due to the use of any drugs which affect the immune system.

There is a known six-fold increase in the risk of PID in the 21 days following IUD insertion in women generally. This increased risk returns to a low risk of infection, similar to women not using an IUD, after this time. Large prospective studies have not suggested an increase in the risk of infective complications following IUD insertion in women with HIV.[10] The *WHO Medical Eligibility*

Criteria supports the use of an IUD in women who are HIV-positive. WHO also recommends that women with AIDS who are clinically well on antiretroviral therapy may use an IUD. The WHO *Selected Practice Recommendations* and the UK version of this document (the FFPRHC *UK Selected Practice Recommendations for Contraceptive Use*) do not recommend the routine use of prophylactic antibiotics for IUD insertion. No evidence was identified to support or refute the use of prophylactic antibiotics during the insertion of an IUD in women who are immunocompromised.

The CEU supports the use of intrauterine contraception by women using ciclosporin/tacrolimus after counselling. The use of prophylactic antibiotics for insertion of an IUD in women who are using ciclosporin is unclear. Antibiotic use may be considered, but the decision should be based on an appropriate sexual history.

QUESTION

In women with a past history of Kawasaki disease, does use of the combined oral contraceptive pill increase cardiovascular risk?

POPULATION: Women with a past history of Kawasaki disease.
INTERVENTION: Combined oral contraception.
OUTCOME: Cardiovascular risk.

ANSWER

Kawasaki disease is an illness of children characterised by inflammation of blood vessels throughout the body. There is an annual incidence of approximately 4–15/100 000 children in the USA.[11] The disease is 1.5 times more common in males than females and 85% of cases occur in children under the age of 5 years. Criteria for diagnosis include bilateral conjunctivitis, oral mucosal changes (such as strawberry tongue), peripheral extremity changes (such as oedema, erythema and skin desquamation), rash and cervical lymphadenopathy. The disease has acute, subacute and convalescent phases. Associated laboratory and clinical findings include raised erythrocyte sedimentation rate, raised white cell count, elevated liver function tests, raised platelet count, low red-cell count, aseptic meningitis, urethritis, enlargement of the gall bladder with upper quadrant pain, irritability, diarrhea and vomiting.[11]

Coronary artery aneurysms are sequelae of vasculitis and occur in 20–25% of untreated cases.[11] The Japanese Ministry (where Dr Kawasaki first identified the disease in 1961) has kept a registry of cases. Some 6500 children have been followed up longitudinally to determine the natural history of the illness. So far, no excess mortality has been attributable to Kawasaki disease after the acute phase.[11]

The CEU identified no evidence directly relating to Kawasaki disease and use of the combined oral contraceptive pill. The degree of cardiac and vessel damage as a result of the acute phase of the disease will determine the WHO category for combined pill use in the individual patient.

The *WHO Medical Eligibility Criteria* gives a WHO category 4 (unacceptable health risk) for combined pill use with vascular disease (unspecified). Some vascular diseases are associated with an increased risk of thrombosis; however, with a past history of Kawasaki disease, after the acute event, there does not appear to be an increased thrombotic risk. The combined pill is given a WHO category 2 (benefits generally outweigh the risks) for women with uncomplicated valvular heart disease, but is given a WHO category 4 for complicated valvular heart disease. The degree of cardiac damage following Kawasaki disease will determine an individual's risk and help decide whether combined oral contraception can be used safely.

QUESTION

For women with lactose intolerance, is the combined oral contraceptive pill an acceptable method of contraception?

POPULATION: Women with lactose intolerance.
INTERVENTION: Combined oral contraception.
OUTCOME: Safety, acceptability, efficacy.

ANSWER

Lactose intolerance is an inability to digest lactose caused by a deficiency in the enzyme lactase (which breaks down galactose into simpler sugars for absorption into the blood).[12] Symptoms include nausea, cramps, bloating and diarrhoea, which may begin half an hour to 2 hours after ingestion of foods containing lactose. Lactose intolerance may have several causes. It is rarely congenital, although there is a genetic form, and certain ethnic groups are more widely affected than others. The condition may also be caused by digestive diseases or injury to the small intestine.[12]

Lactose is used as a base for more than 20% of prescription drugs, including combined oral contraceptive pills and about 6% of over-the-counter medications.[12] These products typically affect only individuals with severe lactose intolerance as the dose of lactose in the base is very small.[12] For this reason, pharmaceutical companies have not fully addressed the issue or manufactured combined pills that may be better tolerated by this particular group of women. Summaries of Product Characteristics for most combined pills state that the medication should be avoided by individuals with sensitivity to any of the listed ingredients.

The CEU found only one letter in the literature which referred to lactose intolerance and combined oral contraception. Garden and Davidson wrote a letter[13] in response to published recommendations for the management of galactosaemia.[14] They had concerns regarding the recommended use of Loestrin 20® (Galen) as a method of long-term estrogen replacement for adult women at risk of osteoporosis. This is because combined oral contraceptives are not licensed for the prevention of osteoporosis (although they were widely used for this purpose before the acceptance of HRT). The authors acknowledge that the dose of lactose in combined pills is small but point out that even this dose may be unacceptable to some women. They also mention that if HRT is taken via a transdermal patch, women with lactose intolerance may be able to avoid ingestion of lactose.[13]

Femulen® (Pharmacia) is the only oral hormonal method of contraception which does not contain lactose.

QUESTION

For women with Legg-Calve-Perthes disease, awaiting surgery, is DMPA a safe method of contraception?

POPULATION: Women with Legg-Calve-Perthes disease.
INTERVENTION: DMPA.
OUTCOME: Safety, acceptability, efficacy.

ANSWER

Legg-Calve-Perthes disease is a childhood hip disorder characterised by idiopathic avascular necrosis of the femoral head.

The CEU was unable to find evidence in the literature on the use of different methods of contraception by women with Legg-Calve-Perthes disease. Studies investigating hormonal contraception and bone mineral density in the general population cannot easily be extrapolated to women with a bone disorder. These studies have found that bone mineral density is reduced at the femoral neck in DMPA users under and over the age of 18 years, compared with non-users.

A Faculty Aid to Continuing Professional Development Topic[15] advises that those with risk factors for low bone mineral density should be discouraged from using DMPA. Thus, DMPA is an unsuitable method of contraception for a woman with Legg-Calve-Perthes disease, who already has a risk of low bone mineral density at the femur.

The *WHO Medical Eligibility Criteria for Contraceptive Use* advises that, because of an increased risk of VTE, combined oral contraceptives should be avoided if a woman will be significantly immobile following major surgery.

A Scottish Intercollegiate Guidelines Network guideline[16] found no evidence that low dose progestogen-only contraception is associated with VTE post-operatively.

Consideration should be given to the progestogen-only pill, implant, LNG-IUS or non-hormonal methods in this case.

QUESTION

> **For a woman with a low-grade malignant abdominal liposarcoma which has been removed, what is the effect of progestogens on prognosis or possible recurrence?**

POPULATION: Women with previous liposarcoma.

INTERVENTION: Progestogen contraception.

OUTCOME: Risk of recurrence.

ANSWER

The malignant tumour, liposarcoma, has an embryologic origin from meso-dermal tissue. It is the most common histological subtype of retroperitoneal soft tissue sarcoma, however it only makes up 0.1% of all human neoplasms.[17] Low-grade liposarcomas are well-differentiated and are not usually aggressive but may recur locally.[18]

The CEU could find no evidence in the literature on the effect of progestogens on the risk of recurrence or prognosis of liposarcomas.

QUESTION

For women with obesity (high BMI), which contraceptive methods are safe and effective? (Four similar enquiries)

POPULATION:	Women with obesity.
INTERVENTION:	Contraception.
OUTCOME:	Safety, efficacy.

ANSWER

Obesity has been defined as a BMI of $30.0–39.9\,kg/m^2$, with morbid obesity defined as a BMI over $40\,kg/m^2$.[19] In England in 1998, 21% of women and 19% of men were obese. Obesity increases with age and there is an increased prevalence in people from lower socioeconomic groups and particular ethnic groups.[19] Women with a family history of myocardial infarction before the age of 45 years who are obese or have abnormal levels of blood lipids are at increased risk of arterial disease.[20]

Combined pills containing 'third-generation' progestogens (desogestrel, gestodene) were thought to be associated with less risk of arterial disease than second generation pills (containing levonorgestrel and norethisterone) but evidence regarding this is inconclusive. There appears to be a direct relationship between the dose of estrogen in a pill and the risk of VTE. The risk of VTE increases with use of combined oral contraception. Women who do not use the pill have an estimated risk of VTE of approximately 5/100 000; the risk increases to 15/100 000 for users of 'second-generation' pills and to 25/100 000 for users of 'third-generation' pills.[21] Other factors which can increase the risk of VTE are pregnancy, obesity, immobility and inherited clotting disorders.[20]

Due to these risks, patients with a BMI greater than $39\,kg/m^2$ are advised in the BNF to avoid combined oral contraception.

The WHO *Medical Eligibility Criteria for Contraceptive Use* classifies the use of combined pills as category 2 (benefits generally outweigh risks) and of all progestogen-only methods as category 1 (unrestricted use) for women with a BMI greater than or equal to $30\,kg/m^2$. However, WHO notes that there may be some concern regarding weight gain with some progestogen-only contraceptives, particularly long-acting methods.

DMPA and obesity

Connor *et al.*[22] performed a retrospective study to investigate whether there was a relationship between DMPA use in obese and overweight women and uterine bleeding. Results showed that obesity was associated with a decreased risk of excessive bleeding while using DMPA. The authors concluded that this finding would be useful in counselling this group of women, as decreased adverse effects are associated with increased compliance and patient satisfaction.

A comparison of users of DMPA and the IUD found that DMPA users increased in weight by 4.3 kg and IUD users increased in weight by 1.8 kg during 5 years of use.[23] The authors concluded that DMPA users had a significantly higher weight increase compared to IUD users. A position paper on the clinical effectiveness and adverse effects of DMPA points out that the main disadvantages of DMPA in UK practice are likely to be menstrual disturbance and weight gain.[24]

The CEU has found no evidence in the literature that women above a certain weight should have repeat DMPA injections every 10 weeks rather than every 12 weeks.

Combined oral contraceptives and obesity

Obese women may be at increased risk of pregnancy if prescribed combined pills containing less than 35 micrograms of ethinylestradiol. A retrospective cohort analysis of 2822 woman-years of combined pill use found that, after controlling for parity, women in the highest body weight quartile had a significantly increased risk of pill failure (relative risk 1.6; 95% CI 1.1–2.4) compared with women of lower weight.[25] Higher elevations of risk associated with weight were seen among very-low-dose pill users (relative risk 4.5; 95% CI 1.4–14.4).[25]

Progestogen-only pills and obesity

A large cohort study investigated associations between oral contraceptive failures and body weight.[26] A total of 17 032 white, married women using oral contraceptives, diaphragms or IUDs were recruited from 17 family planning clinics in the UK between 1968 and 1974. The failure rates (expressed as Pearl Indices) for progestogen-only pills were 3.4/100 woman-years at ages 25–29 years and 0.28/100 woman-years at ages 40–44 years. Failure rates for the progestogen-only pill and combined pill were adjusted for age alone and for age and parity in relation to body weight, height and BMI. No association was found between failure rate and body weight, height or BMI. The overall failure rate (adjusted for age and parity) for women weighing less than 82 kg was 0.24/100 woman-years. The overall failure rate for women weighing 82 kg or more (adjusted for age and parity) was 0.38/100 woman-years. The study did not support the hypothesis that an increase in body weight is related to an increase in contraceptive failure in women using either the combined or progestogen-only pill. However, this study may not have had sufficient power to prove or disprove the hypothesis.[27]

In another study, Kovacs *et al.*[28] evaluated the use of the progestogen-only pill as a precoital contraceptive. Three obese women (who were over 75 kg with BMI greater than 35) did not respond to the pills. The authors suggested that the metabolism of progestogen may be influenced by excessive adipose tissue, rendering it less effective.

Until more evidence becomes available, it would appear that the extra risk of adverse effects with two progestogen-only pills/day is negligible and a two-pill regimen may be appropriate in young obese women. In women who already have decreased fertility, such as women over 45 years, there is no evidence to support the use of two pills daily.

Progestogen-only implants and obesity

Higher failure rates have been shown to occur in obese women using the levonorgestrel implant or levonorgestrel-releasing vaginal ring.[29,30] The low systemic dose of levonorgestrel released by these contraceptives is comparable to that released daily by the progestogen-only pill. No pregnancies have been reported in women using the subdermal progestogen-only implant (Implanon).

QUESTION

For women with osteogenesis imperfecta, which contraceptive methods are suitable?

POPULATION: Women with osteogenesis imperfecta.
INTERVENTION: Contraception.
OUTCOME: Safety, efficacy.

ANSWER

Osteogenesis imperfecta is a genetic disorder caused by an inherited dominant gene defect or spontaneous mutation that affects the production of collagen resulting in brittle bones.

The CEU was unable to find any evidence in the literature on the use of different methods of contraception by women with osteogenesis imperfecta. Studies investigating hormonal contraception and bone mineral density have focused on women in the general population, and therefore the results cannot easily be extrapolated to women who already have brittle bones.

A Faculty Aid to Continuing Professional Development Topic[15] advises that all women who are considering the use of DMPA should be told that studies have found an association between long-term use and loss of bone mass. Additionally, the FACT advises that women should be encouraged to build up, or maintain, their bone mass through diet and exercise, while those with risk factors for low bone mineral density should be discouraged from using this method. DMPA is therefore an unsuitable method of contraception for a woman with osteogenesis imperfecta.

Estrogen-containing contraceptives should also be avoided due to increased risk of VTE if a woman is significantly immobile as a result of fractures with osteogenesis imperfecta. Consideration should be given to progestogen-only contraceptives (other than DMPA) or non-hormonal methods in this case.

QUESTION

For women with a history of ovarian cancer, can hormonal contraception be used safely? (Two similar enquiries.)

POPULATION:	**Women with a history of ovarian cancer.**
INTERVENTION:	**Contraception.**
OUTCOME:	**Safety.**

ANSWER

The *WHO Medical Eligibility Criteria for Contraceptive Use* recommends that combined oral contraception may be used unrestrictedly in women with current or previous ovarian cancer. This is also the case for progestogen-only methods of contraception (progestogen-only pill, DMPA and the implant) (WHO category 1). However, the *WHO Medical Eligibility Criteria for Contraceptive Use* states that the risks of using the IUD or the LNG-IUS generally outweigh the benefits (WHO category 3).

The FFPRHC published guidance on first prescription of combined oral contraception in 2003.[31] Evidence from the literature on the risk of ovarian cancer with combined pill use was reviewed. A systematic review of cohort studies of women using pills containing more than 35 micrograms ethinyl-estradiol identified a 40–50% reduction in risk of ovarian epithelial cancer.[32]

In this systematic review, the association between the progestogen-only pill and ovarian cancer was also examined. The reviewers found one case–control study that addressed the use of the progestogen-only pill. The study found no alteration in risk of ovarian cancer with progestogen-only pill use, either overall or in relation to duration of use.[32]

Despite extensive searching, no information was found regarding whether there is less of a protective effect with combined pill use if the ovarian tumour is estrogen receptor negative.

QUESTION

For women with benign ovarian cysts, is DMPA a safe and effective method of contraception?

POPULATION: Women with benign ovarian cysts.
INTERVENTION: DMPA.
OUTCOME: Safety, efficacy.

ANSWER

The CEU identified no evidence to suggest that benign, functional, ovarian cysts represent a contraindication to, or reported undesirable effect of, DMPA. When used as a contraceptive, DMPA consistently inhibits ovulation and would be expected to reduce the risk of functional cysts. The CEU considers that DMPA is an appropriate method of contraception for women with benign, functional, ovarian cysts. This advice is in line with that included in the *WHO Medical Eligibility Criteria for Contraceptive Use* and in the manufacturer's Summary of Product Characteristics.

QUESTION

For women with PCOS, what contraception can be used safely? (Two similar enquiries.)

POPULATION: Women with PCOS.
INTERVENTION: Contraception.
OUTCOME: Safety.

ANSWER

Polycystic ovary syndrome (PCOS) is characterised by hyperandrogenism, chronic anovulation, and insulin resistance which result in hirsutism, irregular menses, and infertility. Type II diabetes and cardiovascular diseases are potential long-term consequences for women with PCOS and oligomenorrhoeic or amenorrhoeic women with PCOS have an increased risk of endometrial hyperplasia and malignancy.[33]

PCOS can be managed with combined oral contraception in order to regulate menstruation, provide contraception, and reduce the risk of endometrial malignancy.[34] Any combined pill can provide these benefits. For women with acne and hirsutism, combined pill use will increase sex hormone binding globulin and subsequently decrease free testosterone and has been shown to improve symptoms. When oral contraceptives are combined with other treatments, such as flutamide, there is thought to be a more beneficial effect on hirsutism. In terms of risk of cardiovascular events, there is no evidence to suggest that women with PCOS using combined oral contraception experience more cardiovascular events than users without PCOS.

DMPA has been shown to suppress pituitary gonadotrophins and circulating androgens. Medroxyprogesterone acetate has also been associated with a decrease in sex hormone binding globulin in women with PCOS. Progestogen-only contraception is an alternative for endometrial protection, but it is associated with a high incidence of breakthrough bleeding. No studies have addressed the long term use of progestogen-only contraception in the treatment of hirsutism.

The CEU recommends that the IUD or barrier methods can also be safely used in women with PCOS.

QUESTION

For women with PCOS who wish to use combined oral contraception, can drospirenone-containing pills be prescribed?

POPULATION: Women with PCOS.

INTERVENTION: Drosperinine-containing combined oral contraception.

OUTCOME: Safety, efficacy.

ANSWER

Drospirenone/ethinylestradiol (Yasmin®) is marketed by Schering Healthcare.

The Scottish Medicines Consortium has provided advice on the prescribing of drospirenone/ethinylestradiol for oral contraception in Scotland.[35] The Consortium concluded that there is no evidence that drospirenone/ethinyl-estradiol has superior effects compared to other standard strength combined pills on acne, premenstrual symptoms or wellbeing. It is substantially more expensive than competitor products and provides little additional benefit for this additional cost. A statistically significant weight difference of 0.3–0.7 kg is seen with drospirenone/ethinylestradiol, compared with a standard strength combined pill but there is no evidence that women who discontinue other pills because of weight gain tolerate drospirenone/ethinylestradiol any better.

Guidance from the RCOG does not cite combined oral contraception as an option to reduce the long term consequences of PCOS.[33] PCOS can be managed with combined oral contraception in order to regulate menstruation, provide contraception and reduce the risk of endometrial malignancy. Any combined pill can provide these benefits. For women with acne and hirsuitism, combined pill use will increase sex hormone-binding globulin and subsequently decrease free testosterone and has been shown to improve symptoms.

A pill which contains cyproterone acetate (an antiandrogen) with ethinyl-estradiol is not licensed in the UK solely as a contraceptive.[36]

Currently, Yasmin is not recommended for routine use by the Scottish Medi-cines Consortium. Women with PCOS may choose any combined pill to provide effective contraception and to provide a regular withdrawal bleed.

QUESTION

For women with porphyria, is hormonal contraception contraindicated because of adverse effects? (Two similar enquiries.)

POPULATION: Women with porphyria.
INTERVENTION: Hormonal contraception.
OUTCOME: Adverse effects.

ANSWER

Two review articles[37,38] provide a useful overview of porphyria. The porphyrias form a group of inherited disorders of haem biosynthesis. There are seven main types, depending on which of the seven enzymes in the pathway for haem synthesis is deficient. In the UK, the most common form is porphyria cutanea tarda, which occurs in around 1/25 000 of the general population. Acute intermittent porphyria is the most common form associated with acute attacks. The pathogenesis of attacks is poorly understood (but may be related to haem deficiency in nerve tissue). Manifestations include acute abdominal pain and tachycardia, along with neurological and psychiatric features. Acute attacks are often precipitated by exogenous factors including a wide range of prescribed and recreational drugs. Estrogens and progestogens are among the drugs reported to precipitate attacks. Around 1% of acute porphyria attacks are fatal. Treatment of attacks must be undertaken in specialist centres with access to the effective, but expensive, treatment haem arginate.

Some forms of porphyria result in hepatic cirrhosis (which may progress to overt hepatic failure) secondary to deposition of haem precursors in the liver.

The *WHO Medical Eligibility Criteria for Contraceptive Use* makes no specific mention of porphyria. However, estrogen-containing contraception would be contraindicated if severe cirrhosis has arisen secondary to porphyria.

Because the porphyrias are rare and heterogeneous, there is, inevitably, a paucity of robust data on the effects of any individual drug or group of drugs. Kauppinen and Mustajoki reviewed 206 Finnish patients (representing all known patients in Finland with acute intermittent porphyria).[39] They reported that nearly a third of female patients had a cyclical pattern of porphyria symptoms associated with the menstrual cycle; however, these symptoms seldom proceeded to an acute attack. Four percent of pregnancies were associated with acute attacks. Forty-six percent of women had used regular sex-hormone preparations but only two (4.5% of users) experienced associated acute attacks. These authors also noted that low-dose combined oral contraception may be beneficial in reducing the rate of acute attacks.

Gross *et al.*[40] studied the influence of combined oral contraception on porphyrin metabolism in healthy volunteers and found little effect. These authors also reported on their experience with three patients suffering repeated premenstrual exacerbations of acute porphyria who were successfully treated with combined oral contraception to stabilise the disease.

A single case report[41] has shown that suppression of the menstrual cycle with GnRH analogue plus tibolone 'add-back' may be effective for cyclical exacerbations of porphyria.

Available evidence therefore confirms that sex steroid hormones (endogenous and exogenous) have an impact on acute symptoms of porphyria. However, natural cyclical fluctuations and pregnancy appear to be associated with more problems than exogenous hormones in the form of low-dose combined oral contraception. There are reports that low-dose combined oral contraception, by stabilising the disease, may be useful in the treatment of some women with cyclical exacerbations. Because the porphyrias are so rare, most clinicians will encounter few patients in a professional lifetime. It would be advisable for all therapeutic decisions to be made in consultation with a local specialist physician managing the woman's overall care.

QUESTION

Can women with erythropoietic protoporphyria use the LNG-IUS safely?

POPULATION: Women with erythropoetic protoporphyria.
INTERVENTION: LNG-IUS.
OUTCOME: Safety.

ANSWER

The European Porphyria Initiative recommends that combined oral contraceptives should not be used in women with acute porphyrias. The progestogen component of the combined pill can provoke acute attacks. However, many women who have inherited one of the acute porphyrias take the combined pill without any adverse effects. The LNG-IUS contains a progestogen that has mainly a local action within the uterus and only enters the bloodstream in very small amounts. The European Porphyria Initiative advises that experience to date suggests that this sort of device carries only a very low, if any, risk of provoking an acute attack.[42]

Despite extensive searching, the CEU could find no evidence-based information on the use of the LNG-IUS in women with erythropoietic protoporphyria. The CEU recommends that women with erythropoietic protoporphyria can use the LNG-IUS, however they should be advised that there is a lack of evidence on this topic.

References

1. Silverman, M. A. Idiopathic Thrombocytopenic Purpura. eMedicine. 2003 [www.emedicine.com/emerg/topic282.htm].
2. Moake, JL. Thrombotic thrombocytopenic purpura today. *Hosp Pract* 1999;15:53–9.
3. Harrison C, Machin S. Idiopathic thrombocytopenic purpura (ITP). 2005 [www.netdoctor.co.uk/diseases/facts/itp.htm].
4. Allford S, Machin S. Thrombotic thrombocytopenic purpura (TTP). 2005 [www.netdoctor.co.uk/diseases/facts/ttp.htm].
5. Fraser JL, Millenson M, Malynn ER, Uhl L, Kruskall MS. Possible association between

the Norplant contraceptive system and thrombotic thrombocytopenic purpura. *Obstet Gynecol* 1996;87:860–3.

6. Khan MA, Rahid MA, Rahman J. Clinical and haematological profile of idiopathic thrombocytopenic purpura. *Journal of the Medical Teachers Federation* 2000;5:16–19.

7. Bevan JA, Maloney KW, Hillery CA, Gill JC, Montgomery RR, Scott JP. Bleeding disorders: A common cause of menorrhagia in adolescents. *J Pediatr* 2001;138:856–61.

8. Oral E, Cagdas A, Gezer A, Kaleli S, Aydin Y, Öçer F. Hematological abnormalities in adolescent menorrhagia. *Arch Gynecol Obstet* 2002;266:72–4.

9. British Society for Haematology. Guidelines for the investigation and management of idiopathic thrombocytopenic purpura in adults, children and pregnancy. *Br J Haemotol* 1996;95:21–6.

10. Sinei SK, Morrison CS, Sekadde–Kigondu C, Allen M, Kokonya D. Complications of use of intrauterine devices among HIV-1-infected women. *Lancet* 1998;351:1238–41.

11. Burns JC, Kushner HI, Bastian JF, Shike H, Shimizu C, Mastsubara T, Turner CL. Kawasaki disease: a brief history. *Pediatrics* 2000;106:27–37.

12. National Digestive Diseases Information Clearinghouse (NDDIC) of the National Institutes of Health. Lactose intolerance [http:digestive.niddk.nih.gov/ddiseases/pubs/lactoseintolerance/index.htm].

13. Garden AS, Davidson DC. Recommendations for the management of galactosaemia. *Arch Dis Child* 2000;82:266.

14. Walter JH, Collins JE, Leonard JV, on behalf of the UK Galactosaemia Steering Group. Recommendations for the management of galactosaemia. *Arch Dis Child* 1999;80:93–6.

15. Gbolade BA. Depo-Provera and bone density. Faculty Aid to CPD Topics (FACT). *J Fam Plann Reprod Health Care* 2002;28:7–11.

16. Scottish Intercollegiate Guidelines Network Secretariat. *Prophylaxis of Venous Thromboembolism*. Guideline No. 62. Edinburgh: SIGN; 2003.

17. Pascual Samamiego M, Gonzalez Fajardo JA, Fernandez de la Gandara F, Calleja Escudero J, Sanz Lucas FJ, Fernandez Del Busto E. [Giant retroperitoneal liposarcoma]. *Actas Urol Esp* 2003;27:640–4. [Spanish]

18. Lopes RI, Lopes RN, Barbosa Filho CM. Giant retroperitoneal liposarcoma. *Int Braz J Urol* 2002;28:227–9.

19. Department of Health. *Obesity. Prodigy Guidance.* London: DH; 2002.

20. Szarewski A, Guillebaud J. *Contraception: A User's Handbook.* London: Churchill Livingstone; 1999.

21. Gupta S, Hannaford P. *Combined Oral contraceptives – Myocardial Infarction, Stroke and Venous Thromboembolism*. London: Faculty of Family Planning and Reproductive Health Care; 1999 [www.ffprhc.org.uk/meetings/fact_coc.pdf].

22. Connor PD, Tavernier LA, Thomas SM, Gates D, Lytton SM. Determining risk between Depo-Provera use and increased uterine bleeding in obese and overweight women. *J Am Board Fam Pract* 2002;15:7–10.

23. Bahamondes L, Del Castillo S, Tabares G, Arce XE, Perrotti M, Petta C. Comparison of weight increase in users of depot medroxyprogesterone acetate and copper IUD up to 5 years. *Contraception* 2001;64:223–5.

24. Bigrigg A, Evans M, Newton J, Pollard L, Szarewski A, Thomas C, *et al.* Depo Provera discussion paper on clinical care, effectiveness and adverse effects. *Br J Fam Plann* 1999;26:52–3.

25. Holt VL, Cushing-Haugen KL, Daling JR. Body weight and risk of oral contraceptive failure. *Obstet Gynecol* 2002;99:820–7.

26. Vessey M, Painter R. Oral contraceptive failures and body weight: findings in a large cohort study. *J Fam Plann Reprod Health Care* 2001;27:90–1.

27. Guillebaud J. Progestogen-only pills (POPs) and body weight. *J Fam Plann Reprod Health Care* 2001;27:239.

28. Kovacs GT, Hendricks J, Summerbell C, Baker WG. A precoital pill? A preliminary in vitro study. *Br J Fam Plann* 2000;26:239.

29. Sivin I. International experience with Norplant and Norplant-2 contraception. *Stud Fam Plann* 1988;19:81–94.

30. Koetsawang S, Ji G, Kristhna Um Cuadros A, Dhall GI, Wyss R, *et al*. World Health Organization Task Force on Long-Acting Systemic Agents for Fertility Regulation. Microdose intravaginal levonorgestrel contraception: a multicentre clinical trial. III. The relationship between pregnancy rate and body weight. *Contraception* 1990;41:143–50.

31. Faculty of Family Planning and Reproductive Health Care Clinical Effectiveness Unit. First prescription of combined oral contraception. *J Fam Plann Reprod Health Care* 2003;29:209–22.

32. International Agency for Research on Cancer. *Hormonal Contraception and Postmenopausal Hormonal Therapy*. Monographs on the evaluation of carcinogenic risks to humans. Lyons: WHO IARC; 1999.

33. Royal College of Obstetricians and Gynaecologists. *Long-Term Consequences of Polycystic Ovary Syndrome*. Guidline No. 33. London: RCOG; 2003.

34. American College of Obstetricians and Gynecologists. ACOG Practice Bulletin Number 41. Polycystic ovary syndrome. *Obstet Gynecol* 2002;100:1389–402.

35. Scottish Medicines Consortium. Dropirenone ethinylestradiol (Yasmin) – Schering Health Care March 2003rg.uk/press/detail.asp?ICI=63].

36. Committee on Safety of Medicines (CSM). Cyproterone acetate (Dianette): Risk of venous thromboembolism (VTE). *Curr Probl Pharmacovigil* 2002;28:9–10.

37. Thadani H, Deacon A, Peters T. Diagnosis and management of porphyria. *BMJ* 2000;320:1647–51.

38. Gross U, Hoffmann GF, Doss MO. Erythropoietic and hepatic porphyrias. *J Inherit Metab Dis* 2000;23:641–61.

39. Kauppinen R, Mustajoki Pj. Prognosis of acute porphyria: occurrence of acute attacks, precipitating factors, and associated diseases. *Medicine* 1992;71:1–13.

40. Gross U, Honcamp M, Daume E, Frank M, Dusterberg B, Doss MO. Hormonal oral contraceptives, urinary porphyrin excretion and porphyrias. *Horm Metab Res* 1995;27: 379–383.

41. Castelo-Branco C, Vicente JJ, Vanrell JA. Use of gonadotropin-releasing hormone analog with tibolone to prevent cyclic attacks of acute intermittent porphyria. *Metabolism* 2001;50:995–6.

42. European Porphyria Initiative. *Guidelines for Common Prescribing Problems. Hormonal Contraception*. 2003 [www/porphyria-eurpoe.com/oz-drugs/commom-prescribing-pb/hormonal-contraception-asp].

QUESTION

For women using combined oral contraception, who show symptoms of Raynaud's phemonenon, should this method be continued and is there a risk of VTE from the underlying disorder? (Two similar enquiries.)

POPULATION:	Women with Raynaud's phenomenon.
INTERVENTION:	Combined oral contraception.
OUTCOME:	Risk of VTE.

ANSWER

Raynaud's phenomenon was first described by Maurice Raynaud in 1862 and is a condition where the small blood vessels in the fingers or toes constrict.[1] Primary Raynaud's has no known cause; women are affected nine times more often than men and sufferers have fingers or toes that are extremely sensitive to cold. A typical attack of Raynaud's involves the fingers first going white and cool as the vessels constrict, then blue as oxygen is used, and red as vessels dilate. Secondary Raynaud's has an underlying cause such as scleroderma, rheumatoid arthritis or SLE.[1] In young women, SLE frequently occurs concurrently with the acquired thrombophilia, antiphospholipid syndrome, typified by raised lupus anticoagulant and anticardiolipin.[2]

Primary Raynaud's is not a contraindication to use of combined oral contraception. However, secondary Raynaud's may be caused by underlying conditions such as SLE which, if lupus anticoagulant is present, causes increased coagulation. In such cases, the *WHO Medical Eligibility Criteria for Contraceptive Use* guidance for DVT or pulmonary embolism and the combined pill would be applicable.

For women with a family history among first-degree relatives of VTE, the benefits of using the combined pill generally outweigh the risks (WHO category 2). The *WHO Medical Eligibility Criteria for Contraceptive Use* states that women with a personal history of, or current, VTE should not use the combined pill (WHO category 4). The risks of using progestogen-only contraceptives such as the progestogen-only pill, implant, DMPA or the LNG-IUS generally outweigh the benefits (WHO category 3) for women with current VTE. The benefits of using these methods generally outweigh the risks for women with a past history of VTE. Women with these conditions may have unrestricted use of the IUD or barrier methods (WHO category 1).

The evidence below relates specifically to women with systemic lupus erythematosis:

- CEU guidance on first prescription of combined oral contraception advises that for women with a family history of VTE in a first-degree relative under the age of 45 years, who having considered other methods still wish to use a combined pill, a thrombophilia screen should be performed.[3] Antiphospholipid syndrome is uncommon but thrombophila screening in such a case is warranted.[4] The interpretation of a thrombophilia screen should be undertaken in consultation with a haematologist or other expert, and along with a detailed family history.

- Rampone *et al.* performed a study to evaluate the effect of combined oral contraception in women suffering from SLE.[5] Twenty women of childbearing age with SLE were asked to take combined pills containing 20 micrograms ethinylestradiol and were followed up for 1 year. A control group of women with SLE who were not using any medication was also observed. Only five of the 20 patients taking combined pills experienced flare-ups and had to discontinue the pill; a similar number in the control group experienced flare-ups. The authors concluded that modern low-dose combined pills do not produce immediate exacerbation of SLE and can be used under supervision.

- Lakasing and Khamashta performed an observational, questionnaire-based study to determine the past and present contraceptive practices of 86 women with SLE and/or antiphospholipid syndrome.[2] Among women with SLE alone, one of nine using the combined pill at the time of diagnosis reported a severe flare-up. In women with primary or secondary antiphospholipid syndrome, seven of 32 using the combined pill suffered thromboses during use. The women with SLE and/or antiphospholipid syndrome using other contraceptive methods did not report any specific problems. The authors concluded that most contraceptive methods are relatively safe for women with SLE alone but that women with antiphospholipid syndrome should be advised strongly against using combined oral contraception.

QUESTION

For women with Raynaud's phenomenon who take nifedipine, does use of hormonal contraception carry an increased risk of adverse effects? (Two similar enquiries.)

POPULATION: Women with Raynaud's phenomenon taking nifedipine.
INTERVENTION: Combined oral contraception.
OUTCOME: Adverse effects.

ANSWER

The published literature indicates that the exact relationship, if any, between estrogens and progestogens and Raynaud's is unclear. In addition, the studies performed have been short-term and may not identify long-term hormonal effects. One hypothesis is that estrogen may sensitise the peripheral vascular bed to catecholamines, adrenaline and noradrenaline.

Anecdotal evidence suggests that symptoms may worsen if women with Raynaud's use combined oral contraceptive pills. However, short-term studies have shown no effect on, or a marginal increase in, fingertip temperature following administration of estrogen and progestogen. Studies in animal models suggest that progesterone has little effect or may even counter the sensitisation mechanism mentioned above.

The CEU advises that a clinician needs to weigh the contraceptive benefit of an estrogen-containing method against the risk of recurrence of Raynaud's. Primary Raynaud's is not, in itself, a contraindication to combined pill use. If a woman has a secondary Raynaud's due to underlying causes such as SLE with tendency to coagulation, a clinician would have to consider the WHO classifications for use of the combined pill in relation to VTE.

Nifedipine is a dihydropyridine calcium-channel blocker that relaxes vascular smooth muscle and dilates coronary and peripheral arteries. There is no mention of drug interaction between nifedipine and the combined pill. However, there is a cautionary note in BNF that advises that grapefruit juice significantly increases the plasma concentration of dihydropyridine calcium-channel blockers. This is of interest because one study has also suggested that grapefruit juice, which contains nariginen, may increase the bioavailability of ethinylestradiol due to reduction in metabolism.[6]

QUESTION

For women with rheumatoid arthritis, does the use of the LNG-IUS have any impact on symptoms and disease progression?

POPULATION:	Women with rheumatoid arthritis.
INTERVENTION:	LNG-IUS.
OUTCOME:	Effects on rheumatoid arthritis.

ANSWER

One review article provides a useful overview of rheumatoid arthritis.[7] It is a chronic, inflammatory arthritis affecting less than 1% of the population, and affecting women twice as often as men. Typically, rheumatoid arthritis produces a symmetrical polyarthritis, affecting both large and small joints. Diagnosis is based on clinical features, often supported by laboratory findings such as a positive test for rheumatoid factor. It is now recognised that irreversible joint damage can occur early in the history of the disease. Current strategies therefore involve prompt treatment with a range of drugs in order to achieve disease control and minimise joint damage.

It is acknowledged that contraceptive steroids have an impact on the occurrence and progression of rheumatoid arthritis. A review on oral contraception[8] includes a section on non-contraceptive benefits of combined pill use. The authors summarise a meta-analysis of nine studies on the protective effects of combined oral contraception relating to rheumatoid arthritis.[9] These studies suggest that combined oral contraception may decrease the risk of rheumatoid arthritis by around 30% overall, and may prevent progression to more severe disease. The protective role of combined oral contraception has been reiterated in more recent reviews.[10,11]

We were unable to identify any publications which specifically address the impact of the LNG-IUS on rheumatoid arthritis. However, a comprehensive systematic review has examined the safety of implantable contraceptives, including the levonorgestrel implants, Norplant and Jadelle.[12] Data on connective tissue disorders were examined because concerns had been raised about a possible effect of the silicone component of contraceptive implants, rather than the active hormone. Interestingly, Norplant users appeared to have an increased risk of rheumatoid arthritis, although this increase failed to reach statistical significance.

There is, therefore, no robust evidence that levonorgestrel contraception adversely affects the progress of rheumatoid arthritis. However, there is some evidence that estrogen-containing contraceptives may be beneficial. Patients and clinicians may wish to consider this information in making contraceptive choices.

QUESTION

For a woman who has rheumatoid arthritis, taking Arcoxia® (MSD) and methotrexate, is Cerazette or Implanon more suitable than DMPA?

POPULATION: Women with rheumatoid arthritis taking Arcoxia and methotrexate.

INTERVENTION: Methods of progestogen-only contraception.

OUTCOME: Effects on rheumatoid arthritis.

ANSWER

Rheumatoid arthritis is the second most common type of arthritis affecting more than 350 000 people in Britain. As the disease progresses, the ligaments supporting the joints are damaged and there is erosion of bone, leading to deformity.[13] It differs from osteoarthritis in that it is caused by inflammation of the lining of joints, whereas osteoarthritis is a 'wear and tear' process. Some evidence suggests that those with rheumatoid arthritis are at increased risk of developing osteoporosis.[14,15]

Treatment of rheumatoid arthritis is with a variety of drugs including anti-inflammatory analgesics, disease modifying anti-rheumatic drugs (DMARDs) and NSAIDs.[16] In this particular member's enquiry, the patient is receiving methotrexate (a DMARD) and Arcoxia (etoricoxib, a NSAID).

The CEU found no evidence to suggest that there is interaction between drugs for rheumatoid arthritis and oral contraceptives; but did find some limited evidence that combined oral contraception has a protective effect in the disease's development.[9,17] There was no evidence to suggest that any one progestogen-only method is better or worse than any other in its effect on rheumatoid arthritis. No evidence of any association between DMPA and rheumatoid arthritis was identified.

QUESTION

For women who develop Schamberg's disease while using combined oral contraception, what contraceptive methods can be used safely?

POPULATION: Women with Schamberg's disease.

INTERVENTION: Contraception.

OUTCOME: Safety.

ANSWER

People with Schamberg's disease have 'leaky' blood vessel walls, which allow red blood cells to pass through into the skin. The red cells in the skin disintegrate and release their iron, which has a rust colour. The lesions consist of irregular patches of orange or brown pigmentation and usually occur on the legs.[18] Sometimes slight pruritus may occur. Sometimes the eruption may last for many years. Usually there are no symptoms, although some people experience slight itching. Schamberg's disease constitutes a nonpalpable purpura, is more common in males and may occur at any age from childhood onward. It can be secondary to a drug reaction. There is no cure but itching can be controlled with cortisone cream.

The Summaries of Product Characteristics for a combined oral contraceptive (Yasmin), the etonogestrel implant (Implanon) and the LNG-IUS state that pruritus is an uncommon (less than 1/100) reaction in users of these methods. The Summaries of Product Characteristics for various other combined oral contraceptives and progestogen-only pills advise that they are contraindicated in women who have had severe pruritus during pregnancy.

Despite extensive searching, the CEU could find no specific information in the literature on the use of contraceptive methods in women with Schamberg's disease. If a woman developed Shamberg's disease while using combined oral contraception, she could be advised to try a non-hormonal method of contraception, such as the IUD.

QUESTION

For women with Scheuermann kyphosis, are there any contraceptives which are not recommended?

POPULATION: Women with Scheurmann kyphosis.

INTERVENTION: Contraception.

OUTCOME: Safety.

ANSWER

In 1920, Scheuermann first described the structural findings of thoracic kyphosis but it was not until 1964 that the radiographic findings in Scheuermann kyphosis were defined by Sorensen.[19] Scheuermann thoracic kyphosis is a structural deformity of the thoracic spine and is defined by anterior wedging of at least five degrees of three or more adjacent vertebral bodies. The prevalence of Scheuermann kyphosis is estimated to be about 4–8% of the general population.

The aetiology of the kyphosis remains unknown and adolescents usually develop a progressive cosmetic deformity. Scheuermann kyphosis may be entirely asymptomatic but patients who present for medical attention generally have pain, progressive deformity, neurologic compromise, cardiopulmonary complaints or cosmetic issues. Neurologic problems are rare with Scheurmann's kyphosis but stenosis of the lumbar spine below the kyphosis may lead to neurologic claudication in adults. Neurological compromise increases following spinal revision surgery and is the complication that affects quality of life for patients the most. Cardiopulmonary complications are also rare with Scheurmann's kyphosis. Murray *et al.* have reported restrictive lung disease in patients with kyphosis of more than 100 degrees.[20]

The *WHO Medical Eligibility Criteria for Contraceptive Use* advises that women between the ages of 18 and 45 years may have unrestricted use (WHO category 1) of DMPA. There are theoretical concerns about the hypoestrogenic effect of DMPA in women over the age of 45 years. For women over the age of 45 years, WHO advises that the benefits of using this method generally outweigh the risks (WHO category 2). If a woman with Scheuermann kyphosis has associated osteoporosis, DMPA may not be advisable.

A FFPRHC review[21] on DMPA and bone density mentions that studies have shown that after even up to 5 years of use, most women have serum estradiol levels above those seen in postmenopausal women. Additionally, serum estradiol levels are found to be in the early follicular phase range. Therefore DMPA users are not usually estrogen-deficient.

The CEU advises that women with Scheurmann kyphosis who have low bone density should consider methods other than DMPA. This is because of the small risk of reduction in bone density for some women associated with use.

QUESTION

Do women with sickle cell disease and abnormal liver function tests who use DMPA, have an increased risk of adverse effects?

POPULATION: Women with sickle cell disease and abnormal liver function tests.
INTERVENTION: DMPA.
OUTCOME: Adverse effects.

ANSWER

Sickle cell anaemia is an autosomal recessive genetic disorder caused by a defect in the gene which codes for haemoglobin.[22] To have sickle cell anaemia, individuals must have inherited two copies of the defective gene. Individuals who have only one copy of the sickle haemoglobin gene are carriers of the sickle cell trait. The disease is characterised by chronic anaemia and episodes of pain. The sickle-shaped red blood cells, unlike normal round red blood cells, cannot pass through small blood vessels and organs and tissues do not get enough oxygen-carrying blood. Although millions of people are affected worldwide, the disease is particularly prevalent in people with ancestors from sub-Saharan Africa, Spanish-speaking regions, Saudi Arabia, India and Mediterranean countries.

The *WHO Medical Eligibility Criteria for Contraceptive Use* classifies the use of DMPA as WHO category 1 (unrestricted use) for women with sickle cell disease. WHO has further stated that DMPA may have a beneficial effect on sickle cell crises.

WHO has also advised that progestogen-only contraceptives are metabolised by the liver and that use may adversely affect women whose liver function is compromised. WHO has given a category 2 classification for the use of DMPA by women with mild (compensated) cirrhosis (benefits generally outweigh risks). There is a category 3 classification for the use of DMPA by women with severe (decompensated) cirrhosis (risks generally outweigh benefits).

A randomised controlled trial was performed by de Abood *et al.* in 1997 to study the effect of DMPA or Microgynon on the painful crises of sickle cell anaemia.[23] Although no changes were observed in haematological parameters after one year, 70% of women who received DMPA reported no pain and 16% reported a reduction in pain. Women who received Microgynon also reported a reduction in pain but at a slower rate than the depot users; 45.5% still had sickle cell crises. About 50% of controls reported an improvement in pain and the authors postulated that this may be due to better general management.

Kaunitz has written a review of the role of DMPA as a contraceptive.[24] This mentions a study which showed that after long-term depot use, menstrual blood loss decreases and haemoglobin levels increase in patients who become amenorrhoeic.[25] Another study cited showed that depot users with sickle cell anaemia had increased haemoglobin and erythrocyte life expectancy and less painful crises.[26] Kaunitz further mentions a study which showed that depot use has not been associated with clinically significant changes in hepatic function.[27] One Danish study monitored the liver function of DMPA users who also used intravenous drugs and had a high prevalence of viral hepatitis and did not reveal any hepatotoxicity.[28]

In summary, DMPA has been shown to be beneficial to individuals with sickle cell disease in terms of decreasing the number of painful crises and improving haemoglobin and erythrocyte viability. WHO advises that women with sickle cell disease may have unrestricted use of the method. In terms of liver function, it appears that restricted use of DMPA only applies to individuals with active viral hepatitis, severe (decompensated) cirrhosis or benign or malignant liver tumours.

A woman who has abnormal liver function tests must be monitored to observe any changes that may be caused by metabolism of the progestogen-only contraceptive. The CEU advises that a patient with sickle cell disease would benefit from DMPA. However, such a woman would have to be closely monitored after starting the method.

QUESTION

For women with splenectomy, should antibiotic prophylaxis be provided for IUD insertion to prevent infection?

POPULATION: Women with splenectomy undergoing IUD insertion.
INTERVENTION: Antibiotic prophylaxis.
OUTCOME: Risk of infection.

ANSWER

Fulminant infection in post-splenectomy patients is a lifelong risk. A working group for the British Committee for Standards in Haematology has produced recommendations for clinical practice.[29] Lifelong prophylactic antibiotics should be offered in all cases, especially in the first 2 years following splenectomy, for children up to the age of 16 years, or if there is underlying immunosuppression. In addition, patients should be offered amoxycillin to keep at home for use if they develop symptoms of fever, malaise and shivering. Antibiotic prophylaxis may not prevent sepsis. No recommendations were provided regarding dental procedures or IUD insertion.

The CEU, in its guidance on the IUD as long-term contraception,[30] recommended that women with previous endocarditis or with a prosthetic heart valve require intravenous antibiotic prophylaxis to protect against bacterial endocarditis during IUD insertion or removal. However, no information was identified regarding antibiotic prophylaxis to prevent fulminant sepsis for patients post-splenectomy.

As the risk of serious sepsis in post-splenectomy patients is lifelong, the CEU recommends that for IUD or LNG-IUS insertion or removal, antibiotic prophylaxis is given as for women at risk of bacterial endocarditis (intravenous amoxicillin 1 g plus gentamicin 120 mg, followed by oral amoxicillin 500 mg 6 hours later). However, obtaining the advice of a local haematologist and microbioloist may be appropriate.

QUESTION

For women with Takayasu's arteritis is the progestogen-only pill a safe option?

POPULATION: Women with Takayasu's arteritis.

INTERVENTION: Progestogen-only pill.

OUTCOME: Safety.

ANSWER

Takayasu's arteritis is a chronic systemic inflammatory disease that affects the aorta, its primary branches and sometimes the pulmonary and coronary arteries.[31] The incidence of the disease is estimated to be 2.6 cases per million persons per year in the Western world; being a female of reproductive age and Asian origin are factors associated with higher prevalence. There is typically limb or organ ischaemia, illness and fever although occasionally exertional dyspnea may be the initial manifestation.

It is important that women with Takayasu's arteritis recognise the effects of anti-inflammatory and immunosuppressive drugs on pregnancy and fertility.[32] Prednisone and other glucocorticoids are generally considered safe for a developing fetus. Methotrexate is a folic acid antagonist; women taking methotrexate who wish to become pregnant should discontinue treatment under medical supervision at least 3 months before stopping contraception and continue the use of folic acid.[33] Cyclophosphamide is contraindicated in pregnancy as it causes severe birth defects. It also commonly causes ovarian failure, permanent sterility, and premature menopause.[32]

The BNF states that oral contraceptives increase plasma concentrations of corticosteroids but do not appear to interact with methotrexate.

The *WHO Medical Eligibility Criteria for Contraceptive Use* does not refer specifically to contraceptive choices for women with Takayasu's arteritis. However, for women with other vascular diseases, the benefits of using the progestogen-only pill generally outweigh the risks (WHO category 2).

The newer desogestrel-only pill (Cerazette) should be considered as similar to any other progestogen-only pill and would be an option for women with Takayasu's arteritis.

QUESTION

For women with a recent hydatidform mole (trophoblastic disease), which methods of contraception can be safely used? (Five similar enquiries.)

POPULATION: Women with recent trophoblastic disease.
INTERVENTION: Contraception.
OUTCOME: Safety.

ANSWER

Gestational trophoblastic disease encompasses several diseases that originate in the placenta.[34] These include hydatidform mole, invasive mole and chorio-carcinoma. The incidence, which may be under estimated, is 1.54/1000 live births.[35] Of women with a hydatidform mole, 20% develop a trophoblastic malignancy. With a complete mole, uterine invasion occurs in 15% of women and metastasis occurs in 4%. No cases of choriocarcinoma have been reported after a partial mole, although 4% of women with a partial mole develop persistant non-metastatic trophoblastic disease requiring chemotherapy. Almost all women with malignant gestational trophoblastic disease can be cured with preservation of reproductive function.

The CEU was unable to find any evidence in the literature on the safety of progestogen-only emergency contraception if used by women with gestational trophoblastic disease. However, guidelines on the management of the condition advise that combined oral contraceptives can be used when serum levels of hCG are normal.[36]

A guideline from the RCOG on the management of gestational trophoblastic disease recommends that, although the risk of future molar pregnancy is low, women should be advised not to conceive until they have had 6 months of normal hCG levels.[36] The guideline also advises that combined pills can be used safely after hCG levels have returned to normal but, if combined oral contraception is taken while hCG levels are raised, it may increase the need for treatment.

The *WHO Medical Eligibility Criteria for Contraceptive Use* classifies the use of combined pills, progestogen-only pills, DMPA and the implant (specifically Norplant) by women with either benign or malignant gestational trophoblastic disease as WHO category 1 (unrestricted use). WHO classifies the insertion of either a copper IUD or the LNG-IUS as WHO category 3 for women with benign gestational trophoblastic disease (risks generally outweigh benefits). WHO advises that women with malignant gestational trophoblastic disease should not have either an IUD or the LNG-IUS inserted because there is an increased risk of perforation as treatment for the condition may require multiple uterine curettages.

Lan *et al.* studied the pregnancy outcomes of 22 women who conceived within 1 year after chemotherapy for gestational trophoblastic tumour.[37] The average interval between completion of chemotherapy and pregnancy was 10 months in the group who carried their pregnancies to term and 6 months in the group with fetal loss due to repeat hydatidform mole, intrauterine death or miscarriage ($P < 0.05$). Results suggest that the longer the interval between completion of chemotherapy and conception, the lower the risk of gestational trophoblastic disease. Contraception is advised for at least 1 year after chemotherapy for gestational trophoblastic tumour.

Canadian guidelines on gestational trophoblastic disease were developed in 2002.[38] These recommend that women should be advised to avoid pregnancy until hCG levels have been normal for 6 months following the evacuation of a molar pregnancy or for 1 year following chemotherapy for gestational trophoblastic tumour. They also conclude that combined oral contraception is safe for use by women with gestational trophoblastic tumour but do not specifically recommend waiting for hCG levels to normalise. In the Canadian guideline, the use of chemotherapy is recommended even for low-risk women with non-metastatic or metastatic disease.

QUESTION

For a woman with previous gestational trophoblastic disease followed by two normal pregnancies, can hormonal contraception be safely used?

POPULATION: Women with previous trophoblastic disease and subsequent normal pregnancies.

INTERVENTION: Hormonal contraception.

OUTCOME: Safety.

ANSWER

Gestational trophoblastic disease is a rare condition with an incidence of 1.54/1000 live births in the UK. The *WHO Medical Eligibility Criteria for Contraceptive Use* advises that women with either benign or malignant gestational trophoblastic disease may have unrestricted use of combined oral contraceptives, the progestogen-only pill, DMPA and the implant (specifically Norplant) (WHO category 1). The risks of either the copper IUD or the LNG-IUS generally outweigh the benefits for women with benign gestational trophoblastic disease (WHO category 3) and neither method should be used by women with malignant gestational trophoblastic disease (WHO category 4). However, for women who have had further normal pregnancies following hydatidiform mole, there appears to be no contraindication to the use of the LNG-IUS, nor to any other contraceptive method.

Guidelines from the RCOG[36] advise that combined pills can be used by women with gestational trophoblastic disease when serum hCG levels are normal. Guidelines from the RCOG and from Canada[36] both recommend that women with gestational trophoblastic disease should avoid pregnancy until serum hCG levels have been normal for 6 months. The Canadian guidelines suggest pregnancy should be avoided for 1 year following chemotherapy for gestational trophoblastic tumour and conclude that the combined pill may be safely used by these women without waiting for hCG levels to normalise.

QUESTION

For women being treated for tuberculosis, can progestogen-only contraception be used safely?

POPULATION: Women being treated for tuberculosis.

INTERVENTION: Progestogen-only contraception.

OUTCOME: Safety.

ANSWER

BNF guidance on antituberculous drug regimens recommends that tuberculosis is treated in two phases, an initial phase using at least three drugs and a continuation phase using two drugs. During the initial phase, at least three drugs are used concurrently to reduce the bacterial population as rapidly as possible and to prevent the emergence of drug-resistance. Daily use of isoniazid, rifampicin, pyrazinamide and ethambutol is recommended. During the continuation phase, treatment is continued for a further 4 months with isoniazid and rifampicin.

Rifampicin induces liver microsomes and thus increases the metabolism of synthetic estrogen and progestogen. The concurrent use of rifampicin severely compromises the efficacy of all hormonal oral contraception.[39]

Guidance from the FFPRHC on the use of rifampicin and contraceptive steroids states that women who have to use rifampicin over a long period and use oral contraception (combined or progestogen-only pills) should be advised to choose another contraceptive method. Evidence is lacking regarding any interaction between rifampicin and contraceptive implants or injections.

Guidance from the FFPRHC on first prescription of combined oral contraception supported the use of combined oral contraception for women with liver enzyme-inducers but at least 50 micrograms of ethinylestradiol is required and barrier contraception is advised in addition.[40]

The *WHO Medical Eligibility Criteria for Contraceptive Use* has classified the use of the progestogen-only pill and the implant as category 3 for women using liver enzyme-inducing antibiotics such as rifampicin. The use of DMPA is given a category 2 classification for women using liver enzyme-inducers; and the LNG-IUS is given a category 1 classification.

The Summaries of Product Characteristics for Rifadin® (Aventis Pharma) (capsules and infusion), Rifater 150® and Rifater 300® (Aventis Pharma) and Rifinah® (Aventis Pharma) recommend that women using oral contraceptives should be advised to use alternative, non-hormonal methods of birth control during therapy. No evidence of interactions with hormonal contraceptives was reported for isoniazid, pyrazinamide or ethambutol.

The efficacy of the LNG-IUS appears to be unaffected by use of liver enzyme-inducing drugs, because the progestogen is released directly into the uterus. The Summary of Product Characteristics for DMPA does not suggest shortening of the usual 12-week injection interval even for women using liver enzyme-inducing drugs.

In summary, the CEU advises that for women using the potent liver enzyme-inducer, rifampicin, progestogen-only pills should not be used but women can use DMPA or the LNG-IUS. Data regarding progestogen-only implants are lacking and if women use an implant, additional contraceptive protection is advised for the duration of treatment and until 4 weeks after the cessation of rifampicin.

QUESTION

For women with ulcerative colitis who take steroids, will the efficacy of the combined oral contraceptive pill be affected?

POPULATION: Women with ulcerative colitis taking steroids.
INTERVENTION: Combined oral contraception.
OUTCOME: Contraceptive efficacy.

ANSWER

Ulcerative colitis is an inflammatory bowel disease characterised by inflammation and ulcers in the top layers of the gut lining, usually of the rectum and lower part of the colon. It rarely affects the small intestine, apart from the ileum. Ulcerative colitis usually occurs in the 15- to 40-year-old age group and affects men and women in equal numbers. The aetiology is unknown. The most common symptoms include abdominal pain and bloody diarrhoea; other symptoms such as weight loss and fatigue may also occur. Patients with mild disease are usually first treated with sulfonamides, sulfapyridine and salicylates and if they do not respond, may be treated with corticosteroids such as prednisone and hydrocortisone. About 25–40% of patients with ulcerative colitis undergo colectomy when the disease becomes severe.[41]

A Faculty Aid to CPD Topic written in 2000 covered interactions with hormonal contraception.[40] This states that oral contraceptives are absorbed from the upper small intestine, either unaltered or conjugated to sulphates and some glucuronides. Within about 2 hours of ingestion, peak plasma levels of hormones will be observed in most women. Hormones are then transported in a free state, or bound to albumin, to the liver. In the liver, microenzymes act on ethinylestradiol and progestogens thus reducing the amount of active hormone that reaches the bile and ethinylestradiol is conjugated to glucuronides and some sulphates. The conjugated, metabolised, and unaltered ethinylestradiol is excreted into the bile; then in the colon, bacteria hydrolyse the compounds, which can then be reabsorbed into the circulation (enterohepatic circulation). The FACT notes that some women may experience a second peak plasma level but this is variable and probably contributes little to overall levels.

It is noted that the plasma half-life elimination of ethinylestradiol, usually about 5–8 hours, varies among women and depends on the enterohepatic circulation. However, ileostomy patients, with no enterohepatic circulation, do not have a significantly different half-life.[43]

FFPRHC guidance on contraceptive choices for women with inflammatory bowel disease[44] indicates that women with inflammatory bowel disease should have the same contraceptive choices as other women but individual associated medical problems should be taken into account. Currently, based on the limited information found, the CEU advises that the efficacy of the combined pill is unlikely to be affected in women with ulcerative colitis.

Bioavailable corticosteriod may be increased with combined pill use but BNF states that this is unlikely to be clinically important.

QUESTION

For women with von Willebrand's disease, can the LNG-IUS be used safely? (Two similar enquiries.)

POPULATION: Women with von Willebrand's disease.
INTERVENTION: LNG-IUS.
OUTCOME: Safety.

ANSWER

Von Willebrand's disease is a common inherited (autosomal dominant) bleeding disorder. It is a genetically and clinically heterogeneous haemorrhagic disorder due to a deficiency of von Willebrands factor (vWf). This factor mediates platelet adhesion and deficiency can lead to mucocutaneous bleeding due to defective interaction between platelets and the vessel wall. There are three major categories of von Willebrands disease, type I, II and III, which correspond to different molecular variants. Type I produces a mild to moderate deficiency in vWf and, in type III disease, very little vWf is present, resulting in a profound bleeding disorder. Screening studies suggest that approximately 1% of the population may have abnormalities of vWf. Most affected individuals have a manageable bleeding disorder, in which severe haemorrhage only occurs as a result of trauma or invasive procedures. The most common presentation is with nosebleeds, skin bruises and haematomas. Prolonged bleeding from trivial wounds, following dental extraction or menorrhagia are common.[45]

Patients can be treated with desmopressin, a synthetic analogue of the antidiuretic hormone, vasopressin. Infusion of desmopressin results in a rapid increase in vWf. Intranasal desmopressin can be useful in the management of menorrhagia and recurrent nose bleeds and may be indicated prior to major surgery or in the treatment of serious haemorrhage.[45]

A review article on obstetrical and gynecological aspects of von Willebrand's disease summarised the current literature on issues for women with this condition. Studies of women with von Willebrand's disease objectively measured menorrhagia and suggest a prevalence of 7–20%. Oral contraceptives, antifibrinolytics and desmopressin have all been used in the management of menorrhagia in women with von Willebrand's disease.[46]

Despite extensive searching, the CEU could find no specific evidence in the literature on the use of the LNG-IUS in women with von Willebrand's disease.

The Summary of Product Characteristics for the LNG-IUS, Mirena, states that insertion and removal of the device may be associated with some pain and bleeding. Occasionally this may be due to perforation of the uterine corpus or cervix. The risk of heavy or continuous bleeding may be increased in women with von Willebrand's disease.

The FFPRHC has published guidance on the LNG-IUS in contraception and reproductive health.[47] This guidance identified evidence that the LNG-IUS can be used as a first-line option to treat menorrhagia. The LNG-IUS is more effective than oral treatments in the management of menorrhagia,[48–51] and also as effective as conservative surgery (resection and ablation) after the first year of use.[52]

The CEU considers that the LNG-IUS is potentially useful for both contraception and the treatment of menorrhagia in women with von Willebrand's disease. We would, however, recommend close liaison with haematology colleagues, particularly to advise on haemostatic cover during insertion and removal.

QUESTION

For women with von Willebrand's disease undergoing insertion of the progestogen-only contraceptive implant, is there a serious risk of haematoma formation?

POPULATION: Women with von Willebrand's disease.

INTERVENTION: Insertion of progestogen-only implant.

OUTCOME: Risk of haematoma.

ANSWER

Von Willebrands disease is a common inherited disorder due to a deficiency of vWf. This factor mediates platelet adhesion and deficiency can lead to muco-cutaneous bleeding. The clinical presentation varies, with the majority of patients having mild disease. Women can specifically present with menorrhagia or postpartum haemorrhage, but the most common presenting symptoms include nose bleeds, bleeding following dental extraction, and prolonged bleeding following trivial injury.

Following an extensive literature search, we were unable to identify any evidence on the incidence of haematoma formation following insertion or removal of progestogen-only implants in women with von Willebrand's disease. A haematology opinion is advised prior to surgical or dental treatment and perhaps also before considering the implant.

References

1. Department of Health. *Prodigy Guidance. Cold Hands and Raynaud's Phenomenon*. PILS Leaflet L141. London: DH; 2001.
2. Lakasing L, Khamashta M. Contraceptive practices in women with systemic lupus erythematosus and/or antiphospholipid syndrome: What advice should we be giving? *J Fam Plann Reprod Health Care* 2001;27:7–12.
3. Faculty of Family Planning and Reproductive Health Care. First prescription of combined oral contraception. *J Fam Plann Reprod Health Care* 2003;29:209–23.
4. British Society for Haematology. Guidelines on the investigation and management of the antiphospholipid syndrome. *Br J Haematol* 2000;109:704–15.
5. Rampone A, Rampone B, Tirabasso S, Panariello S, Rampone N, Vozza A, *et al.* Contraception with the latest estroprogestogens in women suffering from systemic lupus erythematosus. *Minerva Ginecol* 2001;53:75–7.
6. Weber A, Jager R, Borner G, Klinger G, Vollanth R, Malthey K, *et al.* Can grapefruit juice influence ethinyloestradiol bioavailbility? *Contraception* 1996;53:41–7.
7. Pisetsky DS, St CEW. Progress in the treatment of rheumatoid arthritis. *JAMA* 2001;286:2787–90.
8. Burkman RT, Collins JA, Shulman LP, Williams JK. Current perspectives on oral contraceptive use. *Am J Obstet Gynecol* 2001;185:4–12.
9. Spector TD, Hochberg MC. The protective effect of the oral contraceptive pill on rheumatoid arthritis: an overview of the analytic epidemiological studies using meta-analysis. *J Clin Epidemiol* 1990;43:1221–30.
10. Olsen NJ, Kovacs WJ. Hormones, pregnancy, and rheumatoid arthritis. *J Gend Specif Med* 2002;5:28–37.
11. Symmons DP. Epidemiology of rheumatoid arthritis: determinants of onset, persistence and outcome. *Best Pract Res Clin Rheumatol* 2002;16:707–22.
12. Curtis KM. Safety of implantable contraceptives for women: data from observational studies. *Contraception* 2002;65:85–96.
13. Arthritis Research Campaign ARC. *Rheumatoid Arthritis*. Arthritis Research Campaign

ARC; 2003 [www/arc.org.uk/about_arth/booklets/6033.htm].

14. Parker N, Soy D, Kesiktas N, Erbil M. Osteoporosis in patients with long standing rheumatoid arthritis. *Ftr Turkiye Fiziksel Tip Ve Rehabilitasyon Dergisi* 2004;50:29–33.

15. Van Offel JF. Rheumatic diseases and their repercussions on the skeleton. *Tijdschr Geneeskd* 2004;60:1116–25.

16. Oxford Concise Medical Dictionary. Oxford: Oxford University Press.

17. Dawe F, Meltzer H. *Contraception and Sexual Health*. London, Office for National Statistics; 2002.

18. The Skin Site. Schamberg's Disease. 2003 [www.skinsite.com/info=schambergs-disease.htm].

19. Tribus C. Scheuermann Kyphosis [www.emedicine.com/orthoped/topic555.htm].

20. Murray PM, Weinstein SL, Spratt KF. The natural history and long-term follow-up of Scheuermann kyphosis. *J Bone Joint Surg Am* 1993;75:236–48.

21. Gbolade BA. Depo-Provera and bone density. Faculty Aid to CPD Topics (FACT). *J Fam Plann Reprod Health Care* 2002;28:7–11.

22. National Institute of Health. MedlinePlus. *Genetic Disease Profile: Sickle Cell Anaemia* [www.nlm.nih.gov/medlineplus/sicklecellanemia.html].

23. de Abood M, de Castillo Z, Guerrero F, Espino M, Austin KL. Effect of Depo-Provera or Microgynon on the painful crises of sickle cell anemia in patients. *Contraception* 1997;56:313–16.

24. Kauntiz AM. The role of hormonal contraceptives: Long-Acting injectable contraception with depot medroxyprogesterone acetate. *Am J Obstet Gynecol* 1994;170:1543–9.

25. Schwallie PC, Assenzo JR. Contraceptive use efficacy study utilizing medroxyprogesterone acetate administered as an intramuscular injectiononce every 90 days. *Fertil Steril* 1973;24:331–9.

26. Ceulaer K, Gruber C, Hayes R, Serjeant GR. Medroxyprogesterone acetate and homozygous sickle-cell disease. *Lancet* 1982;2:229–31.

27. Virutamasen P, Wongsrichanalai C, Tangkeo P. Metabolic effects of depot-medroxyprogesterone acetate in long-term users: a cross-sectional study. *Int J Obstet Gynaecol* 1986;24:291–6.

28. Sotaniemi EA, Hynnynen T, Ahlqvist Jea. Effects of medroxyprogesterone on the liver function and drug metabolism of patients with primary biliary cirrhosis and chronic active hepatitis. *J Med* 1978;9:117–28.

29. Working Party of the British Committee for Standards in Heamatology Clinical Haematology Task Force. Guidelines for the prevention and treatment of infection in patients with an absent or dysfunctional spleen. *BMJ* 1996;312:430–4.

30. Faculty of Family Planning and Reproductive Health Care Guidance. The copper intrauterine device as long-term contraception. *J Fam Plann Reprod Health Care* 2004;30:29–42.

31. Neidhart B, Kosek R, Bachmann LM, Stey C. Exertional dyspnea as initial manifestation of Takayasu's arteritis: a case report and literture review. *BMC Pulm Med* 2001;1:3.

32. Merkel PA. Fertility, contraception and pregnancy in patients with Takayasu's arteritis [www.takayasus.com/merkel.html].

33. Janssen NM, Genta MS. The effects of immunosuppressive and anti-inflammatory medications on fertility, pregnancy, and lactation. *Arch Intern Med* 2000;160:610–9.

34. Moore LE, Ware D. Hydatidform mole [www.emedicine.com/med/topic1047.htm].

35. Bagshawe KD, Dent J, Webb J. Hydatidform mole in England and Wales 1973–1983. *Lancet* 1986;2:673–7.

36. Royal College of Obsetricians and Gyanecologists. *The Management of Gestational Trophoblastic Disease*. Guideline No. 18. London: RCOG; 2000.

37. Lan Z, Hongzhao S, Xiuyu Y, Yang X. Pregnancy outcomes of patients who conceived within 1 year of chemotherapy for gestational trophoblastic tumour: a clinical report of 22 patients *Gynecol Oncol* 2001;83:146–8.

38. Gerulath AH, Ehlen TG, Bessette P, Jolicoeur L, Savoie R, Society of Obstetricians and Gynaecologists of Canada.Gynaecologic Oncologists of Canada. Society of Canadian Colposcopists. Gestational trophoblstic disease. *J Obstet Gynaecol Can* 2002;24:434–46.

39. Clinical Effectiveness Unit. Use of rifampicin and contraceptive steroids. *Br J Fam Plann* 1999;24:169–70.

40. Faculty of Family Planning and Reproductive Health Care Clinical Effectiveness Unit. First prescription of combined oral contraception. *J Fam Plann Reprod Health Care* 2003;29:209–22.

41. National Institute of Health. Medline Plus Medical Encyclopedia. Ulcerative Colitis [www.nlm.nih.gov/medlineplus/ency/article/000250.htm].

42. Elliman A. Interactions with hormonal contraception. Faculty Aid to CPD Topics (FACT) *J Fam Plann Reprod Health Care* 2000;26:109–11.

43. Grimmer SFM, Back DJ, Orme ML'E, Cowie A, Gilmore I, Tjia J. The bioavailability of ethinyloestadiol and levonorgestrel in patients with an ileostomy. *Contraception* 1986;33:51–9.

44. Faculty of Family Planning and Reproductive Health Care Clinical Effectiveness Unit. Contraceptive choices for women with inflammatory bowel disease. *J Fam Plann Reprod Health Care* 2003;29:127–34.

45. Pollack ES, Stein ES. Von Willebrands Disease. 2002 [www.emedicine.com/med/topic2392.htm].

46. Kouides PA. Obstetric and gynaecological aspects of von Willebrand disease. *Best Pract Res Clin Haematol* 2001;14:381–99.

47. Faculty of Family Planning and Reproductive Health Care Clinical Effectiveness Unit. The levonorgestrel-releasing intrauterine system (LNG-IUS) in contraception and reproductive health. *J Fam Plann Reprod Health Care* 2004;30:99–109.

48. Irvine GA, Campbell-Brown MB, Lumsden MA, Heikkilä A, Walker JJ, Cameron IT. Randomised comparitive trial of the LNG-IUS and norethisterone for treatment of idiopathic menorrhagia. *Br J Obstet Gynaecol* 1998;105:592–8.

49. Stewart A, Cummins C, Gold L, Jordon R, Phillips W. The effectiveness of the levonorgestrel-releasing intrauterine system in menorrhagia: a systematic review. *BJOG* 2001;108:74–86.

50. Lethaby AE, Cooke I, Rees M. Progesterone/progestin releasing intrauterine systems for heavy menstrual bleeding. *Cochrane Database Syst Rev* 2003;(2).

51. Milsom I, Andersson K, Andersch B, Rybo G. A comparison of flurbiprofen, tranexamic acid, and a levonorgestrel-releasing intrauterine contraceptive device in the treatment of idiopathic menorrhagia. *Am J Obstet Gynecol* 1991;164:879–83.

52. Istre O, Trolle B. Treatment of menorrhagia with the levonorgestrel intrauterine system versus endometrial resection. *Fertil Steril* 2001;76:304–9.

INDEX

abortion *see* induced abortion;
  miscarriage
abstinence, sexual *see* back-up
  contraception/abstinence from sex
access to contraception 251–2
achondroplasia 503
acitretin 323–5, 477
acne
  Dianette® therapy 9, 49, 50–1, 53–4
    in cerebral palsy 52
    combined pill after 55–6
    postpartum, and prior acoustic
      neuroma 368–9
    isotretinoin therapy 320–3
    in polycystic ovary syndrome 542, 543
acoustic neuroma, past history 368–9
acrocyanosis 503–4
ACTH-secreting pituitary tumours 366
Actinomyces israelii 271, 272–3
actinomyces-like organisms
  detected by cervical smears 271, 272–3
  detected prior to IUD insertion 148
  postmenopausal women with IUDs
    178–9
actinomycosis, pelvic 271, 272–3
acute macular neuroretinopathy
  (AMNR) 369
Addison's disease 504–5, 528
adhesions
  intraperitoneal IUD-related 173, 178
  intrauterine (Asherman syndrome)
    506–7
adolescents
  under 16 years, consent issues 258,
    260, 385, 508–9

cerebrovascular disease 384–5
  dysmenorrhoea 35–6
  legal and ethical issues 258–60, 260,
    262–4
  progestogen-only emergency
    contraception 224, 230–1
  progestogen-only injectables 84–6, 90
  smokers with small ventricular septal
    defect 401–2
  walk-in style services 247–9
  see also young women
adrenaline *see* epinephrine
adrenal insufficiency 504–5, 528
adrenocorticotrophic hormone-secreting
  pituitary tumours 366
African Caribbean women,
  perimenopausal 87–8
age restrictions
  progestogen-only injectables 90–1
  progestogen-releasing implants 119
  see also older women; young women
AIDS *see* HIV infection
allergic reactions
  nonoxynol-9 207–8
  progestogen-only injectables 100–5
  see also anaphylactic reactions
alopecia 21–2
  androgenic 21, 22
  areata 21
alpha-1 antitrypsin deficiency 450–1
5-alpha reductase 21
Alport syndrome 473–4
altitudes, extreme 18
amenorrhoea
  in anorexia nervosa 505–6

DMPA-induced 90, 91–2, 96
induction, valvular heart disease and previous stroke 406
lactational 60
LNG-IUS-induced 182–3, 192
perimenopausal 61, 86
post-pill secondary 20
weight-related 20
aminoglutethimide 514
anaesthesia, Chinese steel ring IUD removal 217–18
anaphylactic reactions
LNG-IUS 102, 187–8, 190
progestogen-only injectables 100–5
resuscitation guidance 100–2, 103, 250
androgen therapy 129
angina 429–30
anorexia nervosa 505–6
anovaginal fistula 506
anti-arrhythmic agents 413–14
antibiotics
in cystic fibrosis 515
infections prior to IUD insertion 148–9
liver enzyme-inducing, interactions 309–10
non-liver enzyme-inducing, interactions 311–5
oral regimens for PID 274
pelvic actinomycosis 272–3
pelvic inflammatory disease in IUD users 166
during pill-free interval of combined pill 45–6
progestogen-only pill and 74
prophylactic *see* antimicrobial prophylaxis
timing of induced abortion and 235
anticoagulant therapy 433–5
combined oral contraception 442–3
endocarditis prophylaxis and 189–90
intrauterine contraception 391–2, 433–4, 434–5
progestogen-only implants 411–12, 438–9

see also warfarin
anticonvulsant drugs 343–9, 427
in bipolar affective disorder 511
etonogestrel implants and 300, 349
liver-enzyme inducers 343–4, 349, 391
non-liver-enzyme inducers 345–8, 349
progestogen-only emergency contraception and 307, 343–4
anti-epileptic drugs *see* anticonvulsant drugs
antifibrinolytic agents 193
anti-fungal drugs 315
antihistamines
in anaphylaxis 103, 250
interactions 335–6
antimicrobial prophylaxis
etonogestrel implant insertion/removal 403–4
female sterilisation 402
induced abortion 233–4
IUD insertion/removal 145–7, 153, 186–7
cardiomyopathy 189–90
coronary artery stents 430–1
past history of endocarditis 407–8
post-splenectomy 157–8, 556–7
valvular heart disease 157, 407–8
antiphospholipid syndrome
combined oral contraception 26, 439, 479, 548, 549
LNG-IUS 183–4
progestogen-only contraception 440
anti-retroviral drugs 300, 493–6, 499–501
antisepsis, vaginal 152, 153
antithrombin III deficiency 442–3
antituberculous drugs 561
aortic stenosis 396–8
aortic valve, bicuspid 400–1
appointments-based clinics 247–9
Arcoxia® 552
arrhythmias 413–14
arterial thrombosis
lupus anticoagulants and 26

see also myocardial infarction; stroke
Arthrotec® 335
ascorbic acid 334
Asherman syndrome 506–7
Asperger syndrome 507–9
aspirin 291
atazanavir 493–5
atenolol 467–8
atrial fibrillation 412, 413–14
atrial septal defects 400–1, 405–6
atropine 188, 250
attention deficit disorder, and history of
    stroke 387–3
aura, migraine 350
azathioprine 466
azithromycin 314

back-up contraception/abstinence from
    sex
    after induced abortion 237, 239
    antibiotic users 45–6, 314
    in epilepsy 344, 345
    late DMPA injections 106–7
    late norethisterone acetate injections
        116
    liver enzyme-inducing drugs 300,
        301, 303, 305
    missed combined pills 41, 42, 43
    missed progestogen-only pills 76–7,
        78–9
    prior to stopping progestogen-only
        pill 75
    progestogen-only implant insertion
        124–5
    progestogen-only implant removal
        126
    starting combined pills 11, 14
    starting progestogen-only injectables
        83, 84
    switching combined pills 12–13
    time-expired combined pills 44
bacteria, incidental detection at cervical
    cytology 271–3
bacterial vaginosis 271

IUD or LNG-IUS use 148, 185–6
    prophylaxis, induced abortion 234
    treatment before induced abortion
        235
    treatment prior to IUD or LNG-IUS
        insertion 188–9
barbiturates 339
barotrauma 19
barrier methods 205–8
    back-up *see* back-up contraception/
        abstinence from sex
    in liver disease 454–5
    travellers to high altitudes 18
Behcet's disease 509–10
benign intracranial hypertension 359–63
    plus multiple other pathologies 425–7
Betadine®, vaginal preparations 152,
    153
bicornuate uterus, LNG-IUS use 184
bicuspid aortic valve 400–1
bipolar affective disorder 510–12
bleeding
    delaying *see* menstruation, delaying
    post-abortion, contraceptive methods
        and 237–8, 240–1
bleeding disorders (dyscrasias) 527–8,
    530–2, 563–5
bleeding patterns, abnormal
    combined oral contraception 31–3
    copper IUDs 170, 171
    LNG-IUS 182–5, 192
    in migraine 357
    monthly injectables 216–17
    progestogen-only implants 132–4
    progestogen-only injectables 96–8,
        115, 521
    progestogen-only pill 69–70
    see also breakthrough bleeding;
        intermenstrual bleeding;
        menorrhagia
blood pressure 3–4, 19, 57–8
    see also hypertension
body mass index (BMI) 537
    combined oral contraception and 4–5

drug interactions and 303–4
high *see* obesity
progestogen-only implants and 121–2
progestogen-only injectables and 82,
    97–8, 99
body weight *see* weight, body
bone mineral density
    desogestrel-only pill and 64–5
    in HIV infection 497–8
    in inflammatory bowel disease 512–14
    progestogen-only implants and 130–1,
        198
    progestogen-only injectables and
        84–6, 87–8, 90–6, 114–15
    see also osteoporosis
borage (starflower) oil 331
bosentan 304–6
brain haemorrhage 383–5
BRCA1 and BRCA2 gene mutations
    489, 490, 491
breakthrough bleeding
    combined pill 8, 31–3
    drug interactions causing 335–6
    progestogen-only pill 71
breast cancer 484–92
    combined oral contraception-related
        risk 16, 489–90
    estrogen receptor positive 486
    family history 65–6, 108–9, 489–92
    LNG-IUS as progestogen component
        of HRT and 282–3
    personal history 283–5, 484–9
    progestogen-only contraception-
        related risk 65–7, 108–9, 490–2
    risk factors 67, 484
    tamoxifen therapy 283–5, 484–8
breastfeeding
    combined oral contraception 6, 368
    IUD insertion 142, 155–6
    progestogen-only emergency
        contraception 223
    progestogen-only injectables 83–4
    progestogen-only pill 59–60
breast lumps, in LNG-IUS users 196–7

breast tenderness, premenstrual 287–9
bromocriptine 334
broom-like device, cervical smear
    collection 268–9

caesarean section, IUD insertion after
    155–6
Calista® saliva ovulation test 214–15
candidiasis, vulvovaginal 28–9, 148, 272
cardiac arrhythmias 413–14
cardiac laser surgery 415
cardiac transplant recipients 415–16
cardiomyopathy 410–12
    dilated 410–12
    familial 53–4
    LNG-IUS insertion 189–90
    peripartum 411
    warfarin therapy 411–12
cardiovascular disease 395–446
    DMPA users 109–10, 386–7
    Ehlers-Danlos syndrome and 519–20
    family history 417–18, 425–6
    older combined pill users 277, 278
    renal disease and 317–18, 317–18
    see also cerebrovascular disorders;
        heart disease; stroke
cardiovascular risk factors 419–23
    contribution of family history 417–18
    multiple 53, 109, 427–8
Carpenter syndrome 405–6
catamenial epilepsy 343
centchroman 219–20
Cerazette® *see* desogestrel-only pill
cerebral infarction 386–7
    post-meningitic 390
    see also stroke
cerebral palsy 52, 370–1
cerebral venous sinus thrombosis 390–2
cerebral venous thrombosis 378
cerebrospinal fluid shunts
    benign intracranial hypertension
        362–3, 425–7
    in neurofibromatosis 374–5
cerebrovascular accident *see* stroke

cerebrovascular disorders 383–58
cervical cancer
    risk, hormonal contraception 17
    in young women 253–2
cervical intraepithelial neoplasia (CIN)
    512
cervical smears/screening
    clinical guidelines 267–9
    incidental detection of bacteria
        271–3
    opportunistic chlamydia screening
        270–1
    plastic vs metal speculums 255
    routine pelvic examination 269–70
    in young women 252–4
cervical weakness, history of 137
cervix
    cleansing, prior to IUD insertion 153
    priming for IUD insertion 488
    swabbing *see* microbiology testing
    traction, at IUD insertion 153–4
Charcot Marie Tooth syndrome 371
chasteberry (Vitex agnus castus) 33–1
Chinese steel ring intrauterine devices
    217–18
Chlamydia trachomatis
    bacterial vaginosis and 188–9
    infections in IUD users 164–6
    prophylaxis, induced abortion 234
    screening
        opportunistic 270–1
        prior to IUD insertion 145–6, 147,
            186–7
    treatment
        before induced abortion 235
        prior to IUD insertion 149
chloasma 472–3
chlorpheniramine, in anaphylaxis 103, 250
cholangitis, primary sclerosing 52–3
cholecystectomy 447–9, 516
cholestasis
    combined hormonal contraceptive-
        related 458
    pregnancy-related 449–51

cholesterol, high *see*
        hypercholesterolaemia
chorea, oral contraceptive-induced 378–9
ciclosporin 316–19, 465, 532–3
Cilest®
    in cardiomyopathy 410–12
    venous thromboembolism risk 8–9
cirrhosis of liver 456, 453–5
    in porphyria 544
clerical staff 252
clinics, family planning, drop-in vs
        appointment 247–9
clomifene citrate 285
clotting studies, estrogen-containing
        preparation users 279–80
cocaine 340, 340–2
colitis 448–9, 562–3
colposcopy
    Chinese steel ring IUD users 218
    insertion of IUDs after 144–5
combined hormonal contraception
    3–56
    in breast cancer 484
    cholestasis induced by 458
    drug interactions 494
    in haemophilia 527–8
    in liver disease 453–4, 455
    monthly injectables 216–17
    oral *see* combined oral contraception
    in thrombophilias 439, 441, 443–4
    transdermal *see* combined
        transdermal contraception
    in venous thromboembolism 433–4
    see also estrogen-containing
        preparations
combined oral contraception 3–46
    in achondroplasia 508
    in acquired heart disease 410–12,
        412–16
    in acrocyanosis 503–4
    in acute macular neuroretinopathy
        369
    adverse effects 8–9, 21–30
    after induced abortion 237, 238

after oral emergency contraception 13–14

in anorexia nervosa 505–6

in autoimmune cyclical neutropenia 509

blood tests for gonadotrophins, thyroid function and clotting studies 279–80

breast cancer risk 16, 489–90

in cerebral palsy 52, 370–1

in cerebrovascular disorders 384, 387, 390, 392–3

choice of pill and starting regimens 7–15

in congenital glaucoma 371–2

in congenital heart disease 396, 397, 402–7

in cystic fibrosis 515

diagnosis of menopause 278, 279–80

in DMPA users with abnormal bleeding 97, 98, 521

drug interactions
   antibiotics 311–5
   anti-obesity medications 336, 337
   complementary medicines 326–7, 326–7, 330–1
   illegal recreational drugs 340, 341
   liver-enzyme inducers 303, 305, 306, 494
   retinoids 321, 477
   tacrolimus 319–20
   in tuberculosis 560–1
   vitamin C 334

in dysmenorrhoea 35–6

efficacy 7–8, 9–14, 36–7

in epilepsy 344, 345, 346, 348

'every day' pills 11–12, 37, 42, 43

in gall bladder disease 447-8, 515–16

in haemochromatosis 526–7

in haemophilia 527–8

HIV acquisition/transmission and 495–6

in HIV infection 499, 500

in hyperlipidaemia 392–3, 425–7, 423–4

in idiopathic thrombocytopenic purpura 531, 532

in ischaemic heart disease 417–18, 419–23

in Kawasaki disease 533–4

in lactose intolerance 534–5

in liver disease 449–50, 452, 455–6, 457, 459

managing problems during use 30–9

in migraine 350–9, 357

missed pills and potential failures 9–10, 36–7, 40–6, 232

in multiple sclerosis 373–4

in obesity 4–5, 36, 98, 121, 538

in older women 5, 30–1, 277–9

in otosclerosis 376–7

in ovarian cancer 540–1

past history of acoustic neuroma 368–9

patient selection 3–6

in pituitary tumours 366–7

in polycystic ovary syndrome 542–3

in porphyria 544–5

in progestogen-only implant users 134

in Raynaud's phenomenon 548–50

refusal to prescribe 261–3

in renal disorders 463, 465–7, 469

in rheumatoid arthritis 551

risks and sequelae 16–21

in Schamberg's disease 552–3

in sickle cell disease 554–6

in skin disorders 472–3, 474–5, 476, 478–9

skin disorders caused by 24–6, 472–3, 475, 481

stroke risks *see* under stroke

stroke while taking 386

supply arrangements 251

switching formulations 12–13

switching to progestogen-only implants 124–5

in Sydenham's chorea 378–9

in thrombophilias 436–7, 439, 443–4

time-expired pills 44

'tricycling' 37
in trophoblastic disease 559–60
in ulcerative colitis 562–3
in valvular heart disease 53, 397,
    402–3
venous thromboembolism risks *see*
    under venous thromboembolism
vs combined transdermal
    contraception 46–7
combined transdermal contraception
    46–8
    drug interactions 494
    in haemophilia 527–8
Combivir® 493–5
competence, IUD insertion 155
complementary medicines 325–32
compliance
    failures, combined pill 9–10, 37–8,
        40–3
    strategies for improving 10, 259
condoms 205–6
    back-up use *see* back-up
        contraception/abstinence from sex
    free provision 248
confidentiality
    guidance on breaching 260
    patients aged under 16 years 259
congenital abnormalities *see* fetal
    abnormalities
congenital heart disease 395–409
consent
    written, for IUD insertion 257
    young women under 16 years 258,
        260, 385, 508–9
    young women with learning
        difficulty 262–4
contact lenses 27–8
copper, intrauterine corrosion 141
Copper-7 IUD 172
copper intrauterine devices (IUDs)
    136–81
    after endometrial ablation 523–4
    after induced abortion 143–4, 237,
        239–42

in anticoagulated patients 391–2, 429,
    433
antimicrobial prophylaxis for
    insertion/removal *see under*
    antimicrobial prophylaxis
in breast cancer 487–8
choice of device 139–42
complicated insertion 155–9
discontinuation or removal 174–81
efficacy 139
emergency use 222, 223, 228, 228
in epilepsy 344, 345
expired 161–2
expulsion 137, 155–6, 157–8, 168–9,
    178
failed insertion 487–8
follow-up 163–4, 251
in heart disease 396, 397, 401, 429–31
in HIV infection 499, 501, 532–3
in immunocompromised patients
    532–3
investigations prior to insertion 145–9
in liver disease 454–5, 459–60
lost threads 158–9, 170, 178
misplacement 168–70
patient selection 136–8
problems at insertion 159–3
problems during use 164–74, 274
recall systems for removal 257–9
routine insertion procedures 149–56
in skin lesions 479
timing of insertion 142–5
Copper T380A IUD 160, 171–2
coronary artery bypass 418–19
coronary artery stenting 418–19, 430–1
coronary heart disease *see* ischaemic
    heart disease
corticosteroid therapy 514
    in Addison's disease 504–5
    high-dose, in IUD users 168
    in Takayasu arteritis 380–1, 563
    in ulcerative colitis 562–3
cost-effectiveness
    free condoms 248

progestogen-only emergency
   contraception 260–1
Crohn's disease 512–14
Cushing's disease 366
Cushing syndrome 514
cutaneous lupus erythematosus 26
cyanotic congenital heart disease 407–8
cyclical neutropenia, autoimmune 509
Cyclofem® 216–17
cyclophosphamide 563
Cyklokapron® 193
cyproterone acetate-containing pill see
   Dianette®
cystic fibrosis 515–16

decompression sickness 19
deep vein thrombosis (DVT) see venous
   thromboembolism
deltoid muscle, DMPA injections 99
dental problems 23
depot medroxyprogesterone acetate
   (DMPA) (Depo-Provera®) 82–113
   abnormal bleeding 96–8, 115, 521
   administration 98–100, 104
   adverse effects 22, 23, 108–13, 535
   after induced abortion 238–9
   anaphylactic and allergic reactions
      100–5
   in Asperger syndrome 510–12
   in bipolar affective disorder 510–12
   bone mineral density and 84–6, 90–6,
      114
   in cerebrovascular disorders 386–7
   in Crohn's disease 512–14
   in diabetes 521–2
   dose and regimens 105–7
   drug interactions 299, 301, 309–11,
      322–3, 335–6
   in endometriosis 530
   in epilepsy 344, 346–7, 349
   in heart disease 396, 425, 427–8
   in HIV infection 495, 497–8, 500
   interval between injections 98, 100,
      105, 106, 106–7

in Legg-Calve-Perthes disease 535–6
in liver disease 456
LNG-IUS in peritoneal cavity 191
in migraine 354–5, 357–8
in obesity 82, 97–8, 99, 538
in osteogenesis imperfecta 541
in ovarian cysts 541
patient selection 82–90
in polycystic ovary syndrome 547
in prolactinoma 365–6
in renal disorders 466, 467–8
in retinoblastoma 377–8
in rheumatoid arthritis 552
in Scheuermann kyphosis 554
in sickle cell disease 554–6
in smokers 31, 92–4
switching to norethisterone enanthate
   113–14
in tuberculosis 561
depression
   in DMPA users 110–11, 510–12
   metformin therapy in PCOS and
      291–2
dermatomyositis 474
desmopressin 563–4
desogestrel 198
desogestrel-containing combined pills 7
   acne recurrence and 56
   adverse effects 8, 9
   breakthrough bleeding 32–3
   cardiovascular risk factors and 420
desogestrel-only pill (Cerazette®)
   abnormal bleeding patterns 69, 70
   in benign intracranial hypertension
      361
   bone mineral density and 65
   efficacy 72–3, 74–5
   elective surgery 64
   missed pills 78–9
   in obesity 59, 121
   ovarian cyst risk 68–9
   pregnancy risk after stopping 75
   in renal disorders 464–5
   in rheumatoid arthritis 552

vaginal estrogens with 80
warfarin and 338
DEXA scanning 88, 90, 92
diabetes
    insulin-dependent
        and Addison's disease 522–3
        and high BMI 521
    type II, and Down syndrome 522
diabetic nephropathy 469
Dianette® (cyproterone acetate-
        containing pill) 48–56
    after acoustic neuroma 369
    indications 27, 49, 50, 53–4
    in PCOS and congenital heart disease
        402–3
    prevention of alopecia 22
    venous thromboembolism risk 9, 49,
        50–1
diaphragms 206–8
    in valvular heart disease 397
diathermy treatment, Chinese steel ring
        IUD users 218
diazepam 250
diclofenac sodium 335
dihydrotestosterone 21
discoid lupus erythematosus 478–9
dispensing arrangements 251–2
diving, deep-sea 19
DMPA *see* depot medroxyprogesterone
        acetate
Down syndrome
    competence to give consent 262–4
    type II diabetes and 522
doxycycline 317
drop-in clinics 247–9
drospirenone/ethinylestradiol combined
        pill (Yasmin®) 9
    body weight changes 33–4
    hirsutism and 27
    in polycystic ovary syndrome 542–3
drug interactions 299–42
    complementary medicines 325–32
    in HIV infection 493–5, 501
    illegal recreational drugs 339–42

immunosuppressants 316–21
liver enzyme-inducers 299–11
liver enzyme-inducing antibiotics
        309–10
miscellaneous 335–42
non-liver enzyme-inducing
        antibiotics 311–5
retinoids 321–5
in tuberculosis 560–1
drug use, illicit recreational 339–42
dry-eye syndrome 28
dural sinus thrombosis, postnatal 391–2
dysmenorrhoea
    in adolescents 35–6
    adverse effects of NSAIDs 290–1
    nephrotic syndrome with 465–7

ear disease 376–7
eating disorders 505–6
ecstasy 340–2
ectopic pregnancy
    copper IUD or LNG-IUS after 136–7
    Dianette® and 51
    DMPA users 111–12
    progestogen-only implants and 125
Ehlers-Danlos syndrome 519–20
electrolysis kits, home 171
embolism, paradoxical 396
emergency contraception
    after progestogen-only implant
        removal 128
    copper IUDs 222, 223, 228, 231
    extended pill-free interval 44–5
    late DMPA injections 106–7
    late norethisterone acetate injections
        116
    missed combined pills 42, 43, 232
    missed progestogen-only pills 77–9
    progestogen-only *see* progestogen-
        only emergency contraception
    time-expired combined pills 44
    see also back-up contraception/
        abstinence from sex
emergency situations

equipment and supplies (shock pack)
249–51
LNG-IUS removal 187–8
see also anaphylactic reactions;
resuscitation
endocarditis
past history, IUD insertion/removal
407–8
prophylaxis
etonogestrel implant
insertion/removal 403–4
female sterilisation 398
IUD or LNG-IUS insertion/
removal 157–8, 189–90, 397,
407–8
endocervical brush, cervical smears 268
endometrial ablation, microwave 528–9
endometrial cancer, postmenopausal
retention of IUDs and 178–9, 179,
205
endometrial protection 80, 282–3
endometriosis 131–2, 524–5
epilepsy 343–9
catamenial 343
plus multiple other pathologies 425–7
see also anticonvulsant drugs
epinephrine (adrenaline) 250
in anaphylaxis 103, 250
erectile dysfunction, and solvent abuse
293
erythema multiforme major 475
erythema nodosum 480–1
erythromycin 314
erythropoietic protoporphyria 545
Essure® 209–12
estradiol
monthly injectables 216
serum concentrations
DMPA users 93–4, 106
LNG-IUS users 197
estrogen
conjugated, in migraine 357–8
dose, combined pills
in epilepsy 346

see also ethinylestradiol dose,
combined pills
natural, in migraine 357
receptor positive breast cancer 486
topical vaginal *see* vaginal estrogens,
topical
estrogen antagonist, nonsteroidal
(centchroman) 219–20
estrogen-containing preparations
in benign intracranial hypertension
360
clotting studies 279–80
illegal recreational drug users 340,
341–2
in multiple pathologies 425–7
serum gonadotrophin tests 134–5,
278, 279–80
thyroid function tests 279–80
see also combined hormonal
contraception; hormone
replacement therapy
estrogen replacement therapy
DMPA users 93–4, 95
with LNG-IUS 282–3
in migraine 357–8
post-pill amenorrhoea 20
ethambutol 309–11, 561
ethical issues 257–64
ethinylestradiol dose, combined pills
antibiotic users 46
breakthrough bleeding and 32–3
in epilepsy 346
in HIV infection 500
in hypercholesterolaemia 422–3
missed pill rules in relation to 41–3
in obesity 539
optimal 7–8, 9, 10
switching 12–13
ethinylestradiol–norelgestromin patch
(Evra®) 47
see also combined transdermal
contraception
ethnic minorities, walk-in style services
247, 248

etonogestrel-releasing implant
(Implanon®)
adverse effects 129–32
in anticoagulated patients 411–12,
438–9
in cerebrovascular disorders 387–3,
389–90
drug interactions 300–1, 323–5, 331,
341–2
efficacy 120–2, 125
endocarditis prophylaxis for insertion/
removal 403–4
in epilepsy 345, 349
in fibrodysplasia ossificans
progressiva 525–6
in gall bladder disease 448–9
in HIV infection 493–5
insertion and removal 125–6, 127, 128
in liver disease 456, 458–9
in migraine 357
in obesity 117, 118–19, 121–2
in older women 119
in renal disorders 473
in rheumatoid arthritis 552
in skin disorders 481–2
unscheduled bleeding 132–4
see also progestogen-only implants
etoricoxib (Arcoxia®) 552
etretinate 325
etynodiol diacetate 198
etynodiol diacetate-only pill
missed pills 76–7
in obesity 58–9
pregnancy risk after stopping 75
Eugynon 30® 56
evening primrose oil 287–9
Evra® 47
see also combined transdermal
contraception
experience, clinician, IUD insertion
153–4
expired combined pills 44
expired intrauterine devices 161–2
eye diseases 369, 371–2

facial numbness
occasional, and migraine 351–2
transient, DMPA users 112–13
factor V Leiden deficiency 437–9
family planning services see services,
family planning
female sterilisation 209–12
after induced abortion 242
LNG-IUS as alternative 180–1
obese women awaiting 121–2
in valvular heart disease 397–8
Femodene® ED 12
Femodette® 32
Femulen® 540
fenofibrate 423
fenoprofen 291
fertility awareness-based methods
214–15
fetal abnormalities
combined pill users 14, 37–8
DMPA users 112
fibrodysplasia ossificans progressiva
525–6
fibroids, uterine, LNG-IUS use 203–4
fistula, anovaginal 506
flecainide acetate 413–14
Flexi-T300 IUD 140
flucloxacillin 311–12
fluconazole 315
fluid retention, benign intracranial
hypertension and 361
flushes, hot see menopausal symptoms
focal nodular hyperplasia of liver 462
follicle-stimulating hormone (FSH),
serum 278
DMPA users 86, 522
estrogen-containing preparation users
135, 278, 279–80
IUD users 174, 202–3
progestogen-only pill users 62, 279
tamoxifen users 283–4
follow-up arrangements 251
fractures, osteoporotic 92–4
Fraser guidelines (1985) 258, 260, 385

furosemide 514

gall bladder disease 447–9, 516
gamma linolenic acid 289, 331
gemeprost, medical abortion 238
general anaesthesia, removal of Chinese
    steel ring IUDs 217–18
general practitioners, prescribing of
    IUDs 263–5
genital herpes, recurrence in IUD users
    166–7, 195–6
genital tract infections
    LNG-IUS insertion after 181–3
    prophylaxis see antimicrobial
        prophylaxis
    see also pelvic infections; sexually
        transmitted infections
gestodene-containing combined pills 7
    adverse effects 8, 9
    breakthrough bleeding 32–3
    cardiovascular risk factors and 420
Gilbert's disease 455–6
Gillick vs West Norfolk and Wisbech
    Area Health Authority (1986) 385,
    508–9
gingivitis 23
girls see adolescents
glaucoma, congenital 371–2
gluteal muscle, DMPA injections 99
gonadotrophin-releasing hormone
    (GnRH) agonists
    and add-back HRT, for endometriosis
        524–5
    combined with tamoxifen 284–5
gonadotrophins, serum
    estrogen preparation users 279–80
    tamoxifen users 283–4
    see also follicle-stimulating hormone
        (FSH), serum
gonorrhoea see Neisseria gonorrhoea
grapefruit juice 334, 550
griseofulvin 45–6, 307
group A streptococcus 148, 271
group B streptococcus 148, 271

guardians, consent by 262, 509
gum disease 23
gynaecological problems 265–95
GyneFix® IUD 140, 141, 159–60

haemochromatosis 526–7
haemodialysis 463–4
haemolytic-uraemic syndrome 356
haemophilia 527–8
hair loss 21–2
health visitors 252
heart disease 53–4, 395–432
    acquired 409–32
    congenital 395–409
    ischaemic see ischaemic heart disease
heart transplant recipients 415–16
HELLP syndrome 452–3
hemiparesis 389–90
Henoch-Schönlein purpura 528
heparin, progestogen-only implants and
    438–9
hepatitis 458–61
    acute, combined pill-associated 458
    viral 456, 458–60
hepatitis A 458–9
hepatitis B 459–60
hepatitis C 460
herbal remedies 325–32
herpes, genital, recurrence in IUD users
    166–7, 195–6
high altitude 18
highly active antiretroviral therapy
    (HAART) 495
    see also antiretroviral drugs
hirsutism
    Dianette® therapy 27, 49, 50–1, 53–4
    LNG-IUS use and 198–9
    in polycystic ovary syndrome 547, 543
HIV infection 493–502
    antiretroviral drug interactions 493–6,
        499–501
    bone mineral density and 497–8
    free provision of condoms 248
    IUD use 501, 532–3

nonoxynol-9 use and 206
risk of acquiring/transmitting 495–6
home
    electrolysis kits 171
    LNG-IUS removal at 187–8
hormone replacement therapy (HRT)
    add-back, with GnRH, for
        endometriosis 524–5
    alternatives to 281
    blood tests for gonadotrophins,
        thyroid function and clotting
        studies 279–80
    LNG-IUS for progestogen
        component 282–3
    in otosclerosis 376–7
    personal/family history of VTE and
        281
    progestogen-only implants with
        134–5
    progestogen-only pill with 79–80, 81
    see also estrogen replacement therapy
hot flushes see menopausal symptoms
HRT see hormone replacement therapy
human chorionic gonadotrophin (hCG),
    serum 265–6, 559, 560
human immunodeficiency virus see HIV
hydatidiform mole 558–60
hydrocortisone 250
    in anaphylaxis 103, 250
    long-term therapy 514
hypercholesterolaemia 422–5
    familial 423–4
    fenofibrate-treated 423
    plus family history of stroke 392–3
Hypericum perforatum (St John's wort)
    325–30
hyperlipidaemia 420–4
    plus family history of stroke 392–3
    in renal disease 317–18, 318, 464
hypermobility syndrome 354
hyperprolactinaemia 20, 363–6
hypertension
    adequately controlled 417
    cerebrovascular disease and 387

contraindicating combined pill 3, 19
DMPA use 427–8, 433
in neurofibromatosis 375
pill-induced 19
refusal to prescribe combined pill
    261–3
renal disorders with 463, 464–5,
    467–8
sibutramine hydrochloride and 336,
    337
hyperthyroidism 309–11
hypothyroidism 448–9
hysteroscopy
    IUD identification 178
    tubal occlusion (Essure®) 209–12

idiopathic thrombocytopenic purpura
    530–2
illegal recreational drugs 339–42
immunocompromised women 532–3
immunoglobulin A (IgA) nephropathy
    23–4
immunosuppressants 316–21
    in dermatomyositis 474
    IUD insertion and 532–3
    in Takayasu arteritis 380–1, 563
    in transplant recipients 319, 415–16,
        461, 465
Implanon® see etonogestrel-releasing
    implant
indomethacin 291
induced abortion 233–44
    hormonal contraception after 237–8
    insertion of IUDs after 143–4, 235,
        237–8, 239–42
    medical, regimens 235–6
    sterilisation after 242
infections
    in IUD users 164–8
    prophylaxis see antimicrobial
        prophylaxis
    testing for see microbiology testing
    treatment prior to IUD insertion
        147–9

see also genital tract infections; pelvic infections; sexually transmitted infections
inflammatory bowel disease 52
  combined oral contraception 562–3
  progestogen-only contraception 448–9, 498, 512–14
injectable contraceptives
  monthly 216–17
  progestogen-only *see* progestogen-only injectables
interferon 460
intermenstrual bleeding
  progestogen-only pill 69–71
  smokers aged over 35 years 30–1
intracranial aneurysms 383–4
intracranial haemorrhage 383–5
intracranial hypertension, benign 359–63, 425–7
intrauterine contraception (IUDs) 136–205
  actinomyces-like organisms in cervical smears 272–3
  after endometrial ablation 523–4
  in anovaginal fistula 506
  anticoagulated patients 391–2, 433–4, 435
  antimicrobial prophylaxis for insertion/removal *see* under antimicrobial prophylaxis
  in Asherman syndrome 506–7
  Chinese steel ring 217–18
  in congenital heart disease 397, 405–6
  consent for insertion 257
  copper *see* copper intrauterine devices
  endocarditis prophylaxis for insertion/removal *see* under endocarditis
  follow-up 163–4, 251
  in HIV infection 501, 532–3
  insertion after induced abortion 143–4, 235, 237–8, 239–42
  in ischaemic heart disease 433–6
  prescribing by general practitioners 263–5

recall systems for removal 257–9
  in trophoblastic disease 564
intrauterine system, levonorgestrel-releasing *see* levonorgestrel-releasing intrauterine system
ischaemic heart disease 109, 417–32
  after coronary artery bypass and stenting 418–19
  family history 417–18, 420–1
  risk factors *see* cardiovascular risk factors
  women at increased risk 419–23, 427–8
  women with current disease 424–7, 433–6
isoniazid 561
isotretinoin 321–3, 477
itraconazole 317
IUDs *see* copper intrauterine devices; intrauterine contraception

Jadelle® 123, 129
joint hypermobility 354

Kawasaki disease 533–4
ketoconazole 317
Klippel-Trenaunay-Weber syndrome 445
kyphosis, Scheuermann 553–4

lactational amenorrhoea 60
lactose intolerance 534–5
Lamictal® 348
Lamisil® 333
lamivudine 493–5
lamotrigine 347–8
lansoprazole 306–8
large loop excision of the transformation zone (LLETZ) 144
laser surgery, cardiac 415
learning difficulties
  competence to give consent 262–4
  service provision 251
legal issues 257–64

Legg-Calve-Perthes disease 535–6
letter of competence in intrauterine
    techniques (LoC IUT) 155
levofloxacin 274
Levonelle, vs generic levonorgestrel
    260–1
levonorgestrel
    androgenic effects 198
    in combined pills 7, 8–9, 56, 420
    emergency contraception *see*
        progestogen-only emergency
        contraception
    generic vs branded, for emergency
        contraception 260–1
levonorgestrel-only pill
    efficacy 72–3, 74–5
    missed pills 76
    in obesity 58–9
    pregnancy risk after stopping 74–5
levonorgestrel-releasing implant
    (Norplant®)
    adverse effects 22, 129, 531
    efficacy 122–3
    in obesity 58, 117
    removal 126–7
levonorgestrel-releasing intrauterine
    system (LNG-IUS) 180–203
    after surgical abortion 239–40
    anaphylaxis risk 102, 187–8, 190
    in anticoagulated patients 391–2,
        433–5
    in benign intracranial hypertension
        362–3
    in breast cancer 484–5, 486–7
    in cardiovascular disease 396, 397,
        401, 418–19, 433, 430–1
    in cerebrovascular disorders 385–6,
        388–90, 433
    combined with Dianette® 54–5
    continuation and removal 175, 201–4
    drug interactions 305–6, 477
        liver-enzyme inducers 494
        in tuberculosis 561
    effectiveness 180–1

in Ehlers-Danlos syndrome 520
endocarditis prophylaxis for insertion/
    removal *see* under endocarditis
in epilepsy 344, 345
in erythropoietic protoporphyria 545
expulsion 157–8, 168–9
extrauterine location 191
in HIV infection 499, 501
in inflammatory bowel disease 513
insertion 142–3, 187–91
    complicated 157, 157–8
    investigations before 186–7
in migraine 355–6
misplacement 168–70
patient selection 31, 136–7, 140,
    178–9, 181–7
prescribing by general practitioners
    263–5
problems during use 166–7, 192–200,
    274
for progestogen component of HRT
    282–3
in prolactinoma 364–5
recall systems for removal 257–9
in renal disorders 464–5, 466–7
in rheumatoid arthritis 551–2
in skin disorders 480
in thrombophilias 441–2, 443
in von Willebrand's disease 563–5
libido, decreased 129–30
lichen sclerosus 476–7
life table analysis 181
lipids, serum
    combined pill formulations and 8
    oral vs transdermal contraception 47
    see also hypercholesterolaemia;
        hyperlipidaemia
liposarcoma 536
Lippes Loop IUD 172, 177, 179
liver disease 447–62
    progestogen-only implants 130, 456,
        458–9
    in sickle cell disease 555, 556
liver-enzyme inducers 299–11

antibiotics 309–10
anti-epileptics 343–4
antiretrovirals 493–5, 495, 499–501
antituberculous drugs 561
herbal remedies 329-30
St John's wort 325–30
liver transplant recipients 461
liver tumours, benign 462
LNG-IUS *see* levonorgestrel-releasing
    intrauterine system
Loestrin® 32, 540
Logynon® 12, 56
loin pain haematuria syndrome 23–4
lumboperitoneal shunt 425–7
lumps, around DMPA injection site 104
Lunelle® 216–17
lung transplant, women awaiting 305–6
lupus anticoagulant 26, 440, 441
lupus erythematosus
    cutaneous (CLE) 26
    discoid 478–9
    systemic *see* systemic lupus
        erythematosus

macrolide antibiotics 313–14
macroprolactinaemia 364, 364–5
macular neuroretinopathy, acute 369
magnetic resonance imaging (MRI),
    IUD users 171–2
maladie de Roger 401–2
malaria prophylaxis 314–15
male sterilisation 212–13
manic-depressive illness 510–12
Marfan syndrome 399–400
Marvelon® 33
medical problems, complex 137–8, 425–7
medico-legal issues 257–64
medroxyprogesterone acetate
    depot *see* depot medroxyprogesterone
        acetate
    effect on prolactin levels 365–6
    in epilepsy 343
    monthly injectables 216
mefenamic acid 193, 291

melasma 472–3
Meliane® 33
menarche 276
meningitis, cerebral infarcts after 390
menopausal symptoms
    copper IUD users 174–5
    efficacy of progestogens 280–1
    LNG-IUS users 203
    progestogen-only contraception and
        81, 122–3, 134–5, 279
    see also perimenopause
menopause 276–87
    diagnosis 278–9
        DMPA users 86, 522
        estrogen preparation users 134–5,
            279–80
        IUD users 174–5, 202–3
        progestogen-only pill users 61–2,
            279
        tamoxifen users 283–4
    premature, Shwachman–Diamond
        syndrome 287
menorrhagia
    in anticoagulated patients 434–5
    combined oral contraception 31, 36
    in haemophilia 527–8
    in idiopathic thrombocytopenic
        purpura 531–2
    LNG-IUS 181–5, 192
        in prolactinoma 364–5
    management options 193
    nephrotic syndrome with 465–7
    norethisterone therapy 289–90
    pemphigoid gestationis and 480
    stroke and valvular heart disease and
        406
    in von Willebrand's disease 563–4
menstrual cycle(s)
    after menarche 276
    catamenial epilepsy 343
    insertion of IUDs 143
    porphyria exacerbations 544
    repeat progestogen-only emergency
        contraception 229–31

starting hormonal contraception
10–12, 125
menstrual problems 287–90
see also bleeding patterns, abnormal;
dysmenorrhoea; menorrhagia
menstruation
delaying
Dianette® users 55
DMPA users 115
progestogen-only pill users 72
insertion of IUDs 143
Mercilon® 32–3
Mesigyna® 216–17
mestranol 7
in epilepsy 346
metabolic problems, transdermal
contraception 46–7
metformin 291–5
methicillin-resistant Staphylococcus
aureus (MRSA)
eradication, LNG-IUD users 194–5
identified on vaginal swabs 273–4
in IUD users 166–7, 274
methotrexate 335, 381, 552, 563
metronidazole 274, 313–14
metyrapone 514
microbiology testing
cervical cytology 270–4
induced abortion 233–4
prior to IUD insertion 145–7, 186–7
Staphylococcus aureus identified on
273–4
Microgynon® 11–12, 23, 56
Micronor® 23, 290
Microval, emergency contraception 261
midwives 252
mifepristone (Mifegyne®), medical
abortion 235–6
migraine 350–9
abdominal 351
with aura 350, 389
with focal symptoms 351–2, 353–8,
389
and occasional facial weakness 351–2

during pill-free interval 352–3
without aura 350
Mirena® *see* levonorgestrel-releasing
intrauterine system
miscarriage, IUD insertion after 240
misoprostol
cervical priming for IUD insertion
488
interactions 335
medical abortion 238
missed pill rules 41–3, 77, 232
mitral valve prolapse 402–3
ML 375 IUD 140
molar pregnancy 558–60
monthly injectable contraception 216–17
mood disturbances/swings
in DMPA users 110–11, 510–12
metformin in PCOS 291–3
premenstrual 287–9
mood stabilisers 510–12
MRSA *see* methicillin-resistant
Staphylococcus aureus
Multiload® Cu 375 IUD 155
multiple sclerosis (MS) 372–4
mycophenolate mofetil 461
myocardial infarction
past history
and coronary artery stent 430–1
and multiple other pathologies
425–7
and warfarin therapy 433–4
risks, combined pill 8, 30–1, 420–1

naproxen 291
National Institute for Clinical Excellence
(NICE) 85–6, 87, 210
natural family planning methods
214–15
Neisseria gonorrhoea
bacterial vaginosis and 188–9
prophylaxis, induced abortion 234
screening prior to IUD insertion
145–6, 147, 186–7
treatment prior to IUD insertion 149

nephrotic syndrome 318–19, 465–7
neurofibromatosis 374–5
neurological disorders 343–94
neurosurgical procedures 34–5
neutropenia, autoimmune cyclical 509
NHS Cervical Screening Programme
    (NHSCSP) 252–4
nifedipine 550
nipple discharge 22
non-licensed contraceptive methods
    215–21
nonoxynol-9
    condoms lubricated with 205–6
    spermicides not containing 207–8
non-steroidal anti-inflammatory drugs
    (NSAIDs)
    abnormal bleeding 134, 193
    adverse effects in dysmenorrhoea
        290–1
    in rheumatoid arthritis 552
norethindrone 198
norethisterone
    in combined pills 7, 8, 9, 32, 420
    to delay bleeding, progestogen-only
        pill users 72
    for menorrhagia, contraceptive
        efficacy 289–90
    monthly injectables 216
norethisterone enanthate 113–16
norethisterone-only pill
    missed pills 76–7
    in obesity 58–9
    pregnancy risk after stopping 75
norethynodrel 7
norgestimate 8–9, 198
Norgeston®, emergency contraception
    261
norgestrel 198
Noriday® 290
Norimin® 466
Norinyl-1® 346
Norplant® see levonorgestrel-releasing
    implant
Nova T® 200 IUD 140

Nova T® 380 IUD (previously
    Novagard®) 137–8, 140, 160
Nova TT380S IUD 139, 140
nurses, extended role 251–2
Nuvaring® 215–16

obesity 537–9
    benign intracranial hypertension and
        361
    combined oral contraception 4–5, 36,
        98, 121, 538
    contraception while awaiting
        sterilisation 121–2
    drug interactions 303–4, 335–8
    insulin-dependent diabetes and 521
    progestogen-only emergency
        contraception 223
    progestogen-only implants 116–19,
        121–2, 539
    progestogen-only injectables 82, 97–8,
        99, 538
    progestogen-only pill 58–60, 74, 121,
        538–9
    retinoid users 324–5
ofloxacin 274
older women
    Charcot Marie Tooth syndrome 371
    combined oral contraception 5, 30–1,
        277–9
    continuation of contraception 277–9
    copper IUDs 174–5, 176–9
    high cholesterol and family history of
        stroke 392–3
    IUDs in extrauterine position 173, 178
    LNG-IUS 202–4
    pregnancy risks 277
    progestogen-only emergency
        contraception 224–5
    progestogen-only implants 119,
        122–3, 134–5
    progestogen-only injectables 86–8,
        90–1
    progestogen-only pills 60–2, 73,
        79–80, 81

on retinoids 324
stopping contraception 61, 278
see also menopause; perimenopause;
   postmenopausal women
oral contraceptives
   centchroman (weekly nonsteroidal)
      219–20
   combined *see* combined oral
      contraception
   prescribing for young women under
      16 years 258–60
   progestogen-only *see* progestogen-
      only pill
organisation of family planning services
   see services, family planning
orlistat 337–8
Orthogyn T (Gyne T380S) IUD 178–9
orthopaedic surgery, elective 64
osteogenesis imperfecta 539–40
osteopenia
   in HIV infection 498
   progestogen-only injectables and 92,
      95
   see also bone mineral density
osteoporosis
   in anorexia nervosa 510
   desogestrel-only pill and 65
   in inflammatory bowel disease 512–14
   LNG-IUS and 198
   multiple pathologies with 448–9
   post-pill amenorrhoea 20
   primary biliary cirrhosis and 455
   progestogen-only implants and 130–1,
      198
   progestogen-only injectables and
      87–8, 92–4, 95
   risk factors 92–4
otosclerosis 376–7
ovarian cancer, past history 540–1
ovarian cysts, benign functional 67–9,
   541
ovarian failure, premature 20
overweight *see* obesity
Ovran® 346, 500

Ovranette® 56
ovulation
   after extended combined pill-free
      interval 44–5
   after progestogen-only implant
      removal 128
   after starting combined hormonal
      contraception 10–11
   before/after menarche 276
   Calista® saliva test 214–15
   progestogen-only pill users 74–5,
      79–80
   resumption after DMPA injections
      105, 105–6
oxygen treatment
   in anaphylaxis 103, 250
   vasovagal episodes at IUD insertion
      162

paramedics 252
parents
   consent by 260, 262, 263, 508–9
   disclosure of information to 260
Patient Group Directions 251–2
PCOS *see* polycystic ovary syndrome
Pearl index 7, 36, 58, 73, 125, 180
pelvic examination
   guidance 269–70
   at routine cervical screening 269–70
pelvic infections
   insertion of IUDs after 144
   prophylaxis *see* antimicrobial
      prophylaxis
   testing for *see* microbiology testing
   treatment prior to IUD insertion
      147–9
   see also sexually transmitted infections
pelvic inflammatory disease (PID)
   anovaginal fistula and 506
   high-dose steroid therapy and 168
   in IUD users 164–6
   methicillin-resistant Staphylococcus
      aureus and 166–7
   oral antibiotic regimens 274

treatment prior to IUD insertion 148–9
pemphigoid gestationis 480
penicillin 312
penicillin V 314
perimenopause
  continuing contraception 277–9
  copper IUDs 174–5, 176, 178–9
  LNG-IUS 202–3
  progestogen-only implants 122–3, 134–5
  progestogen-only injectables 86–8, 522
  progestogen-only pill 60–2, 81, 279
  stopping contraception 61, 278
  see also menopause
pharmacists 252
phenytoin 300
pituitary tumours 363–8
pityriasis versicolor 481–2
polycystic kidney disease 467–8
polycystic ovary syndrome (PCOS) 20, 49, 541–3
  and congenital heart disease 402–3
  LNG-IUS users 54–5
  metformin therapy 291–3
polymyositis 448–9
porphyria 543–5
postcoital bleeding, IUD users 171
postmenopausal women 280–3
  with IUDs in place 176–8, 179
  uterine fibroids, and LNG-IUS 203–4
  vasomotor symptoms *see* menopausal symptoms
  see also hormone replacement therapy; menopause; perimenopause
postpartum period
  combined oral contraception 6, 36–7, 368–9
  IUD insertion 142–3, 155–6
  progestogen-only emergency contraception 222–3
  progestogen-only injectables 83–4
  progestogen-only pill 59–60

povidone iodine (Betadine), intravaginal 152, 153
pregnancy
  avoiding starting combined pill during 13–14
  chloasma 472–3
  cholestasis of 449–51
  continuing combined oral contraception in 14, 37–8
  criteria for determining absence 13
  deep-sea diving 19
  during DMPA use 112
  in IUD or LNG-IUS users 175
  molar 558–60
  pemphigoid gestationis 480
  risks in older women 277
  testing 265–6
  unintended, while using contraception 9–10
premenstrual syndrome (PMS)
  progestogen-only implants 131–2
  symptoms 287–8
  treatment 287–9
prescription
  IUDs by general practitioners 263–5
  refusal, patients with contraindications 261–3
primary biliary cirrhosis 454–5
primary sclerosing cholangitis 52–3
progestogen-only contraception 57–135
  after venous thromboembolism 433–4, 435–6
  anaphylaxis risk 102
  in benign intracranial hypertension 361–2
  in breast cancer 484–7, 488
  breast cancer risk 65–7, 108–9, 490–2
  in cerebrovascular disorders 384–8
  in cervical intraepithelial neoplasia 512
  in congenital heart disease 395–6, 397, 405–6
  in Crohn's disease 512–14
  in cystic fibrosis 515–16

drug interactions 327–8, 494
elective surgery 63–4
in gall bladder disease 447, 448–9,
 515–16
in HIV infection 493–5, 497–8, 499,
 500
in hypermobility syndrome 354
in ischaemic heart disease 423, 424–7,
 430
in liposarcoma 536
in liver disease 450–1, 452–5, 457,
 458–9, 462
in migraine 353–6, 357
in neurofibromatosis 374–5
in obesity 537–9
in otosclerosis 376–7
in polycystic ovary syndrome 542
postpartum use 59–60, 83–4
in pulmonary hypertension 410
in renal disorders 317–19, 463–5,
 467–8
in rheumatoid arthritis 551–2
risks and sequelae 66–9
in skin disorders 473, 477, 480, 481–2
in thrombophilias 438–40, 446, 441–2,
 444–5
in tuberculosis 560–2
see also specific types
progestogen-only emergency
 contraception 222–33
continuing contraception after 13–14,
 231–2
dose, timing and efficacy 225–8
drug interactions 302, 306–8, 328–9,
 334, 494
in epilepsy 343–4
generic vs branded levonorgestrel
 260–1
more than once in one cycle 229–31
patient selection 222–5
repeat prescription/advance supply
 224–5
in trophoblastic disease 564
progestogen-only implants 116–35

adverse effects 129–32
after induced abortion 237
in anticoagulated patients 411–12,
 438–9, 442
bone mineral density and 130–1, 198
in cerebrovascular disorders 384,
 387–3
in congenital heart disease 396
drug interactions
 complementary medicines 327–8,
  331
 liver-enzyme inducers 300–1, 303,
  305–6, 306–8, 494
 retinoids 323–4, 324–5
 tacrolimus 320
efficacy 120–4, 125
in endometriosis 131–2, 524–5
in epilepsy 344, 345, 347, 348–9
follow-up 251
in HIV infection 493–5, 500
insertion and removal 11, 124–9
in liver disease 130, 456, 458–9
in multiple pathologies 425–7
in neurofibromatosis 375
in obesity 116–19, 121–2, 539
patient selection 116–20, 131–2
perimenopause 122–3, 134–5
recall systems for removal 257–9
in rheumatoid arthritis 551
in thrombophilias 438–9, 442, 444–5
unscheduled bleeding 132–4
in venous thromboembolism 433–4
in von Willebrand's disease 564–5
see also etonogestrel-releasing
 implant; levonorgestrel-releasing
 implant
progestogen-only injectables 82–116
abnormal bleeding 96–8, 115
administration 98–100, 104
adverse effects 23, 108–13, 114
after induced abortion 237, 238–9
anaphylactic and allergic reactions
 100–5
in anticoagulated patients 442

bone mineral density and 84–6, 87–8,
90–6, 114–15
in cerebrovascular disease 384
dose and regimens 105–7, 116
drug interactions 299, 301, 332–3, 494
in endometriosis 524–5
in epilepsy 344, 347, 349
in neurofibromatosis 375
patient selection 82–90
timing 11
in venous thromboembolism 433–4
see also depot medroxyprogesterone
acetate
progestogen-only pill 57–81
after induced abortion 237
after oral emergency contraception 14
in anticoagulated patients 433–4, 442
in benign intracranial hypertension
361–2
bone mineral density and 65
in breast cancer 485
breast cancer risk 65–6, 490–2
in cerebrovascular disease 384
drug interactions
antibiotics 309–10
antihistamines 333
anti-obesity medications 335–6,
337–8
complementary medicines 327–8
illegal recreational drugs 341
liver-enzyme inducers 303, 305,
309–10, 494
retinoids 477
warfarin 338
efficacy 58, 72–5
elective surgery 63–4
for emergency contraception 260–1
in epilepsy 344, 345
family history of breast cancer and
65–6
in gall bladder disease 447
in heart disease 396, 410–11, 418–19
in HIV infection 500
in liver disease 462

management of adverse effects 69–72
missed pills and potential failures
76–9
in neurofibromatosis 375
in obesity 58–60, 74, 121, 538–9
in ovarian cancer 540, 541
patient selection 57–63
perimenopause 60–2, 81, 279
in renal disorders 464–5
risks and sequelae 66–9
in skin disorders 473
starting 11
supply arrangements 251
in Takayasu arteritis 557–8
with topical vaginal estrogens or
HRT 79–81
travellers to high altitudes 18
in tuberculosis 561
progestogens
androgenic 198
breast cancer risk 282–3
in combined pills 7, 8–9
hair loss related to 22
vaginal estrogen cream users 282
vasomotor symptoms 280–1
prolactin, serum 363–6, 367
prolactinomas 363–6, 367
propylthiouracil 309–11
prostaglandins
cervical priming for IUD insertion
488
see also misoprostol
prostatic cancer, risk after vasectomy
212–13
prosthetic heart valves, IUD
insertion/removal 157, 190, 407–8
protein C/protein S deficiency 443
prothrombin gene mutations 443–4
proton pump inhibitors 309
pruritus
progestogen-only implant users 130
in Schamberg's disease 552
pseudotumour cerebri *see* benign
intracranial hypertension

psoriasis 316–17
puerperal sepsis, insertion of IUDs after
    143
pulmonary embolism
    past history, plus multiple other
        pathologies 425–7
    see also venous thromboembolism
pulmonary (arterial) hypertension 304–6,
    410
pulmonary stenosis 400–1
pyrazinamide 561
pyridoxine (vitamin B6) 287–9, 309–11

Rathke's pouch cyst 366–7
Raynaud's phenomenon 509, 548–50
recall systems, removal of IUDs and
    implants 257–9
reception staff 252
recreational drugs, illegal 339–42
Reductil® 335–6
refusal to prescribe 261–3
renal disorders 463–71
    ciclosporin interactions 317–19
    Henoch-Schönlein purpura 528
renal failure 463–4
renal transplant recipients 464–5
Replens MD® 34, 80, 282
resuscitation
    in anaphylaxis 100–2, 103
    equipment and supplies 249–51
    at LNG-IUS removal 187–8
    vasovagal syncope, at IUD insertion
        162
retinal vascular lesions 372
retinoblastoma 377–8
retinoids 321–5, 477
rheumatoid arthritis 551–2
ribavirin 460
rifabutin 309
rifampicin
    combined oral contraception and
        45–6
    progestogen-only contraception and
        300, 307, 309–10, 561

Saf-T-Coil 177
sagittal sinus thrombosis, postnatal
    391–2
saliva ovulation test, Calista® 214–15
saquinavir 493
Schamberg's disease 552–3
Scheuermann kyphosis 553–4
scleroderma 110
seizures, frequency of 343–4, 348
septic abortion, insertion of IUDs after
    143
services, family planning 247–64
    design 247–56
    legal and ethical issues 257–64
sexual dysfunction, female 129–30
sexual intercourse, unprotected
    contraception after *see* emergency
        contraception
    pregnancy testing after 265–6
    see also back-up contraception/
        abstinence from sex
sexually transmitted infections (STI)
    bacterial vaginosis and 188–9
    insertion of IUDs after 144, 166, 182
    IUD use in HIV infection and 501
    in LNG-IUS users 195–6
    in nonoxynol-9 users 205–6
    screening for *see* microbiology testing
    treatment prior to IUD insertion
        148–9
Shanghai ring 217–18
Shwachman–Diamond syndrome 287
sibutramine hydrochloride 335–7
sickle cell disease 554–5
skin disorders 472–38
    in combined pill users 24–6, 472–3,
        475, 481
smokers
    combined oral contraception 5
        cardiovascular risk factors and 419
        inadvertent use during pregnancy
            37
        for non-contraceptive benefits 30–1
        refusal to prescribe 261–3

sibutramine hydrochloride and 336–7

Takayasu arteritis and 380, 381

venous thromboembolism risk 17–18, 30–1

ventricular septal defects and 401–2

former, combined oral contraception 5

progestogen-only injectables 92–4

on retinoids 324

solvent abuse, and erectile dysfunction 293

spatulas, cervical smears 268

speculums, vaginal

cervical smears 267

correct plural form 254

metal vs plastic 254–6

spermicides

condoms lubricated with 205–6

use with diaphragms 206–8

spider naevi (angiomas) 24–5

spironolactone, premenstrual syndrome 287–9

splenectomy, antibiotic prophylaxis for IUD insertion 157–8, 556–7

Staphylococcus aureus

identified on vaginal swabs 273–4

methicillin-resistant (MRSA) see methicillin-resistant Staphylococcus aureus

vaginal discharge in vaginal ring users and 215–16

starflower oil 331

steel ring intrauterine devices 217–18

sterilisation 209–13

female see female sterilisation

male 212–13

steroid therapy see corticosteroid therapy

Stevens–Johnson syndrome 475

STI see sexually transmitted infections

St John's wort 325–30

streptococcus

group A 148, 271

group B 148, 271

striae, skin 25

stroke

combined pill-related risks 26

hypertension and 19

migraine and 350, 351, 352

smokers aged over 35 years 30–1

family history

and high cholesterol 392–3

and idiopathic thrombocytopenic purpura 531–2

haemorrhagic 383–4

hypercholesterolaemia and 392–3, 422, 423–4

mitral valve prolapse and 399

past history 383–8, 389–90

and valvular heart disease 406

risk factors 393

Takayasu arteritis and 379–81

subarachnoid haemorrhage 383–4

supply of contraceptives 251–2

surgery

combined pill users 447-8

IUD removal 173, 178–9

progestogen-only pill users 63–4

Sydenham's chorea 378–9

syncope, vagovagal see vasovagal episodes

systemic lupus erythematosus (SLE) 440–1

combined oral contraception 26, 478–9, 548, 549

etonogestrel-only implant 448–9

systemic pulmonary shunts, surgical 407–8

tacrolimus 319–20, 461, 465, 532–3

Takayasu arteritis 379–81, 557–8

tamoxifen 283–5, 484–8

tear film 27–8

teenagers see adolescents

teratogenicity see fetal abnormalities

terbinafine 335–6

termination of pregnancy see induced abortion

tetralogy of Fallot 395–6, 405–6, 407–8
thin membrane disease 24
thrombocytopenic purpura
  idiopathic 530–2
  thrombotic 530–1
thromboembolism, venous *see* venous
    thromboembolism
thrombophilias 437–46
  HRT and 281
  women with family history of VTE
    436–7
thrombosis, arterial *see* arterial
    thrombosis
thyroid disease 309–11, 448–9
thyroid function tests 198, 279–80
topiramate 345
toxic epidermal necrolysis 475
toxic shock syndrome 215, 216, 273
training, IUD insertion 155
tranexamic acid (Cyklokapron®) 193
transdermal contraception, combined *see*
    combined transdermal
    contraception
transient ischaemic attacks (TIA) 388–9
transplant recipients 319, 415–16, 461,
    464–5
travel, to extreme altitudes 18
triazole anti-fungals 315
Trichomonas vaginalis 148
trimethoprim 314
trophoblastic disease, gestational 558–60
T Safe® CU 380A IUD 140
T Safe® CU 380A (FP) IUD 139
tuberculosis 309–11, 560–2

ulcerative colitis 562–3
ultrasound scanning, IUDs 178, 217
urticaria, progestogen-only injection-
    associated 102–4
uterine abnormalities
  investigation for, after IUD expulsion
    157–8
  LNG-IUS use 184
uterine fibroids, LNG-IUS use 203–4

uterine perforation
  IUD-related 153–4, 155–6, 159–60,
    168–9, 173
  by uterine sound, management 161
uterine sounding
  perforation complicating 161
  protective benefits 153–4

Vagifem® 80
vaginal antisepsis 152, 153
vaginal bleeding, abnormal *see* bleeding
    patterns, abnormal
vaginal delivery, IUD insertion after
    155–6
vaginal discharge, vaginal ring users
    215–16
vaginal dryness 34, 79–80, 282
vaginal estrogens, topical
  combined pill users 34
  progestogen-only pill users 79–80
  progestogens for endometrial
    protection 282
vaginal rings
  contraceptive 215–16
  estrogen-containing 282
vaginal swabs *see* microbiology testing
vaginal ulceration, in nonoxynol-9 users
    205–6
valvular heart disease 395–9, 407–8
  combined oral contraception 53, 397
  complicated 397, 410
  endocarditis prophylaxis *see*
    endocarditis, prophylaxis
  IUD insertion/removal 157, 407–8
  and past history of stroke 406
  uncomplicated 397
vasectomy 212–13
vasomotor symptoms *see* menopausal
    symptoms
vasovagal episodes
  at IUD insertion 162
  at LNG-IUS removal 188
Veda-scope 255
venous thromboembolism (VTE) 433–46

Behcet's disease and 509–10
cocaine use and 340
combined contraceptive patch users
47–8
combined pill-related risks 7, 8–9,
436–7
in cerebral palsy 370–1
cyproterone acetate-containing
pills 9, 49, 50–1, 403
deep-sea divers 19
in dermatomyositis 474
extreme altitudes 18
gall bladder surgery 448
lupus anticoagulants 26
neurosurgical procedures 34–5
obesity 537
in Raynaud's phenomenon 548–9
smokers 17–18, 30–1
current, treated with anticoagulants
338, 433–5
family history
combined oral contraception 436–7
HRT 281
liver-enzyme inducers and high
BMI 303–4
Klippel-Trenaunay-Weber syndrome
and 445
past history
HRT 281
progestogen-only contraception
435–6–1
progestogen-only contraception-
related risks 435–6, 448
elective surgery 63–4
obesity 82
thrombophilia-related risks 442–3,
443–4
see also thrombophilias
ventricular septal defects (VSD),
asymptomatic 401–2
ventriculoperitoneal shunt, in
neurofibromatosis 374–5
vitamin B6 (pyridoxine) 287–9, 309–11
vitamin C 334

Vitex agnus castus 330–1
von Willebrand's disease 563–5
VTE *see* venous thromboembolism
vulvar epithelial disorders, non-
neoplastic 475–6
vulvovaginal candidiasis 28–9, 148, 272

walk-in centres, NHS 247–9
warfarin
combined oral contraception and
442–3
desogestrel-only pill and 338
endocarditis prophylaxis and 189–90
etonogestrel implant and 411–12
intrauterine contraception and 391–2,
433–4, 434–5
weight, body
gain
benign intracranial hypertension
and 361
DMPA users 82, 538
LNG-IUD users 194–5
Yasmin users 33–4
loss, postpartum 36–7
metformin therapy in PCOS and
291–3
progestogen-only contraception and
58–60, 74, 116–19, 121
-related amenorrhoea 20
see also body mass index; obesity
Wilson's disease 457
Wolff-Parkinson-White syndrome
412–13

Xenical® 337–8
X-rays, IUD identification 173, 176–7

Yasmin® *see* drospirenone/
ethinylestradiol combined pill
young women
under 16 years, consent issues 258,
260, 385, 508–9
cerebrovascular disease 384–5
cervical screening 252–4

dysmenorrhoea 35–6
legal and ethical issues 258–60, 260, 262–4
opportunistic Chlamydia screening 270–1
pregnancy risk after menarche 276
progestogen-only emergency contraception 224, 230–1
progestogen-only injectables 84–6, 90

renal disorders 467–8
severe learning difficulties 251
skin striae 25
walk-in style services 247–9
see also adolescents

zidovudine 493–5
Zoladex® 284–5